# Biochemical Actions of Hormones

Volume IX

# Contributors

Dennis M. DiSorbo
Howard J. Eisen
André Herchuelz
Brian B. Hoffman
Robert J. Lefkowitz
Frances E. Leland
Choh Hao Li
Gerald Litwack
Willy J. Malaisse
Thomas Michel
Tiiu Ojasoo
Jacques Pottier
Jean-Pierre Raynaud
Jean Salmon
S. Stoney Simons, Jr.
Sanford S. Singer
David A. Sirbasku
Thomas C. Spelsberg
Andrew John Szabo
Olga Szabo
E. Brad Thompson

# Biochemical Actions of Hormones

Edited by GERALD LITWACK

*Fels Research Institute and Department of Biochemistry*
*Temple University, School of Medicine*
*Philadelphia, Pennsylvania*

VOLUME IX



1982

ACADEMIC PRESS
A Subsidiary of Harcourt Brace Jovanovich, Publishers

New York London

Paris San Diego San Francisco São Paulo Sydney Tokyo Toronto

ACADEMIC PRESS, INC.
111 Fifth Avenue, New York, New York 10003

*United Kingdom Edition published by*
ACADEMIC PRESS, INC. (LONDON) LTD.
24/28 Oval Road, London NW1 7DX

Library of Congress Cataloging in Publication Data
Main entry under title:

Biochemical actions of hormones.

Includes bibliographies and indexes.
1. Hormones--Collected works. I. Litwack, Gerald.
II. Axelrod, Julius, Date. [DNLM: 1. Hormones.
2. Physiology. WK102 B615]
QP571.B56 574.19'27 70-107567
ISBN 0-12-452809-0 (v. 9) AACR2

PRINTED IN THE UNITED STATES OF AMERICA

82 83 84 85 9 8 7 6 5 4 3 2 1

# Contents

## 6. Chemical Characterization of Nuclear Acceptors for the Avian Progesterone Receptor

*Thomas C. Spelsberg*



## 7. The Use of Pyridoxal 5′-Phosphate as a Tool in the Study of Steroid Receptors

*Dennis M. DiSorbo and Gerald Litwack*



## 8. Affinity Labeling of Glucocorticoid Receptors: New Methods in Affinity Labeling

*S. Stoney Simons, Jr., and E. Brad Thompson*

## 9. Immunochemical Approaches to the Study of Glucocorticoid Receptors

*Howard J. Eisen*



## 10. The Properties and the Endocrine Control of the Production of the Steroid Sulfotransferases

*Sanford S. Singer*



## 11. Chemical Substitution of Steroid Hormones: Effect on Receptor Binding and Pharmacokinetics

*Jean-Pierre Raynaud, Tiiu Ojasoo, Jacques Pottier, and Jean Salmon*

# List of Contributors

*Numbers in parentheses indicate the pages on which the authors' contributions begin.*

Dennis M. DiSorbo (205), Fels Research Institute, and Department of Biochemistry, Temple University, School of Medicine, Philadelphia, Pennsylvania 19140

Howard J. Eisen (255), Developmental Pharmacology Branch, National Institute of Child Health and Human Development, National Institutes of Health, Bethesda, Maryland 20205

André Herchuelz (69), Laboratories of Experimental Medicine and Pharmacology, Brussels University Medical School, Brussels, Belgium

Brian B. Hoffman* (43), Departments of Medicine and Biochemistry, The Howard Hughes Medical Institute, Duke University Medical Center, Durham, North Carolina 27710

Robert J. Lefkowitz (43), Departments of Medicine and Biochemistry, The Howard Hughes Medical Institute, Duke University Medical Center, Durham, North Carolina 27710

Frances E. Leland (115), Departments of Biochemistry and Molecular Biology, The University of Texas Medical School, Houston, Texas 77025

Choh Hao Li (1), Hormone Research Laboratory, University of California, San Francisco, California 94143

*Present address: Department of Medicine, Division of Clinical Pharmacology, Stanford University Medical Center, Stanford, California 94305

Gerald Litwack (205), Fels Research Institute and Department of Biochemistry, Temple University School of Medicine, Philadelphia, Pennsylvania 19140

Willy J. Malaisse (69), Laboratories of Experimental Medicine and Pharmacology, Brussels University Medical School, Brussels, Belgium B-1000

Thomas Michel (43), Departments of Medicine and Biochemistry, The Howard Hughes Medical Institute, Duke University Medical Center, Durham, North Carolina 27710

Tiiu Ojasoo (305), Centre de Recherches Roussel–UCLAF, Paris 75007, France

Jacques Pottier (305), Centre de Recherches Roussel-UCLAF, Paris 75007, France

Jean-Pierre Raynaud (305), Centre de Recherches Roussel–UCLAF, Paris 75007, France

Jean Salmon (305), Centre de Recherches Roussel–UCLAF, Paris 75007, France

S. Stoney Simons, Jr. (221), Laboratory of Chemistry, National Institute of Arthritis, Metabolism and Digestive Diseases, National Institutes of Health, Bethesda, Maryland 20205

Sanford S. Singer (271), Chemistry Department, University of Dayton, Dayton, Ohio 45469

David A. Sirbasku (115), Departments of Biochemistry and Molecular Biology, The University of Texas Medical School, Houston, Texas 77025

Thomas C. Spelsberg (141), Department of Cell Biology, Section of Biochemistry, Mayo Clinic, and Mayo Graduate School of Medicine, Rochester, Minnesota 55901

Andrew John Szabo (93), Department of Medicine, New York Medical College, Valhalla, New York, and The Lincoln Hospital Medical Center, Bronx, New York 10451

Olga Szabo (93), Department of Medicine, New York Medical College, Valhalla, New York, and The Lincoln Hospital Medical Center, Bronx, New York 10451

E. Brad Thompson (221), Laboratory of Biochemistry, National Cancer Institute, National Institutes of Health, Bethesda, Maryland 20205

# Preface

In this volume, the authors present a balanced overview of current research on peptide and steroid hormones. C. H. Li opens the collection with a review of the lipotropins and their active degradation products. An up-to-date chapter on the regulation of adenylate cyclase by adrenergic receptors follows by R. J. Lefkowitz and co-authors· T. Michel and B. B. Hoffman. W. J. Malaisse and A. Herchuelz follow with an intriguing paper on potassium ion conductance in the pancreatic beta cell. A. J. Szabo and O. Szabo introduce a new and exciting concept of the insulin sensitive chemoreceptor of the central nervous system. D. A. Sirbasku and F. E. Leland review their new work on estrogen-induced growth factors with emphasis on their role in tumor cell growth. T. C. Spelsberg reviews his excellent work on nuclear acceptors for the avian progesterone receptor. J.-P. Raynaud presents a cogent work on structural aspects of steroid hormones and their receptors, whereas D. M. DiSorbo and G. Litwack review the current status of using pyridoxal phosphate to provide a better understanding of the functions of steroid receptors. S. S. Simons and E. B. Thompson review their elegant work in producing a new affinity label for glucocorticoid receptors, and H. Eisen reviews his ground-breaking work on the development of a polyclonal antibody to the glucocorticoid receptor. Finally, S. S. Singer appraises us of his work on the regulation of the steroid sulfotransferases, a little-studied but important new area.

The emphasis of this volume, then, has been on new developments along several lines of investigation. I hope that future volumes will continue to cover new developments as well as reviews of classical subjects undergoing experimental revolutions.

Gerald Litwack

# CHAPTER 1

# The Lipotropins

*Choh Hao Li*



## I. INTRODUCTION*

Pituitary extracts have been known for a long time to contain fat-mobilizing or lipolytic activity (Best and Campbell, 1936). After pituitary hormones have been isolated and their primary structures are known, it is possible to conclude that somatotropin (GH), thyrotropin (TSH), corticotro-

*Abbreviations: LPH, lipotropin (subscript h denotes human; s, sheep; p, pig; b, bovine; and t, turkey); CMC, carboxymethylcellulose; MSH, melanotropin; RIA, radioimmunoassay; ACTH, corticotropin; EP, endorphin; CD, circular dichroism.



BIOCHEMICAL ACTIONS OF HORMONES, VOL. IX

ISBN 0-12-452809-0

pin (ACTH), and melanotropins (α- and β-MSH) are active as lipolytic agents. The discovery of a new pituitary lipolytic factor, whose chemical characteristics are completely different from known pituitary hormones, occurred in 1963 during the course of improving the procedure for the isolation of ACTH from sheep pituitary glands. In 1955, we described a method for the isolation of pure ACTH (Li *et al.*, 1955) from acid–acetone extracts of sheep pituitaries with a yield of only 9 mg from 1 kg of glands. In this method, ACTH in the acid–acetone extract was adsorbed onto oxycellulose before purification by means of countercurrent distribution and/or column chromatography on ion-exchange resin. The oxycellulose adsorption step does not remove ACTH completely from the extract and occasionally causes inactivation of the hormone. For these reasons we omitted this step and submitted the extract directly to chromatography on carboxymethylcellulose. By this simplified procedure (Birk and Li, 1964), the yield of ACTH increased considerably and, in addition, a new peak appeared before the elution of ACTH. It was a matter of curiosity that the new peak was isolated and purified. Physicochemical studies revealed it to possess distinct characteristics that are different from those of ACTH and other known pituitary hormones. During that time, we were actively investigating the structure–activity relationship of synthetic peptides relating to the ACTH molecule with regard to adrenocorticotropic, melanotropic, and lipolytic activities. Among these three assay procedures, lipolytic assay was carried out more frequently than the other two. Hence, the newly isolated component was first submitted to lipolytic assay using the rabbit fat pads. It was found to be active with a potency comparable to that of ACTH. Because of these assay data, the name lipotropin (LPH) was proposed (Li, 1964) for the new product. If melanotropic assay had been performed first, we might have called it γ-melanotropin.

## II. ISOLATION AND PRIMARY STRUCTURE OF SHEEP β-LPH

The protocol for the isolation of sheep β-LPH ($\beta_s$-LPH) may be seen in Table I (Li *et al.*, 1966). The steps of acid–acetone extract, NaCl precipitation, and dialysis were carried out at 0°C; the ACTH concentrate was dialyzed against dilute $NH_4OH$ (pH 8); and the insoluble material was centrifuged off. The clear supernatant was lyophilized and yielded approximately 1 gm of fraction D′ from 1 kg of whole or anterior pituitary glands.

Figure 1 presents a chromatographic pattern of 1.5 gm. Fraction D′ when applied to a CMC column (1.5 × 60 cm) equilibrated with 0.01 *M* ammonium acetate buffer of pH 4.6. Gradient elution (pH and buffer concen-

TABLE I
PROTOCOL FOR THE ISOLATION OF $\beta$-LPH FROM SHEEP PITUITARY GLANDS

| Procedure | Yield (gm) |
|---|---|
| Whole sheep pituitaries | 1000 |
| Acid–acetone extract[a] | 25 |
| NaCl precipitate[a] | 4 |
| Dialysis[a]; pH 8 soluble fraction[b] | 1 |
| CM-cellulose chromatography | 0.08 |
| IRC-50 chromatography | 0.05 |

[a]These steps were carried out at 0°C.
[b] Designated as fraction D′.

trations) was performed as previously described (Birk and Li, 1964). The material corresponding to peak $L_3$, after lyophilization several times to remove ammonium acetate, was rechromatographed on a CMC column under identical conditions as shown in Fig. 1. The yield of the lyophilized product ($L'_3$) was approximately 80 mg from 1 kg of sheep pituitaries. Further purification of $L'_3$ was achieved on an IRC-50 ($H^+$) column (2.2 × 26 cm) which was previously equilibrated with 0.01 *M* ammonium acetate buffer of pH 4.6. One hundred milligrams of $L'_3$ in 10 ml starting buffer were applied to the column and eluted with 1 *M* ammonium acetate buffer of pH 6.7; the purified peptide, obtained from the main peak (II) as shown in Fig. 2, was found to be homogeneous when again submitted to chromatography on IRC-50 under the same conditions. The recovered product from the second chromatography on IRC-50 was designated as $\beta$-LPH. One hundred milligrams of $\beta$-LPH were dissolved in 5 ml of 0.1 *M* $NH_4HCO_3$ and applied to a Sephadex G-75 (Pharmacia, Uppsala) column (2.5 × 120 cm). The column was equilibrated with 0.1 *M* $NH_4HCO_3$ and had a hold-up volume of 100 ml. Elution was made with the same solvent. The peptide emerged as a single peak with an elution volume of 158 ml. Thus, 50 mg pure $\beta_s$-LPH were obtained from 1 kg of whole sheep glands. It was also found that acid–acetone extracts of posterior pituitaries contain no $\beta$-LPH. This is in agreement with the histochemical findings (Moon *et al.*, 1973) that the hormone is located in basophila of both the anterior and intermediate lobe cells but not in the posterior lobe of the sheep pituitary.

$\beta_s$-LPH sediments in an ultracentrifuge as a single symmetrical peak at 59,780 rpm with $s_{20,w}$ = 0.88 S. Sedimentation equilibrium studies at a speed of 15,200 rpm with a peptide concentration of 0.5% gave an average molecule weight for $\beta_s$-LPH of 9500 using the calculated partial specified volume of 0.728.

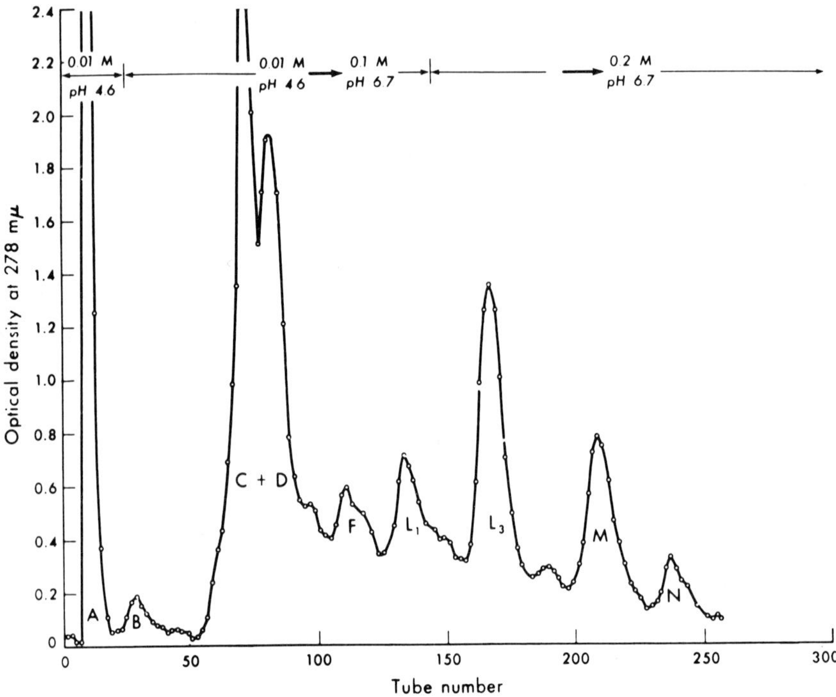


FIG. 1. CMC chromatography of 1.5 gm of fraction D′ obtained from sheep anterior pituitary glands. The initial buffer was 0.01 *M* ammonium acetate of pH 4.6. After 3–4 hold-up volumes (4 ml/tube) had been collected a gradient with respect to pH and concentration was started by introducing 0.1 *M* ammonium acetate buffer of pH 6.7 through a 500 ml mixing flask containing the starting buffer. Later, the gradient was increased by substituting 0.2 *M* ammonium acetate of pH 6.7 as the buffer. Later, the gradient was increased by substituting 0.2 *M* ammonium acetate of pH 6.7 as the solution was flowing into the mixing flask.

The $NH_2$-terminal residue analyses by the quantitative fluorodinitrobenzene procedure (Sanger, 1945; Levy, 1954) indicated glutamic acid as the sole $NH_2$-terminal amino acids with a yield of 0.85 mol/mol of $\beta_s$-LPH. Reactions of the hormone with carboxypeptidase A gave results indicating that -Gly-Gln is at the COOH-terminus. Amino acid composition of $\beta_s$-LPH was found to be $Lys_{10}His_2Arg_5Met_2Asp_4Thr_4Ser_5Glu_{16}Pro_5Gly_8Ala_{13}Val_2$-$Ile_1Leu_6Tyr_3Phe_3Trp_1$. Later structural studies revealed the presence of two residues of Ile (Gráf and Li, 1973). Thus, $\beta_s$-LPH consists of 91 amino acids with a single residue of Trp and two residues each of His, Val, Met, and Ile.

The amino acid sequence of $\beta_s$-LPH was first proposed in 1965 (Li *et al.*, 1965, 1966) and later revised slightly (Chrétien *et al.*, 1972; Gráf and Li, 1973) as shown in Fig. 3. The single Trp residue is in position 52 and the four amino acids occupy the following positions: His-49,87; Val-31,75; Met-47,65; and Ile-82,83. It was pointed out (Li *et al.*, 1965, 1966) that the amino acid sequence 37–58 in $\beta_s$-LPH is identical to that of $\beta_h$-MSH (Harris, 1959; Pickering and Li, 1963) except that the amino acid residues in positions 42 and 46 are serine and lysine, respectively, instead of glutamic acid and arginine as is the case of $\beta_b$-MSH.

$\beta_s$-LPH was found to have no detectable growth-promoting, gonadotropic, or thyrotropic activity as determined by measurement of tibial widths and organ weights and by histological examination of the uterus, ovaries, and thyroid when a total dose of 5 mg $\beta$-LPH was injected subcutaneously once daily for 4 days in hypophysectomized female rats (Long-Evans strain, hypophysectomized at 27 days of age and 14 days postoperative). The same preparation of $\beta$-LPH assayed in the pigeon crop sac assay was found to evoke a minimal positive response at a level of 25 to 25 $\mu$g, a result indicating a 0.5 to 1% contamination with lactogenic hormone; however, $\beta$-LPH

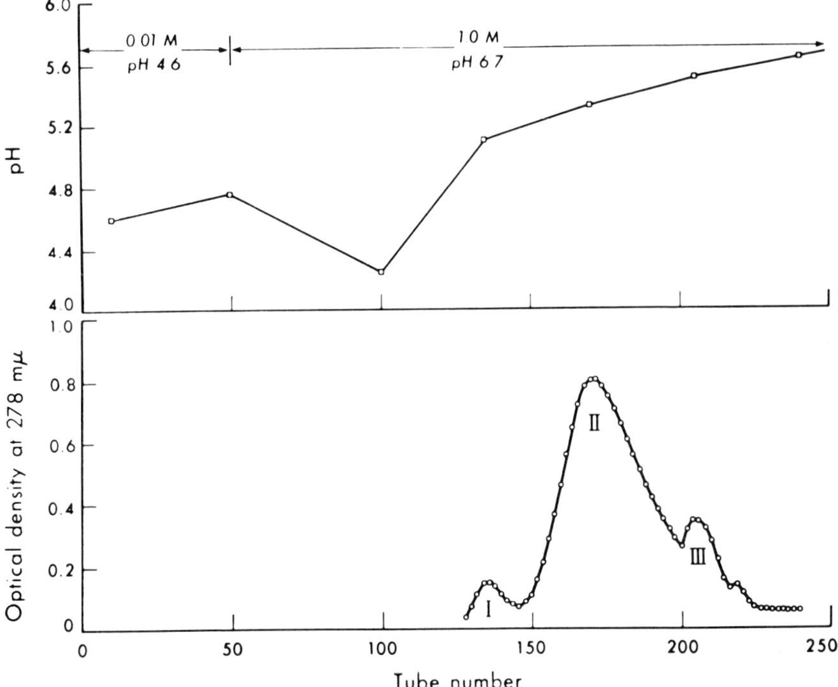


FIG. 2. Chromatography on IRC-50(H+) resin of 100 mg L'$_3$. The initial buffer of 0.01 *M* ammonium acetate of pH 4.6. At tube no. 50 (2 ml/tube), 1.0 *M* ammonium acetate buffer of pH 6.7 was applied.

additionally purified by countercurrent distribution (120 transfers in a system composed of *sec*-butanol/0.2% trichloroacetic acid) was found to be free of detectable crop sac stimulating activity when assayed at a level of 100 $\mu g$ (Lohmar and Li, 1968).

$\beta_s$-LPH has been found to have melanocyte-stimulating activity, lipolytic activity and a small amount of adrenal-stimulating activity (Table II). To estimate the potency of $\beta_s$-LPH in these various assays, ovine ACTH has been used as the standard of comparison. As a melanocyte-stimulating agent, $\beta_s$-LPH is approximately one-half as potent as ACTH. As a lipolytic hormone, $\beta_s$-LPH is also less active than ACTH in adipose tissue of the three species examined, the rabbit, rat, and mouse. In Table II, the minimal effective doses found for ACTH and $\beta_s$-LPH in three typical lipolytic assays are presented. Although the absolute values vary somewhat from one assay

H-Glu-Leu-Thr-Gly-Glu-Arg-Leu-Glu-Gln-Ala-
5 10

Arg-Gly-Pro-Glu-Ala-Gln-Ala-Glu-Ser-Ala-
15 20

Ala-Ala-Arg-Ala-Glu-Leu-Glu-Tyr-Gly-Leu-
25 30

Val-Ala-Glu-Ala-Glu-Ala-Ala-Glu-Lys-Lys-
35 40

Asp-Ser-Gly-Pro-Tyr-Lys-Met-Glu-His-Phe-
45 50

Arg-Trp-Gly-Ser-Pro-Pro-Lys-Asp-Lys-Arg-
55 60

Tyr-Gly-Gly-Phe-Met-Thr-Ser-Glu-Lys-Ser-
65 70

Gln-Thr-Pro-Leu-Val-Thr-Leu-Phe-Lys-Asn-
75 80

Ala-Ile-Ile-Lys-Asn-Ala-His-Lys-Lys-Gly-Gln-OH
85 90

FIG. 3. Amino acid sequence of sheep $\beta$-lipotropin.

TABLE II
SUMMARY OF BIOLOGICAL ASSAYS COMPARING OVINE β-LPH AND OVINE ACTH

| Preparation | Melanocyte-stimulating activity units/gm | Adrenal-stimulating activity units/gm | Lipolytic activity minimal effective dose (μg) | | |
|---|---|---|---|---|---|
| | | | Rabbit[a] | Rat[a] | Mouse[a] |
| β-LPH | $2 \times 10^7$[b] | 1.1 (0.70–1.76)[c] | 0.054 | 0.78 | Inactive (>50) |
| ACTH | $4 \times 10^7$[b] | 179 (122–262)[a] | 0.008 | 0.001 | 0.1–1 |

[a]In each species of adipose tissue, β-LPH and ACTH were assayed simultaneously.
[b]These values were obtained consistently in several *in vitro* assays.
[c]Fiducial limits.

to another, the ratio between the minimal effective doses for $\beta_s$-LPH and ACTH remains fairly constant. Thus, it can be stated that $\beta_s$-LPH is $\frac{1}{5}$ to $\frac{1}{10}$ as active as ACTH in rabbit adipose tissue and that it is approximately 1/1000 as active as ACTH in rat adipose tissue. $\beta_s$-LPH is not active on mouse adipose tissue at a level of 50 μg, although ACTH is active at a level between 0.1 and 1.0 μg (Lohmar and Li, 1968). When assayed for adrenal-stimulating activity *in vitro*, $\beta_s$-LPH consistently evokes a response corresponding to an ACTH activity of 1 IU/mg (Table II).

## III. TOTAL SYNTHESIS OF $\beta_s$-LPH

The total synthesis of $\beta_s$-LPH has now been achieved by Yamashiro and Li (Yamashiro and Li, 1978) employing the improved procedures of the solid-phase method. The anchoring linkage of the COOH-terminal glutamine was to brominated styrene/1% divinyl-benzene polymer. Coupling was performed by a symmetrical anhydride technique. Trifluoroethanol was employed in the second stage of anhydride couplings to enhance the efficiency of this reaction (Yamashiro *et al.*, 1976). The side chain of tryptophan was protected with the formyl group (Yamashiro and Li, 1973a) in view of its susceptibility to destruction under conditions of repeated acidolysis of Boc groups. For histidine, the benzyloxycarbonyl group was used since it has been employed in synthesis of peptide analogs of the carboxyl terminal plasmin fragment of human somatotropin (Blake and Li, 1978). For threonine, serine, and glutamic acid, the very stable *p*-halobenzyl protecting groups were used through residue 66 and benzyl protection thereafter.

Selection of the other protecting groups has been discussed previously (Yamashiro *et al.*, 1972a,b, 1973; Yamashiro and Li, 1973a,b; Yamashiro, 1977). Since methionine was not protected, the last Boc group was removed with TFA to reduce *tert*-butylation that occurs in HF (Noble *et al.*, 1976).

The first purification step was accomplished on CMC chromatography. A peak was detected close to the position previously reported for the natural hormone (Li *et al.*, 1966). It is evident from the recovery of material that this procedure constituted the major purification step in the scheme. The slower moving materials, which represent the major side products of synthesis, apparently consist of shorter sequences as shown by both amino acid analysis and peptide mapping. The formyl group on tryptophan was then removed by brief treatment at pH 11.5 with NaOH (Yamashiro and Li, 1976). Rechromatography on CMC gave a sharply defined peak as does natural $\beta_s$-LPH. The ultraviolet spectrum of this material was identical with that of the natural hormone in the region of 245–360 nm, indicating that deformylation was complete.

Final purification was effected by partition chromatography in a biphasic solvent system on agarose. The $R_f$ value of the major peak, which is a reflection of its distribution constant in the solvent system, was, within experimental error, indistinguishable from that of natural $\beta_s$-LPH. Under these conditions natural $\beta_s$-LPH gave an $R_f$ of 0.285.

The final highly purified material was obtained after dialysis and CMC chromatography in which a single sharp peak was obtained. The synthetic preparation was homogeneous and identical to natural $\beta_s$-LPH on paper electrophoresis at two pH values and on thin-layer chromatography. Amino acid analysis of an HCl hydrolysate was in agreement with expected values. Amino acid analysis of a total enzyme digest was in close agreement with that previously reported for natural $\beta_s$-LPH (Yamashiro and Li, 1978). The synthetic peptide showed only glutamic acid as $NH_2$-terminal as does natural

TABLE III

LIPOLYTIC ACTIVITY OF SYNTHETIC $\beta_s$-LPH

| $\beta_s$-LPH | Dose ($\mu$g/ml) | Glycerol production[a] |
|---|---|---|
| Natural | 0.37 | 2.98 ± 0.07 |
| | 1.10 | 3.70 ± 0.13 |
| Synthetic[b] | 0.37 | 2.85 ± 0.05 |
| | 1.10 | 3.60 ± 0.11 |

[a] $\mu$mol/gm of cells/hour; mean ± SE; determination in triplicate.

[b] Relative potency to the natural hormone, 0.84 times, a confidence limit of 0.58–1.18 and $\lambda$ = 0.11.

TABLE IV
PROPERTIES OF SYNTHETIC $\beta_s$-LPH

| Properties | Synthetic | Natural |
|---|---|---|
| Paper electrophoresis ($R_f^{Lys}$) | | |
| pH 3.7 | 0.56 | 0.56 |
| pH 6.7 | 0.18 | 0.18 |
| Thin-layer chromatography[a] ($R_f$) | 0.25 | 0.25 |
| Partition chromatography[b] | 0.275 | 0.285 |
| $NH_2$-terminal residue | Glu | Glu |
| $[\alpha]_{589}^{27°}$ nm | −110° | −105° |
| Circular dichroism[c] $[\Theta]\lambda$ | | |
| 278 nm | −14,000 | −11,700 |
| 220 nm | −25,000 | −22,500 |
| Isoelectric focusing,[d] p$I$ | 6.33 | 6.33 |
| Relative lipolysis potency[e] | 0.84 | 1.0 |

[a]Solvent system: 1-BuOH/pyridine/HOAc/$H_2O$ (5:5:1:4, v/v).
[b]Solvent system: 2-BuOH/$H_2O$/$HOA_c$/10% $Cl_3COOH$/NaCl (150 nm/97 ml/43 ml/7.5 ml/4.4 gm).
[c]Solvent: 0.1 $M$ HOAc.
[d]On polyacrylamide gel.
[e]Lipolytic activity in isolated rabbit fat cells.

$\beta_s$-LPH. A peptide map of a tryptic digest gave a pattern close to that given by the natural hormone. Since the behavior of peptides on a map can vary from one map to another, a map of a mixture of synthetic and natural materials was obtained. No difference between the two could be discerned including colorations of various peptides to ninhydrin. The synthetic material showed behavior identical to that of natural $\beta_s$-LPH upon isoelectric focusing.

The circular dichroism spectra of the synthetic and natural hormones have been carried out. It was found that the differences between the two spectra are probably within the expected error as determined by multiple runs of different preparations of a single protein. The optical rotations of synthetic hormone taken in a wavelength region of high sensitivity were $[\alpha]_{300nm}^{27°}$ − 604° and $[\alpha]_{250nm}^{27°}$ − 1820° at concentration 0.1% in 0.1 $M$ Tris buffer of pH 8.2. The corresponding values for natural hormone were $[\alpha]_{300nm}^{27°}$ − 590° and $[\alpha]_{25nm}^{27°}$ − 1840°.

The biological activities of synthetic and natural $\beta_s$-LPH were compared in isolated rabbit fat cells as summarized in Table III. The lipolytic activities of the synthetic product is nearly identical to that for the natural hormone. In addition, the immunoreactivity of the synthetic hormone is the same as of the natural $\beta_s$-LPH as revealed by both radioimmunoassay and complement fixation using rabbit antiserum to the natural hormone.

Thus, the synthetic $\beta_s$-LPH has been found to be indistinguishable from the natural hormone in its $R_f$ value on partition chromatography, mobility in paper electrophoresis at two pH values, behavior on thin-layer chromatography, amino acid composition of both acid and enzymatic hydrolysates, $NH_2$-terminal residue, behavior on peptide mapping, p$I$ value in isoelectric focusing, circular dichroism spectra, optical rotation, lipolytic activity, and immunoreactivity (Table IV).

## IV. A $\text{GLU}^1/<\text{GLU}^1$ POLYMORPHISM IN $\beta_s$-LPH

It has been discovered that $\beta_s$-LPH exists in two polymorphic forms by partition chromatography on agarose gel (Yamashiro and Li, 1976). The solvent system was prepared by mixing 2-butanol azeotrope (150 ml, deaerated), water (97 ml, deaerated), glacial acetic acid (4.3 ml), 10% (w/w) aqueous trichloroacetic acid (7.5 ml), and sodium chloride (4.4 gm). As shown in Fig. 4, $\beta_s$-LPH resolved into two components A and B. To demonstrate that the separation was not artifactual, components A and B were isolated and separately rechromatographed. Each component behaved as it did in the original separation. The weight ratio of A to B was 2:3. This partition system on agarose gel was readily reproducible.

The resolution of the hormone into two components obviously led to the question of the identity of $\beta_s$-LPH. Both had identical ultraviolet spectra. Each gave a single band on disc gel electrophoresis with similar mobilities. The amino acid compositions of acid and enzyme hydrolysates were close enough to each other that they could not be distinguished one from another. The electrophoretic patterns at pH 6.7 of chymotryptic digests of the two were identical. The electrophoretic patterns of tryptic digests finally revealed a difference between the two. Component B generated a ninhydrin-positive spot where component A gave no corresponding spot. The former spot gave a positive response to Sakaguchi's reagent, and in the parallel position for component A a spot also appeared. The peptide in the spot generated by component B was isolated, and amino acid analysis of an acid hydrolysate proved it to correspond to the N-terminal hexapeptide portion of $\beta_s$-LPH. Similarly, the corresponding peptide generated by component A was analyzed, and it too had the same composition.

It appeared evident that component B was $\beta_s$-LPH. It was then postulated that component A had the same structure with the exception that the $NH_2$-terminal position was occupied by a pyroglutamyl residue. Indeed, component A was shown to have no end group at all by the dansyl method, whereas component B had glutamic acid as indicated by a combination of the dansyl

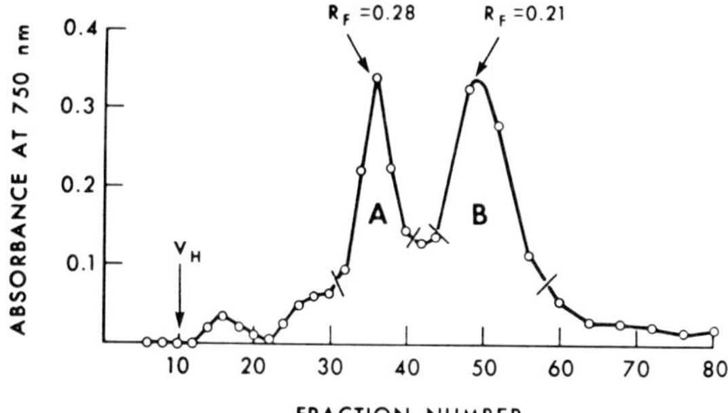


FIG. 4. Partition chromatography of $\beta_s$-LPH (4.9 mg) on a 1.05 × 18.7 cm column of agarose gel. Fraction volume of 0.4 ml. Detection by the Folin–Lowry method.

method and amino acid analysis of a leucine aminopeptidase digest. Furthermore, under conditions known to open the pyrrolidone ring (Dekker *et al.*, 1949), $NH_2$-terminal hexapeptide of component A gave a $NH_2$-terminal glutamic acid residue. For additional confirmation of the identities of $NH_2$-terminal hexapeptides of components A and B, authentic samples of <Glu-Leu-Thr-Gly-Glu-Arg-OH and H-Glu-Leu-Thr-Gly-Glu-Arg-OH were synthesized. In every respect, the synthetic peptides were identical to the natural products. Thus, component B is $\beta_s$-LPH and component A is <Glu$^1$-$\beta_s$-LPH. All preparations of $\beta_s$-LPH have shown the presence of the <Glu$^1$ analog with three more recent preparations giving A to B ratios of 1:1, 3:2, and 3:4.

Bioassays of $\beta_s$-LPH and <Glu$^1$-$\beta_s$-LPH in isolated rabbit fat cells are summarized in Table V. These results indicate that <Glu$^1$-$\beta_s$-LPH is less active than $\beta_s$-LPH. This is somewhat surprising as the two forms of $\beta_s$-LPH differ in only one amino residue at position 1.

TABLE V
LIPOLYTIC ACTIVITY OF OVINE $\beta_s$-LPH AND [1−<GLU]-$\beta_s$-LPH

| Preparation | Dose (μg/ml) | Glycerol production[a] |
|---|---|---|
| $\beta_s$-LPH | 1.1 | 2.58 ± 0.12 |
| | 3.3 | 3.38 ± 0.12 |
| [1−<Glu]-$\beta_s$-LPH[b] | 1.1 | 1.40 ± 0.26 |
| | 3.3 | 3.08 ± 0.09 |

[a] μmol/gm of cells per hour; mean ± SE; determinations in triplicate.
[b] Relative potency to $\beta_s$-LPH, 51.2% with 95% confidence limit of 34.6–68.8 and λ=0.1.

## V. ISOLATION AND PRIMARY STRUCTURE OF HUMAN β-LPH

β-LPH has also been obtained in highly purified form from bovine (Lohmar and Li, 1967), porcine (Cseh *et al.*, 1968; Gilardeau and Chrétien, 1970; Yudeau and Pankov, 1970), rat (Rubinstein *et al.*, 1977a), human (Cseh *et al.*, 1968; Scott and Lowry, 1974; Chrétien *et al.*, 1976a; Li and Chung, 1976a), whale (Kawauchi *et al.*, 1980), turkey (Chang *et al.*, 1980b), and ostrich (Naudé and Oelofsen, 1981) pituitary glands. The complete amino acid sequences of porcine (Gráf *et al.*, 1971; Gilardeau and Chrétien, 1972; Pankov and Yudeau, 1972), bovine (Li *et al.*, 1977a; Nakanishi *et al.*, 1979; Li and Chung, 1981), human (Li and Chung, 1976a), and turkey (Chang *et al.*, 1980b) hormones have also been proposed. Figures 5 and 6 present the primary structure of porcine and bovine, respectively. $\beta_p$-LPH

```
H-Glu-Leu-Ala-Gly-Ala-Pro-Pro-Glu-Pro-Ala-
                  5                   10

Arg-Asp-Pro-Glu-Ala-Pro-Ala-Glu-Gly-Ala-
                  15                  20

Ala-Ala-Arg-Ala-Glu-Leu-Glu-His-Gly-Leu-
                  25                  30

Val-Ala-Glu-Ala-Gln-Ala-Ala-Glu-Lys-Lys-
                  35                  40

Asp-Glu-Gly-Pro-Tyr-Lys-Met-Glu-His-Phe-
                  45                  50

Arg-Trp-Gly-Ser-Pro-Pro-Lys-Asp-Lys-Arg-
                  55                  60

Tyr-Gly-Gly-Phe-Met-Thr-Ser-Glu-Lys-Ser-
                  65                  70

Gln-Thr-Pro-Leu-Val-Thr-Leu-Phe-Lys-Asn-
                  75                  80

Ala-Ile-Val-Lys-Asn-Ala-His-Lys-Lys-Gly-Gln-OH
                  85                  90
```

FIG. 5. Amino acid sequence of porcine β-LPH.

H-Glu-Leu-Thr-Gly-Glu-Arg-Leu-Glu-Gln-Ala-
5 10

Arg-Gly-Pro-Glu-Ala-Gln-Ala-Glu-Ser-Ala-
15 20

Ala-Ala-Arg-Ala-Glu-Leu-Glu-Tyr-Gly-Leu-
25 30

Val-Ala-Glu-Ala-Glu-Ala-Glu-Ala-Ala-Glu-
35 40

Lys-Lys-Asp-Ser-Gly-Pro-Tyr-Lys-Met-Glu-
45 50

His-Phe-Arg-Trp-Gly-Ser-Pro-Pro-Lys-Asp-
55 60

Lys-Arg-Tyr-Gly-Gly-Phe-Met-Thr-Ser-Glu-
65 70

Lys-Ser-Gln-Thr-Pro-Leu-Val-Thr-Leu-Phe-
75 80

Lys-Asn-Ala-Ile-Ile-Lys-Asn-Ala-His-Lys-Lys-Gly-Gln-OH
85 90

FIG. 6. Amino acid sequence of bovine $\beta$-LPH.

and $\beta_t$-LPH consist of 91 amino acids as in the case of $\beta_s$-LPH (see Fig. 3). The amino acid sequence of $\beta_b$-LPH (Li *et al.*, 1977a) has been proposed based on a homologous comparison with the $\beta_s$-LPH structure. Nakanishi *et al.* (1979) reported recently the sequence of $\beta_b$-LPH to consist of 93 amino acids derived from the DNA sequence. The primary structure of both bovine and ovine $\beta$-LPH has subsequently been reinvestigated (Li and Chung, 1981). Results indicated the difference between ovine and bovine $\beta$-LPH is in the region of $Gly^{29}$-$Lys^{41}$ as follows:

29 35 41
Bovine: Gly-Leu-Val-Ala-Glu-Ala-Glu-Ala-Glu-Ala-Ala-Glu-Lys

29 35 39
Ovine: Gly-Leu-Val-Ala-Glu-Ala-Glu-Ala-Ala-Glu-Lys

It appears that the bovine hormone has an additional Ala-Glu in this peptide segment. Thus, bovine β-LPH consists of 93 amino acids (see Fig. 6); ovine β-LPH is different and consists of 91 amino acids (see Fig. 3).

## A. Isolation of $\beta_h$-LPH (Li and Chung, 1981)

The glands were homogenized in 75 ml of distilled water for 1 minute in a Waring blender. The slurry was then added to cold 600 ml acetone plus 15 ml conc. HCl and the mixture stirred for 1 hour. The mixture was filtered using Whatman No. 1 paper and the residue reextracted with 300 ml 80% acetone by stirring for ½ hour. The residue was filtered off and discarded. The combined supernatants were added slowly to 4.5 liters of cold acetone with stirring for 5 minutes. The precipitate was allowed to settle for 2 days. The acetone was siphoned off and discarded. The precipitate was filtered, washed with cold acetone, and dried overnight *in vacuo* over NaOH pellets. The resulting acid–acetone powder (4.1 gm) was dissolved in 125 ml of water at pH 3 and the solution was brought to 0.06 saturation with respect to NaCl. The NaCl precipitate was removed by centrifugation and the solution was brought to saturation with NaCl. The saturated NaCl precipitate was dissolved in 100 ml of 0.1 *M* HOAc and desalted by gel filtration on Sephadex G-10 column (3.5 × 80 cm) in 0.1 *M* HOAc. After lyophilization, the yield of the desalted material (designated fraction D) was 444 mg.

Fraction D was next submitted to chromatography on a CMC column (1.5 × 45 cm) that had been equilibrated with 0.01 *M* $NH_4OAc$ buffer of pH 4.6. Elution was performed as described in Li *et al.* (1975). Further purification was performed with exclusion chromatography on Sephadex G-50 (fine).

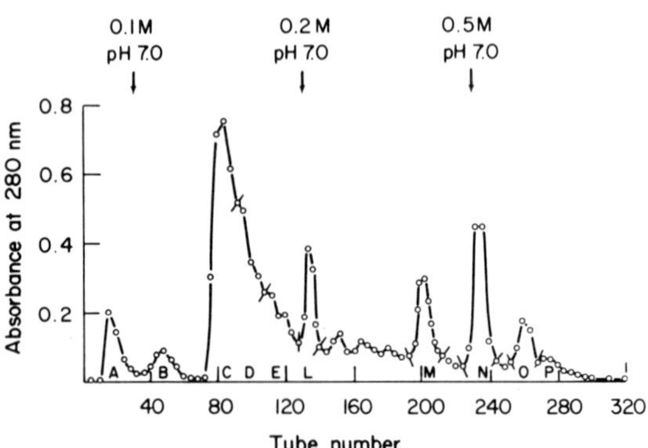


Fig. 7. CMC chromatography of 444 mg fraction D from human pituitaries: column size, 1.5 × 45 cm; flow rate, 12 ml/hour; 4 ml/tube.

TABLE VI
AMINO ACID COMPOSITION OF HUMAN β-LPH

| Amino acid | Residues derived from hydrolysis | Residues derived from sequence | Cseh *et al.* 1972 | Scott and Lowry, 1974 | Chrétien *et al.*, 1976a |
|---|---|---|---|---|---|
| Lys | 8.7 | 9 | 10 | 10 | 10 |
| His | 2.1 | 2 | 2 | 2 | 2 |
| Arg | 5.3 | 5 | 5 | 6 | 6 |
| Asp | 8.9 | 9 | 9 | 10 | 10 |
| Thr | 3.9 | 4 | 4 | 4 | 4 |
| Ser | 3.8 | 4 | 5 | 4 | 4 |
| Glu | 10.8 | 13 | 13 | 13 | 13 |
| Pro | 6.1 | 6 | 6 | 6 | 7 |
| Gly | 11.2 | 11 | 9 | 12 | 12 |
| Ala | 7.9 | 8 | 8 | 9 | 8 |
| Val | 2.5 | 2 | 3 | 3 | 2 |
| Met | 1.8 | 2 | 2 | 2 | 2 |
| Ile | 1.8[a] | 2 | 2 | 2 | 1 |
| Leu | 7.3 | 7 | 7 | 8 | 7 |
| Tyr | 3.1 | 3 | 3 | 4 | 3 |
| Phe | 3.1 | 3 | 3 | 3 | 3 |
| Trp | 1.0[b] | 1 | 1 | 1 | 1 |

[a]72 hour hydrolysis.
[b]Methanesulfonic acid hydrolysis.

Figure 7 presents the chromatographic pattern when 444 mg of fraction D was submitted to a CMC column. The material in tubes 128–140 (peak L) was lyophilized to obtain 18 mg crude $\beta_h$-LPH. Further purification of crude $\beta_h$-LPH (18 mg) was achieved by gel filtration on a Sephadex G-50 column in 0.1 *M* HOAc. The content in the main peak was lyophilized, yielded 13 mg, and was shown to be homogeneous in paper electrophoresis at pH 6.7 and disc electrophoresis. $NH_2$-terminal analysis gave only glutamic acid as the end group. This material was subsequently characterized as human β-LPH.

## B. CHARACTERIZATION OF $\beta_h$-LPH (LI AND CHUNG, 1981)

The molecular weight of $\beta_h$-LPH was determined by sedimentation equilibrium to be 11,700. The amino acid content of $\beta_h$-LPH, summarized in Table VI, is comparable to that reported in the literature (Cseh *et al.*, 1972; Scott and Lowry, 1974; Chrétien *et al.*, 1976a). The $NH_2$-terminal sequence, as analyzed by the dansyl-Edman method, was shown to be:

H-Glx-Leu-Thr-Gly-Glx-Arg-Leu-Arg-

TABLE VII
MELANOCYTE-STIMULATING ACTIVITY OF SHEEP AND HUMAN $\beta$-LIPOTROPIN

| Preparation | Dose (ng) | Response[a] |
|---|---|---|
| $\beta_s$-LPH | 60 | 24.7 ± 4.1 |
| | 180 | 39.0 ± 3.9 |
| $\beta_h$-LPH[b] | 60 | 31.5 ± 2.9 |
| | 180 | 52.7 ± 4.4 |

[a]MSH activity expressed as percent decrease in reflectance. Five skins used per each assay. Values in mean ± SE.

[b]Relative potency to $\beta_s$-LPH, 188% with 95% confidence limit of 108–508 and $\lambda = 0.22$.

The melanocyte-stimulating activity as assayed by the *in vitro* frog skin method is summarized in Table VII. It is evident that $\beta_h$-LPH is somewhat more potent as a melanotropin in comparison withe the sheep hormone. However, the lipolytic potency of the hormone from these two species is identical as shown in Fig. 8.

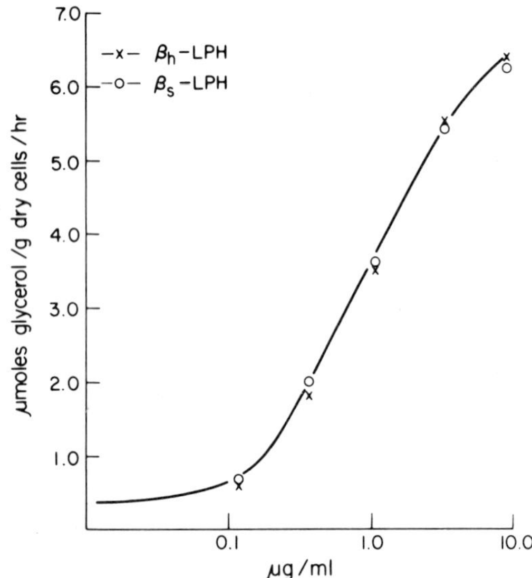


FIG. 8. Lipolytic activity of $\beta$-LPH and $\beta_s$-LPH in rabbit fat cells.

H-Glu-Leu-Thr-Gly-Gln-Arg-Leu-Arg-Gln-Gly-
5 10

Asp-Gly-Pro-Asn-Ala-Gly-Ala-Asp-Asp-Gly-
15 20

Pro-Gly-Ala-Gln-Ala-Asp-Leu-Glu-His-Ser-
25 30

Leu-Leu-Val-Ala-Ala-Glu-Lys-Lys-Asp-Glu-
35 40

Gly-Pro-Tyr-Arg-Met-Glu-His-Phe-Arg-Trp-
45 50

Gly-Ser-Pro-Pro-Lys-Asp-Lys-Arg-Tyr-Gly-
55 60

Gly-Phe-Met-Thr-Ser-Glu-Lys-Ser-Gln-Thr-
65 70

Pro-Leu-Val-Thr-Leu-Phe-Lys-Asn-Ala-Ile-
75 80

Ile-Lys-Asn-Ala-Tyr-Lys-Lys-Gly-Glu-OH
85 89

Fig. 9. Amino acid sequence of human $\beta$-LPH.

### C. Primary Structure of $\beta_h$-LPH (Li and Chung, 1981)

From the tryptic, chymotryptic, peptic, and thermolysin peptides of $\beta_h$-LPH, it is possible to propose the complete amino acid sequence of the hormone as shown in Fig. 9. It consists of 89 amino acids with the single Trp residue in position 50.

The sequence of COOH-terminal 52 residues has been reported by Cseh *et al.* (1972). In addition, these investigations indicated that their $\beta_h$-LPH preparation has the $NH_2$-terminal sequence: $NH_2$-Glx-Gly-Asx-. The sequence, shown in Fig. 9, is in agreement with Cseh *et al.* (1972) on the COOH-terminal sequence but differed on the sequence at the $NH_2$-terminus. It is of interest to note that Chrétien *et al.* (1976a) reported $NH_2$-Glu-Leu-Thr-Gly-Glu- and -Ala-Val-Leu-OH as $NH_2$-terminal and COOH-terminal sequences, respectively, in $\beta_h$-LPH.

## VI. ISOLATION AND CHARACTERIZATION OF $\gamma$-LPH

$\gamma$-LPH was first isolated and sequenced from sheep pituitary extracts (Chrétien and Li, 1967). Its primary structure is identical to the 58 $NH_2$-terminal residues of $\beta_s$-LPH (Li *et al.*, 1965; Li and Chung, 1976a). $\gamma$-LPH from pig glands has subsequently been isolated and characterized (Gráf *et al.*, 1969). The COOH-terminal 18-amino acid segment of $\gamma$-LPH is the entire sequence of $\beta$-MSH (Chrétien and Li, 1967). The presence of $\gamma$-LPH in human pituitaries has recently been described (Udea *et al.*, 1980). The isolation and primary structure of $\gamma$-LPH from human pituitary glands has recently been accomplished (Li *et al.*, 1980).

For isolation of $\gamma_h$-LPH, acid–acetone powder (16 gm) and fraction D (1.7 gm) from 1500 human pituitaries were obtained as previously described (Li *et al.*, 1966). Fraction D (0.5 gm) was submitted to chromatography on CMC column (1.5 × 45 cm) according to the same procedure for the isolation of $\beta_h$-LPH (Li and Chung, 1981) with a pattern similar to that of Fig. 7. The

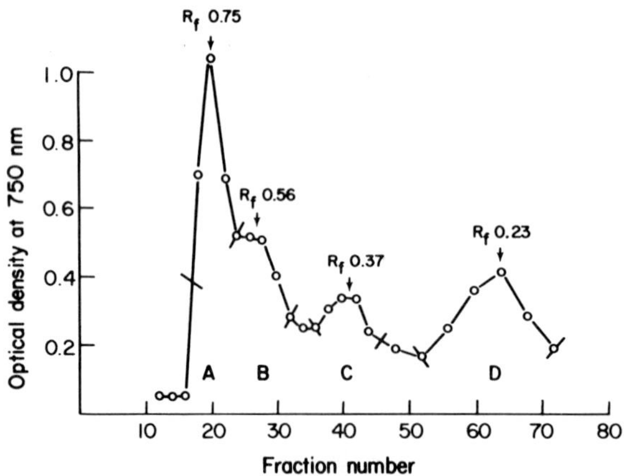


FIG. 10. Partition chromatography of crude natural $\gamma_h$-LPH on Sephadex G-50. Column size, 1.05 × 26.6 cm; solvent system, 1-butanol:pyridine:3.4 *M* NaCl (31:250:320); sample size, 18 mg; fraction volume, 0.45 ml; flow rate, 2 ml/hour; detection, Folin–Lowry; fractions pooled as indicated to give A, B, C, and D.

TABLE VIII
AMINO ACID COMPOSITIONS OF FRACTIONS PC-C AND PC-D[a]

| Amino acid | C | D | Integral values | $\beta_h$-LPH-(1-58)[b] |
|---|---|---|---|---|
| Trp | N.D.[c] | N.D.[c] | N.D.[c] | 1 |
| His | 2.0 | 2.1 | 2 | 2 |
| Lys | 3.1 | 3.2 | 3 | 3 |
| Arg | 4.1 | 4.2 | 4 | 4 |
| Asp | 6.6 | 6.6 | 7 | 8 |
| Thr | 1.1 | 0.9 | 1 | 1 |
| Ser | 2.0 | 1.9 | 2 | 2 |
| Glu | 7.9 | 7.7 | 8 | 8 |
| Pro | 5.0 | 5.2 | 5 | 5 |
| Gly | 7.7 | 7.9 | 8 | 8 |
| Ala | 5.8 | 6.2 | 6 | 6 |
| Val | 1.1 | 1.1 | 1 | 1 |
| Met | 0.9 | 1.0 | 1 | 1 |
| Leu | 5.1 | 5.0 | 5 | 6 |
| Tyr | 1.1 | 1.1 | 1 | 1 |
| Phe | 1.1 | 1.2 | 1 | 1 |

[a]See Fig. 2.
[b]Taken from Li and Chung (1976a).
[c]Not determined.

material in peak C was lyophilized to yield 70 mg (designated CMC-C). From the 1.7 gm fraction D, 220 mg of CMC-C were obtained. CMC-C (132 mg) was next applied to gel filtration on Sephadex G-50 (fine) column in 0.1 *M* HOAc. The content in the main peak was lyophilized, yielded 53 mg, and rechromatographed on Sephadex G-50 under the same conditions. The material recovered from the main peak yielded 33 mg of crude $\gamma_h$-LPH.

A sample (18 mg) of the crude $\gamma_h$-LPH was submitted to partition chromatography on Sephadex G-50 as shown in Fig. 10. Materials in peaks A, B, C, and D were evaporated *in vacuo* to dryness and desalted on Sephadex G-10 in 0.5 *M* HOAc, and are designated as PC-A, PC-B, PC-C, and PC-D. All four fractions behaved identically on paper electrophoresis at pH 3.7 and pH 6.7. Amino acid analyses of PC-A and PC-B showed the presence of cystine. Fractions PC-C and PC-D were isolated in yields of about 0.7 mg and 1.7 mg, respectively. Analytical data indicate that PC-D is $\gamma_h$-LPH and PC-C is probably $<$Glu$^1$-$\gamma_h$-LPH.

Table VIII shows that the amino acid compositions of PC-C and PC-D obtained by partition chromatography are identical to that of the $NH_2$-terminal 1-58 segment of $\beta_h$-LPH (Li and Chung, 1976a) with the exception of two less residues (Leu, Asp).

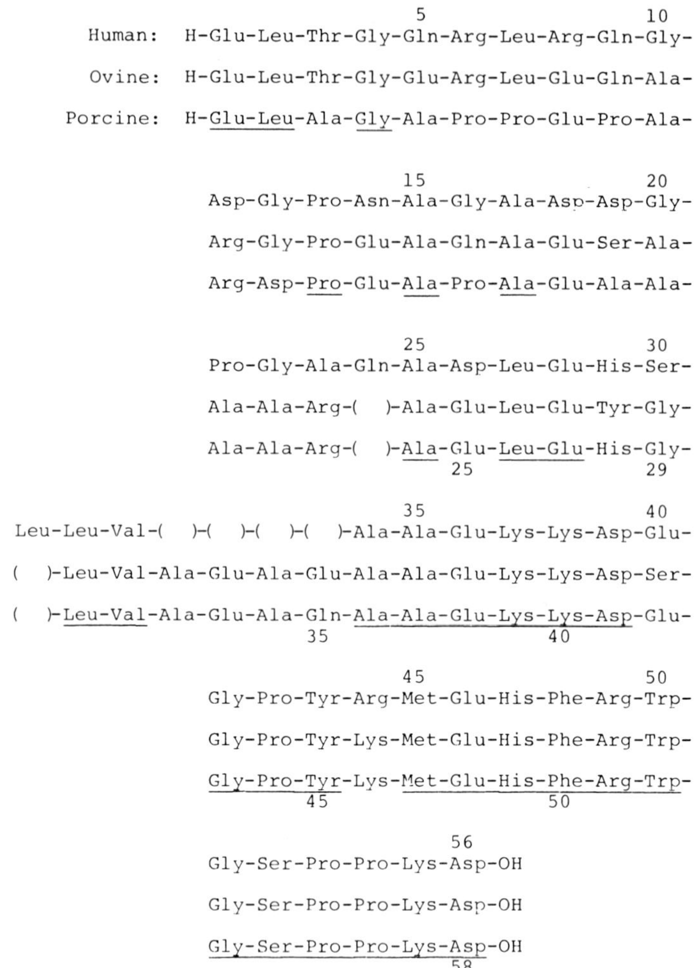

FIG. 11. Amino acid sequence of various γ-LPH.

From the sequence analysis of tryptic, chymotryptic, and thermolysin peptides of $\gamma_h$-LPH, together with the proposed structure of $\beta_h$-LPH (Li and Chung, 1981), the amino acid sequence of $\gamma_h$-LPH is deduced as $\beta_h$-LPH-(1-56) (see Fig. 9).

There are 56 amino acids in $\gamma_h$-LPH (see Table VIII) instead of 58 residues as in the case of $\gamma_s$-LPH (Chrétien and Li, 1967) or $\gamma_p$-LPH (Gráf *et al.*, 1969). For comparison of the proposed amino acid sequence of $\gamma_h$-LPH with that of the ovine (Chrétien and Li, 1967) and porcine (Gráf *et al.*, 1969), it is necessary to have five gaps for the human structure and two gaps for the other two, as shown in Fig. 11. It may be noted that the COOH-terminal 23-amino acid sequence is highly conserved in evolution. This segment contains the entire primary structure of β-MSH.

When assayed for lipolytic potency using isolated rabbit fat cells, it was found that $\gamma_h$- and $\beta_h$-LPH exhibited nearly identical potency. Earlier studies showed that the lipolytic activities of these two hormones from sheep pituitary glands were the same (Chrétien and Li, 1967).

## VII. LIPOTROPINS FROM MOUSE PITUITARY CELL

Tissues other than normal pituitary glands have been shown to contain LPH-like material. Feurle *et al.* (1980) reported the presence of β-LPH in human pancreas and arotial mucosa by four different methods: radioimmunological displacement, Sephadex chromatography, ion exchange chromatography, and immunocytochemistry.

Eipper and Mains (1979) described the isolation and characterization of β-LPH and γ-LPH from mouse pituitary tumor cell AtT culture medium. The molecular weights of β-LPH and γ-LPH from mouse tumor cell are 8200 ± 250 and 4600 ± 200, respectively. These values are significantly lower than the hor-

TABLE IX
AMINO ACID COMPOSITION OF MOUSE TUMOR CELL β-LPH AND γ-LPH

| Amino acid | β-LPH | γ-LPH | Difference between β- and γ-LPH |
|---|---|---|---|
| Lysine | 8 | 2 | 6 |
| Histidine | 2 | 1 | 1 |
| Arginine | 4 | 3 | 1 |
| Aspartic acid | 6 | 4 | 2 |
| Threonine | 3 | 0 | 3 |
| Serine | 4 | 2 | 2 |
| Glutamic acid | 12 | 9 | 3 |
| Proline | 5 | 4 | 1 |
| Glycine | 7 | 3–4 | 3 |
| Alanine | 3–4 | 1–2 | 2 |
| Valine | 3 | 2 | 1 |
| Methionine | 1 | 0 | 1 |
| Isoleucine | 2 | 0 | 2 |
| Leucine | 6 | 4 | 2 |
| Tyrosine | 2 | 1 | 1 |
| Phenylalanine | 3 | 1 | 2 |
| Tryptophan | 1 | 1 | 0 |
| Total residues | 72 | 39 | 31+2 |

mones from other species. The amino acid compositions of the mouse tumor lipotropins are summarized in Table IX. It is interesting that the mouse tumor γ-LPH does not contain methionine, which may be taken to mean that the β-MSH segment has no methionine. All other known β-MSHs have a single methionine (Li, 1978). When the amino acid composition of mouse tumor cell β-LPH was subtracted from that of γ-LPH, it gave us the composition of β-EP. As shown in Table IX, the β-EP segment of mouse tumor cell β-LPH has a composition similar to ovine, bovine, and camel endorphin (Li *et al.*, 1977a).

## VIII. CONFORMATION OF β-LPH

$\beta_s$-LPH has been reported to contain about 12% α-helix in dilute salt solutions, which increased to 30% in 50% dioxane water (St-Pierre *et al.*, 1976). The ability of nonpolar solvents to produce helical structures in $\beta_p$-LPH has also been observed by Makarov *et al.* (1976).

Yang *et al.* (1977) reported on the conformation of $\beta_s$-LPH in water, methanol, and SDS solutions as determined by CD and hydrodynamic studies. In water at pH 5.9, $\beta_s$-LPH appears to have little secondary structure as revealed by the CD spectra. The absence of the double minimum at 210 and 222 nm characteristic of an α-helix and the appearance of a large negative band near 200 nm suggest that the structure is mostly nonperiodic, although a small amount of helix and β-form cannot be completely ruled out. Raising the pH of the polypeptide solution to 12 did not change the CD spectra of $\beta_s$-LPH, suggesting that changes in electrostatic interactions do not cause detectable changes in polypeptide conformation. The changes in CD spectra with temperature are small and reversible. Raising the temperature of the polypeptide solution reduced the magnitude of the negative CD band near 200 nm.

The CD spectra of $\beta_s$-LPH in the region of side chain absorption show that in an aqueous solution the polypeptide exhibits only weak optical activity. The spectra in water and in 6 *M* guanidine–hydrochloride are either equivalent or nearly the same, indicating that the polypeptide has a rigid tertiary structure with aromatic groups buried within asymmetric local environments. The hormone shows negative bands at 269 and 261–262 nm characteristic of phenylalanine residues. The negative bands at 283 and 276 nm for $\beta_s$-LPH can be assigned to tyrosine residues.

The intrinsic viscosity, $[\eta]$, and sedimentation coefficient, $s°$, of $\beta_s$-LPH have been measured in 0.1 *M* KCl at 5°. It had an $[\eta]$ of 0.15 dl/gm and indicating that the polypeptide is not a compact, globular molecule. The corresponding $s^{\circ}_{20,w}$ (converted from data at 5°) was 1.3 S.

Addition of methanol to an aqueous solution of $\beta_S$-LPH induces an $\alpha$-helical conformation. The polypeptide increases in helicity with increasing concentrations of methanol. Equally striking is the helix-promoting effect of SDS on the polypeptide; almost one-half of the molecule becomes helical in SDS solution.

The addition of either methanol or SDS increases the CD intensity of both the phenylalanine and tyrosine bands in the $\beta_S$-LPH molecule, suggesting the production of somewhat more rigid, asymmetric environments for these chromophores in the presence of solvents less polar than water. However, even in SDS solutions no distinct band can be assigned to the tryptophan residue in $\beta_S$-LPH, suggesting that some areas of conformational flexibility still exist.

## IX. RELATIONSHIP OF STRUCTURE TO LIPOLYTIC ACTIVITY OF $\beta_S$-LPH

As already mentioned, the lipolytic activity of $\gamma_S$-LPH is equivalent to that of $\beta_S$-LPH (Chrétien and Li, 1967). Lipolytic activity of various fragments of $\beta_S$-LPH is summarized in Table X. A fragment with a sequence of residues 1-65 (see Fig. 3) obtained by CNBr cleavage of the ovine hormone also exhibits comparable activity (Lohmar and Li, 1968). On the other hand, a fragment with a sequence of residues 47-91 (see Fig. 3) possesses only one-tenth of the activity of $\beta_S$-LPH. A synthetic peptide consisting of 50 amino acid residues, $\beta_S$-LPH-(42-91) has about six times that of $\beta_S$-LPH on a weight basis in isolated rabbit fat cells (Yamashiro and Li, 1974).

TABLE X
LIPOLYTIC POTENCY OF VARIOUS FRAGMENTS OF $\beta_S$-LIPOPROTEIN

| Residue | Rabbit adipose tissue | Relative potency[a] |
|---|---|---|
| 1-91 | Pad/cells | 1.0 |
| 1-47 | Pad | Nil |
| 1-58 | Pad | 1.0 |
| 1-65 | Pad | 1.1 |
| 66-91 | Pad | Nil |
| 41-91 | Cells | 5.4 |
| 41-58 | Pad | ≃10.0 |
| 42-91 | Cells | 6.0 |
| 48-65 | Cells | Nil |
| 47-91 | Pad | 0.1 |
| 61-91 | Cells | Nil |

[a]On-weight basis.

Lemaire *et al.* (1978) reported the synthesis of $\beta_s$-LPH-(41-91), which spans the complete amino acid sequences of both $\beta$-MSH and $\beta$-EP, in good yield. The synthetic $\beta_s$-LPH-(41-91) was homogenous as evidenced by partition chromatography on agarose, thin-layer chromatography in two solvent systems, paper electrophoresis at pH 3.7 and 6.9, polyacrylamide gel electrophoresis, and amino acid analysis of acid and total enzymatic hydrolysates. The lipolytic activity of the synthetic product in isolated rabbit fat cells is 5.4 times more active than the natural hormone on a weight basis and it possesses approximately the same potency of $\beta_s$-LPH-(42-91) as previously reported (Yamashiro and Li, 1974). Apparently, an extension of the hexa- or heptapeptide to the $NH_2$-terminus of $\beta$-LPH-(47-91) greatly increases the lipolytic activity. However, further extension of the $NH_2$-terminal residues to Glu-1 lowers the activity. The optimal number of residues that could be added or substracted from the $NH_2$-terminus of $\beta_s$-LPH-(42-91) to give rise to maximal lipolytic activity remains to be investigated.

## X. RADIOIMMUNOASSAY

Earlier immunological studies of $\beta_s$-LPH showed that the hormone is a poor antigen in rabbits (Lohmar and Li, 1968). A sensitive radioimmunoassay (RIA) for $\beta_s$-LPH has subsequently been developed (Desranleau *et al.*, 1972). Antiserum to the human hormone has recently been raised in rabbits and characterized by gel double diffusion, quantitative precipitin, microcomplement fixation, and biological neutralization tests (Rao and Li, 1977). Using this antiserum, an RIA system for $\beta_h$-LPH has been developed and shown the antiserum to be species specific (Krieger *et al.*, 1977b; Wiedemann *et al.*, 1977). Human plasma concentrations of $\beta_h$-LPH were estimated by this RIA system to be $47.9 \pm 5.7$ pg/ml in five normal subjects (Krieger *et al.*, 1977b). It appears that the plasma level of $\beta_h$-LPH in normal female subjects is higher than that of male subjects (Wiedemann *et al.*, 1977). It is of interest to note that plasma ACTH and $\beta_h$-LPH rose in parallel in response to insulin-induced hypoglycemia (Krieger *et al.*, 1977b).

A specific RIA for $\beta_h$-LPH has also been described by Jeffcoate *et al.* (1978). With extraction of 3 ml plasma samples, the assay is sensitive to measure circulating $\beta_h$-LPH levels in normal individuals at 0900 hours to be 20–200 pg/ml. There is a circadian variation with levels falling to $<$20–80 pg/ml at 2300 hours; $\beta_h$-LPH levels rose after metyrapone and after insulin-induced hypoglycemia, and fell after dexamethasone administration (Jeffcoate *et al.*, 1978).

The half-life of $\beta_h$-LPH in adult male rats after a single intravenous injection of the hormone was found to be $4.2 \pm 0.75$ minutes as estimated by RIA

(Chang *et al.*, 1978). In the same study, the rate of disappearance of $\beta_h$-EP is slower ($t_{\frac{1}{2}}$ – 9.2 minutes) than that of $\beta_h$-LPH.

In another study, the trace of $\beta_h$-EP immunoreactivity in the rabbit antiserum to $\beta_h$-LPH was removed by affinity chromatography (Liotta *et al.*, 1978). The purified antiserum was employed in studies of three normal human subjects in whom the metabolic clearance rate (MCR), apparent volume of distribution ($V_d$), and disappearance half-time ($t_{\frac{1}{2}}$) of $\beta_h$-LPH were determined following bolus injection of 0.27 mg $\beta_h$-LPH. Average values for the three parameters were obtained as follows: MCR, 517 ml/minute; $V_d$, 27,800 ml (48.8% body weight), and $t_{\frac{1}{2}}$, 37.3 minutes. In comparison, $\alpha_h$-ACTH has the following values: MCR, 291 ml/minute; $V_d$, 929 ml (13.9% body weight), and $t_{\frac{1}{2}}$, 21.4 minutes. The markedly different kinetics of $\beta_h$-LPH and $\alpha_h$-ACTH might reflect differing mechanisms for their tissue uptake and metabolism.

## XI. IMMUNOHISTOCHEMICAL LOCALIZATION OF β-LPH IN THE PITUITARY AND BRAIN

The immunofluorescent reactions of the cells of the intermediate lobe and some basophils of the sheep pituitary indicated that both cell types contain β-LPH or an immunologically related substance (Moon *et al.*, 1973). Additional evidence was provided by the studies with rabbit antiserum to $\beta_s$-LPH and peroxidase-conjugated anti-rabbit γ-globulin in which peroxidase reaction product was observed in the intermediate lobe walls and some basophils of the anterior pituitary. The immunofluorescent reactions of these two cell types with antiserum to $\alpha_s$-ACTH also indicated that both are corticotrophs (Moon *et al.*, 1973).

The addition of $\beta_s$-LPH to anti-$\beta_s$-LPH abolished both the fluorescent and peroxidase reactions of the intermediate lobe cells and corticotrophs of the anterior pituitary. When $\alpha_s$-ACTH was added to anti-$\beta_s$-LPH, there was a significant reduction in the fluorescence of the intermediate lobe cells; reduction of fluorescence was also observed in the corticotrophs of the anterior lobe. These data provide evidence for the first time that the intermediate lobe walls (lipotrophs) and probably the anterior lobe corticotrophs contain β-LPH (Moon *et al.*, 1973). These observations were subsequently confirmed and extended by Pelletier *et al.* (1977).

Identification of the β-LPH-producing cells in the pituitary from oxen, sheep, pigs, monkeys, and man was carried out by the technique involving use of the unlabeled antibody and peroxidase–antiperoxidase complex (Pelletier *et al.*, 1977). Serial paraffin and ultrathin sections were treated for the detection of both β-LPH and ACTH at the light and electronmicropic levels.

It was found that β-LPH is located only in the corticotrophs in the pars intermedia and pars distalis of all species studied. It was also shown by electron microscope that β-LPH is contained in all the secretory granulos of positive cells. These results suggest that β-LPH is stored in the same secretory granules as ACTH and that both hormones are released together during granule extension (Pelletier *et al.*, 1977).

Watson *et al.* (1977) described evidence for the localization of β-LPH in hypothalamic cells and beaded axons throughout the brainstem and limbic system of the rat brain using the immunohistochemical technique. No activity was seen in the cerebellum, hippocampus, cerebral cortex, or spinal cord. The system of β-LPH fibers seems to have many points of contact with the catecholamine neuronal networks. Norepinephrine cells of the locus coeruleus appeared to have especially heavy contact with β-LPH fibers. Other points in common with norepinephrine fibers include the periaqueductal central gray area, the region of the dorsal catecholamine bundle, the periventricular nucleus of the thalamus, most of the hypothalamus, the lateral septal nucleus, the nucleus accumbens, the diagonal band of Broca, the stria terminalis, and the medial amygdoloid nucleus.

Dopaminergic systems also have extensive areas of contact with β-LPH containing structures. The dopamine cell areas in midbrain (zona compacta, the medial A10 group and the dopamine cells of the periaqueductal central gray area) have moderate contact with β-LPH fibers. The hypothalamus, nucleus accumbens, stria terminalis, lateral septum, and diagonal band of Broca are potential points of interaction. Of particular interest is the arcuate median eminence area where both dopamine and β-LPH fibers and cells are seen. There were very few β-LPH fibers associated with the serotonin rich raphe dorsalis, magnus, or medianus (Watson *et al.*, 1977).

The presence of immunoassayable β-LPH has been reported in bovine central nervous system, the highest concentration being found in the hypothalmus (Labella *et al.*, 1977; Krieger *et al.*, 1977a). In order to establish the identification of the nervous structures containing β-LPH in the human hypothalamus, Pelletier *et al.* (1978) described immunohistochemical localization of β-LPH in this tissue. In the four hypothalami examined, a rich network of immunostained nerve fibers was observed in an area extending rostrocaudally from the anterior part of the paraventricular nucleus up to the mammillary bodies. The positive fibers were mainly found laterally in the higher portion of the third ventricle but could occasionally be seen along the border of the middle and low portions of the third ventricle. They were particularly abundant in an area of the periventricular nucleus located above the paraventricular nucleus. No immunohistochemical reaction was detected in the neurovascular zone or the pituitary stalk. At high magnification, the immunostained fibers appeared as typical beaded fibers.

Immunostained cell bodies were seen in the basal hypothalamus in an area corresponding to the anterior portion of the infundibular nucleus. They were not infrequently observed below the floor of the third ventricle. These positive cells appeared as small to medium-size neurons of a diameter ranging from 14 to 22 $\mu$m. The immunoperoxidase reaction in the cytoplasm appeared to be in granular form. Numerous positive fibers were observed near the positive cell bodies. No immunostaining was detected when normal rabbit serum or anti-$\beta_h$-LPH serum absorbed with $\beta_h$-LPH was used.

Zimmerman *et al.* (1978) have also shown that $\beta$-LPH is localized in hypothalamus and pituitary of sheep or ox by the immunoperoxidase technique. In both species $\beta$-LPH was found in perikarya of arcuate neurons as well as in cells of the anterior and intermediate lobes of the pituitary. A large number of immunoreactive axons were found in the arcuate region; some appeared to innervate other neurons and others projected to portal capillaries. Stained fiber segments were also scattered throughout the hypothalamus (Zimmerman *et al.*, 1978).

## XII. BIOLOGICAL PROPERTIES

As a lipolytic agent, $\beta$-LPH is most active in rabbit adipose tissue, only weakly active in rat, and appears to be inactive in mouse adipose tissue (Lohmar and Li, 1968). Similar species specificity was observed on the levels of serum free fatty acids when injected with $\beta$-LPH (Tamasi *et al.*, 1969). It stimulated lipolysis by activating the adenylate cyclase system (Lis *et al.*, 1972a). In fasting mice, $\beta$-LPH exhibits fat-mobilizing activity (Lohmar and Li, 1968). $\beta$-LPH also has melanotropic activity of a potency similar to ACTH (Lohmar and Li, 1968). In the rabbit, it lowers plasma calcium (Chrétien *et al.*, 1970; Lis *et al.*, 1972b; Gildersleeve *et al.*, 1975) and raises plasma phosphate (Lis *et al.*, 1972b).

A single injection of $\beta_s$-LPH in the rabbit decreased significantly blood coagulation time with peak effects at 60 and 180 minutes. Prothrombin time was shortened and platelets adhesiveness was increased at 60 minutes only, while thrombin time was maximal at 60 and 180 minutes. Platelets counts and plasma recalcification time were not affected by $\beta_s$-LPH (Chrétien *et al.*, 1971).

Thody and Shuster (1971) reported the sebotropic activity of $\beta_s$-LPH. In the ovariectomized–hypohysectomized rats, a daily dose of 0.1 mg of the hormone for 2 weeks caused a significant increase in the sebum secretion.

TABLE XI
EFFECT OF $\beta_s$-LPH ON SEBUM SECRETION OF OVARIECTOMIZED–HYPOPHYSECTOMIZED RATS[a]

| Hormone treatment | No. rats | Final body wt (gm) | Adrenal (mg) | Preputial gland (mg) | Sebum secretion[b] (mg) |
|---|---|---|---|---|---|
| Control | 6 | 129.8 | 13.7 | 22.8 | 58.1 |
| $\beta_s$-LPH | 5 | 133.2 | 14.0 | 25.4 | 74.5 ($P<0.01$)[c] |

[a] Modified from Thody and Shuster (1971).
[b] mg/4 days.
[c] The $P$ value refers to the significant difference between the hormone-treated rats and the controls.

$\beta_s$-LPH had no effect on the weight of the preputial or adrenal glands (see Table XI).

Behavioral effects of $\beta_s$-LPH in the male rabbit have been described by Bertolini (1971). The experiments were carried out on white New Zealand male rabbits weighing about 3 kg with intraventricular injections of $\beta_s$-LPH. The data summarized in Table XII show that a single dose of 5 $\mu$g of $\beta_s$-LPH was able to induce penile erections, stretchings, and yawning in the rabbit.

Arregui and Iversen (1979) presented evidence that $\beta_h$-LPH is a potent inhibitor to the human brain angiotensin converting enzyme using His-His-Leu as the substrate. The calculated $K_i$ value for the hormone is 0.78 $\mu M$. $\beta$-EP and Met-enkephalin were inactive to inhibit the enzyme at concentrations up to 40 $\mu M$.

Matsuoka *et al.* (1980) have demonstrated that $\beta$-LPH is an aldosterone-stimulating agent in collagenase-dispersed rat adrenal capsular cells. At $10^{-8}$

TABLE XII
BEHAVIORAL EFFECTS OF $\beta_s$-LPH[a]

| | | No. of rabbits showing[b]: | | |
|---|---|---|---|---|
| Dose ($\mu$g) | No. rabbits | Sexual excitement | Stretching | Yawning |
| 100 | 3 | 2 (5) | 2 (10) | 2 (8) |
| 50 | 3 | 3 (6) | 3 (24) | 3 (6) |
| 10 | 10 | 6 (6) | 10 (11) | 9 (8) |
| 5 | 10 | 8 (4) | 10 (6) | 5 (7) |

[a] Modified from Bertolini (1971).
[b] In parentheses are the number of penile erections, stretching, and yawning recorded during the 2 hours following the injection of $\beta_s$-LPH.

to $10^{-7}$ $M$ $\beta_s$-LPH stimulated production of aldosterone by the capsular cells, but not that of corticosterone by the decapsular cells. Human $\beta$-LPH produced a similar effect. In a single experiment with synthetic $\beta_s$-LPH (Yamashiro and Li, 1978), aldosterone stimulation was similar to that caused by the natural product. A significant increase in aldosterone production was obtained with $10^{-9}$ $M$ $\beta$-LPH and the half-maximum increase in aldosterone production was obtained at a $\beta$-LPH concentration between $3 \times 10^{-8}$ and $1 \times 10^{-7}$ $M$. The maximum response obtained with $\beta_s$-LPH (144.9 ± 15.5 ng/100,000 capsular cells) is greater than that obtained with agiotensin II (110.8 ± 16.1 ng/100,000 capsular cells) and the same as that obtained with ACTH (142.7 ± 17.3 ng/100,000 capsular cells). Doses of $\beta_s$-LPH that maximally stimulated production of aldosterone did not significantly increase production of cyclic AMP by the adrenal cells. In contrast, maximally stimulating doses of synthetic $\alpha_h$-ACTH caused a 4.5-fold increase in cyclic AMP production (Matsuoka *et al.*, 1980). It appears that $\beta$-LPH and ACTH have different modes of action in the adrenal cell. At any rate, these data raise the question whether $\beta$-LPH is essential for the aldosterone response during sodium restriction in some types of primary aldosteronism.

## XIII. β-LIPOTROPIN—THE PROHORMONE FOR β-ENDORPHIN

During the course of isolation of melanotropins from camel pituitary glands (Li *et al.*, 1975), we were unable to find the existence of $\beta$-LPH, but obtained an untriakontapeptide (Li and Chung, 1976b) that has an amino acid sequence identical to the COOH-terminal 31-residues of ovine lipotropin [$\beta_s$-LPH-(61-91)] (see Fig. 3). The peptide possesses significant opiate activity (Li and Chung, 1976b), as displayed in a preparation of guinea pig ileum and in the opiate receptor binding assay (Cox *et al.*, 1976). This untriakontapeptide was designated $\beta$-endorphin ($\beta$-EP) (Li and Chung, 1976b). A similar untriakontapeptide with opiate activity was obtained from porcine (Bradbury *et al.*, 1976; Gráf *et al.*, 1976), ovine (Chrétien *et al.*, 1976b), bovine (Li *et al.*, 1977a), and rat (Rubinstein *et al.*, 1977b) pituitary glands. Apparently, a specific intracellular protease in the pituitary causes the cleavage of the Arg-Tyr bond in positions 60 and 61 (see Fig. 3) to generate $\beta$-EP (Gráf *et al.*, 1977).

Isolation of human $\beta$-EP has also been reported (Chrétien *et al.*, 1976b; Li *et al.*, 1976a). From 1000 frozen human glands, only 3 mg of the peptide were obtained (Li *et al.*, 1976a). Structural analysis established that the amino acid sequence of the human peptide is identical to the COOH-terminal 31-amino acid fragment of $\beta_h$-LPH (Li *et al.*, 1977a; see Fig. 9). Figure 12

| | |
|---|---|
| Human: | H-Tyr-Gly-Gly-Phe-Met(5)-Thr-Ser-Glu-Lys-Ser(10)- |
| | Gln-Thr-Pro-Leu-Val(15)-Thr-Leu-Phe-Lys-Asn(20)- |
| | Ala-Ile-Ile-Lys-Asn(25)-Ala-Tyr-Lys-Lys-Gly-Glu(31)-OH |
| Porcine: | Val . . . His . . . Gln-OH |
| Camel, Ovine, Bovine: | Ile . . . His . . . Gln-OH |

FIG. 12. Amino acid sequence of various $\beta$-EP.

presents the amino acid sequence of $\beta$-EP from various species. The only variations occur in residues positions 23, 27, and 31.

Both camel (Li *et al.*, 1976b) and human (Li *et al.*, 1977b) $\beta$-EP have been synthesized by the improved procedures of the solid-phase method. The brominated styrene/1% divinylbenzene polymer was used for the synthesis of $\beta_h$-EP. A yield of 32% was achieved based on starting resin. The opiate activity of the synthetic product was comparable to that of the natural peptide by the guinea pig ileum assay. It was found that the opiate activities of the synthetic camel and human $\beta$-EP are identical even though their amino acid sequences are slightly different (see Fig. 12).

In addition to the analgesic effect of $\beta$-EP, it exhibits a marked and prolonged state of catatonia (Jacquet *et al.*, 1976; Jacquet and Marks, 1976; Bloom *et al.*, 1976; Motomatsu *et al.*, 1977; Tseng *et al.*, 1977) in rats when injected directly into the brain. $\beta$-EP has been shown to induce excess grooming behavior in rats (Gispen *et al.*, 1976). Male sexual behavior in rats was also found to be influenced by the peptide (Meyerson and Terenius, 1977).

An intracerebroventricular dose of 94 $\mu$g $\beta$-EP in rats caused a profound hypothermia (Tseng *et al.*, 1977). The body temperature decreased at 30 minutes after injection and reached a maximum (4° lower than preinjection). A salivation effect of $\beta$-EP was also observed (Holaday *et al.*, 1978). Injections of $\beta$-EP into the anterior horn of the lateral ventricle in rats produced a profound increase in salivation along with a behavioral pattern described as sialogogic seizure.

In addition to its potent analgesic and behavioral activities, $\beta$-EP inhibits striatal dopamine release *in vitro* (Loh *et al.*, 1975). It stimulates somatotropin (Dupont *et al.*, 1976; Rivier *et al.*, 1977) and prolactin (Rivier *et al.*,

1977; Dupont *et al.*, 1977) release when injected intracerebroventricularly in rats. β-EP exhibits antidiuretic activity by intravenous injections in rats (Tseng *et al.*, 1978). This may be related to the observation that β-EP stimulates the release of vasopressin as measured by RIA (Weitzmann *et al.*, 1977).

## XIV. γ-LIPOTROPIN—THE PROHORMONE FOR β-MSH

As pointed out in 1965, the peptide segment comprising the sequence 37–58 in the $\beta_s$-LPH structure is $\beta_h$-MSH (Harris, 1959; Pickering and Li, 1963). In addition, the COOH-terminal 18 amino acids in γ-LPH is the entire sequence of $\beta_b$-MSH (Geschwind *et al.*, 1957). Barát *et al.* (1979) recently showed that brain cathepsin D selectively splits the $Ala^{36}$-$Ala^{37}$ peptide bond of $\beta_h$-LPH (see Fig. 9) to generate $\beta_h$-MSH.

Figure 13 presents the amino acid sequences of β-MSH from various species. All consist of 18 amino acids, except that the human hormone consists of 22 amino acids and one of the dogfish β-MSH has only 16 amino acids. When all β-MSHs are compared (Fig. 13) it is striking that the tetrapeptide His-Phe-Arg-Trp or the pentapeptide His-Phe-Arg-Trp-Gly has been conserved during the evolution from dogfish to man.

The precise function of MSH, except in amphibia and some fish, is not at all clear. It is thought by some to be concerned in visual adaptation (Jores and Glogner, 1933). It has been claimed (Hanaoka, 1951) that MSH concentrates prepared from bovine, equine, and porcine pituitaries, when administered subcutaneously to human subjects, are active in shortening the time of adaptation to darkness and increasing sensitivity to light. It was further reported by the same author (Hanaoka, 1953) that the hormone is capable of accelerating regeneration of visual purple in the retina.

Mussio Fournier *et al.* (1936, 1943) have reported that with MSH concentrates repigmentation was effected in patients with vitiligo. Lerner *et al.* (1954), working with more highly purified MSH preparations, did not succeed in confirming this observation, although they demonstrated darkening of human skin and the formation of new nevi as a consequence of the administration of this hormone. The latter investigators also noted increased pigmentation within a few hours after the administration of large doses of hormone (Lerner and Takahashi, 1956).

Melanotropins have been shown to exert action on the central nervous system. Ferrari (1958) and Ferrari *et al.* (1963) reported that α-MSH produced stretching and yawning movements in dogs. β-MSH enhances the amplitude of spinal cord monosynaptic potentials (Krivoy and Guillemin, 1961). Long *et al.* (1961) postulated that melanotropins play a role in

Human: H-Ala-Glu-Lys-Lys-Asp-Glu-Gly-Pro-Tyr-Arg-Met-Glu-His-Phe-Arg-Trp-Gly-Ser-Pro-Pro-Lys-Asp-OH

Macacus: H-Asp-Glu-Gly-Pro-Tyr-Arg-Met-Glu-His-Phe-Arg-Trp-Gly-Ser-Pro-Pro-Lys-Asp-OH

Porcine: H-Asp-Glu-Gly-Pro-Tyr-Lys-Met-Glu-His-Phe-Arg-Trp-Gly-Ser-Pro-Pro-Lys-Asp-OH

Equine: H-Asp-Glu-Gly-Pro-Tyr-Lys-Met-Glu-His-Phe-Arg-Trp-Gly-Ser-Pro-Arg-Lys-Asp-OH

Bovine: H-Asp-Ser-Gly-Pro-Tyr-Lys-Met-Glu-His-Phe-Arg-Trp-Gly-Ser-Pro-Pro-Lys-Asp-OH

Camel: H-Asp-Gly-Gly-Pro-Tyr-Lys-Met-Glu-His-Phe-Arg-Trp-Gly-Ser-Pro-Pro-Lys-Asp-OH

Camel: H-Asp-Gly-Gly-Pro-Tyr-Lys-Met-Gln-His-Phe-Arg-Trp-Gly-Ser-Pro-Pro-Lys-Asp-OH

Dogfish: (*Scyliorphinus caniculus*) H-Asp-Gly-Ile-Asp-Tyr-Lys-Met-Gly-His-Phe-Arg-Trp-Gly-Ala-Pro-Met-Asp-Lys-OH

Dogfish: (*Squalus acanthias*) H-Asp-Gly-Asp-Asp-Tyr-Lys-Phe-Gly-His-Phe-Arg-Trp-Ser-Val-Pro-Leu-OH

FIG. 13. Amino acid sequence of various $\beta$-MSH.

central neural control. In rats, α-MSH exhibits an inhibitory effect on extinction of conditioned avoidance behavior (De Wied, 1966; De Wied and Bohns, 1966). Sandman *et al.* (1971, 1972) also reported that melanotropins have effects on attention, memory, and certain aspects of learning behavior. Two observed effects of β-MSH on rodents resemble the effects of catecholamines. These are behavior changes, namely, hyperexcitability in mice and lethargy in rats (Sakamoto, 1966), and radioprotection to lethal whole-body X-irradiation (Sakamoto and Prasad, 1967).

The effects of α- and β-MSH on the thyroid were studied in mice injected with $^{131}I$ and pretreated with thyroxine by Bowers *et al.* (1964). It was found that melanotropins cause an increase in blood levels of $^{131}I$ as well as the uptake of $^{131}I$. Melanotropins were found also to stimulate thyroid activity in rabbits (Courrier and Cehovic, 1960) and in guinea pigs (Cehovic, 1962).

α-MSH was shown to act synergistically with testosterone to stimulate the sebaceous, prostate, and preputial glands and the seminal vesicles in hypophysectomized–castrated rats (Ebling *et al.*, 1975; Thody and Shuster, 1975). Ebling *et al.* (1975) also showed that α-MSH not only acted synergistically, but also had a significant effect on the sebaceous glands and this effect was independent of the presence of exogenous testosterone. Thody and Shuster (1975) found that α-MSH acts synergistically with progesterone to stimulate sebum secretion. These authors suggest that α-MSH acts directly on the sebaceous glands to stimulate lipogenesis and, together with steroid hormones, may have an important role in controlling sebaceous gland function in the rat and other hairy mammals. Thody and Shuster (1973, 1975) further propose that, with the evolution of hair, certain of the melanotropin peptides may have lost their significance as pigmentary hormones and have developed a sebotropic function and that melanotropins may be referred to as "sebotropins."

Injections of relatively large doses of α- and β-MSH can cause skin darkening in man (Lerner and McGuire, 1961; McGuire and Lerner, 1963). The epidermal melanocytes of guinea pigs (Snell, 1962), weasel (Rust, 1965), and mouse (Geschwind and Huseby, 1968) are affected by administration of melanotropins. Geschwind and Huseby (1966) reported that a darkening of coat color occurred in mice bearing an MSH-secreting pituitary tumor.

## XV. CONCLUDING REMARKS

β-LPH, like other secreted proteins (Chan *et al.*, 1976; Maurer *et al.*, 1976; Birken *et al.*, 1977; Shields and Blobel, 1977) is initially biosynthesized in a large precursor which contains $NH_2$-terminal extension or leader sequence (Kemper *et al.*, 1974). Studies on the biosynthesis of ACTH

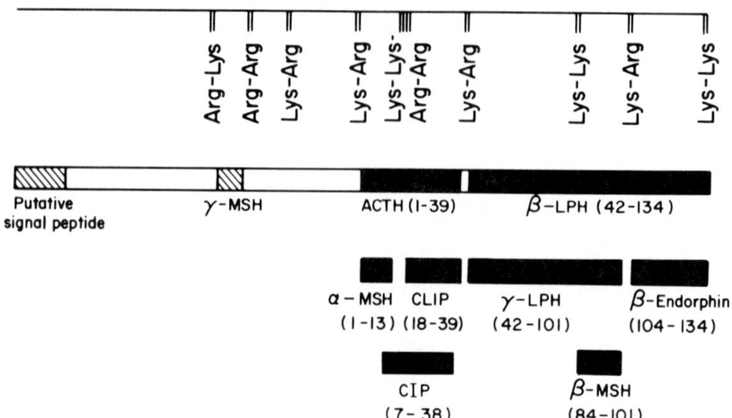


FIG. 14. The primary structure of the ACTH/β-EP precursor as deduced from the DNA sequence (modified from Nakanishi *et al.*, 1979).

and β-LPH in a mouse anterior-pituitary tumor-cell line (AtT-20), in cultured rat pars anterior and pars intermedia cells, in mouse pituitary cells, and in bovine pituitary slices and isolated pars intermedia cells led to the isolation of the common precursor molecule for these two hormones (Chrétien *et al.*, 1979; Herbert *et al.*, 1980; Eipper and Mains, 1980). Nakanishi *et al.* (1979) have recently determined the primary structure of the bovine ACTH/β-LPH precursor by the nucleotide sequence of cloned DNA complementary to the mRNA coding for the precursor proteins. Structure organization of a human genomic DNA encoding the ACTH/β-LPH precursor has also been reported by Chang *et al.* (1980a). Figure 14 presents the schematic representation of the amino acid sequence of the bovine precursor protein as deduced from the DNA structure.

From a comparison of the primary structures of β-LPH from various species as shown in Fig. 15, it is evident that the sequence of COOH-terminal 56 residues is surprisingly homologous whereas the $NH_2$-terminal sequence exhibits considerable variability. In fact, the various chain lengths of $\beta_h$-LPH and $\beta_b$-LPH as compared with ovine and porcine hormones is derived from the differences in the sequence of $NH_2$-terminal 33–37 amino acids. The conservation of the COOH-terminal portion in the β-LPH structure is particularly of interest. As already pointed out, the most potent naturally occurring opioid peptide is β-EP which is the COOH-terminal segment of β-LPH. Figure 16 presents the structural relationship of γ-LPH, β-MSH, Met-enkephalin, and β-EP in the amino acid sequence of $\beta_s$-LPH. The biological function of $\beta_s$-LPH-(1-40) remains to be determined.

```
                              5                   10                  15                  20
   Human:  H-Glu-Leu-Thr-Gly-Gln-Arg-Leu-Arg-Gln-Gly-Asp-Gly-Pro-Asn-Ala-Gly-Ala-Asp-Asp-Gly-
   Ovine:  H-Glu-Leu-Thr-Gly-Glu-Arg-Leu-Glu-Gln-Ala-Arg-Gly-Pro-Glu-Ala-Gln-Ala-Glu-Ser-Ala-
  Bovine:  H-Glu-Leu-Thr-Gly-Glu-Arg-Leu-Glu-Gln-Ala-Arg-Gly-Pro-Glu-Ala-Gln-Ala-Glu-Ser-Ala-
 Porcine:  H-Glu-Leu-Ala-Gly-Ala-Pro-Pro-Glu-Pro-Ala-Arg-Asp-Pro-Glu-Ala-Pro-Ala-Glu-Gly-Ala-

                             25                  30                                      35
            Pro-Gly-Pro-Ala-Gln-Asp-Leu-Glu-His-Ser-Leu-Leu-Val(                   )Ala-Ala-
            Ala-Ala-Arg-Ala(   )Glu-Leu-Glu-Tyr-Gly-Leu-Val-Ala-Glu(       )Ala-Glu-Ala-Ala-
            Ala-Ala-Arg-Ala(   )Glu-Leu-Glu-Tyr-Gly-Leu-Val-Ala-Glu-Ala-Glu-Ala-Glu-Ala-Ala-
            Ala-Ala-Arg-Ala(   )Glu-Leu-Glu-His-Gly-Leu-Val-Ala-Glu(       )Ala-Gln-Ala-Ala-

                             40                  45                  50                  55
            Glu-Lys-Lys-Asp-Glu-Gly-Pro-Tyr-Arg-Met-Glu-His-Phe-Arg-Trp-Gly-Ser-Pro-Pro-Lys-
            Glu-Lys-Lys-Asp-Ser-Gly-Pro-Tyr-Lys-Met-Glu-His-Phe-Arg-Trp-Gly-Ser-Pro-Pro-Lys-
            Glu-Lys-Lys-Asp-Ser-Gly-Pro-Tyr-Lys-Met-Glu-His-Phe-Arg-Trp-Gly-Ser-Pro-Pro-Lys-
            Glu-Lys-Lys-Asp-Glu-Gly-Pro-Tyr-Lys-Met-Glu-His-Phe-Arg-Trp-Gly-Ser-Pro-Pro-Lys-

                             60                  65                  70                  75
            Asp-Lys-Arg-Tyr-Gly-Gly-Phe-Met-Thr-Ser-Glu-Lys-Ser-Gln-Thr-Pro-Leu-Val-Thr-Leu-
            Asp-Lys-Arg-Tyr-Gly-Gly-Phe-Met-Thr-Ser-Glu-Lys-Ser-Gln-Thr-Pro-Leu-Val-Thr-Leu-
            Asp-Lys-Arg-Tyr-Gly-Gly-Phe-Met-Thr-Ser-Glu-Lys-Ser-Gln-Thr-Pro-Leu-Val-Thr-Leu-
            Asp-Lys-Arg-Tyr-Gly-Gly-Phe-Met-Thr-Ser-Glu-Lys-Ser-Gln-Thr-Pro-Leu-Val-Thr-Leu-

                                                                         Total Residues
                             80                  85
            Phe-Lys-Asn-Ala-Ile-Ile-Lys-Asn-Ala-Tyr-Lys-Lys-Gly-Glu-OH           89
            Phe-Lys-Asn-Ala-Ile-Ile-Lys-Asn-Ala-His-Lys-Lys-Gly-Gln-OH           91
            Phe-Lys-Asn-Ala-Ile-Ile-Lys-Asn-Ala-His-Lys-Lys-Gly-Gln-OH           93
            Phe-Lys-Asn-Ala-Ile-Val-Lys-Asn-Ala-His-Lys-Lys-Gly-Gln-OH           91
```

FIG. 15. The amino acid sequence of β-LPH from various species.

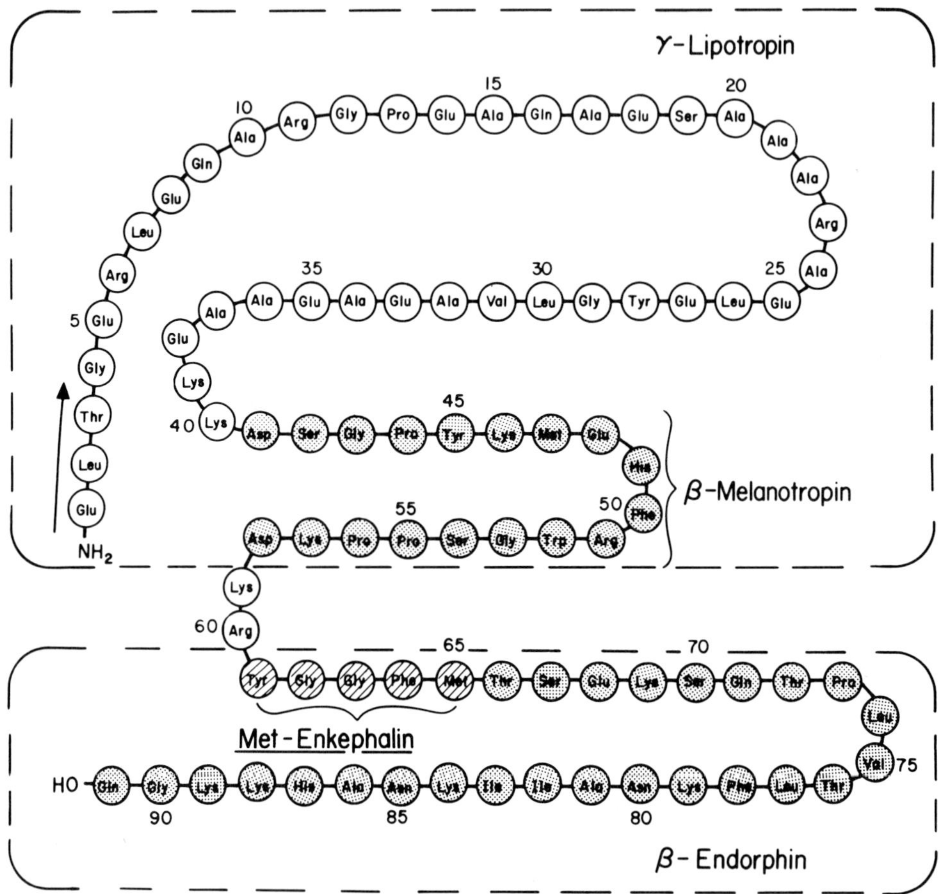


FIG. 16. Structural relationship of γ-LPH, β-MSH, Met-enkephalin, and β-EP to the ovine β-LPH structure.

In 1968, I wrote a brief review (Li, 1968) entitled "β-Lipotropin, A New Pituitary Hormone." I would like to repeat the introduction here as the final remark for this review.

> As a general rule biologically active compounds are isolated on the basis of certain biological effects that have been observed by physiologists, pharmacologists or clinicians. The development of endocrinology depends chiefly upon the observations of the biologist or the physician. Many early discoveries of hormonal principles were derived from the removal of endocrine glands and the subsequent observation of the effect of this removal on the whole organism. Later the chemists investigated extracts of that particular gland, isolated the active substance in pure form, determined its structure, and finally, synthesized the product in the laboratory.
>
> This has been the classical way in which biomedical science has proceeded. Cer-

tainly it was this approach which gave the first clues concerning the existence of the hormonal principles that are known to us at present, and had it not been used, there undoubtedly would have been great delays in obtaining therapeutically useful compounds in medicine. However, the more we learn about chemistry and biology of hormones, the more we begin to find out how complex is their function. We realize that gross observation can be misleading and at times may lead to a false conclusion. This is clearly evident in the case of earlier concepts of pituitary hormones. Activities that were once thought to be contaminants have been found to be intrinsic, and often a major characteristic activity of a hormone has been found to be only one of a number of activities which that hormone can exercise. Growth hormone does more than promote linear and skeletal growth; it is a major metabolic hormone. It enhances immunological reactions and increases resistance to disease, and moreover, growth hormone from human sources has recently been found to exercise all the effects thought of as characteristic of animal lactogenic hormone.

In view of these difficulties, another approach, one that has not been given much attention in the past, is coming to take its place alongside the earlier biological approach. This new procedure involves isolating a chemical compound from natural products and then investigating its biological activity after it has been determined to be a pure substance. What I am suggesting is that previously the parent of hormone study was biology; now this study begins with chemistry. This is not to diminish the importance of the biologist. We need even more biological testing systems available to us, and the new products must constantly be characterized according to their biological criteria. Yet we should be aware of the possibilities of the chemical approach to the discovery of new biologically active compounds.

One example is the recent discovery of a new biologically active peptide, β-lipotropic hormone (β-LPH; β-lipotropin) in sheep pituitaries. This discovery originated from a purely chemical investigation. In the course of improving the method to isolate ACTH from sheep glands, we obtained a new product which differs completely from all the other known pituitary hormones. Its biological behavior was tested after it had been characterized chemically.

## ACKNOWLEDGMENTS

The experimental work, summarized herein, was derived from collaborations with my coworkers whose names appear in the cited publications. This work was supported in part by NIH Grant GM-2907 and the Hormone Research Foundation.

## REFERENCES

Arregui, A., and Iversen, L. L. (1979). *Biochem. Pharmacol.* **28**, 2693–2696.

Barát, E., Patthy, A., and Gráf, L. (1979). *Proc. Natl. Acad. Sci. U.S.A.* **76**, 6120–6123.

Bertolini, A. (1971). *Riv. Farmacol. Terapia* **11**, 43–46.

Best, C. H., and Campbell, J. (1936). *J. Physiol. (London)* **86**, 190–203.

Birk, Y., and Li, C. H. (1964). *J. Biol. Chem.* **239**, 1048–1052.

Birken, S., Smith, D. L., Canfield, R. E., and Boime, I. (1977). *Biochem. Biophys. Res. Commun.* **74**, 106–112.

Blake, J., and Li, C. H. (1978). *Int. J. Pept. Protein Res.* **11**, 315–322.

Bloom, F., Segal, D., Ling, N., and Guillemin, R. (1976). *Science* **194,** 630–632.
Bowers, C. Y., Redding, T. W., and Schally, A. V. (1964). *Endocrinology* **74,** 559–566.
Bradbury, A. F., Smyth, D. G., and Snell, C. R. (1976). *Biochem. Biophys. Res. Commun.* **69,** 950–956.
Cehovic, G. (1962). *C. R. Acad. Sci. (Paris)* **254,** 1872.
Chan, S. J., Keim, P., and Steiner, D. F. (1976). *Proc. Natl. Acad. Sci. U.S.A.* **73,** 1964–1968.
Chang, W.-C., Rao, A. J., and Li, C. H. (1978). *Int. J. Pept. Protein Res.* **11,** 93–94.
Chang, A. C. Y., Cochet, M., and Cohen, S. N. (1980a). *Proc. Natl. Acad. Sci. U.S.A.* **77,** 4890–4894.
Chang, W.-C., Chung, D., and Li, C. H. (1980b). *Int. J. Pept. Protein Res.* **15,** 261–270.
Chrétien, M., and Li, C. H. (1967). *Can. J. Biochem.* **45,** 1163–1174.
Chrétien, M., Daviguon, J., Lis, M., Chan, P. V., Aubry, F., and Gilardeau, C. (1970). *Can. J. Physiol. Pharmacol.* **48,** 762–767.
Chrétien, M., Dufault, C., Gratton, J., and Gilardeau, C. (1971). *Horm. Metab. Res.* **3,** 355–356.
Chrétien, M., Gilardeau, C., and Li, C. H. (1972). *Int. J. Pept. Protein Res.* **4,** 263–265.
Chrétien, M., Gilardeau, C., Seidah, N., and Lis, M. (1976a). *Can. J. Biochem.* **54,** 778–782.
Chrétien, M., Benjannet, S., Dragon, N., Seidah, N. G., and Lis, M. (1976b). *Biochem. Biophys. Res. Commun.* **72,** 472–478.
Chrétien, M., Benjannet, S., Gossard, F., Gianoulakis, C., Seidah, N. G., Crine, P., and Lis, M. (1979). *Can. J. Biochem.* **57,** 1111–1121.
Courrier, R., and Cehovic, G. (1960). *C. R. Acad. Sci. (Paris)* **251,** 832–834.
Cox, B. M., Goldstein, A., and Li, C. H. (1976). *Proc. Natl. Acad. Sci. U.S.A.* **73,** 1821–1823.
Cseh, G., Gráf, L., and Góth, E. (1968). *FEBS Lett.* **2,** 42–44.
Cseh, G., Barát, E., Patthy, A., and Gráf, L. (1972). *FEBS Lett.* **21,** 344–346.
Dekker, C. A., Stone, D., and Fruton, J. S. (1949). *J. Biol. Chem.* **181,** 719–729.
Desranleau, R., Gilardeau, C., and Chrétien, M. (1972). *Endocrinology* **91,** 1004–1010.
De Wied, D. (1966). *Proc. Soc. Exp. Biol. Med.* **122,** 28–32.
De Wied, D., and Bohns, B. (1966). *Nature (London)* **212,** 1484–1486.
Dupont, A., Cusan, L., Garon, M., Labrie, F., and Li, C. H. (1976). *Proc. Natl. Acad. Sci. U.S.A.* **74,** 758–759.
Dupont, A., Cusan, L., Labrie, F., Coy, D. A., and Li, C. H. (1977). *Biochem. Biophys. Res. Commun.* **75,** 76–82.
Ebling, F. J., Ebling, E., Randall, V., and Skinner, J. (1975). *J. Endocrinol.* **66,** 407–412.
Eipper, B. A., and Mains, R. E. (1979). *J. Biol. Chem.* **254,** 10190–10199.
Eipper, B. A., and Mains, R. E. (1980). *Endocr. Rev.* **1,** 1–27.
Ferrari, W. (1958). *Nature (London)* **181,** 925–926.
Ferrari, W., Gossa, G. L., and Vargui, L. (1963). *Ann. N. Y. Acad. Sci.* **104,** 330–345.
Feurle, G. E., Weber, U., and Helmstaedter, V. (1980). *Life Sci.* **27,** 467–473.
Geschwind, I. I., and Huseby, R. A. (1966). *Endocrinology* **79,** 97–105.
Geschwind, I. I., Li, C. H., and Barnafi, L. (1957). *J. Am. Chem. Soc.* **79,** 6394–6401.
Gilardeau, C., and Chrétien, M., (1970). *Can. J. Biochem.* **48,** 1017–1021.
Gilardeau, C., and Chrétien, M. (1972). *In* "Chemistry and Biology of Peptides" (J. Meienhofer, ed.), pp. 609–611. Ann Arbor Science Publ., Ann Arbor, Michigan.
Gildersleeve, D. L., Pearson, T. A., Baghdiantz, A., and Foster, G. V. (1975). *Endocrinology* **97,** 533–534.
Gispen, V. M., Wiegand, V. M., Bradbury, A. F., Hume, E. C., Smyth, D. G., Snell, C. R., and De Wied, D. (1976). *Nature (London)* **264,** 794–795.
Gráf, L., and Li, C. H. (1973). *Biochem. Biophys. Res. Commun.* **53,** 1304–1309.
Gráf, L., Cseh, G., and Medzihradszky-Schweiger, H. (1969). *Biochim. Biophys. Acta* **175,** 444–447.

Gráf, L., Barat, E., Cseh, G., and Sajco, M. (1971). *Biochim. Biophys. Acta* **229,** 276–278.

Gráf, L., Barat, E., and Patthy, A. (1976). *Acta Biochim. Biophys. Acad. Sci. Hung.* **11** *(2–3),* 121–122.

Gráf, L., Kenessey, A., Berzétol, I., and Rónai, A. Z. (1977). *Biochim. Biophys. Acta* **78,** 1114–1123.

Hanaoka, T. (1951). *Jpn. J. Physiol.* **2,** 9–16.

Hanaoka, T. (1953). *Nature (London)* **172,** 866.

Harris, J. I. (1959). *Nature (London)* **184,** 167–169.

Herbert, E., Budarf, M., Phillips, M., Rosa, P., Policastro, P., Oates, E., Roberts, J., Seidah, N. G., and Chrétien, M. (1980). *Ann. N.Y. Acad. Sci.* **343,** 79–93.

Holaday, J., Loh, H. H., and Li, C. H. (1978). *Life Sci.* **22,** 1525–1536.

Jacquet, Y. F., and Marks, N. (1976). *Science* **194,** 632–635.

Jacquet, Y. F., Marks, N., and Li, C. H. (1976). *In* "Opiates and Endogenous Peptides" (H. Kosterlitz, ed.), pp. 411–414. Elsevier, Amsterdam.

Jeffcoate, W. J., Rees, L. H., Lowry, P. J., and Besser, G. M. (1978). *J. Clin. Endocrinol. Metab.* **47,** 160–167.

Jores, A., and Glogner, O. (1933). *Z. Gesamte Exp. Med.* **91,** 91.

Kawauchi, H., Chung, D., and Li, C. H. (1980). *Int. J. Pept. Protein Res.* **15,** 171–176.

Kemper, B., Habener, J. F., Mulligan, R. C., Potts, J. T., Jr., and Rich, A. (1974). *Proc. Natl. Acad. Sci. U.S.A.* **71,** 3731–3735.

Krieger, D. T., Liotta, A., Suda, T., Palkovits, M., and Brownstein, M. J. (1977a). *Biochem. Biophys. Res. Commun.* **76,** 930–936.

Krieger, D., Liotta, A., and Li, C. H. (1977b). *Life Sci.* **21,** 1771–1777.

Krivoy, W. A., and Guillemin, R. (1961). *Endocrinol.* **69,** 170–175.

Labella, F., Queen, G., Senyshyn, J., Lis, M., and Chrétien, M. (1977). *Biochem. Biophys. Res. Commun.* **76,** 930–936.

Lemaire, S., Yamashiro, D., and Li, C. H. (1978) *Int. J. Pept. Protein Res.* **11,** 179–184.

Lerner, A. B., and Takahashi, Y. (1956). *Rec. Prog. Horm. Res.* **12,** 303–320.

Lerner, A. B., and McGuire, J. S. (1961). *Nature (London)* **189,** 176–179.

Lerner, A. B., Shizume, K., and Bunding, I. (1954). *J. Clin. Endocrinol. Metab.* **14,** 1463–1490.

Levy, A. L. (1954). *Nature (London)* **174,** 126–127.

Li, C. H. (1964). *Nature (London)* **201,** 924.

Li, C. H. (1968). *Arch. Biol. Med. Exp.* **5,** 55–61.

Li, C. H. (1978). *In* "Hormonal Proteins and Peptides" (C. H. Li, ed.), Vol. 5, pp. 35–73. Academic Press, New York.

Li, C. H., and Chung, D. (1976a). *Nature (London)* **260,** 622–624.

Li, C. H., and Chung, D. (1976b). *Proc. Natl. Acad. Sci. U.S.A.* **73,** 1145–1148.

Li, C. H., and Chung, D. (1981). *Int. J. Pept. Protein Res.* **17,** 131–142.

Li, C. H., Geschwind, I. I., Dixon, J. S., Levy, A. L., and Harris, J. I. (1955). *J. Biol. Chem.* **213,** 171–185.

Li, C. H., Barnafi, L., Chrétien, M., and Chung, D. (1965). *Nature (London) 208,* 1093–1094.

Li, C. H., Barnafi, L., Chrétien, M., and Chung, D. (1966). *Excerpta Med. Int. Congr. Ser.* **112,** 349–364.

Li, C. H., Danho, W. O., Chung, D., and Rao, A. J. (1975). *Biochemistry* **14,** 947–952.

Li, C. H., Chung, D., and Doneen, B. A. (1976a). *Biochem. Biophys. Res. Commun.* **72,** 1542–1547.

Li, C. H., Lemaire, S., Yamashiro, D., and Doneen, B. A. (1976b). *Biochem. Biophys. Res. Commun.* **71,** 19–25.

Li, C. H., Tan, L., and Chung, D. (1977a). *Biochem. Biophys. Res. Commun.* **77,** 1088–1093.

Li, C. H., Yamashiro, D., Tseng, L-F., and Loh, H. H. (1977b). *J. Med. Chem.* **20,** 325–328.

Li, C. H., Chung, D., and Yamashiro, D. (1980). *Proc. Natl. Acad. Sci. U.S.A.*, in press.
Liotta, A. S., Li, C. H., Schussler, G. C., and Krieger, D. T. (1978). *Life Sci.* **23**, 2323–2330.
Lis, M., Gilardeau, C., and Chrétien, M. (1972a). *Acta Endocrinol.* **59**, 507–516.
Lis, M., Gilardeau, C., and Chrétien, M. (1972b). *Proc. Soc. Exp. Biol. Med.* **139**, 680–683.
Loh, H. H., Brase, D. A., Sampath-Khanna, S., Mar, J. B., Way, E. L., and Li, C. H. (1975). *Nature (London)* **264**, 567–568.
Lohmar, P., and Li, C. H. (1967). *Biochim. Biophys. Acta* **148**, 381–383.
Lohmar, P., and Li, C. H. (1968). *Endocrinology* **82**, 898–904.
Long, J. M., Krivoy, W. A., and Guillemin, R. (1961). *Endocrinology* **69**, 176–181.
McGuire, J. S., and Lerner, A. B. (1963). *Ann. N. Y. Acad. Sci.* **100**, 622–630.
Makarov, A. A., Esipova, N. A., Pankov, Yu. A., Brishkousky, B. A., Lobachev, U. M., and Sukhomudrenko, A. G. (1976). *Mol. Biol. (USSR)* **10**, 704–711.
Maurer, R. A., Stone, R., and Gorski, J. (1976). *J. Biol. Chem.* **251**, 2801–2807.
Matsuoka, H., Mulrow, P. J., and Li, C. H. (1980). *Science* **209**, 307–308.
Meyerson, B. J., and Terenius, L. (1977). *Eur. J. Pharmacol.* **42**, 191–192.
Moon, H. D., Li, C. H., and Jennings, B. M. (1973). *Arch. Biochem. Biophys.* **155**, 95–110.
Motomatsu, T., Lis, M., Seidah, N., and Chrétien, M. (1977). *Can. J. Neurol. Sci.* **4**, 49–52.
Mussio Fournier, J. C., Morato-Manero, J., and Fischer, J. T. (1936). *An. Fac. Med. Univ. Repub. Montevideo* **21**, 8–9.
Mussio Fournier, J. C., Cervino, J. M., and Conti, V. (1943). *J. Clin. Endocrinol.* **3**, 353–356.
Nakanishi, S., Inoue, A., Kita, T., Nakamura, M., Chang, A. C. Y., Cohen, S. N., and Numa, S. (1979). *Nature (London)* **278**, 423–427.
Naudé, R. J., and Oelofsen, W. (1981). *Int. J. Pept. Protein Res.* **18**, 135–137.
Noble, R. L., Yamashiro, D., and Li, C. H. (1976). *J. Am. Chem. Soc.* **98**, 2324–2328.
Pankov, Y. A., and Yudeau, M. A. (1972). *Biokemia* **37**, 991–1031.
Pelletier, G., Leclerc, R., Labrie, F., Cote, J., Chrétien, M., and Lis, M. (1977). *Endocrinology* **100**, 770–776.
Pelletier, G., Désy, L., Lissitszky, J.-C., Labrie, F., and Li, C. H. (1978). *Life Sci.* **22**, 1799–1804.
Pickering, B. T., and Li, C. H. (1963). *Biochim. Biophys. Acta* **74**, 156–157.
Rao, A. J., and Li, C. H. (1977). *Int. J. Pept. Protein Res.* **10**, 166–171.
Rivier, C., Vale, W., Ling, N., Brown, M., and Guillemin, R. (1977). *Endocrinology* **100**, 238–241.
Rubinstein, M., Stein, S., Gerber, L., and Udenfriend, S. (1977a). *Proc. Natl. Acad. Sci. U.S.A.* **74**, 3052–3055.
Rubinstein, M., Stein, S., and Udenfriend, S. (1977b). *Proc. Natl. Acad. Sci. U.S.A.* **74**, 4969–4972.
Rust, C. C. (1965). *Gen. Comp. Endocrinol.* **5**, 222–231.
Sakamoto, A. (1966). *Nature (London)* **211**, 1370–1371.
Sakamoto, A., and Prasad, K. N. (1967). *Int. J. Radiat. Biol.* **12**, 97–99.
Sandman, C. A., Kastin, A. J., and Schally, A. V. (1971). *Physiol. Behav.* **6**, 45–48.
Sandman, C. A., Miller, L. H., Kastin, A. J., and Schally, A. V. (1972). *J. Comp. Physiol.* **80**, 54–58.
Sanger, F. (1945). *Biochem. J. 39*, 507–515.
Scott, A. P., and Lowry, P. J. (1974). *Biochem. J.* **139**, 593–602.
Shields, D., and Blobel, G. (1977). *Proc. Natl. Acad. Sci. U.S.A.* **74**, 2059–2063.
Snell, R. S. (1962). *J. Endocrinol.* **25**, 249–258.
St-Pierre, S., Gilardeau, C., and Chrétien, M. (1976). *Can. J. Biochem.* **54**, 992–998.
Tamasi, G., Cseh, G., and Gráf, L. (1969). *Experientia* **25**, 360–361.
Thody, A. J., and Shuster, S., (1971). *J. Endocrinol.* **50**, 533–534.

Thody, A. J., and Shuster, S. (1973). *Nature (London)* **245**, 207-209.
Thody, A. J., and Shuster, S. (1975). *J. Endocrinol.* **64**, 503-510.
Tseng, L-F., Loh, H. H., and Li, C. H. (1977). *Biochem. Biophys. Res. Commun.* **74**, 390-396.
Tseng, L-F., Loh, H. H., and Li, C. H. (1978). *Int. J. Pept. Protein Res.* **12**, 173-176.
Udea, M., Miyakawa, S., and Abe, K. (1980). *Biomed. Res.* **1**, 141-145.
Watson, S. J., Barchas, J. D., and Li, C. H. (1977). *Proc. Natl. Acad. Sci. U.S.A.* **74**, 5155-5158.
Weitzmann, R. E., Fisher, D. A., Minick, S., Ling, N., and Guillemin, R. (1977). *Endocrinology* **101**, 1643-1646.
Wiedemann, E., Saito, T., Linfoot, J. A., and Li, C. H. (1977). *J. Clin. Endocrinol. Metab.* **45**, 1108-1111.
Yamashiro, D. (1977). *J. Org. Chem.* **42**, 523-525.
Yamashiro, D., and Li, C. H. (1973a). *J. Org. Chem.* **38**, 591-592.
Yamashiro, D., and Li, C. H. (1973b). *J. Org. Chem.* **38**, 2594-2597.
Yamashiro, D., and Li, C. H. (1974). *Proc. Natl. Acad. Sci. U.S.A.* **71**, 4945-4949.
Yamashiro, D., and Li, C. H. (1976). *Biochim. Biophys. Acta* **451**, 124-132.
Yamashiro, D., and Li, C. H. (1978). *J. Am. Chem. Soc.* **100**, 5174-5178.
Yamashiro, D., Noble, R. L., and Li, C. H. (1972a) *In* "Chemistry and Biology of Peptides" (J. Meienhofer, ed.), pp. 197-202. Ann Arbor Science Publ., Ann Arbor, Michigan.
Yamashiro, D., Blake, J., and Li, C. H. (1972b). *J. Am. Chem. Soc.* **94**, 2855-2859.
Yamashiro, D., Noble, R. L., and Li, C. H. (1973). *J. Org. Chem.* **38**, 3561-3565.
Yamashiro, D., Blake, J., and Li, C. H. (1976). *Tetrahedron Lett.* **18**, 1469-1472.
Yang, J. T., Bewley, T. A., Chen, G. C., and Li, C. H. (1977). *Proc. Natl. Acad. Sci. U.S.A.* **74**, 3235-3238.
Yudeau, M. A., and Pankov, Y. A. (1970). *Endocrinology (U.S.S.R.)* **16**, 49-51.
Zimmerman, E. A., Liotta, A., and Krieger, D. T. (1978). *Cell Tissue Res.* **186**, 393-398.

# CHAPTER 2

# Regulation of Adenylate Cyclase by Adrenergic Receptors

*Thomas Michel, Brian B. Hoffman, and Robert J. Lefkowitz*



## I. INTRODUCTION

The catecholamines epinephrine and norepinephrine modulate a variety of physiological responses. Ahlquist (1948) found that the responses to catecholamines were mediated through two distinct types of receptors which he termed α-adrenergic and β-adrenergic receptors. For α receptors, epinephrine is more potent than norepinephrine, which in turn is much more potent than isoproterenol. In contrast, β-adrenergic receptor mediated responses to catecholamines are those for which isoproterenol is more potent than either epinephrine or norepinephrine. Over the years, considerable insight has been gained into the molecular mechanisms whereby these physiological responses are elicited, and both similarities and differences between α- and β-adrenergic systems have been elucidated. β-Adrenergic responses are mediated primarily, if not exclusively, by stimulation of the enzyme adenylate cyclase (see Robison *et al.*, 1971; Hoffman and Lefkowitz, 1980). In contrast, α-adrenergic receptors generally stimulate cells through



BIOCHEMICAL ACTIONS OF HORMONES, VOL. IX

ISBN 0-12-452809-0

mechanisms other than adenylate cyclase activation (for review, see Jones and Michell, 1978). However, there are $\alpha$-adrenergic receptors that inhibit adenylate cyclase (for review, see Jakobs, 1979). The focus of this review is the discussion of the mechanisms whereby $\alpha$- and $\beta$-adrenergic receptors are thought to respectively inhibit and stimulate adenylate cyclase.

## II. $\alpha$- AND $\beta$-ADRENERGIC RECEPTOR SUBTYPES

Both $\alpha$- and $\beta$-adrenergic responses are initiated by the interaction of a catecholamine (or other agonist drug) with specific integral plasma membrane receptor proteins (see Cuatrecasas, 1974). It has become apparent that each type of adrenergic receptor, both $\alpha$ and $\beta$, exists in more than one subtype. Lands *et al.* (1967) provided evidence for two $\beta$-adrenergic receptor subtypes which were termed $\beta_1$ and $\beta_2$ receptors. $\beta_1$ receptors, such as those mediating the positive inotropic effects of catecholamines on the heart, are those at which epinephrine and norepinephrine are approximately equipotent. $\beta_2$ receptors are those at which epinephrine is much more potent than norepinephrine; the receptors that mediate bronchial smooth muscle relaxation exemplify $\beta_2$ receptors. There exist a variety of agonist and antagonist compounds with differential potency at the $\beta$-adrenergic receptor subtypes; these differences presumably reflect structural dissimilarities in the receptors. Nonetheless, agonist occupation of either $\beta_1$ or $\beta_2$ receptors results in the activation of the membrane bound adenylate cyclase and the increased intracellular production of cAMP (Lefkowitz, 1975). The synthesis of cAMP and the consequent activation of cAMP-dependent protein kinase (for review, see Glass and Krebs, 1980) is thought to be the common mechanism whereby $\beta$-adrenergic receptor binding is transduced into the diverse physiological responses characteristic of different cell types.

The $\alpha$-adrenergic receptors have also been classified recently into distinct subtypes, termed $\alpha_1$ and $\alpha_2$, using both anatomical and pharmacological criteria (Berthelsen and Pettinger, 1977). The $\alpha_1$ receptors are the classical $\alpha$-adrenergic receptors and are widely distributed among peripheral tissues. Typical $\alpha$-adrenergic responses such as smooth muscle contraction are mediated by $\alpha_1$ receptors. The recognition of $\alpha$ receptor subtypes was facilitated by observations that norepinephrine release from nerve terminals, although primarily limited by the rate of firing of the nerve, could also be inhibited by norepinephrine in the synaptic cleft (see Langer 1974; Langer, 1976; Starke, 1977; Wikberg, 1979). The sites at which norepinephrine acts to feedback inhibit norepinephrine release from nerve terminals were found to be $\alpha$-adrenergic receptors. Nonetheless, these "presynaptic" autoregulatory $\alpha$ receptors had pharmacological characteristics that were distinctly different from the "postsynaptic" alpha receptors that mediate typical $\alpha$-adrenergic responses. The "presynaptic" and "postsynaptic" $\alpha$-receptors differ in their affinities for a wide variety of $\alpha$-adrenergic agonists and antagonists. With the discovery that receptors with the pharmacological specificity of "presynaptic" $\alpha$ receptors could be found in nonneural tissues including adipocytes (Hoffman *et al.*, 1979; Garcia-Sainz *et al.*, 1980), the anatomical classification has been largely supplanted by the demarcation of the $\alpha$-adrenergic receptor subtypes as $\alpha_1$ ("postsynaptic") and $\alpha_2$ ("presynapic"). The different pharmacological characteristics of the $\alpha$-adrenergic receptor subtypes have been of great importance both in physiological and radioligand binding studies of $\alpha$ receptor regulation. The plant alkaloid yohimbine has a greater affinity at $\alpha_2$ than $\alpha_1$ receptors (Doxey *et al.*, 1977). In contrast, the antagonist prazosin may be up to several thousandfold more potent at $\alpha_1$ than $\alpha_2$ receptors (Cambridge *et al.*, 1977; Doxey *et al.*, 1977; Cavero *et al.*, 1977). Other antagonist compounds, including dihydroergocryptine (Hoffman *et al.*, 1980a) and phentolamine (Hoffman *et al.*, 1979) are approximately equipotent at $\alpha_1$ and $\alpha_2$ receptors in a number of tissues. Other $\alpha$-adrenergic antagonist drugs exhibit varying degrees of $\alpha$ receptor subtype selectivity in different tissues (Hoffman and Lefkowitz, 1980). The determination of subtype selectivity of agonist compounds in radioligand binding studies presents a particular difficulty in analysis and will be discussed further below.

Since $\alpha$ and $\beta$ receptors have opposed effects in many tissues (for review, see Williams and Lefkowitz, 1978) it was proposed (Robison *et al.*, 1967) that $\alpha$ receptors functioned by inhibiting adenylate cyclase activity. This general hypothesis was refuted by evidence that the activation of some $\alpha$ receptors was independent of changes in cAMP levels (Robison *et al.*, 1968). This conflict has been clarified by the recognition of $\alpha$ receptor subtypes. The $\alpha_2$ receptors have been found to inhibit adenylate cyclase activity in a variety of tissues, including the adipocyte in which adenylate cyclase inhibition is associated with decreased adipocyte lipolysis (for review, see Fain, 1980) and in the platelet, in which adenylate cyclase inhibition may be associated with platelet aggregation (for review, see Steer and Salzman, 1980). There is evidence, however, that a variety of $\alpha_1$ receptors do *not* directly interact with a membrane-bound adenylate cyclase (Jones and Michell, 1978). Whereas considerable controversy exists regarding the precise nature of stimulus-response coupling in $\alpha_1$-adrenergic systems, alterations in $Ca^{2+}$ flux may be important (for review, see Exton, 1980).

Biochemical aspects of the $\beta$-adrenergic receptor–adenylate cyclase system have been extensively studied and are the subject of several recent reviews (Ross and Gilman, 1980; Johnson *et al.*, 1980; Stadel *et al.*, 1981). However, an understanding of the biochemistry of $\alpha$-adrenergic regulation of adenylate cyclase is thus far not as advanced. Preliminary studies have shown some striking similarities and other obvious differences between these adenylate cyclase-coupled receptor systems. The following sections will review briefly interactions among the components of the $\beta$ receptor–adenylate cyclase system, and then examine the extent to which these components may have analogous expression in the $\alpha$-adrenergic receptor systems.

## III. $\beta$-ADRENERGIC RECEPTOR REGULATION OF ADENYLATE CYCLASE

A variety of experimental approaches have been used to study the mechanisms of adenylate cyclase activation by $\beta$-adrenergic agonists. It is generally agreed that there are at least three classes of components involved in $\beta$-adrenergic membrane transduction (Rodbell, 1980). The hormone receptor (R) and the catalytic moiety of the adenylate cyclase (C) are both integral membrane proteins responsible, respectively, for the recognition of the specific ligand at the external surface of the plasma membrane and for the intracellular synthesis of cAMP. Modulation both of hormone binding and of adenylate cyclase catalytic activity is achieved by a membrane protein exposed on the inner surface of the plasma membrane and termed the guanine nucleotide regulatory protein, or N protein. The N protein appears to function via the formation of noncovalent associations with both the receptor and the adenylate cyclase. Guanine nucleotides are an obligate cofactor for hormone stimulation of adenylate cyclase, and guanine nucleotide binding to the N protein modulates the interactions of the N protein with the other components of the adenylate cyclase system.

Radioligand binding studies have revealed fundamental differences in the regulation by guanine nucleotides of the $\beta$-adrenergic receptor's affinity for agonists and antagonists (Maguire *et al.*, 1976; Williams and Lefkowitz, 1977). Figure 1 shows a competition curve of the $\beta$-adrenergic antagonist (−)-alprenolol with the antagonist radioligand [$^3$H]dihydroalprenolol ([$^3$H]DHA) in frog erythrocyte membranes (Kent *et al.*, 1980). Computer modeling of these data using nonlinear least squares curve-fitting techniques (Feldman, 1972; De Lean *et al.*, 1978; Hancock *et al.*, 1979) reveals that the antagonist is interacting with a single homogeneous class of receptor sites. Moreover, the competition curve is unaffected by the presence of guanine nucleotides. A competition curve of the $\beta$-adrenergic agonist (−)-isoproterenol with [$^3$H]DHA is shown in Fig. 2; computer analysis indicates the presence of two distinct affinity states for the agonist compound. However, in the presence of guanine nucleotides such as guanyl-5′-yl-

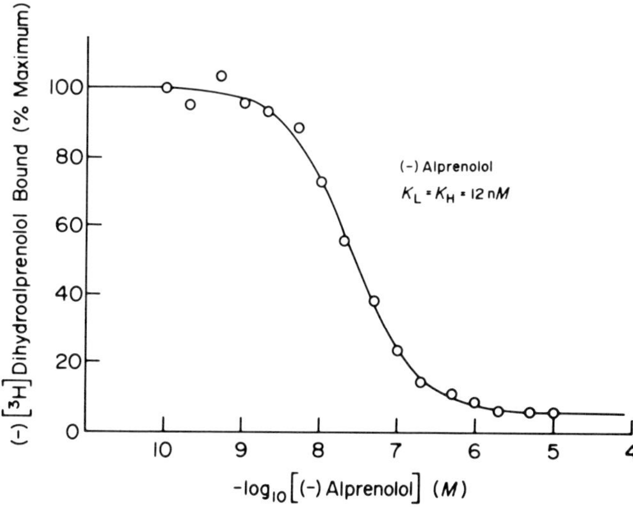


FIG. 1. Computer modeled curves of competition for [$^3$H]DHA binding to frog erythrocyte membrane $\beta$-adrenergic receptors by the antagonist compound (−)-alprenolol. Experiments were performed as described elsewhere using purified frog erythrocyte membranes and [$^3$H]DHA at a concentration of ~2 n$M$. Data points represent means of duplicate determinations from a representative experiment. The curve is a theoretical one drawn by computer modeling procedures for a model with a single affinity state for (−)-alprenolol with $K_D = 12$ n$M$. These binding data were not better fit by a model with two affinity states for (−)-alprenolol. $K_L$, the low affinity dissociation constant, is thus equal to $K_H$, the high affinity dissociation constant. Data from Kent *et al.* (1980).

imidodiphosphate [Gpp(NH)p], a nonhydrolyzable analog of GTP, the competition curve is shifted to lower agonist affinity and appears to represent interactions with a homogeneous class of receptors. The overall affinity for agonists in the presence of guanine nucleotides corresponds to the lower of the two affinity states seen in the absence of added guanine nucleotides; there is no change in the total number of receptors present. Thus, guanine nucleotides appear to mediate a transition between the two states of the receptor, with the receptor population of uniformly lower affinity for agonists in the presence of guanine nucleotides. $\beta$-Adrenergic agonist radioligands such as [$^3$H]hydroxybenzylisoproterenol ([$^3$H]HBI) may be used to label only the high affinity state of the $\beta$-adrenergic receptor of the frog erythrocyte (Williams and Lefkowitz, 1977). Guanine nucleotides promote a dissociation of this high affinity agonist–receptor complex (Fig. 2), and it can be shown that the transition from high to low affinity states of the receptor promoted by guanine nucleotides reflects an increased rate of agonist dissociation from the receptor.

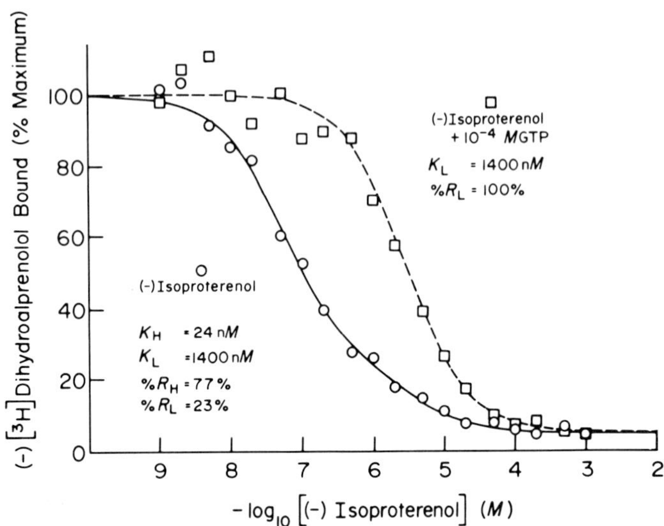


FIG. 2. Computer modeled curves of competition for [$^3$H]DHA binding to frog erythrocyte $\beta$-adrenergic receptors by (−) isoproterenol in the presence and absence of GTP. Procedures as described in legend to Fig. 1. Data points represent means of duplicate determinations from a representative experiment. The curve for isoproterenol alone was significantly better fitted ($p < .01$) by a two-state binding model, whereas in the presence of GTP a one-state model was adequate to fit the data points. $K_H$ and $K_L$ as defined in legend to Fig. 1. % $R_H$,% receptors in high affinity state; %$R_L$, % receptors in low affinity state. Data from Kent *et al.* (1980).

Antagonist compounds, by definition, have zero intrinsic (biological) activity; guanine nucleotides do not affect their interaction with the $\beta$-adrenergic receptor. In contrast, the binding of agonists is strongly influenced by guanine nucleotides, and there is an excellent positive correlation between an agonist's intrinsic activity and the extent to which its overall affinity is modified by guanine nucleotides (Kent *et al.*, 1980). Thus, the ability of a ligand to form a high affinity complex with the $\beta$ receptor reflects its intrinsic activity for the stimulation of adenylate cyclase. These observations, combined with theoretical considerations of receptor-effector coupling and tested using computer modeling of agonist binding data, led to the development of a "ternary complex" model to explain agonist–receptor interactions (Boeynaems and Dumont, 1975; Dehaen, 1976; Jacobs and Cuatrecasas, 1976; De Lean *et al.*, 1980). In this model, $\beta$ receptor binding of agonist ligands leads to an interaction between the agonist–receptor complex and an additional membrane component. The formation of this complex is responsible for stabilizing the agonist receptor interaction, thus increasing the proportion of receptors in the high affinity state and eventually activating the adenylate cyclase. The identity of the additional membrane component as the guanine nucleotide regulatory protein is suggested by the notable modulation of the $\beta$ receptor's affinity for agonists by guanine nucleotides. Whereas the analysis of radioligand binding data supports the notion that the hormone receptor complex interacts with an additional membrane component, this does not, of course, establish the biochemical identity of this component.

The central role of guanine nucleotides in hormone stimulation of adenylate cyclase has been established in a variety of receptor systems (see Rodbell *et al.*, 1971; Rodbell, 1980). It is generally observed that hormone stimulation of adenylate cyclase in purified plasma membranes requires the continued presence of GTP. Nonhydrolyzable derivatives of GTP, such as Gpp(NH)p, may cause an apparently irreversible activation of adenylate cyclase (Salomon *et al.*, 1975). Guanine nucleotide activation of adenylate cyclase exhibits a characteristic 2–4-minute lag before enzyme activity begins to increase linearly; the duration of this lag is significantly reduced by the presence of hormone. The presence of such guanine nucleotides is absolutely required for hormone stimulation of adenylate cyclase. The long-lived activation of the enzyme by Gpp(NH)p but not GTP led Cassel and Selinger (1976) and Blume and Forster (1976) to postulate that GTP hydrolysis might be involved in the regulation of adenylate cyclase. Indeed, a high affinity GTPase was described in turkey erythrocyte membranes by Cassel and Selinger (1976) which could be stimulated by $\beta$-adrenergic agonists. Antagonists did not stimulate the GTPase, and partial agonists did so for a lesser extent than full agonists (Pike and Lefkowitz, 1981). Nonhydrolyzable GTP analogs inhibited the GTPase activity, in contrast to their stimulatory effect on adenylate cyclase activity. GTP hydrolysis thus presumably reflected the "turn off" mechanism whereby adenylate cyclase activity was regulated. Hormones were envisioned as facilitating the binding of guanine nucleotides, thus accelerating the rate at which the adenylate cyclase was activated and increasing GTPase activity.

The search for an adenylate cyclase-coupled membrane protein that bound GTP with high affinity led to the discovery by Pfeuffer (1977) of a 42,000 $M_r$ protein, which could be labeled with a photoreactive GTP derivative and which was found to comigrate with the adenylate cyclase activity upon gel filtration of detergent solubilized membrane preparations. The GTP-binding fraction could be separated from the adenylate cyclase activity by affinity chromatography on GTP-Sepharose. Cholera toxin, long known to activate adenylate cyclase in a variety of tissues (for review, see Moss and Vaughn, 1979), was found to catalyze the NAD-dependent ADP-ribosylation of a similar if not identical 42,000 $M_r$ protein (Cassel and Pfeuffer, 1978; Gill and Meren, 1978). The covalent modification of this putative GTP-binding guanine nucleotide regulatory protein correlates with the potentiation of hormone plus GTP stimulated adenylate cyclase activity and the concurrent inhibition of hormone stimulated GTPase. The reciprocal activation of adenylate cyclase and inhibition of hormone-stimulated GTPase by cholera toxin led Cassel and Selinger (1977) to conclude that inactivation of adenylate cyclase is the result of the hydrolysis of GTP to GDP.

The fate of the nucleotide bound to the guanine nucleotide regulatory protein (N protein) after GTP hydrolysis has been investigated by Cassel and Selinger (1978) and Pike and Lefkowitz (1980). In turkey erythrocyte membranes preincubated with [$^3$H]GTP, $\beta$-adrenergic agonists promoted the release of [$^3$H]GDP. Antagonists did not potentiate the release of [$^3$H]GDP, and partial agonists release GDP at a slower rate than full agonists. Since GTP hydrolysis is correlated with adenylate cyclase deactivation, presumably GDP release and subsequent GTP binding are required for reactivation of the adenylate cyclase. An acceleration of GDP release by agonists would increase the rate of GTP binding to the N protein, thus increasing adenylate cyclase activity. Indeed, both the rate of GDP release and the amount of GTP hydrolysis are correlated with the intrinsic activity of an agonist for the stimulation of adenylate cyclase.

The central role of the guanine nucleotide regulatory protein in hormone stimulation of adenylate cyclase is exemplified by studies of a $\beta$-adrenergic receptor system genetically deficient in this protein (for review, see Johnson *et al.*, 1980). Mutants of the S49 mouse lymphoma cell have been described in which a functional N protein is lacking. A mutant cell line, containing $\beta$-adrenergic receptors and an intact adenylate cyclase but lacking a functional guanine nucleotide regulatory protein, demonstrates no effects of guanine nucleotides on agonist binding nor hormone-stimulated adenylate cyclase (Bourne *et al.*, 1975; Insel *et al.*, 1976) and absence of the 42,000 $M_r$ GTP-binding protein identifiable with cholera toxin (Johnson *et al.*, 1978). These effects of guanine nucleotides could be reconstituted (Ross and Gilman, 1977) by detergent extracts from cells containing intact guanine nucleotide regulatory proteins. The interaction between the receptor and N protein implied by these data and the theoretical considerations of the ternary complex model discussed above suggest that a stable association between the receptor and N protein might be promoted by agonist compounds. Indeed, an increase in the apparent molecular weight of the detergent solubilized frog erythrocyte $\beta$-adrenergic receptor was noted when the receptor was occupied by the $\beta$ agonist radioligand [$^3$H]HBI relative to the apparent molecular weight of the receptor occupied by the antagonist [$^3$H]DHA (Limbird and Lefkowitz, 1978). The increase in molecular weight assessed by gel filtration chromatography was accompanied by the comigration of the receptor and the N protein, the latter of which was identified by its specific ADP-ribosylation by cholera toxin plus [$^{32}$P]NAD (Limbird *et al.*,

1980). The stable association of receptor and N protein could not be induced by agonists in the presence of guanine nucleotides, or by antagonist ligands.

Whereas guanine nucleotides result in the apparent destabilization of the receptor–N protein complex, they appear to facilitate the interaction of the N protein with the adenylate cyclase catalytic moiety. Sucrose density gradient centrifugation of detergent solubilized adenylate cyclase revealed an increased sedimentation coefficient for adenylate cyclase activity when the enzyme had been stimulated with nonhydrolyzable GTP analogs prior to solubilization (Pfeuffer, 1979). Pfeuffer (1979) has shown that the N protein has a higher affinity for the adenylate cyclase catalytic moiety when the former is occupied by a guanine nucleotide triphosphate.

A working model for the molecular interactions between the elements of the $\beta$ receptor adenylate cyclase system, which accommodates the various concepts developed above, is presented in Fig. 3. Each of the components (R, N, and C) is envisioned as alternating between "active" and "inactive" states. Binding of agonists but not antagonists to the receptor (R) promotes the association of the receptor with the N protein. Interaction of the hormone–receptor complex (HR) with the N protein facilitates the exchange of GTP for GDP bound to the N protein. GTP binding has a twofold effect. First, the ternary complex between hormone-bound receptor and the N protein dissociates, as does the hormone from the receptor. Second, the GTP-charged N protein, now in its "active" form, potentiates the activity of the adenylate cyclase catalytic moiety (C). Deactivation of the N-protein–adenylate cyclase complex appears to occur when the GTP is hydrolyzed by the GTPase associated with the N protein. Treatments that inhi-

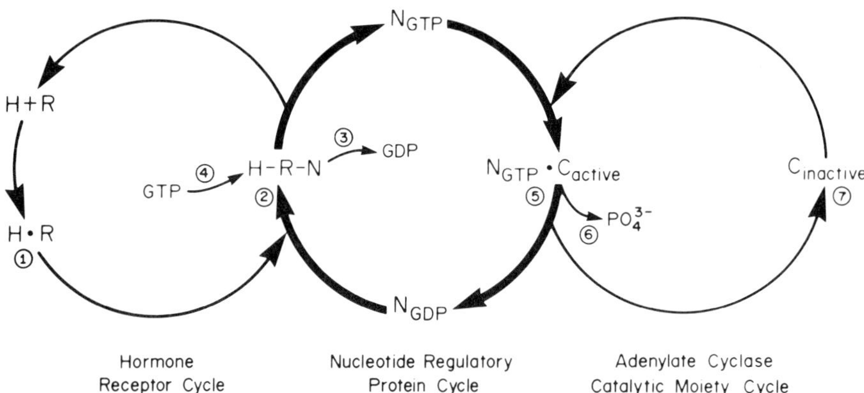


FIG. 3. Working model for adenylate cyclase regulation by $\beta$-adrenergic agonists and GTP. H,$\beta$-adrenergic agonist; R,$\beta$-adrenergic receptor; N, guanine nucleotide regulatory protein; C, catalytic moiety of adenylate cyclase. See text for details.

bit the GTPase, such as nonhydrolyzable GTP analogs or cholera toxin, result in a maximal stimulation of the adenylate cyclase. GTP hydrolysis being the "turn off" reaction for the activated adenylate cyclase, another cycle of activation can be achieved only when GTP replaces the GDP bound to the N protein. GDP tightly bound to the N protein could thus serve as an endogenous inhibitor of adenylate cyclase. The role of the agonist receptor complex is thus to promote the binding of GTP to the N protein, which now activates the adenylate cyclase. Whereas this working model is compatible with radioligand binding data and biochemical observations, the precise sequence of certain events remains obscure. For example, it is not known whether GDP dissociates from the N protein prior to, concomitant with, or just after the interaction between the N protein and the agonist–receptor complex (e.g., Lad *et al.*, 1980). Likewise, the precise timing of GTP hydrolysis and deactivation of the N–C complex is not known. The model is useful, however, in indicating how ligand binding data can be used to elucidate the molecular mechanisms of activation of adenylate cyclase.

## IV. α-ADRENERGIC RECEPTOR INHIBITION OF ADENYLATE CYCLASE

The molecular mechanisms whereby α-adrenergic receptors regulate adenylate cyclase activity are poorly understood. This may be due primarily to the fact that α-adrenergic physiological responses, until recently, were investigated primarily in intact cell systems, thus hampering the biochemical identification of individual components. In the last few years, however, work has progressed not only in elucidating the relevant binding sites for α-adrenergic regulation of adenylate cyclase and the physiological correlates of adenylate cyclase inhibition (see Table I), but also in the study of the mechanisms whereby ligand binding is transduced into inhibition of this enzyme. This section will focus on studies of α-adrenergic receptor regulation using radioligand binding techniques, discuss these techniques in relation to investigation of α-adrenergic receptors in the adipocyte, and evaluate the implications of these studies for the mechanism of hormone receptor transduction of adenylate cyclase inhibition.

Radioligand binding studies of α-adrenergic receptors have revealed fundamental differences between $\alpha_1$ and $\alpha_2$ receptors (see Section II). The proportion of $\alpha_1$ and $\alpha_2$ receptors in a given tissue, as well as the affinity constants of a selective drug for each subtype, may be determined by computer analysis of competition curves (Hoffman *et al.*, 1979). Using the antagonist radioligand [$^3$H]dihydroergocryptine ([$^3$H]DHE), which has been

TABLE I

EXAMPLES OF TISSUES IN WHICH α-ADRENERGIC RECEPTOR-MEDIATED ADENYLATE CYCLASE INHIBITION IS CORRELATED WITH PHYSIOLOGICAL RESPONSES

| Tissue | Physiological response | References |
| --- | --- | --- |
| Platelet | Platelet aggregation | Salzman and Neri, 1969; Cole *et al.*, 1971; Harwood *et al.*, 1972; Jakobs *et al.*, 1976; Lasch and Jakobs, 1979 |
| Adipocyte | Inhibition of lipolysis | Burns and Langley, 1970; Burns *et al.*, 1974; Fain, 1980; Schimmel *et al.*, 1980 |
| Thyroid | Inhibition of thyroid stimulating hormone effects | Yamashita *et al.*, 1977; Maayan *et al.*, 1977; Desmedt, 1980; Yamashita *et al.*, 1980 |
| Parathyroid | Inhibition of parathyroid hormone release | Brown *et al.*, 1978 |
| Melanocyte | Inhibition of melanocyte stimulating hormone-induced granule dispersion | Abe *et al.*, 1969; Pettinger, 1977 |
| Pancreatic islet | Inhibition of insulin secretion | Turtle and Kipnis, 1967 |
| Toad bladder | Decreased water permeability | Turtle and Kipnis, 1967 |
| Kidney | Inhibition of renin release | Pettinger *et al.*, 1976 |

shown to have equal affinity for $\alpha_1$ and $\alpha_2$ receptors in a variety of tissues (Hoffman *et al.*, 1980a), competition curves with the highly $\alpha_1$ selective antagonist prazosin have been analyzed. The proportion of sites labeled by [$^3$H]DHE which are competed for at low prazosin concentrations are $\alpha_1$ receptors, and the [$^3$H]DHE sites competed for only at high prazosin concentrations are $\alpha_2$ receptors (see Fig. 4). The rat liver has been found to have predominantly $\alpha_1$ receptors (~80%) with fewer $\alpha_2$ receptors (~20%), the rabbit uterus has primarily $\alpha_2$ receptors, and the human (and rabbit) platelet contains exclusively $\alpha_2$ receptors. Radiolabeled derivatives of the subtype selective antagonists may also be used to directly identify the α receptor subtype characteristics of a given tissue (Hoffman *et al.*, 1981a). Thus, in the rat liver, [$^3$H]prazosin and [$^3$H]yohimbine label ~80% and ~20% of the sites labeled by the [$^3$H]DHE, which labels the entire α receptor population.

### A. α-ADRENERGIC REGULATION IN ADIPOSE TISSUE

To illustrate the application of the notion of an α receptor that inhibits adenylate cyclase activity and its identification with radioligands, we will now discuss adipose tissue. A wide variety of hormones modulate lipolysis in adipose tissue (for review, see Fain, 1980). In this section we focus on α-adrenergic receptor-mediated inhibition of lipolysis.

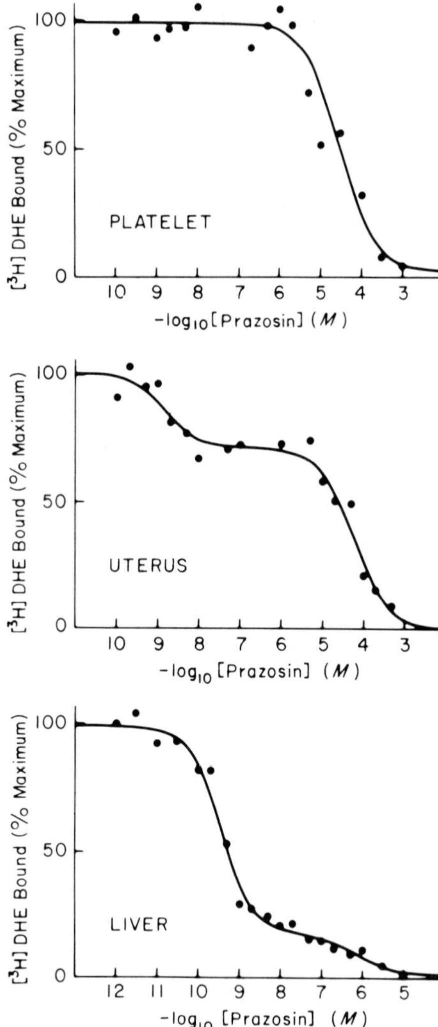


FIG. 4. Computer modeled curves of competition for [$^3$H]DHE binding by the $\alpha_1$-selective antagonist prazosin in platelet, uterus, and liver. Data points are means of duplicate determinations from a representative experiment. The platelet competition curve was best fit by a model with one class of receptors of low affinity for prazosin, suggesting that the platelet's $\alpha$ receptors are 100% $\alpha_2$. The complex competition curves in uterus and liver membranes are best fit by a mixture of $\alpha_1$ and $\alpha_2$ receptors. In this experiment, this mixture was: for uterus, $\alpha_1$ = 35%, $\alpha_2$ = 65%; for liver, $\alpha_1$ = 78%, $\alpha_2$ = 22%. Maximum binding represents the binding of [$^3$H]DHE in the absence of added drug. Data from Hoffman *et al.* (1980a).

$\alpha$-Adrenergic receptors that inhibit lipolysis have been noted in several species, most notably human and hamster adipocytes. Burns and Langley (1970) first established that $\alpha$ agonists inhibited lipolysis in isolated human adipocytes. These investigators also noted that adipose tissue from rats lacked an $\alpha$ receptor-mediated inhibition of lipolysis. While the overall metabolic importance of $\alpha$ receptor-mediated inhibition of lipolysis remains to be determined, the response has been shown to occur in man, *in vivo* (Burns *et al.*, 1974). This was demonstrated by measuring free fatty acid concentrations in blood in response to epinephrine infusions in the presence and absence of $\alpha$ and $\beta$ blocking drugs. It has been suggested that the sympathetic nervous system conserves rather than mobilizes fuel during fasting (Burns *et al.*, 1980).

cAMP plays an important role in lipolysis induced by $\beta$-adrenergic stimulation (Fain, 1980). There is good evidence that the observed $\alpha$ receptor mediated inhibition of lipolysis is associated with reduced cAMP concentrations. It was demonstrated that $\alpha$ receptors reduced both basal and isoproterenol-stimulated cAMP concentrations in isolated human adipocytes (Burns and Langley, 1971; Robison *et al.*, 1972). These results were extended by experiments that directly demonstrated that $\alpha$ receptors inhibited adenylate cyclase activity in human adipocyte membrane preparations (Burns and Langley, 1975; Kather *et al.*, 1979). Recently, it has been demonstrated that the $\alpha$ receptors inhibiting lipolysis and adenylate cyclase activity in human adipocytes are $\alpha_2$ receptors, with yohimbine a more potent antagonist of these responses than prazosin (Lafonton and Berlan, 1980; Burns *et al.*, 1981). Indeed, it may be generally true that the $\alpha$ receptors that inhibit adenylate cyclase activity are of the $\alpha_2$ subtype (Fain and Garcia-Sainz, 1980; Hoffman and Lefkowitz, 1980).

Interestingly, it has also been shown recently that human adipocytes also possess $\alpha_1$ receptors; these $\alpha_1$ receptors do not regulate intracellular cAMP but rather stimulate $^{32}P$ incorporation into phosphatidylinositol (Burns *et al.*, 1981). Although rat adipocytes lack $\alpha_2$ receptors inhibiting lipolysis, these cells also possess $\alpha_1$ receptors that increase phosphatidylinositol turnover and inactivate glycogen synthase (Garcia-Sainz and Fain, 1980).

A useful model for human fat may well be adipocytes derived from hamsters, in some ways preferable to the more extensively studied rat adipocyte. Indeed, hamster adipocytes contain both $\alpha_1$ and $\alpha_2$ receptors which seem to function analogously to their human counterparts. Hamster adipocytes have $\alpha$ receptors which inhibit lipolysis and inhibit cAMP accumulation (Hittelman *et al.*, 1973; Hittelman and Butcher, 1973; Schimmel, 1976; Rosak and Hittelman, 1977; Guidicelli *et al.*, 1977). These inhibitory $\alpha$ receptors have recently been demonstrated to be $\alpha_2$ receptors (Garcia-Sainz *et al.* 1980; Schimmel *et al.*, 1980). Also, in a fashion analogous to human adipocytes, hamster adipocytes possess distinct $\alpha_1$ receptors which increase phosphatidylinositol turnover (Garcia-Sainz *et al.*, 1980).

The $\alpha$-adrenergic receptors of hamster adipocytes have been characterized using radioligand binding techniques (Pecquery *et al.*, 1979; Garcia-Sainz *et al.*, 1980). By analyzing competition curves of the $\alpha_1$ selective antagonist prazosin with the nonsubtype selective radioligand [$^3$H]DHE, the proportion of $\alpha_1$ and $\alpha_2$ receptors in hamster adipocytes was determined. In a series of experiments, $\alpha_1$ receptors were found to constitute 10% of the total $\alpha$ receptors in hamster adipocytes (Garcia-Sainz *et al.*, 1980). Similar radioligand studies in human adipocytes have demonstrated $\alpha$ receptors with the $\alpha_2$ receptors predominating in human subcutaneous fat (Burns *et al.*, 1981). The mechanisms whereby these and other $\alpha_2$ receptors may function to inhibit adenylate cyclase activity are discussed in the next section.

### B. Mechanisms of Adenylate Cyclase Inhibition

Investigations of the effects of guanine nucleotides on $\alpha$-adrenergic receptors using radioligand binding techniques have been particularly informative. U'Prichard and Snyder (1978a) found in brain membranes that GTP reduced the affinity of $\alpha$ receptors for [$^3$H]epinephrine and [$^3$H]norepinephrine, both agonists, whereas there was no effect of GTP on the binding of [$^3$H]WB4101, a radiolabeled antagonist compound. Originally interpreted to represent binding to separate "agonist" and "antagonist" states of $\alpha$ receptors, it is now clear that these sites represent binding to $\alpha_2$ and $\alpha_1$ receptors, respectively (U'Prichard and Snyder, 1979), with agonist affinity only at $\alpha_2$ receptor sites being affected by GTP. The hypothesis that $\alpha_2$ but not $\alpha_1$ receptors are regulated by guanine nucleotides seems reasonable, in that the former appear to inhibit adenylate cyclase whereas the latter do not interact directly with adenylate cyclase in a variety of tissues. Therefore, the characterization of a heterogeneous $\alpha$-adrenergic receptor population may be complicated not only by the presence of $\alpha$-adrenergic receptor subtypes by also by their differential regulation by guanine nucleotides. Neither agonist nor antagonist binding to $\alpha_1$ adrenergic receptors appears to be affected by guanine nucleotides, whereas guanine nucleotides reduce agonist but not antagonist affinity at $\alpha_2$ receptor sites (U'Prichard and Snyder 1978b; Hoffman *et al.*, 1980a). Competition curves of the agonist epinephrine with [$^3$H]DHE in rat liver plasma membranes are only slightly affected by guanine nucleotides and this effect can be shown to arise from the small fraction of $\alpha_2$ receptors in the predominantly $\alpha_1$-adrenergic receptor population of this tissue (Hoffman *et al.*, 1981a). This was demonstrated by noting that competition curves of epinephrine with [$^3$H]prazosin ($\alpha_1$ selective) are unaffected by guanine nucleotides, whereas epinephrine competition curves with the $\alpha_2$ selective radioligand [$^3$H]yohimbine are shifted to lower affinity in the presence of guanine nucleotides. Thus, in a tissue such as the liver, heterogeneity of agonist binding may reflect not only the presence of $\alpha$ receptor subtypes but also the differential regulation of these subtypes by guanine nucleotides.

Since the platelet $\alpha$-adrenergic receptor population is exclusively of the $\alpha_2$ subtype, this tissue has served as an excellent model for these receptors in radioligand binding studies. Figure 5 shows competition curves of prazosin, phentolamine, and yohimbine with [$^3$H]DHE at the human platelet $\alpha_2$ receptor. Computer modeling of these data indicates that the antagonist com-

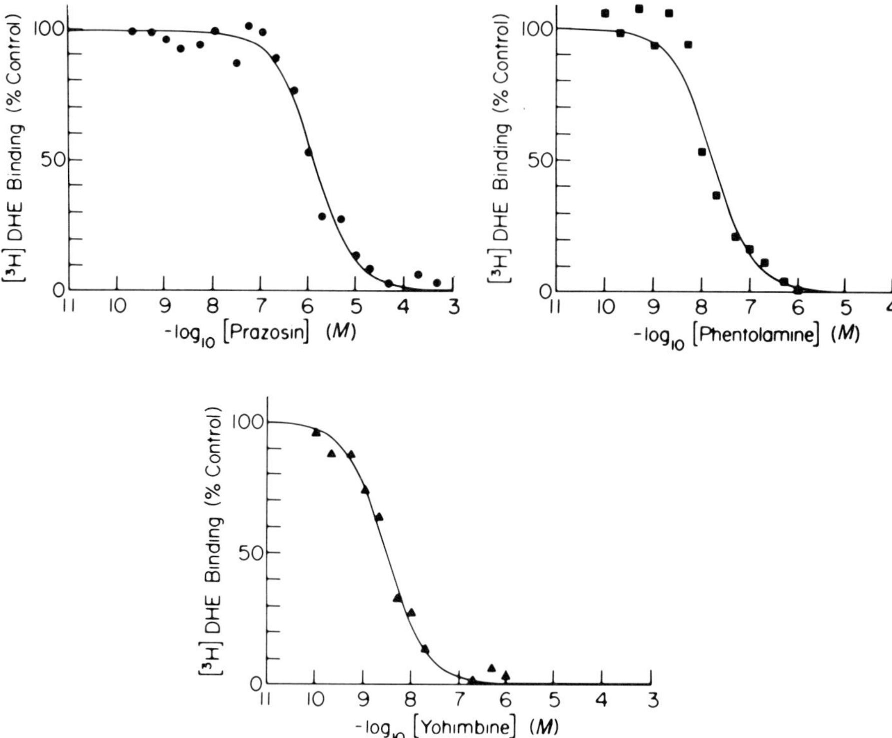


FIG. 5. Computer modeled curves of competition for [$^3$H]DHE binding to human platelet $\alpha$-adrenergic receptors by prazosin, phentolamine, and yohimbine. The data points are means of duplicate determinations from a representative experiment. Each curve is steep and monophasic, and the data are best fit by a model with a single class of $\alpha$-adrenergic receptors. The potency order of yohimbine > phentolamine > prazosin confirms that these $\alpha$-adrenergic receptors are of the alpha$_2$ subtype. Data from Hoffman *et al.* (1979).

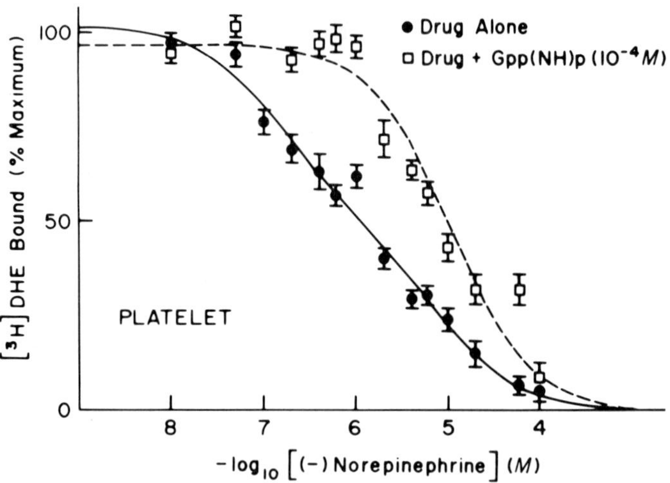


FIG. 6. Computer modeled curves for inhibition of [$^3$H]DHE binding in human platelet membranes by norepinephrine in the presence and absence of GppNHp ($10^{-4}$ $M$). The data points are means of duplicate determinations from a representative experiment. The competition curve in the absence of added GppNHp may be resolved into two affinity states for norepinephrine. In the presence of GppNHp the norepinephrine competition curve becomes steeper and of lower overall affinity; this curve is best fit by a model with a single binding affinity for epinephrine, with this affinity not different from the lower affinity state seen in the absence of GppNHp. Compare Fig. 2; see text for details. Data from Hoffman *et al.* (1980a).

pounds are interacting with a homogeneous $\alpha_2$ receptor population with uniform affinity for antagonists. The affinity of these antagonists is unaffected by guanine nucleotides. Figure 6 shows competition curves of the full $\alpha$ agonist norepinephrine with [$^3$H]DHE at the platelet $\alpha_2$ receptor. There is a marked reduction in the overall affinity for epinephrine in the presence of $10^{-4}$ $M$ Gpp(NH)p. Computer modeling of these data may be interpreted to indicate that, in the absence of added guanine nucleotides, there are two distinct affinity states for epinephrine, one of higher ($\alpha_{2_H}$) and the other of lower affinity ($\alpha_{2_L}$). In the presence of guanine nucleotides the $\alpha_2$ receptor population is of uniform, lower affinity for norepinephrine; this affinity is not different from the lower affinity form of the receptor seen in the absence of Gpp(NH)p and there is no change in the total number of receptors present. Thus, guanine nucleotides appear to promote a transition between high and low agonist affinity states of the $\alpha_2$ receptor such that at high guanine nucleotide concentrations all the $\alpha_2$ receptors are in the low affinity state. This may also be demonstrated directly by binding of [$^3$H]epinephrine to the platelet $\alpha_2$ receptor (Hoffman *et al.*, 1980b). Saturation curves with [$^3$H]epinephrine label only a fraction of the sites labeled by [$^3$H]DHE. This fraction is equivalent to the proportion of receptors in the high affinity state for epinephrine observed in competition curves of unlabeled epinephrine with [$^3$H]DHE. Direct binding of [$^3$H]epinephrine to the high affinity state of the receptor is abolished by guanine nucleotides. These results, demonstrating the apparent interconversion of $\alpha_2$ receptor agonist affinity states by guanine nucleotides, are entirely analogous to those observed for the beta-adrenergic receptors (see Section III). It thus appears that the mechanisms whereby guanine nucleotides modulate $\alpha_2$ receptor affinity for agonists may be similar to those postulated for the $\beta$-adrenergic receptor system. Indeed, $\alpha$ receptor mediated inhibition of adenylate cyclase requires GTP in a variety of tissues (Jakobs *et al.*, 1978; Sabol and Nirenberg, 1978; Aktories *et al.*, 1979; Steer and Wood, 1979). Additionally, in platelet lysates the extent to which an agonists overall affinity is reduced by guanine nucleotides is proportional to the intrinsic activity of that agonist in the $\alpha$ receptor mediated inhibition of adenylate cyclase (Tsai and Lefkowitz, 1979a). Taken together, these observations strongly suggest that a GTP binding nucleotide regulatory protein is a component involved in $\alpha_2$ receptor inhibition of adenylate cyclase. The functional and structural relationships of this putative "adenylate cyclase inhibitory N protein" with the analogous component in the adenylate cyclase stimulatory $\beta$-adrenergic receptor system remain to be determined.

Investigations in a variety of receptor systems are being directed toward an understanding of the biochemistry of guanine nucleotide regulation of hormone-mediated adenylate cyclase inhibition. The adenylate cyclase inhibitory receptor systems have been less amenable to study in cell free systems than adenylate cyclase stimulatory receptors. Whereas hormone stimulation of adenylate cyclase was demonstrated in particulate preparations of liver cells two decades ago (Sutherland and Rall, 1960), hormone inhibition of adenylate cyclase was demonstrated in membrane fractions only in 1975 (Burns and Langley, 1975). Inhibition of cAMP production by $\alpha$-adrenergic agents was noted in platelets in 1969 (Salzman and Neri, 1969) and in adipocytes in 1970 (Burns and Langley, 1970) but conclusive demonstration that this effect was mediated by an inhibition of adenylate cyclase activity awaited cell-free studies several years later (Burns and Langley, 1975; Jakobs *et al.*, 1976). Inhibition of adenylate cyclase by hormones is generally only 40–60% of control activity (Jakobs, 1979); studies of adenylate cyclase inhibition thus deal with a relatively small range of experimental values (see Fig. 7). Additionally, receptor mediated inhibition of adenylate cyclase activity appears to be relatively more labile in membrane preparations. Nevertheless, several generalizations have emerged concerning hormone inhibition of adenylate cyclase based on observations in a variety of receptor systems. Most importantly, these include $\alpha_2$ receptors of platelet, adipocyte, and neuroblastoma × glioma (N×G) cells (Sabol and Nirenberg, 1978), mus-

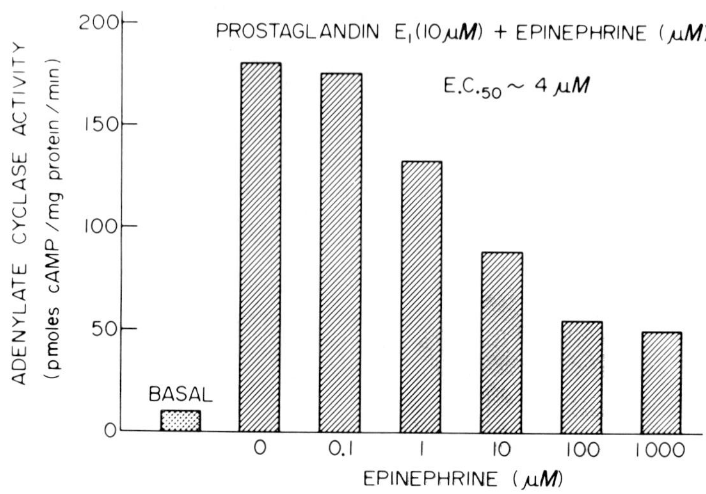


FIG. 7. Stimulation and inhibition of adenylate cyclase in human platelet membranes. Adenylate cyclase assays were performed as described elsewhere. The data shown are means of triplicate determinations from a representative experiment. Basal adenylate cyclase activity is stimulated ~20-fold by $10^{-5}$ *M* $PGE_1$. Increasing concentrations of epinephrine inhibit up to 60% of the $PGE_1$-stimulated adenylate cyclase activity. There is a similar inhibitory effect of epinephrine on the basal adenylate cyclase activity (not shown). These effects of epinephrine can be shown to be α-adrenergic in nature, as they are blocked by phentolamine but not by propranolol.

carinic cholinergic receptors in heart (Watanabe *et al.*, 1978; Jakobs *et al.*, 1979) and N×G cells (Lichtshtein *et al.*, 1979), and opiate receptors in N×G cells (Blume *et al.*, 1979). These tissues, which contain adenylate cyclase inhibitory receptors, also contain receptors that stimulate the enzyme, suggesting that perhaps *in vivo* the inhibitory receptors serve primarily to attenuate responses to stimulatory hormones. Most adenylate cyclase inhibitory receptors inhibit both "basal" and hormone stimulated enzyme activity to the same fractional extent, usually between 40 and 60% (see Jakobs, 1979). In these receptor systems, GTP exhibits a biphasic effect on adenylate cyclase activity (Cooper *et al.*, 1979; Steer and Wood, 1979; Tsai and Lefkowitz, 1979b), stimulating the enzyme at lower concentrations and inhibiting adenylate cyclase activity at higher concentrations. Hormonal stimulation and inhibition of the enzyme also demonstrate a similar bimodal GTP requirement, with higher GTP concentrations required for hormone inhibition of adenylate cyclase than for hormone stimulation. Conflicting data exist regarding whether nonhydrolyzable GTP analogs [e.g., Gpp(NH)p] show a similar biphasic effect in these receptor systems (cf. Jakobs *et al.*, 1978; Steer and Wood, 1979). Biochemical studies of guanine nucleotide metabolism as regulated by adenylate cyclase inhibitory receptor systems are as yet unavailable. Cholera toxin-stimulated adenylate cyclase does not appear to be inhibited by GTP (Cooper *et al.*, 1979) or inhibitory hormones (Jakobs and Schultz, 1979). A cholera toxin substrate associated either with an adenylate cyclase inhibitory receptor or coupled in an inhibitory fashion to the enzyme has not been demonstrated. Thus, whereas considerable indirect evidence exists for the existence of similar but distinct modes of guanine nucleotide inhibition and stimulation of adenylate cyclase, biochemical identification of the membrane components that regulate hormone receptor mediated inhibition of adenylate cyclase remains to be achieved.

Some insight into the molecular components that mediate adenylate cyclase inhibition is provided by recent investigations with digitonin-solubilized human platelet $\alpha_2$ adrenergic receptors (Michel *et al.*, 1981; Smith and Limbird, 1981). Following receptor solubilization, the binding of antagonist compounds remained of high affinity, but the binding of agonist drugs was of markedly lower affinity than in particulate preparations (see Fig. 8) and was no longer sensitive to guanine nucleotides. This may reflect an uncoupling of the alpha$_2$ receptor from the nucleotide regulatory component as a consequence of solublization. Since high affinity [$^3$H]epinephrine binding to the particulate membrane preparations is stable upon solubilization, it is likely that an epinephrine (agonist)-promoted alteration in the receptor takes place prior to solubilization. Using sucrose density gradient centrifugation techniques, it was found that the sedimentation coefficient of the solubilized platelet alpha$_2$ receptor, which had been labeled in the membranes with the agonist [$^3$H]epinephrine, was significantly greater than that of the receptor similarly labeled with the antagonist [$^3$H]yohimbine (Fig. 9).

For the adenylate cyclase stimulatory $\beta$-adrenergic receptor, gel chromatography of the solubilized receptor indicated an apparent increased molecular size of the agonist-liganded receptor due to the agonist-promoted association of the receptor with a guanine nucleotide regulatory protein (see Section III). Changes in one or several hydrodynamic parameters may explain the observed differences in the sedimentation properties of agonist- and antagonist-labeled alpha$_2$ receptors. However, since both hormone receptor mediated stimulation and inhibition of adenylate cyclase appear to be similarly regulated by guanine nucleotides, it seems likely that the increased sedimentation coefficient of the agonist-labeled alpha$_2$ receptor reflects increased receptor molecular size due to an analogous alpha$_2$ receptor–guanine nucleotide regulatory protein interaction promoted by agonists in the platelet.

In addition to their regulation by guanine nucleotides and in contrast to most $\beta$-adrenergic receptors, some $\alpha_2$ adrenergic receptor systems apear to be regulated by monovalent cations, most notably $Na^+$ (U'Prichard and Snyder, 1978a; Tsai and Lefkowitz, 1978; Glossman and Presek, 1979). The affinity of some $\alpha$-adrenergic receptors for agonists compounds is reduced not only by guanine nucleotides but also by monovalent cations. The decrease in the platelet $\alpha_2$ receptor affinity for agonists promoted by $Na^+$ is proportional to the intrinsic activity of that agonist for inhibition of adenylate cyclase (Tsai and Lefkowitz, 1978). In a variety of receptor systems, $Na^+$ potentiates hormone mediated inhibition of adenylate cyclase (Blume and Boone, 1979; Aktories *et al.*, 1979, Michel *et al.*, 1980). Despite the resemblance of these

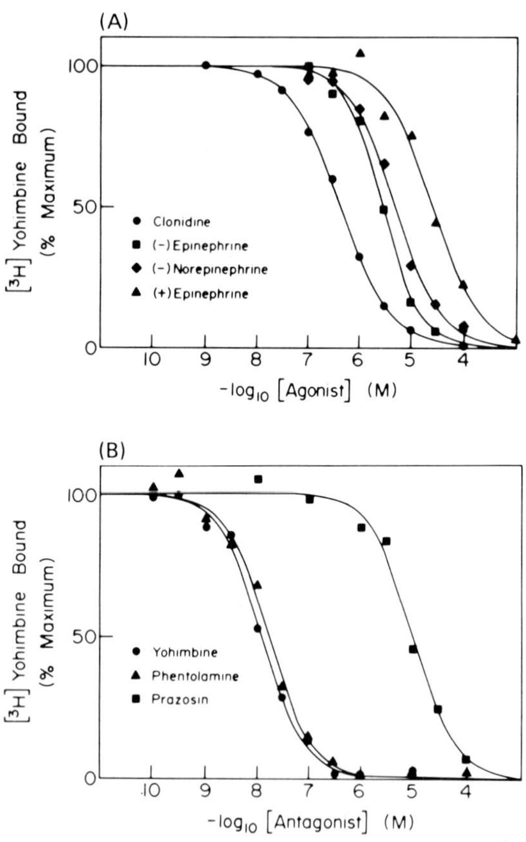


FIG. 8. Competition curves with [$^3$H]yohimbine in digitonin-solubilized human platelet $\alpha_2$adrenergic receptors. The soluble preparation was incubated with [$^3$H]yohimbine at a concentration of ~5 n$M$ plus the indicated concentrations of drugs. Bound radioligand was determined by gel filtration over Sephadex G-50. (A) A series of competition curves with agonist drugs showing the characteristic $\alpha$-adrenergic potency series. This experiment is representative of three such experiments performed in duplicate. (B) Competition curves of antagonist drugs showing the characteristic alpha$_2$ adrenergic potency series. The experiment shown is representative of four such experiments performed in duplicate. Data from Michel *et al.*, 1981.

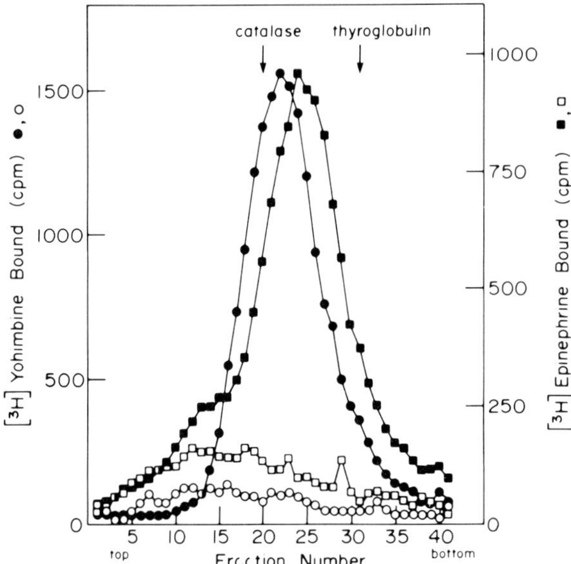


FIG. 9. Sucrose density gradient profiles of platelet $\alpha_2$-adrenergic receptors labeled with [$^3$H]yohimbine (an antagonist) or [$^3$H]epinephrine (an agonist). The platelet alpha$_2$ receptors in lysates were labeled with either ~5 n$M$ [$^3$H]yohimbine (●,○) or ~10 n$M$ [$^3$H]epinephrine (□,■, solubilized with digitonin and spun on 8–20% sucrose density gradients. Open symbols represent nonspecific binding, defined by labeling the platelet lysate in the presence of $10^{-5}$ $M$ phentolamine for [$^3$H]yohimbine or with $10^{-4}$ $M$ guanyl-yl-imidodiphosphate for [$^3$H]epinephrine ($10^{-5}$ $M$ phentolamine yielded equivalent results). The closed symbols represent total radioligand bound. In this representative experiment, the peak of [$^3$H]epinephrine binding represents an S of 15.0, and the [$^3$H]yohimbine peak is at S = 12.6. In four such experiments mean S values were respectively 14.6 ± 0.2 and 12.9 ± 0.4 (mean ± standard error; $p < .01$, paired t-test). Data from Michel *et al.*, 1981.

phenomena to those associated with guanine nucleotides, radioligand binding studies suggest that monovalent cations and guanine nucleotides regulate agonist affinity, and presumably membrane transduction, by distinct mechanisms (Michel *et al.*, 1980). However, the locus of action of $Na^+$ and its precise role in membrane transduction of $\alpha_2$ receptor mediated adenylate cyclase inhibition remains unknown.

The study of guanine nucleotide effects on $\alpha$-adrenergic ligand binding and adenylate cyclase inhibition may provide insight into the molecular constituents of this receptor system. The biochemical roles of individual components of the $\alpha$-adrenergic receptor–adenylate cyclase system are not firmly established; nonetheless, many observations analogous with the more fully characterized $\beta$-adrenergic receptor system allow comparisons to be made. As discussed above, both $\alpha$- and $\beta$-adrenergic ligands interact with discrete membrane receptors, and agonist interactions with each receptor type appear to be similarly regulated by guanine nucleotides. Indeed, it seems likely that both $\alpha$ and $\beta$ receptors form ternary complexes of agonist, receptor, and guanine nucleotide regulatory protein. Although guanine nucleotides are required for both hormone stimulation and inhibition of adenylate cyclase, it is unclear whether $\alpha_2$- and $\beta$-adrenergic receptors interact with a common or distinct pool of nucleotide regulatory proteins. The notion that adenylate cyclase inhibitory and stimulatory receptors interact with discrete classes of nucleotide regulatory proteins is supported by several lines of investigation (Steer and Wood, 1979; for reviews, see Jakobs, 1979; Rodbell, 1980). For example, in the rat adipocyte, the inhibition and stimulation of adenylate cyclase by GTP showed differential sensitivity to a variety of chemical and enzymatic treatments (Yamamura *et al.*, 1977; Cooper *et al.*, 1979); PGE stimulation and $\alpha_2$ receptor mediated inhibition of adenylate cyclase in platelets are differentially regulated by guanine nucleotides (Steer and Wood, 1979) and $Mn^{2+}$ (Hoffman *et al.*, 1981b). Furthermore, target size analysis suggests that these inhibitory and stimulatory processes are carried out by structures of different size (Schlegel *et al.*, 1980). Additionally, differential guanine nucleotide and monovalent cation requirements of hormonal stimulation and inhibition of adenylate cyclase have been noted above. These results suggest that $\alpha$- and $\beta$-adrenergic receptor regulation of adenylate cyclase proceeds through distinct intermediates to exert opposing effects on a common adenylate cyclase catalytic moieties. Nevertheless, these observations are not incompatible with the hypothesis that these distinct effects reflect only functional and not structural differences within a single class of nucleotide regulatory proteins. It could thus be conceivable that $\alpha_2$ receptor inhibition of adenylate cyclase could be achieved by a GTP-dependent receptor mediated "inactivation" of a common pool of nucleotide regulatory proteins, thereby reducing the number of these proteins available for stimulation of adenylate cyclase. This hypothesis is supported by radioligand binding studies which demonstrated that guanine nucleotide regulation of $\beta$ receptors is affected by the presence of agonist compounds active at endogenous adenylate cyclase inhibitory muscarinic cholinergic receptors in myocardium (Watanabe *et al.*, 1978) and $\alpha_2$ receptors in kidney (Woodcock and Johnston, 1980). However, in the platelets binding of agonist ligands to either inhibitory of stimulatory receptors is unaffected by the presence of ligands exerting opposed effects of adenylate cyclase in that tissue (T. Michel, unpublished observations).

Whatever the structural similarities between the stimulatory and inhibitory nucleotide regulatory proteins, the fate of the guanine nucleotide in the inhibitory receptor system remains totally obscure. If there exist structurally distinct but functionally analogous inhibitory and stimulatory regulatory proteins, then hormone inhibition of adenylate cyclase might be expected to stimulate GTPase activity and promote turnover of GDP; no studies to date report on this possibility, although differences in $\alpha_2$ receptor regulation by hydrolyzable and nonhydrolyzable GTP analogues have been observed (Jakobs and Schulz, 1979). An alternative and equally plausible hypothesis is that $\alpha_2$ receptors might "inactivate" stimulatory nucleotide regulatory proteins by inhibiting their release of GDP, thus retarding the reactivation of the regulatory protein by GTP and inhibiting the adenylate cyclase. Other models may be proposed as well, but the current level of understanding does not permit their rigorous evaluation. Further investigations of guanine nucleotide metabolism as regulated by $\alpha_2$ receptors should provide additional information on the molecular mechanisms whereby these receptors inhibit adenylate cyclase.

## REFERENCES


Abe, K., Robison, A. G., Liddle, G. W., Butcher, R. W., Nicholson, W. E., and Baird, C. E. (1969). *Endocrinology* **85**, 674–682.

Ahlquist, R. P. (1948). *Am. J. Physiol.* **153**, 586–600.

Aktories, K., Schultz, G., and Jakobs, K. H. (1979). *FEBS Letters* **107**, 100–104.

Berthelson, S., and Pettinger, W. A. (1977). *Life Sci.* **21**, 595–606.

Blume, A. J., and Boone, G. (1979). *Fed. Proc. Fed. Am. Soc. Exp. Biol.* **38**, 628.

Blume, A. J., and Foster, C. J. (1976). *J. Biol. Chem.* **251**, 3399–3404.

Blume, A. J., Lichtstein, D., and Boone, G. (1979). *Proc. Natl. Acad. Sci. U.S.A.* **76**, 5626–5630.

Boeynaems, J. M., and Dumont, J. E. (1975). *J. Cyclic Nucleotide Res.* **1**, 123–142.

Bourne, H. R., Coffino, P., and Tomkins, G. M. (1975). *Science* **187**, 750–752.

Brown, E. M., Hurwitz, S. H., and Aurbach, G. D. (1978). *Endocrinology* **103**, 893–899.

Burns, T. W., and Langley, P. E. (1970). *J. Lab. Clin. Med.* **75**, 983–997.

Burns, T. W., and Langley, P. E. (1971). *Ann. N. Y. Acad. Sci.* **185**, 115–128.

Burns, T. W., and Langley, P. E. (1975). *J. Cyclic Nucleotide Res.* **1**, 321–328.

Burns, T. W., Mohs, J. M., Langley, P. E., Yawn, R., and Chase, G. R. (1974). *J. Clin. Invest.* **53**, 338–341.

Burns, T. W., Terry, B. E., Langley, P. E., and Robison, G. A. (1980). *Adv. Cyclic Nucleotide Res.* **12**, 329–341.

Burns, T. W., Langley, P. E., Terry, B. E., Bylund, D. B., Hoffman, Hoffman, B. B., Tharp, M. D., Lefkowitz, R. J., Garcia-Sainz, J., and Fain, J. N. (1981). *J. Clin. Invest.* **67**, 467–475.

Cambridge, D., Davey, M. J., and Massingham, R. (1977). *Med. J. Aust. Suppl.* **2**, 2–6.

Cassel, D., and Pfeuffer, T. (1978). *Proc. Natl. Acad. Sci. U.S.A.* **75**, 2669–2673.

Cassel, D., and Selinger, Z. (1976). *Biochim. Biophys. Acta* **452**, 538–551.

Cassel, D., and Selinger, Z. (1977). *Proc. Natl. Acad. Sci. U.S.A.* **74**, 3307–3311.

Cassel, D., and Selinger, Z. (1978). *Proc. Natl. Acad. Sci. U.S.A.* **75**, 4155–4159.

Cavero, I., Lefèvre, F., and Roach, A. G. (1977). *Br. J. Pharmacol.* **61**, 469 (abstract).

Cole, B., Robison, G. A., and Hartmann, R. C. (1971). *Ann. N.Y. Acad. Sci.* **185**, 477–487.

Cooper, D. M. F., Schlegel, W., Lin, M. C., and Rodbell, M. (1979). *J. Biol. Chem.* **254**, 8927–8931.

Cuatrecasas, P. (1974). *Annu. Rev. Biochem.* **43,** 169–214.
Dehaen, C. (1976). *J. Theor. Biol.* **58,** 383–400.
De Lean, A., Munson, P. J., and Rodbard, D. (1978). *Am. J. Physiol.* **235,** E97–E102.
De Lean, A., Stadel, J. M., and Lefkowitz, R. J. (1980). *J. Biol. Chem.* **255,** 7108–7117.
Desmedt, D. H. (1980). *Biochem. Pharmacol.* **29,** 1967–1968.
Doxey, J. C., Smith, C. F. C., and Walker, J. M. (1977). *Br. J. Pharmacol.* **60,** 91–96.
Exton, J. H. (1980). *Am. J. Physiol.* **238,** E3–E12.
Fain, J. N. (1980). *In* "Biochemical Actions of Hormones" (G. Litwack, ed.), Vol. 7, pp. 119–204. Academic Press, New York.
Fain, J. N., and Garcia-Sainz, J. A. (1980). *Life Sci.* **26,** 1183–1194.
Feldman, H. A. (1972). *Anal. Biochem.* **48,** 317–338.
Garcia-Sainz, J. A., and Fain, J. N. (1980). *Biochem. J.* **186,** 781–789.
Garcia-Sainz, J. A., Hoffman, B. B., Li, S.-Y., Lefkowitz, R. J., and Fain, J. N. (1980). *Life Sci.* **27,** 953–961.
Gill, D. M., and Meren, R. (1978). *Proc. Natl. Acad. Sci. U.S.A.* **75,** 3050–3054.
Glass, D. B., and Krebs, E. G. (1980). *Annu. Rev. Pharmacol. Toxicol.* **20,** 363–388.
Glossman, H., and Presek, P. (1979). *Naunyn-Schmiedeberg's Arch. Pharmacol.* **366,** 67–73.
Guidicelli, Y., Agli, B., Brulle, D., and Nordmann, R. (1977). *FEBS Lett.* **83,** 225–230.
Hancock, A. A., De Lean, A., and Lefkowitz, R. J. (1979). *Mol. Pharmacol.* **16,** 1–9.
Harwood, J. P., Moskowitz, J., and Krishna, G. (1972). *Biochim. Biophys. Acta* **261,** 444–456.
Hittelman, K. J., and Butcher, R. W. (1973). *Biochim. Biophys. Acta* **316,** 403–410.
Hittleman, K. J., Wu, C. F., and Butcher, R. W. (1973). *Biochim. Biophys. Acta* **304,** 188–196.
Hoffman, B. B., and Lefkowitz, R. J. (1980). *Annu. Rev. Pharmacol. Toxicol.* **20,** 581–608.
Hoffman, B. B., De Lean, A., Wood, C. L., Schocken, D. D., and Lefkowitz, R. J. (1979). *Life Sci.* **24,** 1739–1745.
Hoffman, B. B., Mullikin-Kilpatrick, D., and Lefkowitz, R. J. (1980a). *J. Biol. Chem.* **255,** 4645–4652.
Hoffman, B. B., Michel, T., Mullikin-Kilpatrick, D., Lefkowitz, R. J., Tolbert, M. E., Gilman, H., and Fain, J. (1980b). *Proc. Natl. Acad. Sci. U.S.A.* **77,** 4569–4573.
Hoffman, B. B., Dukes, D. S., and Lefkowitz, R. J. (1981a). *Life Sci.* **28,** 265–272.
Hoffman, B. B., Yims, S. Y., Tsai, B. S., and Lefkowitz, R. J. (1981b). *Biochem. Biophys. Res. Comm.* **100,** 724–731.
Innes, I. R. (1962). *Br. J. Pharmacol.* **19,** 120–128.
Insel, P. A., Maguire, M. E., Gilman, A. G., Bourne, H. R., Coffino, P., and Melmon, K. L. (1976). *Mol. Pharmacol.* **12,** 1062–1069.
Jacobs, S., and Cuatrecasas, P. (1976). *Biochim. Biophys. Acta* **433,** 482–495.
Jakobs, K. H. (1979). *Mol. Cell. Endocrinol.* **16,** 147–156.
Jakobs, K. H., and Schultz, G. (1979). *Naunyn-Schmiedeberg's Arch. Pharmacol.* **310,** 121–127.
Jakobs, K. H., Saur, W., and Schultz, G. (1976). *J. Cyclic Nucleotide Res.* **2,** 381–392.
Jakobs, K. H., Saur, W., and Schultz, G. (1978). *FEBS Lett.* **85,** 167–170.
Jakobs, K. H., Aktories, K., and Schultz, G. (1979). *Naunyn-Schmiedeberg's Arch. Pharmacol.* **310,** 113–119.
James, R. C., Burns, T. W., and Chase, G. R. (1971). *J. Lab. Clin. Med.* **77,** 254–266.
Johnson, G. L., Kaslow, H. R., and Bourne, H. R. (1978). *J. Biol. Chem.* **253,** 7120–7123.
Johnson, G. L., Kaslow, H. R., Farfel, Z., and Bourne, H. R. (1980). *Adv. Cyclic Nucleotide Res.* **13,** 2–37.
Jones, L. M., and Michell, R. H. (1978). *Biochem. Soc. Trans.* **6,** 673–688.
Kather, H., Pries, J., Schrader, J. B., and Simon, B. (1979). *Brit J. Clin. Pharm.* **8,** 594–595.
Kent, R. S., De Lean, A., and Lefkowitz, R. J. (1980). *Mol. Pharmacol.* **17,** 14–23.
Lad, P. M., Nielsen, T. B., Preston, M. S., and Rodbell, M. (1980). *J. Biol. Chem.* **255,** 988–995.

Lafontan, M., and Berlan, M. (1980). *Eur. J. Pharmacol.* **66,** 87–93.
Lands, A. M., Arnold, A., McAuliff, J. P., Ludvena, F. P., and Brown, T. G., Jr. (1967). *Nature (London)* **214,** 597–598.
Langer, S. Z. (1974). *Biochem. Pharmacol.* **23,** 1793–1800.
Langer, S. Z. (1975). *Clin. Sci. Mol. Med. Suppl.* 3. **51,** 423s–6s.
Lasch, P., and Jakobs, K. H. (1979). *Naunyn-Schmiedeberg's Arch. Pharmacol.* **306,** 119–125.
Lefkowitz, R. J. (1975). *Biochem. Pharmacol.* **24,** 583–590.
Lichtshtein, D., Boone, G., and Blume, A. (1979). *J. Cyclic Nucleotide Res.* **5,** 367–375.
Limbird, L. E., and Lefkowitz, R. J. (1978). *Proc. Natl. Acad. Sci. U.S.A.* **75,** 228–232.
Limbird, L. E., Gill, D. M., and Lefkowitz, R. J. (1980). *Proc. Natl. Acad. Sci. U.S.A.* **77,** 775–779.
Maayan, M. C., Debons, A. F., Krimsky, I., Volpert, E. M., From, A., Dawry, F., and Siclari, E. (1977). *Endocrinology* **101,** 284–291.
Maguire, M., Van Arsdale, P. M., and Gilman, A. G. (1976). *Mol. Pharmacol.* **12,** 335–339.
Michel, T., Hoffman, B. B., and Lefkowitz, R. J. (1980). *Nature (London)* **288,** 709–711.
Michel, T., Hoffman, B. B., Lefkowitz, R. J., and Caron, M. G. (1981). *Biochem. Biophys. Res. Commun.* **100,** 1131–1136.
Moss, J., and Vaughn, M. (1979). *Annu. Rev. Biochem.* **48,** 581–600.
Pecquery, R., Malagrida, L., and Guidicelli, Y. (1979). *FEBS Lett.* **98,** 241–246.
Pettinger, W. A. (1977). *J. Pharmacol. Exp. Ther.* **201,** 622–626.
Pettinger, W. A., Keeton, T. K., Campbell, W. B., and Harper, D. C. (1976). *Circ. Res.* **38,** 338–346.
Pfeuffer, T. (1977). *J. Biol. Chem.* **252,** 7224–7234.
Pfeuffer, T. (1979). *FEBS Lett.* **101,** 85–89.
Pike, L. J., and Lefkowitz, R. J. (1980). *J. Biol. Chem.* **255,** 6860–6867.
Pike, L. J., and Lefkowitz, R. J. (1981). *J. Biol. Chem.* **256,** 2207–2212.
Robison, G. A., Butcher, R. W., and Sutherland, E. W. (1967). *Ann. N.Y. Acad. Sci.* **139,** 703–723.
Robison, G. A., Butcher, R. W., and Sutherland, E. W. (1968). *Annu. Rev. Biochem.* **37,** 149–174.
Robison, G. A., Butcher, R. W., and Sutherland, E. W. (1971). "Cyclic AMP." Academic Press, New York.
Robison, G. A., Langley, P. E., and Burns, T. W. (1972). *Biochem. Pharmacol.* **21,** 589–592.
Rodbell, M. (1980). *Nature (London)* **284,** 17–22.
Rodbell, M., Birnbaumer, L., Pohl, S. L., and Krans, H. M. (1971). *J. Biol. Chem.* **246,** 1877–1882.
Rosak, C., and Hittelman, K. J. (1977). *Biochem. Biophys. Acta* **496,** 458–474.
Ross, E. M., and Gilman, A. G. (1977). *Proc. Natl. Acad. Sci. U.S.A.* **74,** 3715–3719.
Ross, E. M., and Gilman, A. G. (1980). *Annu. Rev. Biochem.* **49,** 533–564.
Sabol, S. L., and Nirenberg, M. (1978). *J. Biol. Chem.* **254,** 1913–1920.
Salomon, Y., Lin, M. C., Londos, C., Rendell, M., and Rodbell, M. (1975). *J. Biol. Chem.* **250,** 4239–4245.
Salzman, E. W., and Neri, L. L. (1969). *Nature (London)* **224,** 609–610.
Schimmel, R. J. (1976). *Biochim. Biophys. Acta* **428,** 379–387.
Schimmel, R. J., Serio, R., Hsueh, A. Y., and Firman-Whiate, L. (1980). *Biochem. Biophys. Acta.* **630,** 71–81.
Schlegel, W., Cooper, D. M. F., and Rodbell, M. (1980). *Arch. Biochem. Biophys.* **201,** 678–682.
Smith, S. K., and Limbird, L. E. (1981). *Proc. Natl. Acad. Sci. U.S.A.* **78,** 4026–4030.
Stadel, J. M., De Lean, A., and Lefkowitz, R. J. (1981). *Adv. Enzymol.,* in press.
Starke, K. (1977). *Rev. Physiol. Biochem. Pharmacol.* **77,** 1–124.

Steer, M. L., and Wood, A. (1979). *J. Biol. Chem.* **254**, 10791-10797.
Steer, M. L., and Salzman, E. W. (1980). *Adv. Cyclic Nucleotide Res.* **12**, 71-92.
Sutherland, E. W., and Rall, T. (1960). *Pharmacol. Rev.* **12**, 165.
Tsai, B. S., and Lefkowitz, R. J. (1978). *Mol. Pharmacol.* **14**, 540-548.
Tsai, B. S., and Lefkowitz, R. J. (1979a). *Mol. Pharmacol.* **16**, 61-68.
Tsai, B. S., and Lefkowitz, R. J. (1979b). *Biochim. Biophys. Acta* **587**, 28-41.
Turtle, J. R., and Kipnis, D. M. (1967). *Biochem. Biophys. Res. Commun.* **28**, 797-802.
U'Prichard, D. C., and Snyder, S. H. (1978a). *J. Biol. Chem.* **253**, 3444-3452.
U'Prichard, D. C., and Snyder, S. H. (1978b). *J. Supramol. Struct.* **9**, 189-206.
U'Prichard, D. C., and Snyder, S. H. (1979). *Life Sci.* **24**, 79-88.
Watanabe, A. M., McConnaughey, M. M., Strawbridge, R. A., Fleming, J. W., Jones, L. R., and Besch, H. R., Jr. (1978). *J. Biol. Chem.* **253**, 4833-4836.
Wikberg, J. E. S. (1979). *Acta Physiol. Scand., Suppl.* 468. **106**, 1-99.
Williams, L. T., and Lefkowitz, R. J. (1977). *J. Biol. Chem.* **252**, 7207-7213.
Williams, L. T., and Lefkowitz, R. J. (1978). "Receptor Binding Studies in Adrenergic Pharmacology." Raven, New York.
Woodcock, E. A., and Johnston, E. I. (1980). *Nature (London)* **286**, 159-160.
Yamamura, H., Lad, P. M., and Rodbell, M. (1977). *J. Biol. Chem.* **252**, 7964-7966.
Yamashita, K., Yamashita, S., and Ogata, E. (1977). *Life Sci.* **21**, 607-612.
Yamashita, K., Yamashita, S., and Aiyoshi, Y. (1980). *Life Sci.* **27**, 1127-1130.

# CHAPTER 3

# Nutritional Regulation of $K^+$ Conductance: An Unsettled Aspect of Pancreatic B Cell Physiology

*Willy J. Malaisse and André Herchuelz*



## I. INTRODUCTION

### A. Mechanism of Insulin Release

The stimulation of insulin release from the pancreatic B cell as provoked by D-glucose or other nutrients is currently viewed as the outcome of a sequence of metabolic, ionic, and motile events (Malaisse *et al.*, 1977). In a simplified manner, it is postulated that the metabolism of the nutrient in the



BIOCHEMICAL ACTIONS OF HORMONES, VOL. IX

ISBN 0-12-452809-0

B cell generates second messengers, e.g., reducing equivalents (NADH, NADPH, reduced glutathione), protons ($H^+$), and high-energy phosphate intermediates (ATP), which act as coupling factors between metabolic and ionic events (Malaisse *et al.*, 1979b). The latter events consist of an extensive remodeling of ionic fluxes across the plasma membrane and the membrane of intracellular organelles in the B cell. Thus, glucose is known to affect the handling of $Cl^-$, inorganic phosphate, $Na^+$, $K^+$, and $Ca^{2+}$ by islet cells (Malaisse *et al.*, 1981a). A dramatic illustration of this remodeling in ionic fluxes is given by the changes in membrane potential and resistance recorded in B cells stimulated with glucose (Matthews, 1975).

The last step in the secretory sequence consists of the migration of secretory granules to the cell boundary, and their extrusion into the interstitial fluid via exocytosis. It is thought that the activation of the effector system controlling the release of secretory granules is secondary to the changes in ionic variables (Malaisse *et al.*, 1978b). For instance, the accumulation of $Ca^{2+}$ in the cytosol, or its ectoplasmic compartment, could trigger insulin release by provoking the contraction of the microfilamentous cell web (Malaisse and Orci, 1979) and/or by removing an electrostatic energy barrier between the surface of secretory granules and the inner face of the plasma membrane (Dean, 1974). It is also conceivable that a change in the electrical polarization of the plasma membrane is essential for exocytosis to occur.

Each of these three major series of functional events is the object of detailed investigations, and the significance of metabolic (Ashcroft, 1980; Hedeskov, 1980), ionic (Sehlin, 1980; Herchuelz and Malaisse, 1981), and motile events (Ostlund, 1980; Malaisse and Orci, 1979) in the insulin secretory sequence is constantly reevaluated in appropriate reviews. Moreover, increasing attention is paid to feedforward or feedback regulatory processes that are superimposed to the main axis of the stimulus–secretion process. For instance, the recent observation that islet cells contain the calcium-dependent regulatory protein calmodulin and that calmodulin stimulates in a $Ca^{2+}$-dependent fashion both adenylate cyclase (Valverde *et al.*, 1979) and protein kinase (Schubart *et al.*, 1980) in islet homogenates apparently ascribes to the cytosolic concentration of ionized $Ca^{2+}$ a new regulatory role, in addition to its long postulated role to trigger motile events in the pancreatic B cell (Grodsky and Bennett, 1966).

It is conceivable but not proved that the release of insulin from the pancreatic B cell is influenced by intraislet regulatory processes including both the effect of different islet hormones (insulin, glucagon, somatostatin, pancreatic polypeptide) on the insulin-secreting cell and changes in junctional complexes (gap junction, tight junction) between adjacent islet cells (Orci, 1976; Meissner, 1976).

### B. Glucose-Induced Changes in $K^+$ Conductance

The hypothesis that ascribes the role of triggering insulin release to the accumulation of $Ca^{2+}$ in a critical site of the B cell is supported by several findings. For instance, insulin release can be stimulated in the absence of exogenous nutrient when the concentration of extracellular $Ca^{2+}$ is sufficiently increased, and such a process of calcium-induced insulin release is abolished by agents blocking the entry of $Ca^{2+}$ into the islet cells (Devis *et al.*, 1975; Hellman, 1976). It is generally accepted that glucose stimulates the entry of $Ca^{2+}$ into islet cells (Herchuelz and Malaisse, 1981). A current view is that the increase in $Ca^{2+}$ inflow into the B cell is attributable to the gating of voltage-dependent $Ca^{2+}$ channels (Meissner and Schmelz, 1974; Meissner and Preissler, 1979). And indeed, glucose depolarizes the B cell plasma membrane and, by doing so, may cause the gating of $Ca^{2+}$ channels. When the glucose concentration of the extracellular fluid is suddenly increased from a nonstimulatory to an insulinotropic concentration, the depolarization of the B cell plasma membrane occurs in two steps, a slow one followed by a rapid depolarization. The slow step (and, according to some authors, also the subsequent fast step of depolarization) is attributed mainly if not exclusively to a decrease in $K^+$ conductance of the B cell plasma membrane. This view is supported, inter alia, by the decrease in the fractional outflow rate of $^{42}K$ (or $^{86}Rb$, the latter being used as a tracer for $^{39}K$) from isolated islets indeed observed when the extracellular concentration of glucose is increased (Sehlin and Täljedal, 1975).

It would thus appear that the capacity of glucose to affect $K^+$ conductance represents a discrete but essential phenomenon in the sequence of events leading to insulin release. The present account deals specifically with the effect of glucose on $K^+$ conductance in the B cell. Three aspects of this phenomenon will be discussed. First, the influence of glucose on $K^+$ conductance will be defined in greater detail. Second, the consequence(s) of a change in $K^+$ conductance will be considered. Last, the mechanism(s) by which glucose affects $K^+$ conductance will be scrutinized.

## II. CHRONOLOGY AND MAGNITUDE OF THE CHANGES IN $K^+$ CONDUCTANCE

Two methods are currently used to ascertain the effect of glucose on the $K^+$ conductance of the B cell plasma membrane. The first depends on the use of either $^{42}K^+$ or $^{86}Rb^+$ as a tracer for the movements of $^{39}K^+$ in the islet cells. The second depends on simultaneous measurements of membrane electrical polarization and resistance in impaled B cells.

## A. Radioisotopic Data

### 1. *General Considerations*

The fluxes of $K^+$ in islet cells have been measured by use of either $^{42}K$ or the more convenient isotope $^{86}Rb$. Although in the islets as in other tissues, the fractional outflow rate of $^{86}Rb$ is lower than that of $^{42}K$, the use of $^{86}Rb$ was proved to be suitable to characterize the absolute inflow–outflow rate of $K^+$, as well as the relative magnitude of environmental changes in either $K^+$ content in the islet cells or fractional turnover rate (Malaisse *et al.*, 1978a).

Glucose fails to significantly affect the inflow of $K^+$ into islet cells, as judged from either the net uptake of $^{86}Rb$ over short periods of incubation or the values for $K^+$ inflow–outflow rate, the latter values being taken as the product of the fractional outflow rate by the cellular pool size measured at isotopic equilibrium (Malaisse *et al.*, 1978a). Under steady-state conditions, the major effect of glucose is to decrease the fractional outflow rate of $K^+$ and, as a result, to increase the cellular pool size of $K^+$.

In order to study the dynamics of changes in $^{86}Rb$ fractional outflow rate, the efflux of $^{86}Rb$ from prelabeled islets is monitored in a perfusion system. It is assumed that changes in $^{86}Rb$ fractional outflow rate reflects changes in $K^+$ conductance of the plasma membrane. The latter assumption may not always be correct. For instance, it was suggested that the changes in $^{86}Rb$ fractional outflow rate evoked by either intracellular acidification or mitochondrial inhibitors may be due, to a limited extent, to an intracellular redistribution of the tracer cation (Carpinelli and Malaisse, 1980b,c).

The outflow of $K^+$ from the islet cells is thought to represent a passive movement driven by the electrochemical gradient across the plasma membrane and mediated by a native transport system, e.g., $K^+$ channels (Boschero and Malaisse, 1979). Depolarization of the plasma membrane as evoked by a rise in extracellular $K^+$ concentration or by administration of veratridine enhances $^{86}Rb$ fractional outflow rate (Boschero and Malaisse, 1979). Verapamil decreases and valinomycin facilitates $^{86}Rb$ outflow from the perfused islets. Ouabain does not markedly affect $^{86}Rb$ fractional outflow rate (Boschero and Malaisse, 1979). The outflow of $^{86}Rb$ is dramatically reduced in the absence of extracellular $K^+$ (Boschero and Malaisse, 1979). These findings are indeed compatible with the view that $K^+$ extrusion corresponds to a passive ionic movement.

### 2. *Timing of the Response to Glucose*

In a recent study, the precise timing of the glucose-induced decrease in $^{86}Rb$ fractional outflow rate was established by monitoring $^{86}Rb$ outflow over successive periods of 12 seconds each and by comparing these data to simultaneous measurements of glucose, lactic, and pyruvic acid, $^{45}Ca$, $^{32}P$, and insulin in the samples of effluent medium (Malaisse *et al.*, 1981b). The concentration of glucose in the effluent progressively increased from zero to 16.7 m$M$ within 132 seconds. After 60 seconds of exposure to glucose, the $^{86}$Rb fractional outflow rate decreased to reach its nadir value after a further 96 seconds of stimulation. This time course was superimposable to that characterizing the glucose-induced fall in $^{45}$Ca fractional outflow rate (Fig. 1). The decrease in $^{86}$Rb outflow was preceded by an increase in both lactic and pyruvic acid output, but was initiated 36 seconds or more before any increase in $^{32}$P fractional outflow rate, any secondary rise in $^{45}$Ca outflow, or any increase in insulin output could be detected. Incidentally, in four out of five experiments, the decrease in $^{86}$Rb fractional outflow rate was preceded by a minor increase in outflow rate after 36 seconds of exposure to glucose. This phenomenon is reminiscent of the transient and slight hyperpolarization often observed in mouse B cells shortly after changing from a glucose-free solution to one containing glucose (Atwater *et al.*, 1978).

In all experiments there was a modest reascension in $^{86}$Rb fractional outflow rate after the initial fall, the value reached after 217 to 228 seconds of exposure to glucose being 0.16 ± 0.05%/minute higher than the paired value reached about 1 minute earlier. This should be compared to values of 3.46 ± 0.29%/minute and 1.90 ± 0.17%/minute corresponding to the basal value for $^{86}$Rb fractional outflow rate measured just prior to exposure to glucose and the nadir value enregistered after 157–168 seconds of stimulation (Malaisse *et al.*, 1981b). A secondary reascension in $^{86}$Rb fractional outflow rate in response to glucose administration had already been observed in islets pretreated with quinine in which case this phenomenon was much more pronounced and was interpreted as indicative of a dual or discontinuous effect of glucose on $^{86}$Rb handling by the islet cells (Carpinelli and Malaisse, 1980a).

In conclusion, the glucose-induced fall in $^{86}$Rb fractional outflow rate is a rapid phenomenon preceded by changes in metabolic variables and itself preceding such events as the phosphate flush, the secondary rise in $^{45}$Ca outflow, and the stimulation of insulin release.

### 3. *Dose-Action Relationship for the Glucose-Induced Decrease in $^{86}$Rb Fractional Outflow Rate*

As judged from the steady-state values for $^{86}$Rb fractional outflow rate reached after 17 to 21 minutes of exposure of the islets to media of different glucose concentrations, glucose decreases $^{86}$Rb outflow in a dose-dependent and sigmoidal fashion, with the steepest part of the curve corresponding to the 2.8–4.4 m$M$ range of glucose concentrations (Fig. 2). The steady-state value of $^{86}$Rb fractional outflow rate is little affected once the concentration of glucose exceeds 8.3 m$M$. The pattern illustrated in Fig. 2 is in good agreement with dynamic data obtained when the concentration of D-glucose in the

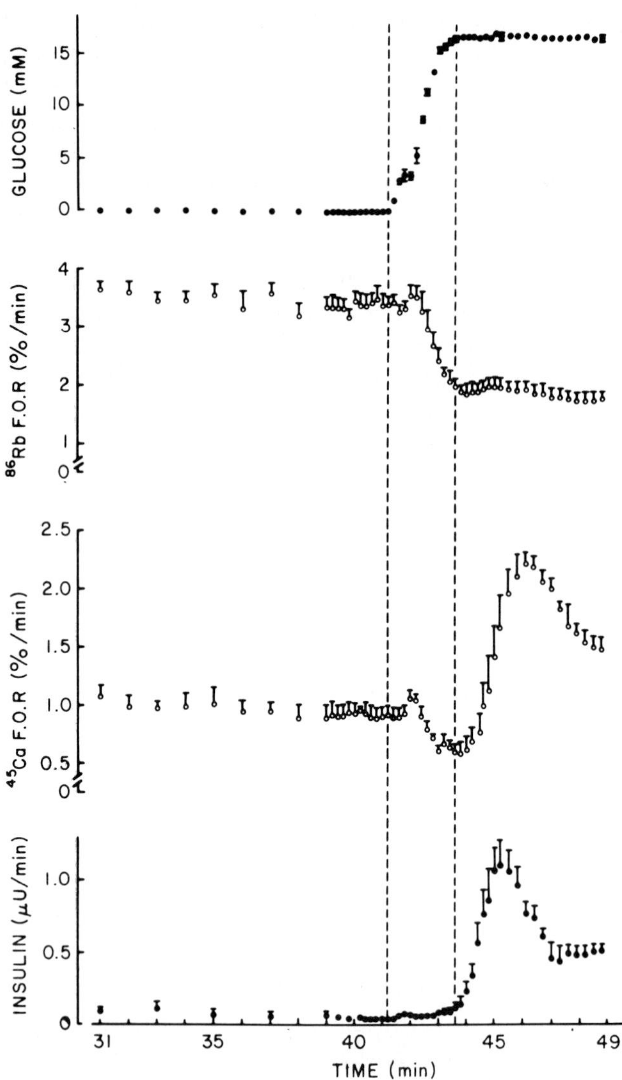


FIG. 1. Timing for the changes in glucose concentration (upper panel), $^{86}$Rb and $^{45}$Ca fractional outflow rates (middle panels), and insulin release (lower panel) in perfused islets (Malaisse *et al.*, 1981b).

perfusate is suddenly changed. In this case, a change of glucose concentration from zero to 1.7 m*M*, from 1.7 to 2.8 m*M*, from 2.8 to 4.4 m*M*, from 4.4 to 5.6 mM, and from 5.6 to 8.3 m*M* invariably causes a sizable fall in $^{86}$Rb fractional outflow rate (Carpinelli and Malaisse, 1981). Such is not the case, however, when the glucose concentration is raised from 8.3 to 11.1 m*M* (or

16.7 m$M$) and from 11.1 to 16.7 m$M$, in which conditions no fall in $^{86}$Rb fractional outflow rate can be detected and, instead, a transient increase in $^{86}$Rb outflow always occurs. The significance of the latter phenomenon will be considered later.

These data indicate that the dose–action relationship for the inhibitory effect of glucose on $^{86}$Rb fractional outflow rate is shifted far to the left (i.e., toward lower glucose concentrations) relative to the sigmoidal curve relating the steady-state values for insulin release to the sugar concentration. In other words, a dramatic fall in $^{86}$Rb outflow is observed at glucose concentrations which do not stimulate insulin secretion and dramatic increases in insulin output are observed in a ranged of glucose concentrations (8.3 to 16.7 m$M$) in which the steady-state values for $^{86}$Rb fractional outflow rate remain virtually constant.

## B. Bioelectrical Data

The record of electrical activity in impaled individual B cells offers considerable advantages over the radioisotopic procedure in that the experimental data refer to a presumably pure B cell population and provide information on a time scale (fractions of a second) which is unaccessible by current perfusion techniques.

### 1. *Effect of Glucose on Membrane Potential*

Five critical levels of membrane potential have been recognized in the B cell. In the absence of glucose or at very low glucose concentration (2.8

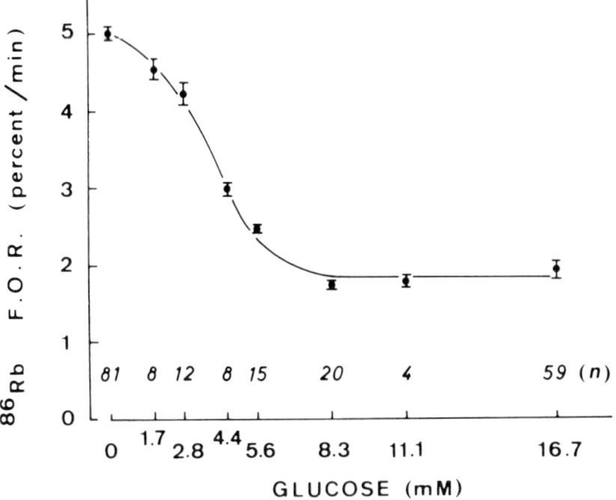


FIG. 2. Dose–action relationship for the steady-state values of $^{86}$Rb fractional outflow rate at increasing concentrations of glucose (Carpinelli and Malaisse, 1981).

m$M$), the B cell displays a stable membrane potential of about −45 to −60 mV, values as high as −80 mV having been occasionally reported (Atwater *et al.*, 1978; Meissner *et al.*, 1980). This resting membrane potential ($V_0$) is affected by stepwise replacement of extracellular $Na^+$ by $K^+$ in a manner that suggests that such a resting potential depends mainly but not solely on the $K^+$ permeability (Atwater *et al.*, 1978; Meissner *et al.*, 1978). The concentration of extracellular $K^+$ required to annihilate the membrane potential (ca. 120 m$M$) was used to estimate the intracellular activity of $Na^+$ (ca. 30 m$M$). The latter value, which depends on an assumed total concentration of intracellular free cations of 150 m$M$, is somewhat lower than the intracellular $Na^+$ concentration derived from radioisotopic studies, even if one takes into account the compartmentation of $Na^+$ in different intracellular pools (Kawazu *et al.*, 1978).

When the concentration of glucose is raised from a low value (e.g., 2.8 m$M$) to a stimulating concentration of glucose (e.g., 16.7 m$M$), the following changes in membrane potential are observed. (Meissner *et al.*, 1980).

A slow depolarization of about 15 mV is first observed over a period of 20–30 seconds. It brings the membrane potential to a threshold value ($V_t$) from which the membrane depolarizes rapidly to a plateau potential ($V_p$).

Once the membrane potential has reached the plateau value ($V_p$), fast spike activity is seen, the membrane potential oscillating rapidly between the plateau potential ($V_p$) and a fourth critical level corresponding to the reversal potential of spikes ($V_s$) (Fig. 3).

The first burst of spikes is of longer duration than a subsequent burst of spikes, so that the electrical activity in response to a "square wave" stimulation with glucose displays a typical biphasic pattern (Meissner and Atwater, 1976).

At the end of each burst of spikes, the membrane repolarizes and reaches the maximum repolarization potential ($V_r$). Incidentally, the resting membrane potential ($V_0$) is about 10 mV lower than the value reached between successive spikes when the islets are exposed to stimulating concentration of the sugar (e.g., 11.1 m$M$) (Meissner *et al.*, 1980). During such a silent phase, the membrane slowly depolarizes back to the threshold potential ($V_t$). A new cycle then takes place so that the electrical response to glucose under steady-state conditions is mainly characterized by a regular burst pattern.

### 2. *Dose–Action Relationship for the Effect of Glucose on Bioelectrical Activity*

Changes in the glucose concentration in the range of values above the threshold level required to evoke electrical activity does not affect the threshold potential ($V_t$), the plateau potential ($V_p$), the reversal potential of spikes ($V_s$), and the maximum repolarization potential ($V_r$). The major effect

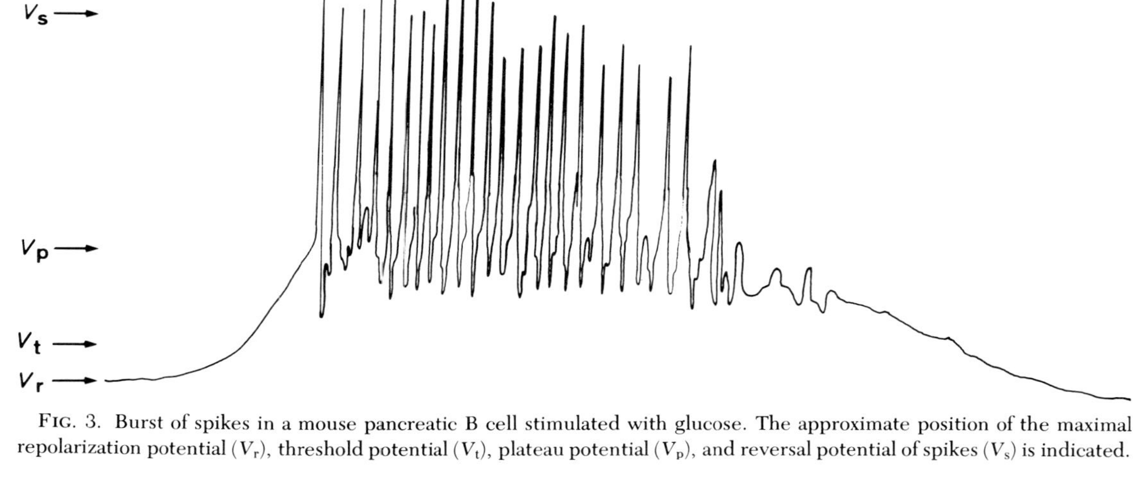


FIG. 3. Burst of spikes in a mouse pancreatic B cell stimulated with glucose. The approximate position of the maximal repolarization potential ($V_r$), threshold potential ($V_t$), plateau potential ($V_p$), and reversal potential of spikes ($V_s$) is indicated.

of glucose is to affect the course of the slow waves. Thus, with increasing concentrations of glucose, the duration of the slow waves increases, the spike periods being consequently prolonged. At very high glucose concentration (above 16.7 m*M*) the burst pattern disappears and the spike activity is continuous. A sigmoidal relationship characterizes the percent of time spent by the B cell in the active phase as a function of the concentration of glucose (Meissner and Preissler, 1979). This relationship is virtually superimposable to that characterizing the rate of insulin release at increasing glucose concentrations.

Another aspect of this dose–action relationship is that, when the B cell is exposed to glucose for only short periods (e.g., 20 seconds), the onset of electrical activity and its duration both depend on the concentration of glucose administered during the 20 second period of exposure to the sugar. The lag period prior to the electrical response is shortened and the duration of spike activity is increased as the glucose concentration is raised. Likewise when glucose at a fixed concentration is administered in pulses of variable duration, the duration of spike activity depends on the length of prior exposure to glucose. In this kind of experiments, when the concentration of glucose or duration of the glucose pulse are not sufficient, a silent depolarization may be seen (Malaisse *et al.*, 1978b; Beigelman and Ribalet, 1980).

### 3. *Interpretation of Bioelectrical Data*

The interpretation of the bioelectrical data described above suggests that changes in $K^+$ conductance of the plasma membrane play a critical role in the regulation of membrane polarization.

*a. The Slow Depolarization.* There is general agreement that the slow depolarization from the resting membrane potential ($V_0$) to the threshold potential ($V_t$) in response to glucose stimulation and the slow depolarization from the maximum repolarization potential ($V_r$) to the threshold potential ($V_t$) between successive bursts is mainly attributable to a decrease in $K^+$ conductance. This slow depolarization does not depend on the presence of extracellular $Na^+$ and does not require the integrity of $Ca^{2+}$ inward transport into the islet cells, being still observed in the presence of $Co^{2+}$. The slow depolarization is prevented by addition to the $K^+$-ionophore valinomycin (Henquin and Meissner, 1978). Furthermore, the glucose-induced depolarization is associated with an increased resistance of the B cell plasma membrane. These convergent findings do not exclude that changes in the fluxes of other ions (e.g., $Cl^-$) also participate in the slow depolarization (Sehlin, 1978).

In our opinion, a crucial aspect of the regulation of membrane polarization has so far been somewhat neglected. This refers to the influence of a change in glucose concentration on membrane potential in the low range of glucose concentrations in which the effect of glucose on $^{86}Rb$ fractional outflow rate is most obvious. According to Beigelman *et al.* (1977), the resting membrane potential in cells without electrical activity tends to progressively depolarize as the glucose concentration is raised from zero to 8.3 m*M*. According to a more recent study, the glucose concentration must exceed 5 m*M* in order to slightly depolarize the membrane of B cells in the silent state (Meissner and Preissler, 1979). However, these observations are based on measurements performed in distinct cells, with large individual variations. To our knowledge, no detailed study on the influence of glucose in low concentrations on resting membrane potential has yet been performed by continuous record in the same cell(s).

*b. The Rapid Phase of Depolarization.* According to Meissner and Preissler (1979), the rapid depolarization from the threshold potential ($V_t$) to the plateau potential ($V_p$) is attributable to an increase of the calcium permeability. This increased calcium permeability leads to an influx of calcium ions eliciting the exocytotic process. In support of such a view, it was observed that $Co^{2+}$ prevents the appearance of the electrical activity, although the membrane potential is depolarized beyond the threshold value from which the slow waves usually start.

An alternative hypothesis to account for the rapid phase of depolarization was recently formulated (Ribalet and Beigelman, 1979). According to this hypothesis, the rapid depolarization is also attributable to a decrease in $K^+$ conductance. The latter view is based on the two following series of observations. First, by recording resistance changes at frequent intervals (0.6 second), Ribalet and Beigelman (1979) were able to show that the resistance was highest during the first few hundred milliseconds of the active phase, after the membrane had depolarized. Second, $Co^{2+}$, $Mn^{2+}$, or excess of $Mg^{2+}$ are known to inhibit the burst pattern, the membrane potential repolarizing at the maximal repolarization potential ($V_r$). However, during sustained exposure to these calcium antagonists, the membrane depolarizes slowly, eventually arriving at the plateau potential ($V_p$). When the competing cation is removed, action potentials occur without further depolarization, and finally the burst pattern is recovered. Similar effects have been observed with antagonists of calcium conductance such as verapamil, D-600, and nifedipine (Atwater, 1980). When 11.1 m*M* glucose and 2 m*M* $Co^{2+}$ are added to the perfusion medium simultaneously, the membrane again depolarizes to the plateau potential ($V_p$). These observations indicate that glucose is capable of depolarizing the membrane to the plateau potential even when the entry of $Ca^{2+}$ into the islet cells is impaired. These latter observations, however, do not rule out that, under normal conditions, the rapid depolarization is indeed attributable to $Ca^{2+}$ influx which would prevent the much slower and progressive depolarization seen in the presence of $Co^{2+}$ from occurring.

*c. The Spikes* It is currently thought that the ascending phase of each spike corresponds to a facilitated influx of $Ca^{2+}$ and possibly $Na^+$. The descending phase of each spike could correspond to an increase in $K^+$ conductance. The hypothesis that the occurrence of spikes may also be somehow secondary to the exocytosis of secretory granules cannot be ruled out (Meissner and Preissler, 1979).

*d. The Repolarization at the End of Each Burst.* Two proposals have been made to account for the repolarization phenomenon terminating each burst of spikes.

The first proposal postulates that the repolarization phenomenon is attributable to activation of an electrogenic Na–K pump. According to the second hypothesis,the repolarization is attributable to activation of a Ca-dependent modality of $K^+$ extrusion from the islet cells. The regulation of such a modality of $K^+$ extrusion would depend mostly on the concentration of cytosolic ionized $Ca^{2+}$.

The first hypothesis is supported by the finding that the presence of ouabain or the removal of extracellular $K^+$, two procedures known to inhibit the activity of the Na–K pump, results in suppression of the burst pattern and induction of continuous spike activity (Atwater and Meissner, 1975). However, the sole participation of an electrogenic Na–K pump seems insufficient to account for the full magnitude of the repolarization phenomenon (Atwater, 1980).

The view that the B cell is equipped with a $Ca^{2+}$-sensitive modality of $K^+$ extrusion is supported, inter alia, by the observation that conditions thought to be associated with high cytosolic concentrations of $Ca^{2+}$ provoke an increase in $^{86}Rb$ fractional outflow rate. Such is the case, for instance, when mitochondrial poisons are administered to the islets (Henquin, 1979; Boschero and Malaisse, 1979; Carpinelli and Malaisse, 1980c). A rise in extracellular $Ca^{2+}$ concentration may also increase $^{86}Rb$ fractional outflow rate (Boschero and Malaisse, 1979; Henquin, 1979).

Whether attributable to the cytosolic accumulation of $Ca^{2+}$ or not, an important contribution of the $K^+$ permeability to the repolarization phase is supported by the observation that agents blocking $K^+$ channels, such as tetraethylammonium, quinine, and 9-aminoacridine, inhibit the repolarization phase and provoke continuous spike activity (Henquin *et al.*, 1979). Moreover, exposure of the islets to mitochondrial poisons or an increase in extracellular $Ca^{2+}$ concentration hyperpolarizes the B cell during the silent phase and prolongs the duration of such a phase (Ribalet and Beigelman, 1979; Atwater *et al.*, 1979a).

*e. Conclusion* This far from exhaustive review of bioelectrical data confirms and extends the conclusion derived from radioisotopic data, i.e., that changes in $K^+$ conductance of the plasma membrane in response to glucose stimulation represent a fundamental aspect of stimulus–secretion coupling in the B cell.

## III. CONSEQUENCES OF THE GLUCOSE-INDUCED CHANGE IN $K^+$ PERMEABILITY

The effect of glucose in decreasing $K^+$ conductance in islet cells is thought to have two major consequences: the first consequence is a depolarization of the B cell plasma membrane, which could lead to the gating of voltage-dependent channels; the second consequence consists in an increase in the intracellular $K^+$ content of the islet cells. These two consequences differ from one another in both their time course and possible physiological implications.

### A. Gating of Voltage-Dependent Channels

#### *1. Evidence and Significance of Voltage-Dependent Channels*

The idea that glucose increases calcium inflow into the islets by causing the gating of voltage-sensitive calcium channels has largely been confirmed by recent studies on the efflux of $^{45}Ca$ from prelabeled and perfused islets. Glucose provokes a dual modification of $^{45}Ca$ efflux consisting in an initial fall followed by a secondary rise in $^{45}Ca$ efflux. The initial fall was shown to reflect a true inhibition of $^{40}Ca$ efflux and may correspond to the inhibition by glucose of calcium extrusion from the B cell by a process of Na–Ca countertransport. The secondary rise in $^{45}Ca$ outflow apparently corresponds to a process of Ca–Ca exchange in which the influent $^{40}Ca$ displaces $^{45}Ca$ from intracellular binding sites (Kikuchi *et al.*, 1978; Herchuelz and Malaisse, 1978). In agreement with such a view, an increased calcium inflow into the B cell, as induced by an increase in the extracellular concentration of calcium, stimulates the efflux of $^{45}Ca$ from perfused islets (Herchuelz *et al.*, 1980a).

There are several findings to suggest that the secondary rise in $^{45}Ca$ efflux reflects the rate of calcium influx into the B cell through gated voltage-sensitive calcium channels. First, the glucose-induced secondary rise in $^{45}Ca$ efflux is impaired under several experimental conditions known to interfere with calcium entry into the B cell, e.g., the presence of verapamil or high concentrations of extracellular $Mg^{2+}$. It is completely abolished in the absence of extracellular $Ca^{2+}$ or presence of either $Co^{2+}$ or $Ni^{2+}$, two specific blockers of the voltage-sensitive calcium channels (Bukowieki and Freinkel, 1976; Herchuelz and Malaisse, 1978; Herchuelz *et al.*, 1980a). Second, an increase in $^{45}Ca$ efflux is observed in response to a depolarization of the B cell membrane as induced by veratridine (a drug known to increase $Na^+$ inflow in the islets) or an increase in the extracellular $K^+$ concentration (Herchuelz and Malaisse, 1980; Herchuelz *et al.*, 1980c). In the presence of a high concentration of $K^+$, a close correlation was found between the ability of glucose to stimulate $^{45}Ca$ efflux and to depolarize the B cell membrane (Atwater *et al.*, 1978; Herchuelz *et al.*, 1980c). Likewise, tetraethylammonium, a specific blocker of $K^+$ conductance, acts synergistically with glucose to depolarize the B cell membrane, stimulate $^{45}Ca$ net uptake, and increase $^{45}Ca$ efflux from perfused islets (Henquin *et al.*, 1979; Atwater *et al.*, 1979b; Herchuelz *et al.*, 1980d). Quinine and 9-aminoacridine, which are more potent than TEA in reducing $K^+$ conductance in the B-cell, also reproduce the effect of glucose in depolarizing the membrane, stimulating $^{45}Ca$ net uptake, and increasing $^{45}Ca$ efflux from perfused islets (Henquin *et al.*, 1979; Herchuelz *et al.*, 1981).

If the existence of voltage-dependent channels in the B cell is taken as an acceptable hypothesis, it is likely that the repolarization of the plasma membrane at the end of each burst of spikes, whatever its mechanism, will suppress facilitated $Ca^{2+}$ inflow into the islet cells. Thus, the precise timing of the bursting pattern may condition the amount of $Ca^{2+}$ entering the islet cells over a given length of time. For instance, under conditions in which a process of Ca–Ca exchange accounts for most of the release of $^{45}Ca$ from prelabeled islets, the amount of effluent $^{45}Ca$ released by the islets over successive periods of 1 minute each may reflect the time spent by each islet cells in the active spiking state.

### 2. *Is the Glucose-Induced Increase in $Ca^{2+}$ Inflow Solely Attributable to the Gating of Voltage-Dependent $Ca^{2+}$ Channels?*

At this point, it should be mentioned that there are several theoretical mechanisms by which glucose could increase the inflow of $Ca^{2+}$ into the islet cells in concert with, or even independently of, the postulated gating of voltage-dependent $Ca^{2+}$ channels. For instance, Hellman *et al.* (1974) have proposed that disulfide bridges in the plasma membrane may be split to sulfhydryl groups, as a consequence of glucose metabolism, and so lead to an increase in ion permeability. A change in redox state could also affect the intrinsic properties, e.g., the affinity for $Ca^{2+}$, of native ionophores conceivably involved in the transport of $Ca^{2+}$ (Valverde and Malaisse, 1980). Last, a glucose-induced increase in membrane fluidity, as recently documented in isolated cells (Deleers *et al.*, 1981), could also facilitate the transport of ions by mobile carriers, in a manner comparable to that observed for the ionophore-mediated transport of $Ca^{2+}$ in liposomes (Deleers and Malaisse, 1980).

So far, however, there is only limited experimental evidence to imply that glucose indeed facilitates $Ca^{2+}$ influx independently of the change in $K^+$ conductance. A first observation in support of such a view is the finding that, in islets exposed to high concentrations of valinomycin, glucose is still able to provoke a modest increase in $^{45}Ca$ outflow rate, provided that the islets are exposed to a normal extracellular concentration of $Ca^{2+}$ (Boschero *et al.*, 1979). Under these experimental conditions, the glucose-induced decrease in $^{86}Rb^+$ fractional outflow rate is abolished. We recently encountered a second situation in which there is an apparent facilitation of $Ca^{2+}$ entry, despite a paradoxical increase in $^{86}Rb$ fractional outflow rate. Such is the case when the concentration of glucose is increased from 8.3 to 11.1 or 16.7 m*M* (Fig. 4). This increase in glucose concentration causes a rapid stimulation of the process of exchange between influent $^{40}Ca$ and effluent $^{45}Ca$, and yet no decrease in $K^+$ conductance but a transient increase in $^{86}Rb$ fractional outflow rate is observed (Carpinelli and Malaisse, 1981). The latter increase appears attributable to activation of the $Ca^{2+}$-dependent modality of $K^+$ extrusion, being suppressed in the absence of extracellular $Ca^{2+}$. For reasons already discussed, the increase in Ca–Ca exchange could merely reflect the fact that the B cell spends a greater proportion of time in the active state in the presence of 16.7 m*M* glucose than at 8.3 m*M* glucose. But, even so, it

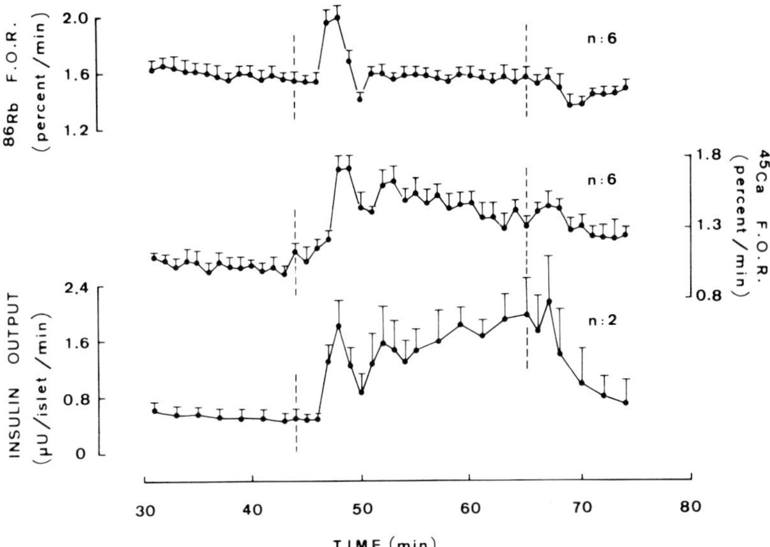


FIG. 4. Effect of an increase in glucose concentration from 8.3 to 16.7 m*M* (forty-fourth minute) and the reverse change (sixty-fifth minute) upon $^{86}Rb$ and $^{45}Ca$ fractional outflow rates (upper panels) and insulin release (lower panel) (Carpinelli and Malaisse, 1981).

remains paradoxical that an increase in $^{86}Rb$ fractional outflow rate occurs under a condition that, according to the interpretation of bioelectrical data, precisely coincides with the suppression by glucose of the $Ca^{2+}$-activated $K^+$ permeability.

### B. Accumulation of $K^+$ in Islet Cells

A second apparent consequence of the glucose-induced decrease in $K^+$ conductance, which occurs in face of an unaltered rate of $K^+$ inflow into the islet cells, consists in an increase in the concentration (or content) of $K^+$ inside the islet cells. That glucose increases the steady-state content of $K^+$ in the islet cells was demonstrated by measuring both $^{86}Rb$ and $^{42}K$ net uptake by isolated islets and by measuring their $^{39}K$ content (Boschero *et al.*, 1977; Malaisse *et al.*, 1978a).

The increase in $K^+$ content apparently compensates for the decrease in $K^+$ conductance so that, under steady-state conditions, the estimated absolute outflow rate of $K^+$ from the islets was the same in the presence or absence of glucose (Malaisse *et al.*, 1978a).

Changes in the intracellular concentration of $K^+$ may in turn affect several biochemical and functional variables in the islet cells. For instance, Sener *et al.* (1980) observed that, when the intracellular $K^+$ content is severely reduced as the consequence of a prolonged deprivation of extracellular $K^+$, the rate of glycolysis is significantly reduced possibly as a result of a decrease in pyruvate kinase activity. In the $K^+$-deprived islets proinsulin biosynthesis is virtually abolished, whatever nutrient is used to stimulate biosynthetic activity (Sener and Malaisse, 1979). Data were also obtained to suggest that the intracellular $K^+$ content may play a role in the memory for glucose of the pancreatic B cell (Sener and Malaisse, 1979). In considering these proposals, it should be kept in mind that, because of the relatively low fractional turnover rate of $K^+$ into islet cells (5.5 to 8.9%/minute, as judged from the outflow of $^{42}K^+$ in the presence and absence of glucose, respectively), the effect of glucose in increasing the $K^+$ content is a slowly rising and slowly reversible phenomenon. As a matter of fact it was calculated that the exponential increase in the $K^+$ content, when raising the glucose concentration from zero to 16.7 m*M*, occurs with a half-life of about 16 minutes (Malaisse *et al.*, 1979a).

## IV. MECHANISM OF THE GLUCOSE-INDUCED CHANGES IN $K^+$ CONDUCTANCE

The last but crucial issue to be discussed in this chapter concerns the mechanism(s) by which glucose may influence the plasma membrane conductance to $K^+$ in islet cells. We will consider three aspects of this problem. First, emphasis will be given to experimental data that strongly suggest that the glucose-induced decrease in $K^+$ conductance is tightly linked with metabolic events evoked by glucose in the islet cells. Second, the nature of the coupling factor(s) between metabolic and ionic events will be considered. Last, the mechanism by which glucose affects the rhythmic pattern of electrical activity will be discussed.

## A. Metabolic Control of $K^+$ Conductance

There is strong evidence to indicate that the decrease in $K^+$ conductance evoked by glucose is tightly linked with the metabolism of the sugar in the islet cells. The effect of glucose is suppressed by mannoheptulose, iodoacetate, glucosamine, and 2-deoxyglucose (Boschero and Malaisse, 1979; Henquin, 1980) and mimicked by such insulinotropic nutrients as glyceraldehyde, 2-ketoisocaproate, leucine, and mannose (Hutton *et al.*, 1980; Malaisse *et al.*, 1980a; Henquin, 1980). Nonmetabolized sugars, e.g., 3*O*-methylglucose, have no effect on $^{86}Rb$ fractional outflow rate (Boschero and Malaisse, 1979; Henquin, 1980).

## B. Nature of the Factor(s) Coupling Metabolic to Ionic Events

### 1. *Redox State and $K^+$ Conductance*

The idea that reducing equivalents (NADH, NADPH, reduced glutathione) play a key role in the coupling of metabolic to ionic events in the pancreatic B cell has been defended by several investigators (Hellman *et al.*, 1974; Malaisse *et al.*, 1979b). For instance, reducing equivalents could affect disulfide bridges in membrane-associated proteins acting as ionic channels.

Glucose and other nutrients are known to increase the islet content of reducing equivalents, and it was recently reported that glucose indeed affects the cytosolic redox potential (Ashcroft and Christie, 1979). The latter finding is important in that it is compatible with the postulated role of reducing equivalents affecting a target system located at the plasma membrane.

A role for NAD(P)H in the control of $K^+$ conductance was proposed on the basis of observations indicating that agents that lower the islet content of reduced pyridine nucleotides but fail to affect glycolysis, glucose oxidation, and the islet content of ATP indeed suppress the ability of glucose to cause a fall in $^{86}Rb$ fractional outflow rate. Such is the case in the presence of $NH_4^+$ (Sener *et al.*, 1978) or low concentrations of menadione (Malaisse *et al.*,

1978c,d). In a further study, Henquin (1980) also reached the conclusion that the glucose-induced decrease in $K^+$ permeability results, at least in part, from an increase in the concentrations of reduced nicotinamide nucleotides and possibly also of reduced glutathione.

### 2. *Other Possible Coupling Factors*

According to Malaisse *et al.* (1979c), the steady-state values for the islet content of reduced pyridine nucleotides at increasing concentrations of D-glucose display a sigmoidal pattern not vastly different from that seen for insulin release. Such a pattern was not observed by Ammon *et al.* (1978) and differs from that seen with other nutrient secretagogues, e.g., 2-ketoisocaproate (Hutton *et al.*, 1979), in which case the dose–action relationship rather appears hyperbolic. Whether the curve relating steady-state islet content of reduced pyridine nucleotides to ambient nutrient concentration displays a sufficiently low "$K_m$" to account for the changes in $K^+$ conductance, such as illustrated in Fig. 2, thus remains debatable. Anyhow, the participation of factors other than the cytosolic redox state in the control of plasma membrane $K^+$ conductance should not be ruled out.

At least three other factors could play a role in the coupling of metabolic to ionic events. These are the islet content (or generation rate) of $H^+$, high-energy phosphate intermediates (ATP), and cyclic AMP. In addition, the regulation of $K^+$ conductance may be indirectly coupled to metabolic events, e.g., through changes in the cytosolic concentration of $Ca^{2+}$.

A direct or indirect role for either $H^+$ or ATP availability in the regulation of $K^+$ conductance is compatible with the knowledge that biochemical variables such as the net output of $H^+$ from isolated islets or the islet content of ATP are significantly affected by glucose in a range of concentrations lower than or similar to that in which a dose-related change in $^{86}Rb$ fractional outflow rate is observed (Malaisse *et al.*, 1979c).

The possible role of $H^+$ was investigated by measuring changes in $^{86}Rb$ fractional outflow rate in response to intracellular acidification, as provoked by a rise in $pCO_2$ (Carpinelli and Malaisse, 1980b). A rapid but poorly sustained decrease in $^{86}Rb$ outflow rate was indeed observed in response to intracellular acidification. However, the magnitude of such a phenomenon was not sufficient to account for the effect of glucose on $K^+$ conductance.

The possible role of ATP will be discussed later in Section IV,B,3, since it is currently considered within the framework of a hypothesis ascribing a key role to cytosolic ionized $Ca^{2+}$ in the control of $K^+$ conductance.

For reasons discussed elsewhere (Carpinelli and Malaisse, 1980d), the influence of cyclic AMP on $^{86}Rb$ fractional outflow rate does not suggest that this nucleotide plays any major role in the glucose-induced decrease in $K^+$ conductance.

### 3. *Is the Glucose-Induced Decrease in $K^+$ Conductance Attributable to a Primary Change in Cytosolic $Ca^{2+}$ Concentration*

Recently, a new hypothesis was proposed to account for the glucose-induced change in $K^+$ permeability (Ribalet and Beigelman, 1979; Atwater *et al.*, 1980). This hypothesis postulates that the $K^+$ conductance is mainly under the control of the concentration of ionized $Ca^{2+}$ in the cytosol. When the B cell is stimulated by glucose, the cytosolic $Ca^{2+}$ concentration may fall. This could be due, inter alia, to activation of an ATP-driven Ca pump mediating Ca transport across the plasma membrane into the interstitial fluid and/or into intracellular organelles. The fall in $Ca^{2+}$ concentration would lead to the decrease in $K^+$ conductance associated with a slow depolarization and an increase in membrane resistance. When the plateau potential is reached, regenerative activation of voltage-dependent $Ca^{2+}$ and $K^+$ channels would occur, causing electrical spiking and a decrease in membrane resistance. The resulting inflow of $Ca^{2+}$ would eventually overcome the capacity of the system(s) responsible for maintaining a low $Ca^{2+}$ concentration in the cytosol and, hence, activation of the $K^+$ conductance would take place, causing repolarization at the end of each burst of spikes. In this model, the duration of the burst would be longer at high glucose concentration because of a better aptitude in maintaining a low cytosolic $Ca^{2+}$ concentration, despite enhanced $Ca^{2+}$ inflow, when more glucose is metabolized and, hence, when the generation of ATP would occur at a higher rate.

This attractive hypothesis raises several questions. It would appear, at the first glance, incompatible with the view that the intracellular accumulation of $Ca^{2+}$ triggers insulin release. Indeed, the cytosolic concentration of $Ca^{2+}$ would be lowest at the onset of each burst of spikes. However, the model does not deny that each spike coincides with the inflow of a $Ca^{2+}$ quantum, which could cause a localized biophysical effect such as the neutralization of negative surface charges on the inner face of the plasma membrane and surface of secretory granules or the contraction of microfilaments located in the cell web. In this perspective, we have recently indicated that the estimation of the amount of $Ca^{2+}$ entering the B cell during each spike, as derived from bioelectrical measurements, is in good agreement with radioisotopic estimation of $Ca^{2+}$ inflow into the islet cells (Malaisse *et al.*, 1981a).

The hypothesis is also compatible with the fact that both the dose–action relationship and time course for the glucose-induced decrease in $^{45}Ca$ fractional outflow rate are virtually superimposable to those characterizing the decrease in $^{86}Rb$ fractional outflow rate (Malaisse *et al.*, 1979b, 1981b). It could thus be postulated that the effect of glucose to decrease $^{45}Ca$ fractional outflow rate reflects a sequestration of the cation in intracellular organelles rather than a true decrease in the rate of Ca outward transport across the cell membrane.

The latter view would be strengthened if factors other than nutrients, known to provoke trapping of calcium in intracellular organelles, would be able to mimic the effect of D-glucose on $K^+$ conductance. To our knowledge, this has not yet been directly explored; however, Hellman and co-workers (Hellman and Andersson, 1978; Hellman *et al.*, 1980) have shown that addition of either 20 m*M* phosphate or a mixture of succinate and rotenone to the perfusate decreases the outflow of $^{45}Ca$ from perfused islets. However, neither addition provoked any secondary rise in $^{45}Ca$ efflux and, in static experiments, the presence of phosphate failed to significantly enhance basal insulin release and even reduced glucose-stimulated insulin output (Hellman and Andersson, 1978). These data would suggest that trapping of calcium in intracellular organelles is not sufficient to provoke the sequence of events (decrease in $K^+$ conductance, gating of $Ca^{2+}$ channels) assumed to be involved in the process of glucose-stimulated insulin secretion.

## C. Influence of Glucose on the Rhythmic Pattern of Bioelectrical Activity

We have already underlined that, once the B cell is exposed to glucose concentrations in excess of the threshold value required to evoke electrical activity and insulin release, the dose-related effect of the sugar in increasing both $Ca^{2+}$ inflow and insulin release cannot be solely attributed to a graded change in $K^+$ conductance. The magnitude of $Ca^{2+}$ inflow and insulin release appears to be conditioned by the time spent by each cell in the active state. As the glucose concentration is raised, such time increases and, eventually, permanent spiking is observed. Therefore, the mechanism(s) by which glucose prolongs the duration of each burst of spikes, shortens the delay between successive burts, and eventually suppresses the repolarization ending each burst is of fundamental importance for understanding the graded effect of glucose on insulin release. Any speculation as to the modality by which glucose prevents the repolarization of the plasma membrane otherwise occurring at the end of each burst of spikes depends on current views concerning the factor(s) held for responsible of such a repolarization phenomenon. To our knowledge there are at least three hypotheses that have been proposed to account for the suppression by high concentrations of glucose of the repolarization phenomenon.

The first hypothesis takes into consideration the view that the metabolic events, to which ionic events appear tightly coupled, may follow a rhythmic pattern in the B cell and that such a rhythmic or discontinuous pattern would disappear at high concentrations of glucose (Malaisse, 1976). This first hypothesis, which is reminiscent of the situation described for the regulation of glycolysis in acellular systems (Torrheim and Lowenstein, 1974), meets with several objections. Indeed, no evidence is yet available to convincingly document oscillations in metabolic fluxes during constant exposure of the B cell to stimulating concentrations of glucose or other nutrients. Indirect attempts to demonstrate metabolic oscillations, such as the effort made to establish whether the frequency distribution of NAD(P)H content in single islets would follow a bimodal pattern, have failed to produce conclusive data (Malaisse *et al.*, 1980b). Moreover, a recent report (Cook *et al.*, 1980) indicates that it is possible to shift the rhythm of electrical bursts, as if a pacemaker is reset, by either depolarizing (e.g., 8 $\mu$A, 2 s-long) or hyperpolarizing (e.g., 18 $\mu$A, 0.1 second long) currents. The depolarizing current, when applied during the silent phase, initiates a premature plateau potential. The hyperpolarizing current, when applied during a burst of spikes, prematurely terminates the endogenous plateau potential. This suggests that the islet cell plateau potential is a persistent, voltage-dependent action potential and that membrane events cannot be merely driven by electrically insensitive pacemaker mechanisms such as autonomous biochemical oscillators.

The second hypothesis would be that glucose prevents activation of an electrogenic $Na^+,K^+$-ATPase (Atwater and Meissner, 1975). The validity of this hypothesis obviously depends on the validity of the concept that the repolarization phenomenon, at the end of each burst, indeed reflects activation of an electrogenic pump. At intermediate glucose concentrations, the stimulation of the Na–K pump at the end of each burst could be secondary to facilitated $Na^+$ influx during the active phase, as a result of the gating of voltage dependent $Na^+$ channels (Atwater, 1980). Along this line of thought, it should be mentioned that $Na^+,K^+$-activated ATPase activity was indeed characterized in islet homogenates, and that according to one study, glucose inhibits this ATPase (Levin *et al.*, 1978). The latter finding, however, has not yet been confirmed.

The third hypothesis postulates that glucose, in high concentration, somehow prevents the activation by cytosolic $Ca^{2+}$ of the $Ca^{2+}$-dependent modality of $K^+$ extrusion (Henquin, 1979). For instance, an increased rate of glucose metabolism could augment the capacity of the B cell to maintain a low cytosolic concentration of $Ca^{2+}$, e.g., by facilitating Ca sequestration in intracellular organelles. Alternatively, the metabolic state of the B cell may directly regulate the sensitivity to $Ca^{2+}$ of the $K^+$ permeability system (Henquin, 1979). The hypothesis that glucose somehow prevents the activation of the $Ca^{2+}$-dependent $K^+$ channel meets with at least one objection already discussed, i.e., that a rise in glucose concentration from 8.3 to 16.7 m$M$ paradoxically augments $^{86}$Rb fractional outflow rate.

## V. CONCLUDING REMARKS

The present account emphasizes the essential role currently attributed to changes in $K^+$ conductance as a key step in the sequence of cytophysiological events leading to the release of insulin in the glucose-stimulated pancreatic B cell. However, the review of the literature on this topic also indicates that several aspects of this phenomenon remain poorly understood. For instance, the intimate mechanism(s) by which glucose causes a decrease in $K^+$ conductance and, in high concentrations, apparently prevents the reactivation of the $K^+$ channels remains to be fully elucidated.

## REFERENCES


Ammon, H. P. T., Grimm, A., Wagner-Tescher, D., Verspohl, E. J., and Händel, M. (1978). *Diabetes* **27**, 466.

Ashcroft, S. J. H. (1980). *Diabetologia* **18**, 5–15.

Ashcroft, S. J. H., and Christie, M. C. (1979). *Biochem. J.* **184**, 697–700.

Atwater, I. (1980). *Cienc. Biol. C. Biol. Mol. Cel.*, **5**, 299–314.

Atwater, I., and Meissner, H. P. (1975). *J. Physiol. (London)* **247**, 56–58.

Atwater, I., Ribalet B., and Rojas, E. (1978). *J. Physiol. (London)* **278**, 117–139.

Atwater, I., Dawson, C. M., Ribalet, B., and Rojas, E. (1979a). *J. Physiol. (London)* **288**, 575–588.

Atwater, I., Ribalet, B., and Rojas, E. (1979b). *J. Physiol. (London)* **288**, 561–574.

Atwater, I., Dawson, C. M., Scott, A., Eddlestone, G., and Rojas, E. (1980). *Horm. Metab. Res., Suppl.* **10**, 100–107.

Beigelman, P. M., and Ribalet, B. (1980). *Diabetes* **29**, 263–265.

Beigelman, P. M., Ribalet, B., and Atwater, I. (1977). *J. Physiol. (Paris)* **73**, 201–207.

Boschero, A. C., and Malaisse, W. J. (1979). *Am. J. Physiol.* **236**, E139–E146.

Boschero, A. C., Kawazu, S., Duncan, G., and Malaisse, W. J. (1977). *FEBS Lett.* **83**, 151–154.

Boschero, A. C., Kawazu, S., Sener, A., Herchuelz, A., and Malaisse, W. J. (1979). *Arch. Biochem. Biophys.* **196**, 54–63.

Bukowieki, L., and Freinkel, N. (1976). *Biochim. Biophys. Acta* **436**, 190–198.

Carpinelli, A. R., and Malaisse, W. J. (1980a). *Mol. Cell. Endocrinol.* **17**, 103–110.

Carpinelli, A. R., and Malaisse, W. J. (1980b). *Diabet Métab.* **6**, 193–198.

Carpinelli, A. R., and Malaisse, W. J. (1980c). *J. Endocrinol. Invest.*, **4**, 365–370.

Carpinelli, A. R., and Malaisse, W. J. (1980d). *Acta Diabet Lat.* **17**, 199–205.

Carpinelli, A. R., and Malaisse, W. J. (1981). *J. Physiol. (London)* **315**, 143–156.

Cook, D. L., Crill, W. E., and Porte, D. (1980). *Nature (London)* **286**, 404–406.

Dean, P. M. (1974). *Diabetologia* **10**, 427–430.

Deleers, M., and Malaisse, W. J. (1980). *Biochem. Biophys. Res. Commun.* **95**, 650–657.

Deleers, M., Ruysschaert, J.-M., and Malaisse, W. J. (1981). *Biochem. Biophys. Res. Commun.*, **98**, 255–260.

Devis, G., Somers, G., and Malaisse, W. J. (1975). *Biochem. Biophys. Res. Commun.* **67**, 525–529.

Grodsky, G. M., and Bennett, L. L. (1966). *Diabetes* **15**, 910–913.

Hedeskov, C. J. (1980). *Physiol. Rev.* **60**, 442–509.

Hellman, B. (1976). *FEBS Lett.* **63**, 125–128.

Hellman, B., and Andersson, T. (1978). *Biochim. Biophys. Acta* **541**, 483–491.
Hellman, B., Idahl, L. A., Lernmark, A., Sehlin, J., and Täljedal, I.-B. (1974). *In* "Diabetes" (W. J. Malaisse and J. Pirart, eds.), Int. Congress Series n° 312, pp. 65–78. Excerpta Medica, Amsterdam.
Hellman, B., Abrahamsson, H., Andersson, T., Berggren, P. O., Flatt, P., Gylfe, E., and Hahn, H. J. (1980). *Horm. Metab. Res. Suppl.* **10**, 122–130.
Henquin, J. C. (1979). *Nature (London)* **280**, 66–68.
Henquin, J. C. (1980). *Biochem. J.* **186**, 541–550.
Henquin, J. C., and Meissner, H. P. (1978). *Biochim. Biophys. Acta* **543**, 455–464.
Henquin, J. C., Meissner, H. P., and Preissler, M. (1979). *Biochim. Biophys. Acta* **587**, 579–592.
Herchuelz, A., and Malaisse, W. J. (1978). *J. Physiol. (London)* **283**, 409–424.
Herchuelz, A., and Malaisse, W. J. (1980). *J. Physiol. (London)* **302**, 263–280.
Herchuelz, A., and Malaisse, W. J. (1981). *In* "Calcium in Normal and Pathological Biological Systems" (L. J. Anghileri, ed.), *CRC Press, Cleveland, Ohio, in press.*
Herchuelz, A., Couturier, E., and Malaisse, W. J. (1980a). *Am. J. Physiol.* **238**, E96–E103.
Herchuelz, A., Sener, A., and Malaisse, W. J. (1980b). *J. Membr. Biol.*, **57**, 1–12.
Herchuelz, A., Thonnart, N., Sener, A., and Malaisse, W. J. (1980c). *Endocrinology* **107**, 491–497.
Herchuelz, A., Thonnart, N., Carpinelli, A., Sener, A., and Malaisse, W. J. (1980d). *J. Pharmacol. Exp. Ther.* **215**, 213–220.
Herchuelz, A., Lebrun, P., Carpinelli, A., Thonnart, N., Sener, A., and Malaisse, W. J. (1981). *Biochim. Biophys. Acta* **640**, 16–30.
Hutton, J. C., Sener, A., and Malaisse, W. J. (1979). *Biochem. J.* **184**, 303–311.
Hutton, J. C., Sener, A., Herchuelz, A., Atwater, I., Kawazu, S., Boschero, A. C., Somers, G., Devis, G., and Malaisse, W. J. (1980). *Endocrinology* **106**, 203–219.
Kawazu, S., Boschero, A. C., Delcroix, C., and Malaisse, W. J. (1978). *Pflugers Arch.* **375**, 197–206.
Kikuchi, M., Wollheim, C. B., Cuendet, G. S., Renold, A. E., and Sharp, G. W. G. (1978). *Endocrinology* **102**, 1339–1349.
Levin, S. R., Kasson, B. G., and Driessen, J. F. (1978). *J. Clin. Invest.* **62**, 692–701.
Malaisse, W. J. (1976). *In* "Diabetes Research Today" (A. E. Renold, W. Creutzfeldt, and E. F. Pfeiffer, eds.), pp. 191–206, Schattauer, Stuttgart.
Malaisse, W. J., and Orci, L. (1979). *Methods Achiev. Exp. Pathol.* **9**, 112–136.
Malaisse, W. J., Sener, A., Herchuelz, A., Hutton, J. C., Devis, G., Somers, G., Blondel, B., Malaisse-Lagae, F., and Orci, L. (1977). *In* "Diabetes" (J. S. Bajaj, ed.), Int. Congr. Ser. n° 413, pp. 95–102. Excerpta Medica, Amsterdam.
Malaisse, W. J., Boschero, A. C., Kawazu, S., and Hutton, J. C. (1978a). *Pflugers Arch.* **373**, 237–242.
Malaisse, W. J., Herchuelz, A., Devis, G., Somers, G., Boschero, A. C., Hutton, J. C., Kawazu, S., Sener, A., Atwater, I. J., Duncan, G., Ribalet, B., and Rojas, E. (1978b). *Ann. N.Y. Acad. Sci.* **307**, 562–582.
Malaisse, W. J., Hutton, J. C., Kawazu, S., and Sener, A. (1978c). *Eur. J. Biochem.* **87**, 121–130.
Malaisse, W. J., Sener, A., Boschero, A. C., Kawazu, S., Devis, G., and Somers, G. (1978d). *Eur. J. Biochem.* **87**, 111–120.
Malaisse, W. J., Sener, A., and Herchuelz, A. (1979a). *In* "Treatment of Early Diabetes" (R. A. Camerini-Davalos and B. Hanover, eds.), pp. 85–96. Plenum, New York.
Malaisse, W. J., Sener, A., Herchuelz, A., and Hutton, J. C. (1979b). *Metab. Clin. Exp.* **28**, 373–386.

Malaisse, W. J., Hutton, J. C., Kawazu, S., Herchuelz, A., Valverde, I., and Sener, A. (1979c). *Diabetologia* **16**, 331–341.

Malaisse, W. J., Hutton, J. C., Carpinelli, A. R., Herchuelz, A., and Sener, A. (1980a). *Diabetes* **29**, 431–437.

Malaisse, W. J., Sener, A., Herchuelz, A., Valverde, I., Hutton, J. C., Atwater, I., and Leclercq-Meyer, V. (1980b) *Horm Met Res (Supplement 10)*, 61–66.

Malaisse, W. J., Herchuelz, A., and Sener, A. (1981a). *In* "Biochemistry, Physiology and Pathology of the Islets of Langerhans" (S. J. Cooperstein and D. T. Watkins, eds.), Academic Press, New York, in press.

Malaisse, W. J., Carpinelli, A. R., and Sener, A. (1981b). *Metab., Clin. Exp.* **30**, 527–532.

Matthews, E. K. (1975). *In* "Calcium Transport in Contraction and Secretion" (E. Carafoli, F. Clementi, W. Drabikowsky, and A. Margreth, eds.), pp. 203–210. North-Holland Publ., Amsterdam.

Meissner, H. P. (1976). *Nature (London)* **262**, 502–504.

Meissner, H. P., and Atwater, I. J. (1976). *Horm. Metab. Res.* **8**, 11–16.

Meissner, H. P., and Preissler, M. (1979). *In* "Treatment of Early Diabetes (R. A. Camerini-Davalos and B. Hanover, eds.), pp. 97–107. Plenum, New York.

Meissner, H. P., and Schmelz, H. (1974). *Pflugers Arch.* **351**, 195–206.

Meissner, H. P., Henquin, J. C., and Preissler, M. (1978). *FEBS Lett.* **94**, 87–89.

Meissner, H. P., Preissler, M., and Henquin, J. C. (1980). *In* "Diabetes" (W. K. Waldhäusl, ed.), Int. Congress Series n° 500, pp. 166–171. Excerpta Medica, Amsterdam.

Orci, L. (1976). *Metab., Clin. Exp.* **25**, 1303–1313.

Ostlund, R. E., Jr. (1980). *In* "Handbook of Diabetes Mellitus" (M. Brownlee, ed.), Vol. 2, pp. 27–40. Garland STPM Press, New York.

Ribalet, B., and Beigelman, P. M. (1979). *Am. J. Physiol.* **237**, C137–C146.

Schubart, U. K., Erlichman, J., and Fleischer, N. (1980). *J. Biol. Chem.* **255**, 4120–4124.

Sehlin, J. (1978). *Am. J. Physiol.* **235**, E501–E508.

Sehlin, J. (1980). *Horm. Metab. Res., Suppl.* **10**, 73–80.

Sehlin, J., and Täljedal, I.-B. (1975). *Nature (London)* **253**, 635–636.

Sener, A., and Malaisse, W. J. (1979). *Endocrinology* **106**, 778–785.

Sener, A., Hutton, J. C., Kawazu, S., Boschero, A. C., Somers, G., Devis, G., Herchuelz, A., and Malaisse, W. J. (1978). *J. Clin. Invest.* **62**, 868–878.

Sener, A., Kawazu, S., and Malaisse, W. J. (1980). *Biochem. J.* **186**, 183–190.

Torrheim, K., and Lowenstein, J. M. (1974). *J. Biol. Chem.* **249**, 3241–3247.

Valverde, I., and Malaisse, W. J. (1980). *IRCS Med. Sci.* **8**, 191–192.

Valverde, I., Vandermeers, A., Anjaneyulu, R., and Malaisse, W. J. (1979). *Science* **206**, 225–227.

# CHAPTER 4

# Insulin-Sensitive Glucoregulator Chemoreceptors in the Central Nervous System: Their Putative Role in Glucose Homeostasis

*Andrew John Szabo and Olga Szabo*



## I. HEPATIC GLUCOSE METABOLISM AS THE FINAL COMMON PATHWAY OF BLOOD SUGAR REGULATION

The mammalian liver is the central target organ of the immensely complicated interaction of regulatory influences (neural, neurohormonal, and hormonal) that developed in response to the undesirable fluctuation of blood sugar concentration resulting from the postabsorptive overabundance of nutrients, and from the intermittent accelerated caloric requirements charac-



BIOCHEMICAL ACTIONS OF HORMONES, VOL. IX

ISBN 0-12-452809-0

teristic for the periodicity of environmental conditions on earth. The central role of the liver in glucose homeostasis stems from the fact that this organ not only takes up glucose from the circulation, and stores it at times of plenty, but is also capable of glucose synthesis and release into the circulation, if required (Soskin and Levine, 1946; Cahill *et al.*, 1959; Levine and Haft, 1970). While there is evidence for some "built-in" metabolic autoregulation in the liver itself (Soskin and Levine, 1946; Bucolo *et al.*, 1974; Bergman, 1977), the rapid *in vivo* hepatic response to hormonal influences is undoubtedly the major force in the regulation of blood sugar concentration. Because of the latter, it was felt natural that insulin and glucagon, the major glucoregulatory hormones, having been secreted into tributaries of the portal vein, which perfuses the liver with hormone rich blood, exert their initial, most important action directly on the hepatic cells (Madison and Unger, 1958; Felig, 1974). The liver is also a major site of insulin degradation (Mirsky and Broh-Kahn, 1949; Tomizawa *et al.*, 1955; Mahler and Szabo, 1967). Thus, plasma insulin concentration is highest in the portal system of the liver, and falls considerably upon leaving this organ (Kanazawa *et al.*, 1966). Lastly, the liver was recently found to be rich in specific insulin receptors on the plasma membrane of the hepatic cells (Freychet *et al.*, 1971; Kahn *et al.*, 1974). All these observations pointed toward a direct action of insulin on the hepatic cells as the major regulator of carbohydrate metabolism.

It was therefore disturbing, that while *in vivo* (in the intact animal) glucose metabolism of the liver responds rapidly to changes in the concentration of circulating insulin (Bishop *et al.* 1965; Felig and Wahren, 1971; Harding *et al.*, 1975; Matsuura *et al.*, 1975), *in vitro*, in perfusion systems hepatic glucose metabolism responded sluggishly to insulin, and then only if specific conditions were rigidly met (Mortimore, 1963; Williamson *et al.*, 1966; Exton *et al.*, 1966; Mortimore *et al.*, 1967; Haft, 1967; Glinsmann and Mortimore 1968; Mackrell and Sokal, 1969; Parilla *et al.*, 1974; and Mondon *et al.*, 1975). This was in sharp contrast to muscle and adipose tissues, in which *in vitro* insulin effects on glucose metabolism were readily demonstrated (Gemmill, 1940; Hechter *et al.*, 1941; Winegrad and Renold, 1958; Ball and Jungas, 1964).

Since in sophisticated *in vitro* liver perfusion systems many of the physiological parameters of the intact animal were closely mimicked (ionic, osmotic, nutrient, and pH requirements were met; partial pressure of oxygen, perfusate temperature, hydrostatic pressure, and flow rate were normalized; presence of albumin and red cells in the perfusate were provided; chamber temperature and humidity were regulated), a possible explanation for the dichotomy between the effects of insulin on *in vivo* and *in vitro* perfused livers should have been easily provided: that is, that intact neural connections to the central nervous system (CNS) are necessary for a brisk insulin action on the liver. This conclusion was however difficult to formulate, because (1) insulin, a large molecular peptide hormone, was thought to cross the blood–brain barrier very slowly (Margolis and Altszuler, 1967; Woods and Porte, 1977), and (2) because the brain as a whole was shown to be a non-insulin-responsive organ (Himwich *et al.*, 1941).

Recent evidence indicates, however, that the blood–brain barrier is incomplete at certain points (Weindl, 1973), and thus insulin may enter the CNS, that there are structures in the CNS with physicochemical characteristics identical to insulin receptors in other insulin responsive tissues, that the concentration of the insulin receptors is high in some, and low in other regions of the brain (suggesting a functional topography), and that exposure of some of the CNS areas to insulin results in measurable physiological effects. It is therefore timely to reevaluate the role of the CNS in carbohydrate homeostasis in light of this new evidence.

The present review will discuss insulin receptors in the CNS, and will attempt to consider them within the framework of a new concept of glucose homeostasis. It is regretful, that because this field of investigation has opened up very recently, more questions will be posed than firm answers given. We hope, however, that this will stimulate further work in this important area.

## II. CNS GLUCORECEPTORS

The capacity to utilize glucose is a physiological property common to all mammalian cells, including the cells of the CNS. Some form of transport system for glucose exists in all tissues, different systems having developed to assure adequate intracellular glucose for energy requiring functions while simultaneously excluding a harmful excess of glucose. In spite of these transport systems, which serve to minimize the metabolic consequences of the fluctuations in extracellular glucose concentration, most mammalian cells will show impaired function if exposed to extreme alterations in ambient glucose cocentration. Glucose is the most important metabolic substrate of the CNS (for review, see Lund-Andersen, 1979), and glucose uptake by the bulk of the CNS correlates directly with the blood glucose concentration (Kerr and Ghantus, 1936; Flock *et al.*, 1969). It is therefore not surprising that grave impairment of CNS function has been observed following major alterations in the extracellular glucose milieu. It is of interest, however, that considerable differences in sensitivity to glucose concentration changes exist between specific areas of the brain. In some regions changes in the rate of firing by neurons have been recorded after relatively modest alterations in the ambient glucose concentration (Anand *et al.*, 1964; Oomura *et al.*, 1969). Hence, CNS glucoreceptors were operationally defined as neurons that change their rate of firing in response to alterations in blood glucose concentrations (Marrazzi, 1976), without physicochemical or morphological identification of the receptor structures, as now customary with peptide hormone receptors. As these glucose sensitive neurons were located in the hypothalamus, a CNS structure long known to be the site of metabolic regulatory functions, it was suggested that some hypothalamic neurons may have specific, glucose-dependent metabolic regulatory roles. Feedback inhibitions had already been demonstrated in a multitude of biological, hormonal, and metabolic systems; therefore it was logical to expect that some of the hypothalamic glucose-sensitive neurons would have a regulatory role in glucose homeostasis. This assumption was supported by the finding of rapid increases in blood glucose concentration following systemic administration of 2-deoxyglucose (Landau and Lubs, 1958; Brown, 1962) and other nonmetabolizable glucose analogs (Meldrum and Horton, 1973; Ritter and Slusser, 1980) which compete with glucose for the glucose transport and for some enzyme systems. As the hyperglycemic effect of 2-deoxyglucose could be eliminated by adrenalectomy (Friedmann and Wertheimer, 1966), or by adrenergic blocking agents (Muller *et al.*, 1973), a sympathoadrenal pathway for this effect was postulated. Central origin of the pathway was suggested, when the hyperglycemic response was eliminated by spinal chord transection (Niijima, 1974). Proof that intracellular cerebral glucopenia was the cause of the 2-deoxyglucose induced increase in sympathoadrenal activity was provided when increases in the systemic blood sugar concentration were observed after local administration of the nonmetabolizable glucose analog into the cerebral ventricles (Muller *et al.*, 1973) or into the carotid blood flow (Sakata *et al.*, 1963).

The above quoted studies present a good case for the hypothesis that glucose metabolism by certain areas in the brain is the sensory arc of the glucoregulatory reflex in glucoprivation. As 2-deoxyglucose administered to CNS areas can be accepted as a reasonable tool to produce local intracellular glucoprivation, it seems safe to assume that in other types of severe cerebral glucopenia, such as may be caused by very low blood sugar levels, similar glucoregulatory impulses would be generated. This establishes glucose itself as the glucoregulatory feedback signal in situations of systemic, and particularly in cerebral glucoprivation, which initiates, through a CNS mechanism, increases in the secretion of glycogenolytic and gluconeogenic hormones, such as glucagon, ACTH, cortisol, growth hormone, and epinephrine (Abramson and Arky, 1968; Donald, 1971; Brodows *et al.*, 1973; Walter *et al.*, 1974; Gerich *et al.*, 1974; Garber *et al.*, 1976; Gerich *et al.*, 1979; DeFronzo *et al.*, 1980; Gauthier *et al.*, 1980), the coordinated effect of which is a rapid increase in hepatic glucose output.

The role of glucose as a feedback regulatory signal in the case of hyperglycemia has been less extensively studied. There is ample evidence showing that increased glucose concentration is a powerful and specific secretory stimulus for the pancreatic $\beta$ cell itself (Grodsky *et al.*, 1963; Coore and Randle, 1964; Matchinsky *et al.*, 1972; Lacy *et al.*, 1972; Malaisse *et al.*, 1973). Though neural influences undoubtedly play some role in modulating insulin responses (Britton, 1925; Porte *et al.*, 1973; Woods and Porte, 1974), their role in the defense against local cerebral hyperglycemia has been questioned (Chieri *et al.*, 1975), and is generally considered to be secondary to the glucoreceptors located in the pancreatic islets.

In a study suggesting that cerebral hyperglycemia may have an inhibitory effect on hepatic glucose output, Sakata *et al.*, (1963) measured arterial plasma glucose levels in rabbits after infusion of glucose into either an ear vein or the internal carotid artery. In these studies systemic blood glucose paradoxically declined, when glucose was infused into the carotid artery. Although the changes were small, the findings pointed to a possible physiological role for the CNS glucoreceptors in the homeostatic regulatory mechanism responsive to cerebral hyperglycemia.

While the above observations may be correct, their biological significance remains questionable. If glucose were the major signal in hyperglycemic animals for a CNS regulatory response to inhibit hepatic glucose output and/or to increase peripheral and hepatic glucose uptake, the diabetic syndromes related to insulin deficiency (alloxan, streptozotocin, or pancreatectomy induced diabetes in animals, type I "juvenile" diabetes in human subjects) would not exist: when the hypothalamic sensor would register the elevation of glucose concentration, it would emit a signal to the liver to cease glucose release, and the hyperglycemic condition would be self-corrected.

It may therefore be concluded that cerebral glucoreceptors probably have an important role in the correction of *hypoglycemia*, and that glucose itself is the signal for the glucoregulatory response to hypoglycemia, but cerebral glucoreceptors have at best a minor role in the regulatory attempts to alleviate *hyperglycemia*.

## III. INSULIN-SENSITIVE CNS RECEPTORS

### A. Physiological Observations on Glucoregulatory Functions

By the early 1970's, five lines of indirect evidence pointed to the existence of a possible insulin-sensitive CNS glucoregulatory function:

1. The somewhat sluggish response of the *in vitro* perfused liver, as opposed to the brisk *in vivo* response of this organ to insulin (see

Section I), suggested that intact neural connections may be essential for normal hepatic glucose dynamics.

2. In spite of early observations (Donald, 1931) that denied the importance of hepatic innervation in carbohydrate metabolism, Shimazu (1967), and Shimazu and Amakawa (1968) were able to show that both glycogenolytic and the opposing glycogen synthetic enzymes of the liver are under the influence of autonomic nerves. The same group of investigators also provided evidence for reciprocal hypothalamic (ventromedial and lateral) representation of the above functions (Shimazu *et al.*, 1966).
3. Although results of gross perfusion and incubation experiments regarding insulin effect on glucose metabolism of the brain as a whole were largely inconclusive (Rafaelsen, 1961a), some insulin effect was observed in incubated brain slices (Rafaelsen, 1961b). More importantly, Debons *et al.* (1970) have shown a direct effect of insulin on the hypothalamus, though this effect could not be directly related to regulatory CNS functions.
4. While glucoprivation was clearly a signal for CNS induced secretion of all gluconeogenic–glycogenolytic hormones (see Section II), overabundance of glucose in the CNS circulation results in only minimal decline of the systemic blood sugar concentration (Sakata *et al.*, 1963), indirectly suggesting that if CNS has a regulatory role in biological responses to hyperglycemia, it may be triggered by another (nonglucose) signal system.
5. Observations on the hemodynamics of the portal vein suggested uneven distribution of the markers in the liver, characteristic of laminar flow systems (Gates and Dore, 1973). Accordingly, insulin, in its first passage through the liver, if its action on this organ were only dependent on hormone/cell contact, would evoke a grossly uneven metabolic response.

The methodology to obtain direct evidence for the existence of a putative insulin-dependent CNS mediated glucoregulatory system became available in the early 1970's. To study the possible effect on the blood sugar level of insulin reaching the brain from the circulation, without exposing the liver or other insulin sensitive peripheral organs to high insulin concentration, Szabo and Szabo (1972) designed the technique of regional insulinization of the CNS. In lightly anesthesized rats a small quantity of insulin (approximately 2 $\mu$U/gm rat weight) was injected into the carotid artery (i.c. injection), while simultaneously an excess of anti-insulin serum (AIS) was injected into the jugular vein (i.j. injection). Blood was collected from the tail for glucose determination before and several times after the injections (Fig. 1).

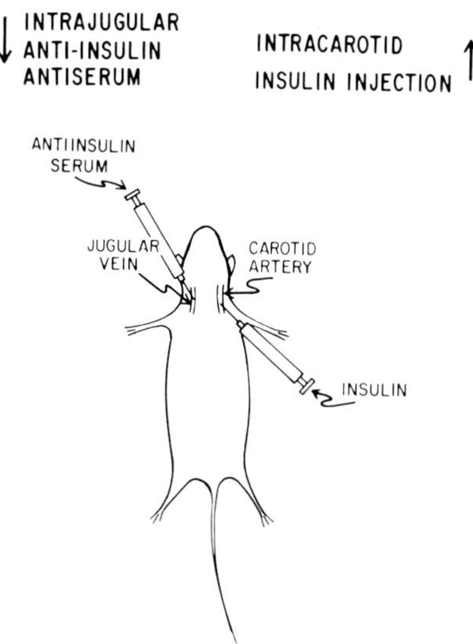


FIG. 1. Graphic illustration of the experimental design. Reproduced from Szabo and Szabo (1975b) with permission of the authors and the publisher.

A significant decrease of blood glucose was seen as early as 2 minutes after intracarotid insulin (with intrajugular AIS) injection. The fall of the blood sugar continued for 10 minutes, after which a rebound took place. Control experiments, in which the injection sites were reversed (i.e., insulin was injected into the jugular vein and AIS into the carotid artery) or in which buffer was injected into the carotid artery, did not result in decreases of blood glucose (Fig. 2). These results pointed to a central site of insulin action, which somehow resulted in rapid lowering of the blood glucose concentration in samples obtained from a part of the body remote from the site of insulin injection.

The observation of a more rapid and deeper fall of blood glucose concentration after intracarotid than after intrajugular insulin injection was independently confirmed by Garcia-Viveros *et al.* (1974) in dogs, suggesting that the phenomenon of central action of insulin on blood glucose is not a peculiarity of rats (or rodents in general), but that it is likely to be universal to other mammalian species as well.

The glucose fall after intracarotid insulin administration was greater in alloxan diabetic than in healthy rats (Szabo and Szabo, 1972). This mitigated against endogenous pancreatic insulin release as the possible mechanism of action, and suggested that a direct CNS reflex influencing hepatic glucose metabolism may be involved in the production of hypoglycemia.

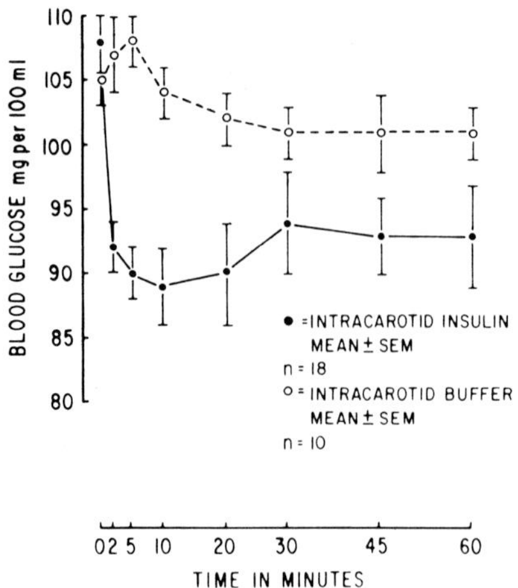


FIG. 2. Plasma glucose values following intracarotid buffer (interrupted line) or 500 $\mu$U intracarotid insulin (solid line) injection in rats. Reproduced from Szabo and Szabo (1975b) with permission from the authors and the publisher.

A possible mediation by the pituitary gland of the CNS–insulin effect on blood glucose concentration was excluded by repeating the intracarotid injection experiments in hypohysectomized rats (Szabo and Szabo, 1975a). In spite of the obvious differences between healthy and hypophysectomized rats in the later part of the blood glucose curves following intracarotid insulin injection (i.e., the deeper fall of glucose and the delayed, deficient rebound in the hypophysectomized animals), the initial fall in glucose concentration was superimposable in the two groups of rats. This suggested that the reflex does not reach the effector organ through a neurohumoral link involving the pituitary gland.

The $\alpha$-adrenergic blocking agent phentolamine and the $\beta$-adrenergic blocker propranolol were not effective as blocking agents, but atropine and vagotomy were both potent inhibitors of the hypoglycemic effect that followed intracarotid insulin injection (Szabo and Szabo, 1975c) (Fig. 3). These observations supported the hypothesis that direct autonomic neural connections (the muscarinic, cholinergic fibers of the vagus nerves) participate in the efferent loop of the hypoglycemic reflex arc.

In acute experiments, in animals subjected to evisceration and functional hepatectomy (i.e., removal of the gastrointestinal tract from the cardia to the rectum, including the pancreas and the spleen, to ligation of the hepatic artery and vein as well as the portal vein, preserving intact the renal and adrenal circulation), the fall of blood sugar was identical in those receiving insulin or control buffer injection into the carotid artery (Szabo and Szabo,

1975). When in a similar acutely eviscerated preparation the hepatic artery and vein were left intact (only the portal vein was ligated), the differential glycemic response to insulin and buffer was reestablished. Thus, a functioning liver was essential for the demonstration of the insulin-induced centrally originated glucoregulatory reflex. This established the liver as the effector organ of the CNS mediated glucoregulation. Calculation of the glucose area in these studies yielded the estimation of glucose appearance and disappearance rates, and led to an approximation of the hepatic glucose output and uptake. These calculations indicated that glucoregulation was affected both

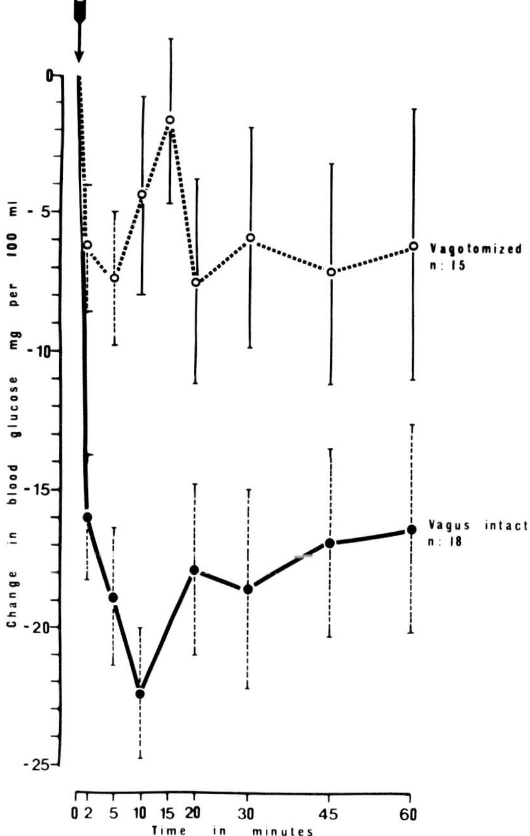


FIG. 3. Changes in blood sugar levels following simultaneous injection of 500 $\mu$U insulin into carotid artery (i.e.) and excess AIS into jugular vein: mean ± SEM. Differences between two treatment groups are significant ($p < .001$) in every time period. Vertical lines of SEM illustrated with interrupted lines represent significant changes from respective time 0 starting point, $p < .05$ in vagotomized and $p < .001$ in control group. Reproduced from Szabo and Szabo (1975c) with permission from the authors and the publisher.

by inhibiting hepatic glucose output, and by facilitating glucose uptake, the former being quantitatively more significant. Similar data were obtained in experiments that estimated the hepatic glucose balance by [2-$^3$H]glucose tracer methodology (Szabo and Szabo, 1978).

The mechanism of signal recognition by the putative CNS receptor was investigated in alloxan diabetic rats and in rats made hyperinsulinemic by repeated growth hormone injections (Szabo and Szabo, 1972). Insulinopenia (i.e., alloxan diabetes) accentuated while hyperinsulinemia abolished the effect of intracarotid insulin injections. In rats with growth hormone-induced hyperinsulinemia eliminated by a subsequent subdiabetogenic dose of alloxan, the hypoglycemic effect of intracarotid insulin injection was restored. These observations suggested that the putative CNS glucoregulator recognized changes in insulin concentration, but probably not via an alteration of glucose metabolism in the regulator cells. This notion was further supported when pretreatment of the rats with an intracarotid injection of 2-deoxyglucose failed to eliminate the hypoglycemic effect of a subsequent intracarotid insulin injection (Szabo and Szabo, 1975b).

These physiological observations were derived from studies in which insulin was injected into the carotid artery of the experimental animals. Thus, localization of the insulin sensitive glucoregulator areas within the CNS could not be attempted through these experiments. There is, however, a large body of information that links the hypothalamus, and more specifically the ventromedial hypothalamic nucleus (VMN), to a variety of metabolic control functions. Destruction of the VMN has been linked to hyperphagia and obesity (Hetherington and Ranson, 1940) and to hyperinsulinemia (Hales and Kennedy, 1964; Frohman and Bernardis 1968), whereas electrical stimulation of this structure was followed by hyperglycemia (Frohman and Bernardis, 1971; Frohman *et al.*, 1974). A direct effect of insulin on gold thioglucose uptake in the VMN was reported by Debons *et al.* (1970), and implantation of insulin crystals into this area caused reduction of food intake in normal and in diabetic rats (Hatfield *et al.*, 1973). Surgical isolation of the medial hypothalamus by stereotaxic surgery resulted in decreased insulin sensitivity of the experimental animals (Hefco *et al.*, 1975).

Sterotaxic injection of 40 mU insulin into the VMN of rats resulted in significant decrease of blood sugar (Storlien *et al.*, 1975), whereas injection into the lateral hypothalamic area evoked only minimal decrease, and injection into the cortex evoked no response at all. This study was confirmed and extended by Iguchi *et al.* (1981), giving microinjections of 10, 50, and 100 $\mu$U insulin into the VMN, which resulted in stepwise graded changes of the glucose concentration in hepatic venous plasma glucose samples, obtained through an indwelling cannula (Iguchi *et al.*, 1979). These studies, preliminary they may be, tentatively localize the insulin sensitive glucoregulator center to the hypothalamic VMN region.

### B. Physicochemical Observations: *In Vitro* Characterization of the CNS Insulin Receptor

The early observations of Levine and Goldstein (1955), derived from experiments on the space distribution of poorly metabolized sugars, which suggested that the primary function of insulin is to facilitate the membrane transport of glucose, received renewed interest in the late 1960s, when the newly developed isotope technology permitted the conclusion that binding of the hormone to the cell membrane is indeed the first step in achieving its biological action (Pastan *et al.*, 1966; Cuatrecasas, 1969). A flurry of investigations on the nature, specificity, and physical characteristics of the hormone–receptor binding began. Most early work was carried out on the three classically insulin-sensitive tissues, adipose tissue, muscle, and liver. Adipose tissue cells, which demonstrated *in vitro* metabolic effect of insulin were noted to become unresponsive to the hormone, when pretreated with proteolytic enzymes, but regained their insulin responsiveness after the enzymes were washed off and time was allotted for recovery from the insult. This suggested that a specific protein moiety of the cell membrane is responsible for the binding of insulin, that this part is easily accessible and removable, and can be rapidly resynthesized by the cells (Kono, 1969). Successful solubilization of the membrane fraction, which was responsible for the binding of the hormone (Cuatrecasas, 1972), led to its partial purification, and enabled subsequent studies of its physical and chemical properties (Kahn *et al.*, 1974; De Meyts *et al.*, 1976), whereas demonstration of insulin receptors on circulating mononuclear cells with identical properties to those previously seen in less easily accessible adipose tissue or liver cell membranes (Olefsky and Reaven, 1974; Bar *et al.*, 1976) permitted the studies of receptor physiology in human subjects. An excellent review of insulin receptors in general has been reported in a previous volume of this treatise (Ginsberg, 1977).

Utilizing the above mentioned isotope methodology, Posner *et al.* (1974) showed the presence of insulin receptors in membrane preparations obtained from a wide variety of species and tissues, including the brain of monkeys and pigeons. The presence of insulin receptors in monkey brain was confirmed by Landau *et al.* (1976) who found greater binding of [$^{125}$I]iodoinsulin to membrane preparations derived from the hypothalamus than to those obtained from the cortex or the thalamus. In the same report Landau *et al.* (1976) also showed biochemical evidence for insulin action on glucose metabolism of the hypothalamus: the hormone appeared to enhance the incorporation of [$^{14}$C]glucose and 3-*o*-Methyl [$^{14}$C]glucose into this area.

Conflicting results were reported by Goodner and Berrie (1977) who infused [$^{125}$I]iodoinsulin intravenously to rats, and found no significant uptake (as immunoprecipitable radioactivity in tissue homogenates) in deep

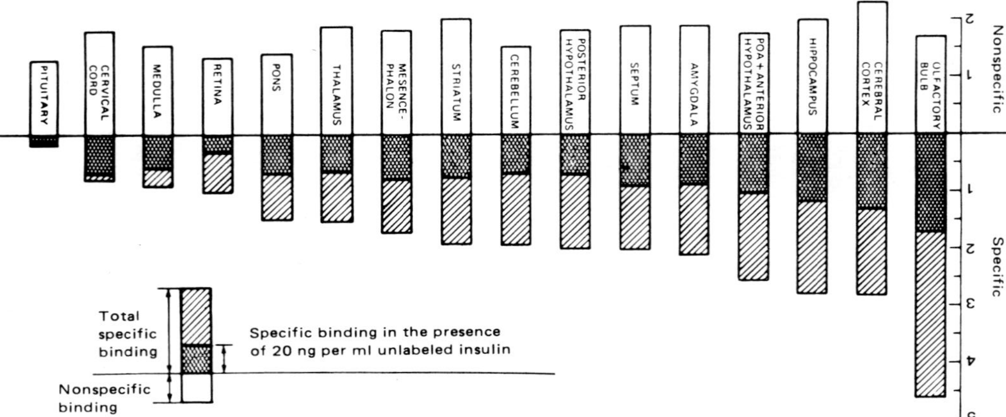


FIG. 4. Regional distribution of the insulin receptor in the CNS of the rat. 20,000 g pellets were prepared and the radioreceptor assay performed as described previously. The specific binding (as % of total radioactivity added) is indicated by the whole hatched bar above the baseline; the double hatched part represents the specific binding in the presence of 20 ng/ml of unlabeled insulin. The empty bar below the baseline represents the nonspecific binding (in the presence of 100 $\mu$U/ml of unlabeled insulin). The total, specific and nonspecific binding was adjusted for each region to the protein concentration of 500 $\mu$g/ml. It was shown in a preliminary experiment that specific binding was linear between protein concentrations 150–700 $\mu$g/ml. Degradation of [$^{125}$I]insulin was determined using the precipitation with trichloroacetic acid (10%) at the end of incubation in every supernatant, and ranged between 5 and 10%. Reproduced from Havrankova *et al.* (1978a) with permission from the authors and the publisher.

hypothalamic structures (such as the VMN), only in the medial eminence. These investigators also failed to observe an effect of insulin on the incorporation (metabolism) of [$^{14}$C]glucose into lipids or carbon dioxide by incubated brain slices.

Further evidence for the existence of insulin receptors in the CNS was reported by Havrankova *et al.* (1978a), who found specific insulin-binding properties in particulate membrane preparations obtained from different CNS regions of rats. The specificity of the binding was shown by displacement of [$^{125}$I]iodoinsulin from the receptor by unlabeled hormone, while proinsulin, desalanine-desasparagine insulin, and isolated A and B chains of the insulin molecule competed less effectively for the binding sites. Uneven distribution of the receptors (Fig. 4) in fifteen CNS regions suggested a functional topography, although finding the highest concentrations of specific binding sites in the olfactory bulb and the cortex, areas that showed no glucoregulatory properties when exposed to insulin through a stereotaxically placed needle (Iguchi *et al.*, 1981), was disappointing. The question related to the site of maximal insulin receptor concentration in the CNS is far from being settled. More recently, investigating the specific binding of [$^{125}$I]iodoinsulin to homogenates of rat brains Pacold and Blackard (1979) found that binding to the hypothalamus [an area that showed only mediocre receptor concentration in the study of Havrankova *et al.* (1978a)] considerably exceeded that of the cortex. A recent communication, using sucrose gradient centrifugal separation of the subcellular fractions, localized the cortical insulin receptors to the synaptic membranes, suggesting the possibility that insulin has a possible neurotransmitter role in this area of the brain (Gameltoft *et al.*, 1980).

It was somewhat surprising that specific [$^{125}$I]iodoinsulin binding to different areas of the rat brain did not vary with the endogenous plasma insulin concentration of the animals (Havrankova *et al.*, 1979). Whereas in other tissues hyperinsulinemia reduces and insulinopenia increases the receptor concentration, in these studies neither obesity (as a prototype of endogenous hyperinsulinemia) nor streptozotocin diabetes (i.e., insulinopenia) caused changes in specific binding sites.

## C. Morphological Observations: Localization of Insulin Receptors in the CNS

The *in vitro* study of hormone receptors in tissues, discussed in section III,B, employs the technique of quantifying the binding of the tracer-labeled hormone to the cell or cell fraction (in case of insulin, to the cell membrane). Specificity of the binding is assumed if addition of excess unlabeled hormone prevents the binding of the tracer labeled hormone to the cell fraction, or if the unlabeled hormone displaces the tracer hormone from its binding, and addition of other related or unrelated proteins and hormones fail to do so. The nature of the procedure, therefore, is that tissues are disrupted, homogenized, the different subcellular particles are isolated by centrifugal or sucrose gradient separation, and are washed to remove contaminations, before the labeled hormone is added. The procedure thus precludes the investigation of *in vivo* access by the hormone to the receptor.

The technique of quantitative radioautography eliminates this shortcoming of the *in vitro* receptor assay, while preserving one of its most advantageous features—its specificity—which is demonstrated by the displacement of the labeled ligand by the unlabeled hormone. In this procedure the labeled hormone is injected *in vivo* (with or without competing excess unlabeled hormone). The animal is subsequently sacrificed, and after appropriate perfusion or washing of the tissue (to rinse out the unbound label remaining in the vascular tree), the silver grains that represent the radioactive tracer are quantified on photoemulsion coated histological sections.

Utilizing this technique, van Houten *et al.* (1979) found rapid, specific binding of [$^{125}$I]iodoinsulin (administered by intracardiac injections) to the parenchyma of the so called "circumventricular organs," the medial basal hypothalamus and the medial paravagal region in rats (Table I). The circumventricular organs were known to possess an incomplete blood–brain barrier (Weindl, 1973). The new information supported the concept that these circumventricular structures may have sensory and hormone responsive regulatory functions (van Houten and Posner, 1980).

Although insulin receptors were found to be widespread on microvascular endothelium throughout the CNS (van Houten and Posner, 1979), binding of [$^{125}$I]iodoinsulin to axonal and synaptic elements in the median eminence and in the arcuate nucleus (van Houten *et al.*, 1980) is of greater significance, because it suggests that insulin rapidly enters the neuronal elements of these hypothalamic structures from the circulation, and may indeed perform regulatory influence over neurally mediated metabolic functions (van Houten and Posner, 1981).

An alternate histological method to demonstrate insulin receptors in the CNS utilized double antibody immunofluorescence (Pansky and Hatfield, 1978). In this procedure acetone-fixed, sliced mouse brain tissue was incubated with insulin, then subsequently with guinea pig anti-insulin serum, and finally with fluorescein-labeled goat anti-guinea pig serum. The procedure does not specifically utilize the vascular route for the delivery of insulin; therefore neither information regarding bioavailability of circulating insulin (i.e., the effectiveness of the blood–brain barrier) nor data regarding possible receptors deep in the tissue block (i.e., distant from the cut surface) could be

TABLE I

COMPARISON OF INTENSITIES OF RADIOAUTOGRAPHIC REACTIONS OVER VARIOUS REGIONS OF RAT BRAIN 5 MINUTES AFTER SYSTEMIC INJECTION OF [$^{125}$I]IODOINSULIN IN THE ABSENCE (E) OR PRESENCE (C) OF A 500-FOLD EXCESS OF UNLABELED INSULIN[a]

| Brain region | Grains/unit area | | % Region reduction |
|---|---|---|---|
| | E | C | [(E − C)/E × 100][b] |
| Organum vasculosum lamina terminalis | 246 ± 11 | 89 ± 7 | 63.8 ± 1.2 |
| Subfornical organ | 399 ± 12 | 92 ± 23 | 71.8 ± 2.9 |
| Median eminence | | | |
| Internal region | 255 ± 44 | 238 ± 40 | 6.1 ± 1.2 (NS) |
| External region | 540 ± 44 | 117 ± 5 | 77.9 ± 1.7 |
| Hypothalamic arcuate nucleus | 370 ± 13 | 111 ± 10 | 70.2 ± 1.6 |
| Hypothalamic ventromedial n. posterior ventrolateral | 170 ± 12 | 41 ± 4 | 76.1 ± 1.2 |
| Area postrema | 257 ± 4 | 65 ± 2 | 74.7 ± 0.6 |
| Paravagal region | 369 ± 13 | 159 ± 9 | 56.6 ± 3.1 |
| Choroid epithelium | 132 ± 16 | 130 ± 3 | 0.75 ± 1.1 (NS) |
| Neocortex | 4.9 ± 0.3 | 4.8 ± 0.3 | 2.0 ± 0.1 (NS) |
| Thalamus | 5.0 ± 0.2 | 4.9 ± 0.2 | 1.0 ± 0.9 (NS) |
| Cerebellum | 5.1 ± 0.1 | 4.9 ± 0.1 | 3.8 ± 0.1 (NS) |

[a] Reproduced from van Houten *et al.* (1979) with permission from the authors and the publisher. All values are the mean ± SEM. Background fog, 4.8 ± 0.1 grains/unit area (6959 $\mu m^2$).

[b] All statistically significant ($p < .0001$), except those marked NS.

derived from it. Immunofluorescence was demonstrated, however, in the ependymal cells lining the third and fourth ventricles, and in tanycytes in these regions, as well as in the choroid plexi.

## IV. DEMONSTRATION OF INSULIN IN THE CNS

The most recent development in the neuroendocrinology of carbohydrate regulation is related to finding native insulin, in considerable amounts, in the central nervous system (Havrankova *et al.*, 1978b). Rat brains were extracted with acid–ethanol, and following neutralization the extracts were stored in lyophilized state, until reconstituted with buffer for further characterization. Insulin was identified by double antibody radioimmunoassay, by radioreceptor assay, by bioassay (using the conversion of [$^{14}$C]glucose to $^{14}CO_2$ by fat cell suspensions), and by Sephadex G-50 gel chromatography. All these methods yielded results, which showed that the extracted material is indistinguishable from native insulin.

The surprising conclusion in this study was not the mere presence of insulin in the CNS, but that after correcting for losses during the extraction (based on the loss of added and coextracted [$^{125}$I]iodoinsulin), Havrankova *et al.* (1978b) found concentrations of insulin that exceeded 25 times the concentration of the hormone in the plasma. Such high concentrations in tissues are difficult to explain by trapping of insulin entering from the circulation. Therefore, the possibility that insulin was synthesized in the CNS was entertained. Although this suggestion may seem to be farfetched for those of us brought up with the idea that insulin is synthesized in, and is secreted from, the islets of the pancreas only, one has to concede that other hormones of the digestive system, such as vasoactive intestinal polypeptide, (Bryant *et al.*, 1976), cholecystokinin (Muller *et al.*, 1977), and others, have also been shown to occur in central nervous system tissue, and are presumed to be produced there, and are thought to fulfill neurotransmitter or neuromodulator roles. Analogous to the latter gastrointestinal hormones, it is possible to consider that insulin may also be synthesized in some part of the CNS.

The presence of insulin in the CNS was confirmed by Eng and Yalow (1980), but these investigators found much smaller quantities, at most two times that of the plasma concentration, and accordingly favored the more conservative contention that insulin found in the CNS could conceivably come from the bloodstream, and that if its concentration exceeds that of the plasma level, it may be due to elution of receptor-bound insulin.

It is of considerable interest that Havrankova *et al.* (1979), Rosenzweig *et al.* (1980), and Oomura and Kita (1981) found little or no variation in brain insulin concentration in hyperinsulinemic state (obese mice) or in hypoinsulinemic (streptozotocin treated) rats, and concluded that insulin concentration in the CNS is independent of the plasma insulin concentrations, whereas Hahn *et al.* (1980) found decreased insulinlike immunoreactivity in brains of streptozotocin diabetic rats.

## V. BIOLOGICAL PERSPECTIVES AND UNANSWERED QUESTIONS

The surprising observation that the net decrease in peripheral blood glucose concentration is not smaller after peripheral venous than after portal venous insulin administration (Madison and Unger, 1958) has been confirmed by many (Erwald *et al.*, 1974; Baruch, 1975), and has been extended to show that the quantitative insulin requirements to achieve similar glycemic control are not different for both routes of administration (Botz *et al.*, 1976; Albisser *et al.*, 1977). Moreover, using more sensitive methods ([3-$H^3$]glucose infusion for the estimation of glucose output and glucose disposal, and computer assisted glucose infusion to hold plasma glucose concentration unchanged—the "glucose clamp technique"), Putnam *et al.* (1980) reported that peripheral insulin administration caused greater inhibition of hepatic glucose output and necessitated greater quantities of glucose infusions to maintain euglycemia than did portal insulin infusion. These *in vivo* studies lend considerable support to the hypothesis (developed in this chapter), that the effect of insulin on hepatic glucose metabolism is mediated, at least in part, by a neural reflex originating in a hypothalamic insulin-sensitive glucoregulator area.

What then is the role of insulin secreted into the portal vein? Perhaps it is a growth and maintenance factor for the hepatocytes, as suggested by the experiments of Starzl *et al.* (1976) in dogs with portocaval shunts, or perhaps the hepatic insulin degrading system (Mirsky and Broh-Kahn, 1949) developed in response to the lability of, or the wide range of oscillation in the insulin secretory rate? And if insulin exerts its metabolic effect on the liver via a neural relay through the CNS, do other hormones act similarly? What is the role of insulin receptors in CNS areas into which injection of insulin was not followed by any known biological effect? What is the role of the high insulin concentration in the CNS? Is insulin a growth factor for the developing brain (Yang and Fellows, 1980)? What is the explanation for the marked differences between CNS receptor concentrations as estimated by different (i.e., radioautographic versus *in vitro* receptor assay) methods?

Is insulin in the CNS a glucoregulator feedback signal, or a modulator of neural transmission adjusting the body to the minute by minute changes in glycemic–insulinemic metabolic state, or is it an independent, specific neurotransmitter substance? Does insulin in the cerebrospinal fluid have a completely different role, such as being a regulator of body weight and obesity (Woods and Porte, 1977)? Will emission transaxial tomography, a new technique that so graphically demonstrated regional glucose dynamics in the CNS of intact humans (Greenberg *et al.*, 1981) clarify some of these issues? As mentioned Section I, the questions greatly outnumber the answers, making this rapidly progressing area of biological science particularly exciting.

## VI. SUMMARY

Research carried out in the last decade provided solid evidence for the existence of glucoreceptors as well as insulin receptors in the central nervous system. Both glucoreceptors and insulin receptors were shown to have glucoregulatory functions: the former to increase, the latter to decrease hepatic glucose output. Both neural and neurohormonal efferent pathways have been described in these glucoregulatory functions; glucoreceptors appear to function more through neurohormonal than pure neural pathways, while insulin-sensitive receptors convey the impulse more through direct neural than through neurohormonal pathways. The sympathetic, adrenergic system emerged as the neural mediator of the former, while the parasympathetic, cholinergic system of the latter function.

Insulin receptors have been recognized in the CNS by several methods: physiological, physicochemical (i.e., *in vitro* radioreceptor assay), and radioautographic techniques have been used. The receptor concentration shows considerable variation from one region of the CNS to the other. Functional mapping of these have started, but will take many years to complete.

Native, endogenous insulin has also been found in the CNS. Its site of origin and biological function remain to be elucidated.

## ACKNOWLEDGMENTS

The critical review of this manuscript by Dr. Adrienne Fleckman, and the secretarial help by Ms. Nancy Quirindongo is gratefully acknowledged. This work was supported by grant AM 17347-08 awarded by the United States Public Health Service, National Institute of Arthritis, Metabolic and Digestive Diseases.

## REFERENCES

Abramson, E. A., and Arky, R. A. (1968). *Diabetes* **17,** 141–146.

Albisser, M. A., Leibel, B. S., Zinman, B., Murray, F. T., Zingg, W., Botz, C. K., Denoga, A., and Marliss, E. B. (1977). *Arch. Intern. Med.* **137,** 639–649.

Anand, B. K., Chhina, G. S., Sharma, K. N., Dua, S., and Singh, B. (1964). *Am. J. Physiol.* **207,** 1146–1154.

Ball, E. G., and Jungas, R. L. (1964). *Recent Progr. Horm. Res.* **20,** 183–214.

Bar, R. S., Gorden, P., Kahn, C. R., Roth, J., and De Meyts, P. (1976). *J. Clin. Invest.* **58,** 1123–1135.

Baruch, S. (1975). *Am. J. Med. Sci.* **269,** 25–35.

Bergman, R. N. (1977). *Fed. Proc. Fed. Am. Soc. Exp. Biol.* **36,** 265–270.

Bishop, J. S., Steele, R., Altszuler, N., Dunn, A., Bjerknes, C., and DeBodo, R. C. (1965). *Am. J. Physiol.* **208,** 307–316.

Botz, C. K., Leibel, B. S., Zingg, W., Gander, R. E., and Albisser, A. M. (1976). *Diabetes* **25,** 691–700.

Britton, S. W. (1925). *Am. J. Physiol.* **74,** 291–308.

Brodows, R. G., Pi-Sunyer, F. X., and Campbell, R. G. (1973). *J. Clin. Invest.* **52,** 1841–1844.

Brown, J. (1962). *Metab., Clin. Exp.* **11,** 1098–1112.

Bryant, M. G., Polak, S. M., Modlin, G., Bloom, S. R., Albuquerque, R., and Pearse, A. G. E., (1976). *Lancet* **1,** 991–993.

Bucolo, R. J., Bergman, R. N., Marsh, D. J., and Yates, F. E. (1974). *Am. J. Physiol.* **227**, 209–217.

Cahill, G. F., Jr., Ashmore, J., Renold, A. E., and Hastings, A. B. (1959). *Am. J. Med.* **26**, 264–282.

Chieri, R. A., Farina, J. M. S., Halperin, J., and Basabe, J. C. (1975). *Diabetologia* **11**, 175–180.

Coore, H. G., and Randle, P. J. (1964). *Biochem. J.* **93**, 66–78.

Cuatrecasas, P. (1969). *Proc. Natl. Acad. Sci. U.S.A.* **63**, 450–457.

Cuatrecasas, P. (1972). *Proc. Natl. Acad. Sci. U.S.A.* **69**, 318–322.

Debons, A. F., Krimski, I., and From, A. (1970). *Am. J. Physiol.* **219**, 938–943.

DeFronzo, R. A., Hendler, R., and Christensen, N. (1980). *Diabetes* **29**, 125–131.

De Meyts, P., Bianco, A. R., and Roth, J. (1976). *J. Biol. Chem.* **251**, 1877–1888.

Donald, J. M. (1931). *Am. J. Physiol.* **98**, 605–609.

Donald, R. A. (1971). *J. Clin. Endocrinol. Metab.* **32**, 225–231.

Eng, J., and Yalow, R. S. (1980). *Diabetes* **29**, 105–109.

Erwald, R., Hed, R., Nygren, A., Rojdmark, S., and Wiechel, K. L. (1974). *Acta Med. Scand.* **195**, 351–357.

Exton, J. H., Jefferson, L. S., Jr., Butcher, R. W., and Park, C. R. (1966). *Am. J. Med.* **40**, 709–715.

Felig, P. (1974). *N. E. J. Med.* **291**, 1031–1032.

Felig, P., and Wahren, J. (1971). *J. Clin. Invest.* **50**, 1702–1711.

Flock, E. V., Tyce, G. M., and Owen, C. A., Jr. (1969). *Endocrinology* **85**, 428–437.

Freychet, P., Roth, J., and Neville, D. M., Jr. (1971). *Proc. Natl. Acad. Sci. U.S.A.* **68**, 1833–1937.

Friedmann, N., and Wertheimer, H. E. (1966). *Metab., Clin. Exp.* **15**, 222–229.

Frohman, L. A., and Bernardis, L. L. (1968). *Endocrinology* **82**, 1125–1132.

Frohman, L. A., and Bernardis, L. L. (1971). *Am. J. Physiol.* **221**, 1596–1603.

Frohman, L. A., Bernardis, L. L., and Stachura, M. E. (1974). *Metab., Clin. Exp.* **23**, 1047–1056.

Gameltoft, S., Staun-Olsen, P., and Fahrenkrug, J. (1980). *Diabetologia* **19**, 275.

Garber, A., Cryer, P., Santiago, J., Haymond, M., Pagliara, A., and Kipnis, D. (1976). *J. Clin. Invest.* **58**, 7–15.

Garcia-Viveros, M., Dib, C. A., Bordes, J., Valverde-R., C., and Lozano-Castaneda, O. (1974). *Rev. Invest. Clin.* **26**, 299–308.

Gates, G. F., and Dore, E. K., (1973). *J. Nucl. Med.* **14**, 79–83.

Gauthier, C., Vranic, M., and Hetenyi, G., Jr. (1980). *Am. J. Physiol.* **238**, E131–E140.

Gemmill, C. L. (1940). *Bull. Johns Hopkins Hosp.* **66**, 232–236.

Gerich, J. E., Schneider, V., Dippe, S. E., Langlois, M., Noacco, C., Karam, J. H., and Forsham, P. H. (1974). *J. Clin. Endocrinol. Metab.* **38**, 77–82.

Gerich, J., Davis, J., Lorenzi, M., Rizza, R., Bohannon, N., Karam, J., Lewis, S., Kaplan, R., Schultz, T., and Cryer, P. (1979). *Am. J. Physiol.* **236**, E380–E385.

Ginsberg, B. H. (1977). In "Biochemical Actions of Hormones" (G. Litwack, ed.), Vol. 4, pp. 313–349. Academic Press, New York.

Glinsmann, W. H., and Mortimore, G. E. (1968). *Am. J. Physiol.* **215**, 553–559.

Goodner, C. J., and Berrie, M. A. (1977). *Endocrinology* **101**, 605–612.

Greenberg, J. H., Reivich, M., Alavi, A., Hand, P., Rosenquist, A., Rintelmann, W., Stein, A., Tusa, R., Dann, R., Christman, D., Fowler, J., MacGregor, B., and Ord Wolf, A. (1981). *Science* **212**, 678–680.

Grodsky, G. M., Batts, A. A., Bennett, L. L., Voella, C., McWilliams, N. B., Smith, D. F. (1963). *Am. J. Physiol.* **205**, 638–644.

Haft, D. E. (1967). *Am. J. Physiol.* **213,** 219–230.

Hahn, J. H., Dorn, A., Besch, W., Bernstein, H. G., Klöting, I., and Ziegler, B. (1980). *Diabetologia* **19,** 279–280.

Hales, C. N., and Kennedy, G. S. (1964). *Biochem. J.* **90,** 620–624.

Harding, P. E., Bloom, G., and Field, J. B. (1975). *Am. J. Physiol.* **228,** 1580–1588.

Hatfield, J. S., Millard, W. J., and Smith, C. J. V. (1973). *Pharmacol., Biochem. Behav.* **2,** 223–226.

Havrankova, J., Roth, J., and Brownstein, M. (1978a). *Nature (London)* **272,** 827–828.

Havrankova, J., Schmechel, D., Roth, J., and Brownstein, M. (1978b). *Proc. Natl. Acad. Sci. U.S.A.* **75,** 5737–5741.

Havrankova, J., Roth, J., and Brownstein, M. J. (1979). *J. Clin. Invest.* **64,** 636–642.

Hechter, O., Levine, R., and Soskin, S. (1941). *Proc. Soc. Exp. Biol. Med.* **46,** 390–393.

Hefco, V., Rotenberg, P., and Jitariu, P. (1975). *Endocrinologie* **65,** 191–197.

Hetherington, A., and Ranson, S. W. (1940). *Anat. Rec.* **78,** 149–172.

Himwich, H. E., Bowman, K. M., Daly, C., Wortis, J., and Goldfarb, W. (1941). *Am. J. Physiol.* **132,** 640–647.

Iguchi, A., Burleson, P. D., and Szabo, A. J. (1979). *Am. J. Physiol.* **237,** H730–H733.

Iguchi, A., Burleson, P. D., and Szabo, A. J. (1981). *Am. J. Physiol.* **240,** E95–E100.

Kahn, C. R., Freychet, P., Roth, J., and Neville, D. M., Jr. (1974). *J. Biol. Chem.* **249,** 2249–2257.

Kanazawa, Y., Kuzuya, T., Ide, T., and Kosaka, K. (1966). *Am. J. Physiol.* **211,** 442–448.

Kerr, S. E., and Ghantus, M. (1936). *J. Biol. Chem.* **116,** 9–20.

Kono, T. (1969). *J. Biol. Chem.* **244,** 1772–1778.

Lacy, P. E., Walker, M. M., and Fink, C. J. (1972). *Diabetes* **21,** 987–998.

Landau, B. R., and Lubs, H. A. (1958). *Proc. Soc. Exp. Biol. Med.* **99,** 124–127.

Landau, B. R., Abrams, M. A., White, R. J., Takaota, Y., Taslitz, N., Austin, P., Austin, J., and Chernicky, C. (1976). *Diabetes, Suppl. 1,* **25,** 322.

Levine, R., and Goldstein, M. S. (1955). *Recent Progr. Horm. Res.* **11,** 343–380.

Levine, R., and Haft, D. E. (1970). *N. E. J. Med.* **283,** 175–183.

Lund-Anderson, H. (1979). *Physiol. Rev.* **59,** 305–352.

Mackrell, D. J., and Sokal, J. (1969). *Diabetes* **18,** 724–732.

Madison, L. L., and Unger, R. H. (1958). *J. Clin. Invest.* **37,** 631–639.

Mahler, R. J., and Szabo, O. (1967). *Proc. Soc. Exp. Biol. Med.* **125,** 879–882.

Malaisse, W. J., Pipeleers, D. G., and Mahy, M. (1973). *Diabetologia* **9,** 1–5.

Margolis, R. V., and Altszuler, N. (1967). *Nature* (*London*) **215,** 1375–1376.

Marrazzi, M. A. (1976). In "Hunger: Basic Mechanisms and Clinical Implications" (D. Novin, W. Wyrwicka, and G. Bray, eds.), pp. 171–178. Raven, New York.

Matchinsky, F. M., Landgraf, R., Ellerman, J., and Kotler-Brajtburg, J., (1972). *Diabetes, Suppl.* 2, **21,** 555–569.

Matsuura, N., Cheng, J. S., and Kalant, N. (1975). *Can. J. Biochem.* **53,** 28–36.

Meldrum, B. S., and Horton, R. W. (1973). *Electroencephalog. Clin. Neurophysiol.* **35,** 59–66.

Mirsky, I. A., and Broh-Kahn, R. H. (1949). *Arch. Biochem.* **20,** 1–9.

Mondon, C. E., Dolkas, C. B., Olefsky, J. M., and Reaven, G. M. (1975). *Diabetes* **24,** 225–229.

Mortimore, G. E. (1963). *Am. J. Physiol.* **204,** 699–704.

Mortimore, G. E., King, E., Jr., Mondon, C. E., and Glinsmann, W. H. (1967). *Am. J. Physiol.* **212,** 179–183.

Muller, E. E., Frohman, L. A., and Cocchi, D. (1973). *Am. J. Physiol.* **224,** 1210–1217.

Muller, J. E., Straus, E., and Yalow, R. S. (1977). *Proc. Natl. Acad. Sci. U.S.A.* **74,** 3035–3037.

Niijima, A. (1974). *J. Physiol.* (*London*) **251,** 231–243.

Olefsky, J. M., and Reaven, G. M. (1974). *J. Clin. Invest.* **54,** 1323-1328.
Oomura, Y., and Kita, H. (1981). *Diabetologia* **20,** 290-298.
Oomura, Y., Ono, T., Ooyama, H., and Wayner, M. J. (1969). *Nature (London)* **222,** 283-284.
Pacold, S. T., and Blackard, W. G. (1979). *Endocrinology* **105,** 1452-1457.
Pansky, G., and Hatfield, J. S. (1978). *Am. J. Anat.* **153,** 459-467.
Parrilla, R., Goodman, M. N., and Toews, C. J. (1974). *Diabetes* **23,** 725-731.
Pastan, I., Roth, J., and Macchia, V. (1966). *Proc. Natl. Acad. Sci. U.S.A.* **56,** 1802-1809.
Porte, D., Jr., Girardier, L., Seydoux, J., Kanazawa, Y., and Posternak, J. (1973). *J. Clin. Invest.* **52,** 210-214.
Porte, D., Jr., Woods, S. C., Chen, M., Smith, P. H., and Ensinck, J. W. (1975). *Pharmacol., Biochem. Behav. Suppl. 1,* **3,** 127-133.
Posner, B. I., Kelly, P. A., Shiu, R. C., and Friesen, H. G. (1974). *Endocrinology* **95,** 521-531.
Putnam, W. S., Andersen, D. K., Hanks, J. B., Jones, R. S., and Lebovitz, H. E. (1980). *Diabetes, Suppl. 2,* **29,** 15a.
Rafaelsen, O. J. (1961a). *Metab., Clin. Exp.* **10,** 99-114.
Rafaelsen, O. J. (1961b). *J. Neurochem.* **7,** 45-51.
Ritter, R. C., and Slusser, P. (1980). *Am. J. Physiol.* **238,** E141-E144.
Rosenzweig, J. L., Havrankova, J., Lesniak, M. A., Brownstein, M., and Roth, J. (1980). *Proc. Natl. Acad. Sci. U.S.A.* **77,** 572-576.
Sakata, K., Hayano, S., and Sloviter, H. A. (1963). *Am. J. Physiol.* **204,** 1127-1132.
Shimazu, T. (1967). *Science* **156,** 1256-1257.
Shimazu, T., and Amakawa, A. (1968). *Biochim. Biophys. Acta* **165,** 335-348.
Shimazu, T., Fukuda, A., and Ban, T. (1966). *Nature (London)* **210,** 1178-1179.
Soskin, S., and Levine R. (1946). "Carbohydrate Metabolism." Univ. of Chicago Press, Chicago, Illinois.
Starzl, T. E., Watanabe, K., Porter, K. A., and Putnam, C. W. (1976). *Lancet* **1,** 812-825.
Storlien, L. H., Bellingham, W. P., and Martin, G. M. (1975). *Brain Res.* **96,** 156-160.
Szabo, A. J., and Szabo, O. (1975). *J. Physiol. (London)* **253,** 121-133.
Szabo, O., and Szabo, A. J. (1972). *Am. J. Physiol.* **223,** 1349-1353.
Szabo, O., and Szabo, A. J. (1975a). *Endocrinology* **97,** 734-738.
Szabo, O., and Szabo, A. J. (1975b). *Diabetes* **24,** 328-336.
Szabo, O., and Szabo, A. J. (1975c). *Am. J. Physiol.* **229,** 663-668.
Szabo, O., and Szabo, A. J. (1978). *60th Ann. Meet. Endocr. Soc.,* p. 276. Abstr. No. 403.
Tomizawa, H. H., Nutley, M. L., Narahara, H. T., and Williams, R. H. (1955). *J. Biol. Chem.* **214,** 285-294.
van Houten, M., and Posner, B. I. (1979). *Nature (London)* **282,** 623-625.
van Houten, M., and Posner, B. I. (1981). *Diabetologia,* **20,** 255-267.
van Houten, M., Posner, B. I., Kopriwa, B. M., and Brawer, J. R. (1979). *Endocrinology* **105,** 666-673.
van Houten, M., Posner, B. I., Kopriwa, B. M., and Brawer, J. R. (1980). *Science* **207,** 181-183.
Walter, R., Dudl, R., Palmer, J., and Ensinck, J. (1974). *J. Clin. Invest.* **54,** 1214-1220.
Weindl, A. (1973). *In* "Frontiers in Neuroendocrinology" (W. F. Ganong and L. Martini, eds.), pp. 1-32. Oxford Univ. Press, London and New York.
Williamson, J. R., Garcia, A., Renold, A. E., and Cahill, G. F., Jr. (1966). *Diabetes* **15,** 183-187.
Winegrad, A. I., and Renold, A. E. (1958). *J. Biol. Chem.* **233,** 267-272.
Woods, S. C., and Porte, D., Jr. (1974). *Physiol. Rev.* **54,** 596-619.
Woods, S. C., and Porte, D., (1977). *Am. J. Physiol.* **233,** E331-E334.
Yang, J. W., and Fellows, R. E., (1980). *Endocrinology* **107,** 1717-1729.

# CHAPTER 5

# Estrogen-Inducible Growth Factors: Proposal of New Mechanisms of Estrogen-Promoted Tumor Cell Growth

*David A. Sirbasku and Frances E. Leland*



## I. INTRODUCTION

In this chapter we will discuss two aspects of our original hypothesis (Sirbasku, 1978a) that estrogens may act indirectly *in vivo* to promote the growth of some types of estrogen-responsive tumors via induction of new



BIOCHEMICAL ACTIONS OF HORMONES, VOL. IX

ISBN 0-12-452809-0

polypeptide growth factors that we have tentatively designated estromedins (Sirbasku and Benson, 1979; Sirbasku, 1980).

In most studies of estrogen-induced mitogenesis, the prevailing concepts rest on the extensive characterization of the well-known estrogen receptor proteins of several target tissues (Jensen and DeSombre, 1972; Meites *et al.*, 1972; O'Malley and Means, 1974). Clearly, the evidence to date abundantly supports the role of estrogens (and other steroid hormones) functioning as controllers of specific protein synthesis in cells.

Several laboratories appear to be well on the way to a very detailed molecular analysis of steroid action that includes isolation of the receptor proteins, characterization of nuclear acceptor sites, and the isolation of the messenger RNA and genes controlled by estrogens. Nevertheless, the role of estrogens in target cell growth remains a matter of considerable contention (Sirbasku, 1978a; Allegra and Lippman, 1978; Sonnenschein *et al.*, 1980a,b; Sirbasku and Benson, 1980), with the main question being whether estrogens are directly mitogenic, presumably through the estrogen–receptor mechanism, or instead, function through indirect or secondary signals.

We will not review here our reasons for believing that the control of estrogen-responsive tumor cells is more complex than represented by the interaction of estrogenic steroids with their specific cytosolic receptors and nuclear acceptor sites. The working hypothesis for the direct mitogenic action is based on the identification of specific receptors in tissues that grow *in vivo* in response to estrogens. However, our laboratory, as well as others (Wyche and Noteboom, 1979; Soto and Sonnenschein, 1979), have found a lack of correlation between estrogen-responsive growth and presence of receptors. Cells that have estrogen receptors may well show completely autonomous growth (D. A. Sirbasku, unpublished; Sonnenschein *et al.*, 1980b). Another group (McGuire and Howitz, 1979) has concluded that the presence of the estrogen receptor is necessary, but not sufficient for a growth response *in vivo*. These matters have been reviewed by us recently (Sirbasku, 1978a; Sirbasku and Benson, 1979; Sirbasku, 1980; Sirbasku and Benson, 1980). We need only state here that all evidence to date suggests that estrogens alone show either no mitogenic capacity when tested with many types of tumor cells or tissue explants *in vitro*, or if estrogen mitogenicity is shown, it is of limited magnitude (1.5- to 2.0-fold) and usually dependent on the presence of growth factors (Barnes and Sato, 1979), or growth factors plus high concentrations of insulin (Allegra and Lippman, 1978; Lippman *et al.*, 1979).

The first purpose of this chapter is then to describe the studies we have conducted to reconcile the apparent discrepancies seen between *in vivo* estrogen responsive growth, and the lack of growth responses seen *in vitro*. In this review, three new models or mechanisms of estrogen-dependent tumor growth are introduced, all involving estrogen-inducible growth factors. The role of growth factors in proliferation of cells in culture (see Holley,

1975; Gospodarowicz and Moran, 1976; Pledger *et al.*, 1978) has been recognized for some time with cell types of fibroblastic or embryonic origins, but until most recently, less attention has been paid to their role in growth of epithelial origin cells, and especially their role in the growth of cells that form hormone-responsive normal or tumor tissues (Kirkland *et al.*, 1976; Sirbasku and Kirkland, 1976; Sirbasku, 1978a). The initial concepts of growth factor control of both fibroblastic and epithelial cells have now been further refined by Sato and colleagues (Sato and Reid, 1978; Bottenstein *et al.*, 1979; Barnes and Sato, 1980) who have developed completely hormonally defined media for many cell types, or at least, media with minimal serum additions supplemented with various hormones, serum spreading factors, and such metal ion transport proteins as transferrin. The lessons to be learned from their studies are that not only can defined media be established for cells in culture, but almost more importantly, that many factors and hormones are required for growth of one cell type. Most notably, no cell line is known that grows in response solely to only steroid hormone (Sato and Reid, 1978; Bottenstein *et al.*, 1979; Barnes and Sato, 1980). For the purpose of this review, it is important to emphasize that this fact is true for such cell lines as the human mammary tumor MCF-7 line that is known to form estrogen-responsive tumors in nude mice (Shafie, 1980), and is known to have estrogen receptor proteins (Chong and Lippman, 1980), but still responds only slightly (i.e., 20% cell number increase) to addition of estrogens to the culture medium. The problems generated by all of these observations suggested to us that a fresh approach was needed to resolve the paradox between the positive estrogen effects *in vivo* and the lack of effects *in vitro* (Sirbasku, 1978a; Sonnenschein *et al.*, 1980a,b; Shafie, 1980). First, we will discuss some of our experimental approaches to this problem, some of the difficulties with our current available methods, and the essential experiments that are yet to be conducted to define further whether these growth factors function *in vivo* in the role of intermediate or secondary signals. Second, we will summarize our interpretation of the relationship between the estromedin hypothesis and other proposed indirect mechanisms described by Sonnenschein *et al.* (1980a,b) and Shafie (1980), as well as how our hypothesis fits with the evidence that at least one cell type (see Lippman *et al.*, 1979) shows an apparent directly mitogenic estrogen response in culture.

## II. THREE POSSIBLE ESTROMEDIN MECHANISMS

In the following section we will review the general concepts of three new mediator (estromedin) mechanisms of hormone-responsive growth, pointing out some of the requirements and limitations of each model. These three models are summarized in Fig. 1.

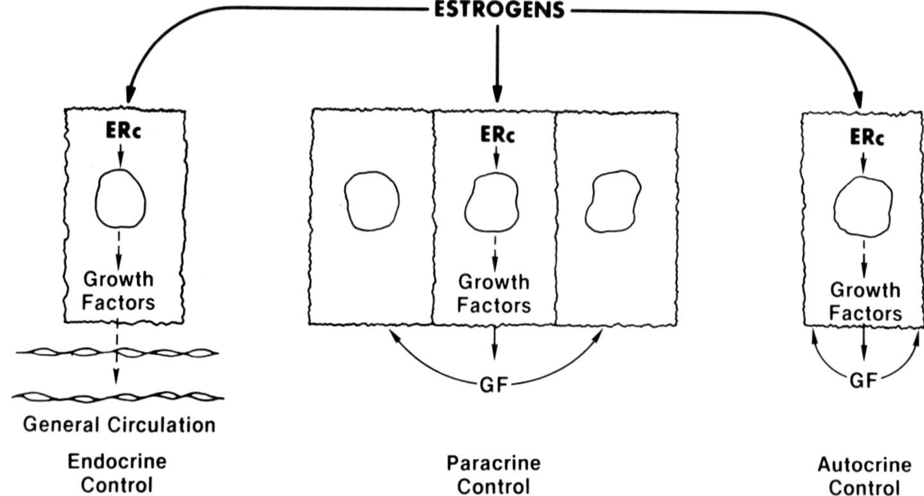


FIG. 1. Three new models for estrogen-responsive tumor growth *in vivo*.

## A. Endocrine Tumor Growth Promotion

In the first model (Fig. 1, left panel) estrogens interact with estrogen target tissues (presumably through the specific estrogen–receptor system) causing production and/or secretion of growth factor(s) which then enter the general circulation (plasma or lymph) and are ultimately made available to distant target tumor cells. By this mechanism, we would expect that tissues could be identified that contained estrogen-elevated activities for cell types that formed estrogen-responsive tumors, and that these activities are secreted and ultimately appear in the general circulation. One possible limitation to these studies might be a situation similar to that observed for somatomedins (Daughaday *et al.*, 1975), in that the active growth factor is not stored in the source tissues. The production of somatomedins by liver was only established by organ perfusion studies. A second major limitation that makes these studies potentially very complex is that, if there were more than one producing tissue, this would clearly complicate any attempts to eliminate surgically the source of the activity *in vivo*. This situation is in clear contrast to the case of the classical pituitary hormones in which hypophysectomy alone resulted in loss of the measured biological responses.

Finally, it must be emphasized that the endocrine–estromedin type control proposed in Fig. 1 (left panel) is consistent with other known functions of estrogens. These steroid hormones are known already to cause the synthesis and secretion of other hormones (Meites *et al.*, 1972), as well as controlling the production of extracellular proteins in uterus (Meglioli, 1976), liver (Skipper and Hamilton, 1977), and oviduct (O'Malley and Means, 1974).

If indeed, an endocrine–estromedin control of growth does exist, it should be possible to identify on the target tumor cells specific receptors for the purified growth factor, and ultimately to develop a radioimmunoassay method of specifically measuring the growth factor presence in the plasma under various conditions that influence the rate of estrogen-dependent tumor growth *in vivo*.

### B. Paracrine Tumor Growth Promotion

In the second mechanism, designated paracrine control (Fig. 1, middle panel), estrogens may interact with some or all cells of a target tissue, but only a fraction of these cells produce growth factor that would be secreted locally, or possibly retained on the membrane of the producing cell causing growth of neighboring cells in the immediate area. This paracrine mechanism would not require the presence of a growth factor in the general circulation, although it may be possible that the activity could find its way through lymph to plasma. When considering paracrine control of tumor growth, it is evident from the studies of Kim and Depowski (1975), Sirbasku (1978b), and Bennett *et al.* (1978) that several different cell types are present in experimentally induced rat mammary tumors. These cell types appear to be derived from both the myoepithelial and the epithelial cell types of normal mammary gland. Thus, it is possible that one of these cell types could produce growth factors for other cells in the population.

Another major consideration is that the paracrine control could be achieved by secretion of a protease or other activator substance from the estrogen stimulated cell leading to the activation of a pro-growth factor already present in the plasma filtrate (lymph) which bathes the tumor cell. This type of mechanism has not been sought specifically, although there is a very recent report (Butler *et al.*, 1980) of estrogen induction of proteases (plasminogen activators) in MCF-7 cells in culture.

One possible problem associated with identifying a paracrine type of activity may be that the growth factor is associated with the membrane of the producing cells, thus requiring various extraction techniques for removal of peripheral and integral membrane proteins to identify the activity. The techniques for extraction of integral proteins require the use of detergents that are difficult to remove, and often interfere with bioassays of growth factors by the usual cell growth methodologies.

### C. Autocrine Tumor Growth Promotion

The third mechanism (Fig. 1, right panel) simply requires that the well known estrogen–receptor interactions with the target cell causes it to produce growth factor(s) that stimulate the producing cell to grow. Indeed, a

Buffalo rat liver cell line (Dulak and Temin, 1973a,b) produces multiplication stimulating activity (MSA) in serum-free medium, and the amount of secreted MSA supports the continued growth of these cells for generations. The medium from the liver cells is used as a major source of MSA for purification (Dulak and Temin, 1973b). Sporn and Todaro (1980) have recently described an autocrine mechanism for growth of malignant cells. Their model is very well developed, and offers new and very interesting insights into tumor growth promotion. Applying the concepts of Sporn and Todaro (1980), it seems possible that estrogen-target tumor cells could possess the same capacity, especially in view of the recent reports (Rowe and Kasper, 1980) that human mammary tumor extracts contain growth factor activities, and our identification of growth factors in extracts of rat mammary tumor cells growing *in vivo* in response to estrogen (Benson *et al.*, 1980; Sirbasku, 1980; Sirbasku and Benson, 1980).

The approach to this problem will be to determine if estrogen-inducible growth factors can be identified in cultures of estrogen-responsive tumor cells growing in hormonally defined serum-free medium.

## III. EVIDENCE FOR AN ENDOCRINE ESTROMEDIN CONTROL OF ESTROGEN-RESPONSIVE TUMOR CELL GROWTH

In this section we will discuss our experimental approaches and the results that have encouraged us to pursue the endocrine estromedin mechanism *in vivo*.

### A. Source of Estrogen-Inducible Growth Factors

Our first question was whether we could identify rat or hamster tissues that contained estrogen-inducible growth factors for three types of tumor cell lines that produced estrogen-reponsive tumors in these species. These cell lines were the MTW9/PL rat mammary tumor cells (Sirbasku, 1978b) that require estrogens, prolactin, and thyroid hormones for tumor formation *in vivo*; the GH3/C14 rat pituitary tumor cell line (Sorrentino *et al.*, 1976a, b; Kirkland *et al.*, 1976) that requires estrogens and thyroid hormones for tumor formation *in vivo*; and finally the H-301 Syrian hamster kidney tumor cells that require estrogens for growth *in vivo* (Sirbasku and Kirkland, 1976).

In all three cases, we could identify at least two tissues in rats and hamsters that had estrogen-elevated growth factors for these cell lines. Both uterine and kidney extracts (prepared as described in Sirbasku, 1978a) con-

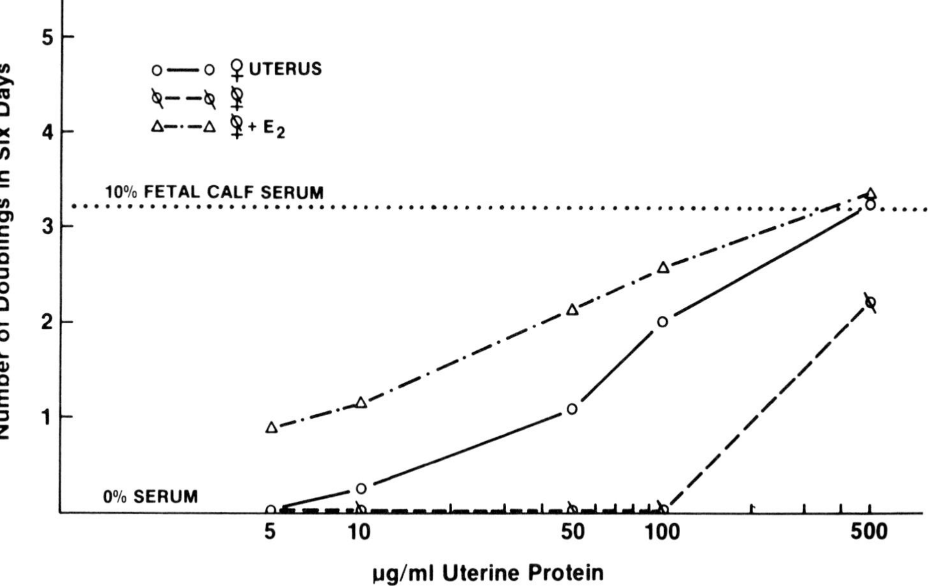


FIG. 2. Growth of GH3/C14 rat pituitary tumor cells in serum-free DME supplemented with the designated concentrations of protein from uterine extracts of estrogen-treated, ovariectomized rats (open triangles), ovariectomized rats (divided circles), and normal female rats (open circles). Methods are those described in Sirbasku (1978a). The data presented here is reproduced from Sirbasku and Benson (1979) with permission of the Cold Spring Harbor Press.

tained growth factors for GH3/C14 pituitary and MTW9/PL mammary tumor cells. The effects of uterine extracts on growth of the MTW9/PL and GH3/C14 cells are shown in Figs. 2 and 3, respectively. A summary of the protein concentrations of uterine and kidney extracts required to achieve half-maximal growth of both the MTW9/PL and GH3/C14 cell lines is presented in Table I. Clearly, the extracts prepared from ovariectomized rats were less effective growth promoters than were extracts prepared from exogenously estrogen-treated castrated females.

The important implications of these data are twofold: First, tissues with mammary and pituitary growth factor activity can be identified, and more than one tissue appears as a possible source. The presence of a significant amount of activity in kidney (see Sirbasku and Benson, 1979) suggests that one of the complications we had anticipated above (see Section II,A), namely, that the potential growth factor sources could not be eliminated completely *in vivo*, proved to be the case, since removal of one kidney and the uterus (Table II) did not inhibit the estrogen-dependent growth of the GH3/C14 pituitary cells *in vivo*; the remaining kidney, which undergoes compensatory hypertrophy, was more than adequate to sustain the life of the

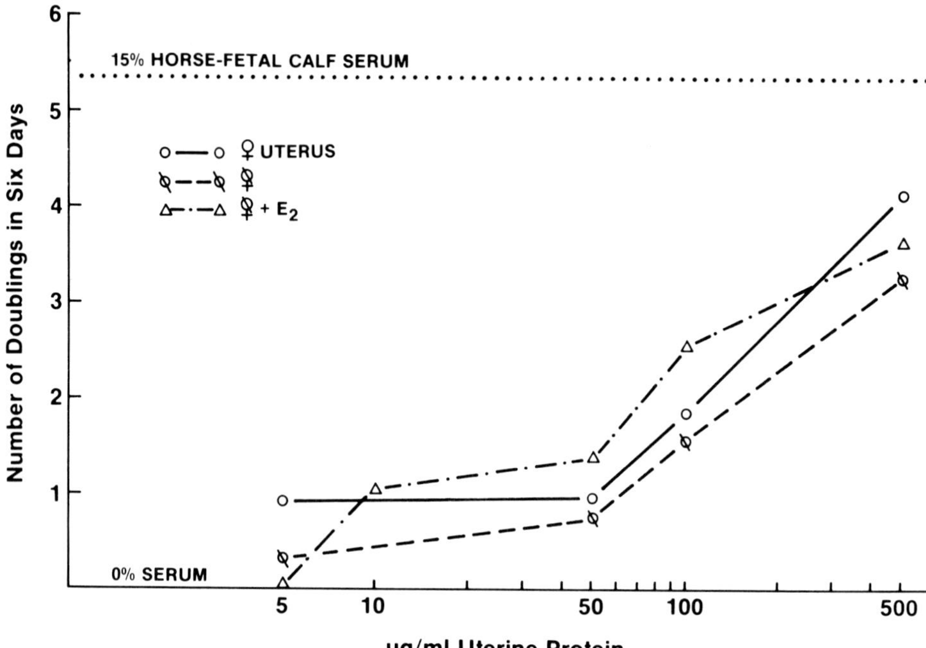


FIG. 3. Growth of MTW9/PL rat mammary tumor cells in serum-free DME supplemented with the designated concentrations of protein from uterine extracts of estrogen-treated, ovariectomized rats (open circles), ovariectomized rats (closed circles), and uterine luminal fluid collected from the estrogen-treated, ovariectomized females (open triangles). Methods are those described in Sirbasku (1978a).

animal, leaving open the possibility that one kidney is an adequate source of growth factor. The removal of both kidneys from a rat results in the animal's death in 96 hours or less (D. A. Sirbasku, unpublished).

In a second series of experiments, organ extracts (Sirbasku, 1978a) from estrogen-treated male hamsters were compared to extracts of organs from normal male hamsters for growth effects on the H-301 hamster kidney tumor cell line. These studies showed that liver (Fig. 4) and kidney (Fig. 5) were both potential sources of estrogen-inducible growth factor for this tumor cell line. The presence of this activity in liver extracts would support an endocrine control mechanism for the H-301 cells, especially in view of our findings that the H-301 cells both *in vivo* (D. A. Sirbasku, unpublished) and *in vitro* (Sirbasku and Kirkland, 1976) have either no estrogen-specific receptors, or receptor numbers at least 8- to 10-fold below that of normal target tissues (i.e., 10,000 to 20,000 sites per cell in uterus). Hence, the relative absence of estrogen receptors in the tumor cells, and the very marked estrogen dependence of this cell line *in vivo* (Table III), are further indications that the role of estrogens in kidney cell growth may be indirect.

TABLE I

SUMMARY OF THE HALF-MAXIMAL ACTIVITIES OF GROWTH FACTORS IN RAT UTERINE AND RAT KIDNEY EXTRACTS[a]

| Animal group | Half-maximal activity of growth factors: MTW9/PL mammary cells, Uterine extract | MTW9/PL mammary cells, Kidney extract | GH3/C14 pituitary cells, Uterine extract | GH3/C14 pituitary cells, Kidney extract |
|---|---|---|---|---|
| Normal females | 75 | 210 | 185 | 170 |
| Ovariectomized females | 320 | 400 | 300 | 450 |
| Estrogen-treated ovariectomized females | 22 | 260 | 130 | 165 |

[a]The half-maximal activities are expressed as $\mu g$ of extract protein added/ml of medium to give 50% the maximum number of cell population doublings growth (Sirbasku, 1978a). Data obtained from experiments presented in Figs. 1–4.

In summary, the data suggest that estrogen-inducible growth factors can be identified in rodent organ extracts for rodent cell lines that form estrogen-responsive tumors *in vivo*, and that these growth factors are identified in extracts of vital organs.

TABLE II

GH3/C14 CELL TUMOR FORMATION IN NORMAL, HYSTERECTOMIZED, AND NEPHRECTOMIZED FEMALE W/FU RATS[a]

| Animal groups[b] | No. with tumor/ no. in group | Average weight (gm + SD): Tumor | Right kidney | Uterus |
|---|---|---|---|---|
| Normal female | 8/8 | 2.7 ± 1.8 | 0.988 ± 0.102 | 0.545 ± 0.148 |
| Ovariectomized female | 4/7 | 0.3 ± 0.14 | 0.709 ± 0.058 | 0.095 ± 0.017 |
| Female + hysterectomy | 8/8 | 6.2 ± 3.1 | 1.143 ± 0.142 | — |
| Female + hysterectomy + nephrectomy[c] | 7/7 | 6.1 ± 2.5 | 1.730 ± 0.313 | — |
| Female + nephrectomy[c] | 7/8 | 2.4 ± 2.4 | 1.259 ± 0.325 | 0.351 ± 0.134 |
| Ovariectomized female + hysterectomy + nephrectomy[c] + $E_2$ | 6/6 | 4.6 ± 3.1 | 1.281 ± 0.212 | — |

[a]Data taken from Sirbasku and Benson (1979) with permission of the Cold Spring Harbor Press.

[b]GH3/C14 cells ($3.8 \times 10^6$) inoculated per animal; tumors harvested and weighed after 40 days. Organ weights were determined at the time of sacrifice.

[c]Nephrectomy indicates unilateral left nephrectomy.

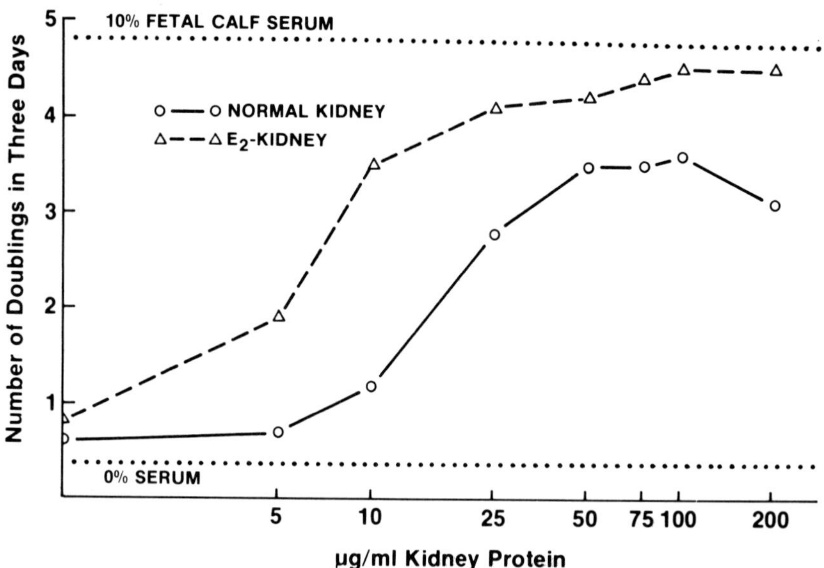


FIG. 5. Growth of H-301 hamster kidney tumor cells in response to hamster kidney extracts prepared from normal male hamsters (open circles) and estradiol treated males (open triangles). Growth was assayed as described in Sirbasku (1978a).

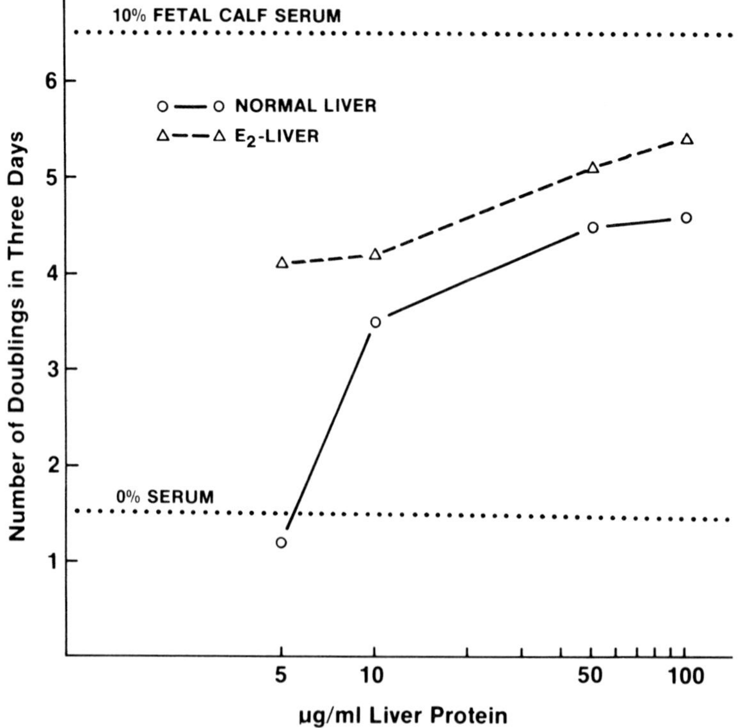


FIG. 4. Growth of H-301 hamster kidney tumor cells in response to hamster liver extracts prepared from normal male hamsters (open circles) and estradiol treated male hamsters (open triangles). Growth was assayed as described in Sirbasku (1978a).

TABLE III

EFFECT OF STEROID HORMONE TREATMENTS ON TUMOR FORMATION BY H-301 CELLS[a]

| Animal group[b] | Steroid treatment[c] | Number with tumor/ number in group | Tumor mass ($g \pm SE$) |
|---|---|---|---|
| Males | None | 0/10 | — |
| Castrated males | None | 0/10 | — |
| Males | Diethylstilbestrol | 13/13 | $4.3 \pm 2.0$ |
| Males | Estrone | 8/8 | $5.5 \pm 2.7$ |
| Males | Estradiol | 8/8 | $6.7 \pm 2.8$ |
| Males | Estriol | 8/8 | $4.3 \pm 2.7$ |
| Males | Estradiol plus progesterone | 8/8 | $1.1 \pm 0.4$ |
| Males | Estradiol plus 3 × progesterone | 5/5 | $1.4 \pm 0.3$ |
| Males | Estradiol plus hydrocortisone | 8/8 | $3.9 \pm 2.5$ |
| Males | Estradiol plus 2 × hydrocortisone | 5/5 | $1.2 \pm 0.4$ |
| Males | Estradiol plus 4 × deoxycorticosterone acetate | 5/5 | $4.2 \pm 0.8$ |
| Males | Estradiol plus testosterone | 8/8 | $1.1 \pm 0.9$ |
| Males | Progesterone | 0/8 | — |
| Males | Hydrocortisone | 0/8 | — |
| Males | Testosterone | 0/8 | — |
| Males | Deoxycorticosterone acetate | 0/8 | — |
| Females | None | 0/10 | — |
| Ovariectomized females | None | 0/10 | — |
| Females | Estradiol | 8/8 | $5.1 \pm 2.6$ |
| Female | Testosterone | 5/8 | $1.0 \pm 0.9$ |

[a] Data taken from Sirbasku and Kirkland (1976) with permission of the editors of *Endocrinology*.

[b] $1.0 \times 10^6$ cells were inoculated sc in each animal in 0.5 ml of standard tissue culture medium. Tumors were harvested after 34 days.

[c] Steroid hormone treatment was a single 25 mg pellet implanted sc 1 to 7 days before inoculation of cells. In some cases 2× to 4× steroid hormone indicates the number of 25 mg pellets implanted.

### B. Cell Type Specificity of Growth Factors

The next major question was whether the growth activities in these extracts were specific for only cell types which form estrogen-responsive tumors, or whether they could promote the growth of any cell type. As shown in Table IV, the rat uterine extracts were most active with cells that formed estrogen-responsive tumors (i.e., MTW9/PL, GH3/C14, and H-301). These extracts also promoted the growth of an ACTH producing AtT20 mouse pituitary cell line, and two Syrian hamster kidney cell lines (HAK and BHK21) that are not estrogen related for growth *in vivo* (Sirbasku and Benson, 1979).

Several other types of cells did not grow significantly in response to rat uterine extract (Table IV). Also, as shown in Table IV (and see Sirbasku and Benson, 1979), the effect of hamster liver extracts on the growth of all of the same cell lines were tested, and it is apparent that the estrogen-inducible liver activity is most potent with and quite specific for the hamster H-301 cells. Most remarkably, the concentrations of hamster liver extract that promote such apparent growth of the H-301 Syrian hamster kidney tumor cells are largely inactive with two related hamster lines, the HAK epithelial cells

TABLE IV
Cell Type Specificity of Growth Activities from Rat Uterus and Hamster Liver[a]

| | Cell population doublings in rat uterus extract[b] | | Cell population doublings in hamster liver extract[c] | |
|---|---|---|---|---|
| Cell lines | Ovariectomized | Estrogen-treated ovariectomized | Normal | Estrogen-treated |
| MTW9/PL | 2.4 | 3.4 | 1.2 | 1.0 |
| GH3/C14 | 2.6 | 3.8 | 1.5 | 0.8 |
| H-301 | 4.2 | 5.1 | 2.7 | 4.0 |
| R2C | 0 | 0 | 0 | 0 |
| $MH_1C_1$ | 0.1 | 0.3 | 1.0 | 1.3 |
| Y1 | 1.2 | 1.4 | 0.4 | 0.3 |
| AtT20 | 2.4 | 2.1 | 0.6 | 1.0 |
| HAK | 2.1 | 2.2 | 0.4 | 0.4 |
| BHK21 | 2.4 | 2.6 | 1.2 | 0.8 |
| BALB/3T3[d] | 1.2 | 0.6 | 0.5 | 0 |

[a] Data taken from Sirbasku (1978a).

[b] Extracts of rat uterus were added at a final protein concentration of 500 μg/ml. Unless otherwise noted, the cell growth assays were of 6 days duration with uterine extracts.

[c] Extracts of hamster liver were added at a final protein concentration of 200 μg/ml. Unless otherwise noted, the cell growth assays were of 3 days duration with liver extracts.

[d] All growth assays with 3T3 cells were of 5 days duration.

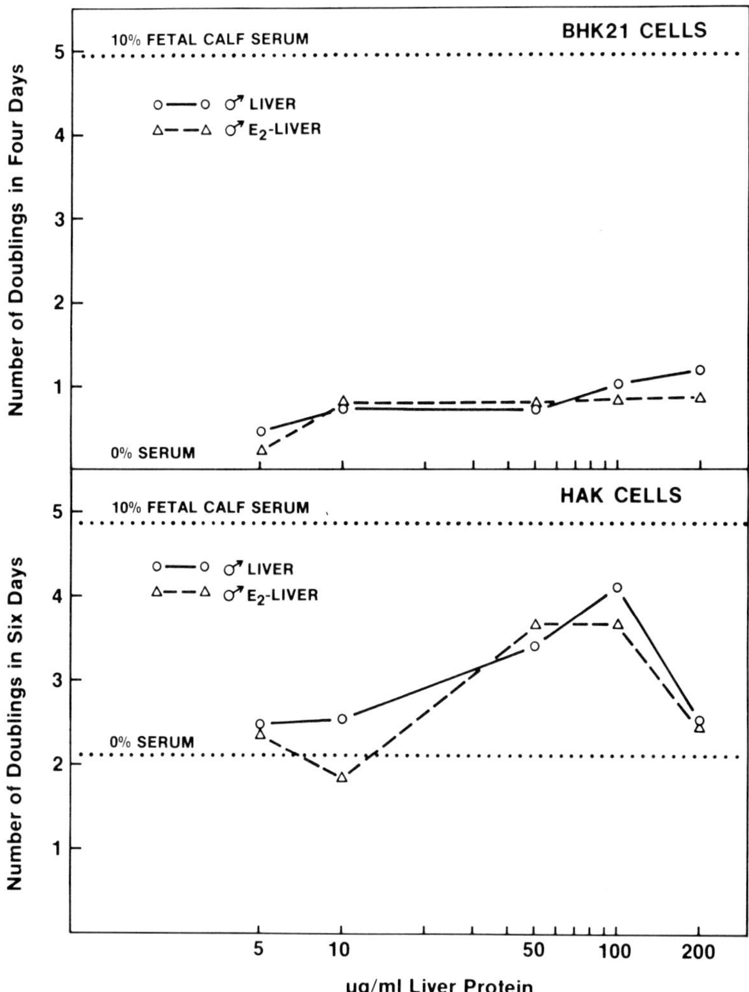


FIG. 6. Growth of BHK21 hamster fibroblasts (top) and HAK hamster epithelial tumor cells (bottom) in extracts of liver from normal and estradiol treated male hamsters. Methods are from Sirbasku (1978a). These data are reproduced from Sirbasku and Benson (1979) with permission of the Cold Spring Harbor Press.

and the BHK21 fibroblasts (see Fig. 6), both of which were derived from cultures of the kidneys of Syrian hamsters.

Beyond these studies, we have asked if the uterine extract activity could promote the growth of any type of rat mammary tumor cell line in culture. As shown in Fig. 7, the uterine activity was a more potent mitogen for the RAMA-29 myoepithelial rat mammary tumor cells than it was with the re-

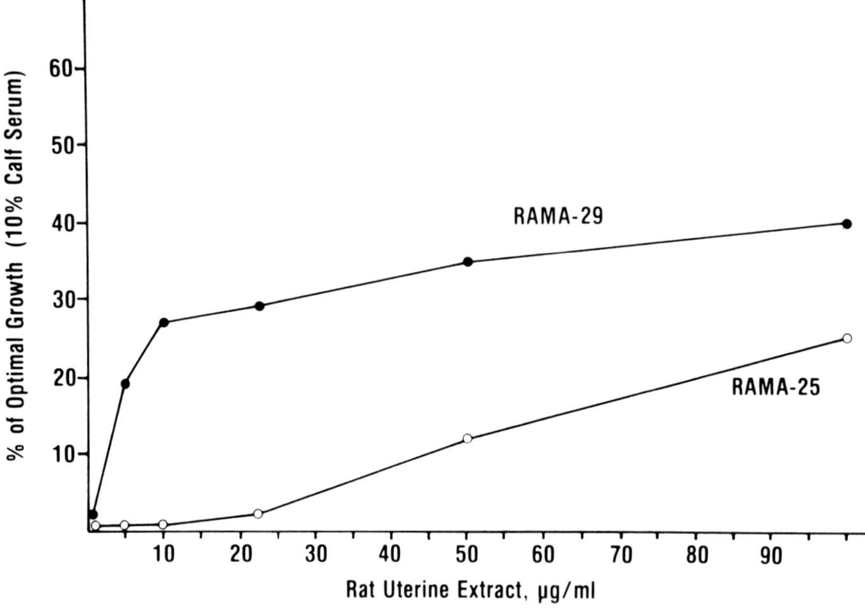


FIG. 7. Growth of the RAMA-29 and RAMA-25 cells in serum-free medium supplemented with the designated concentrations of rat uterine extract. The data are reproduced from Sirbasku and Benson (1980).

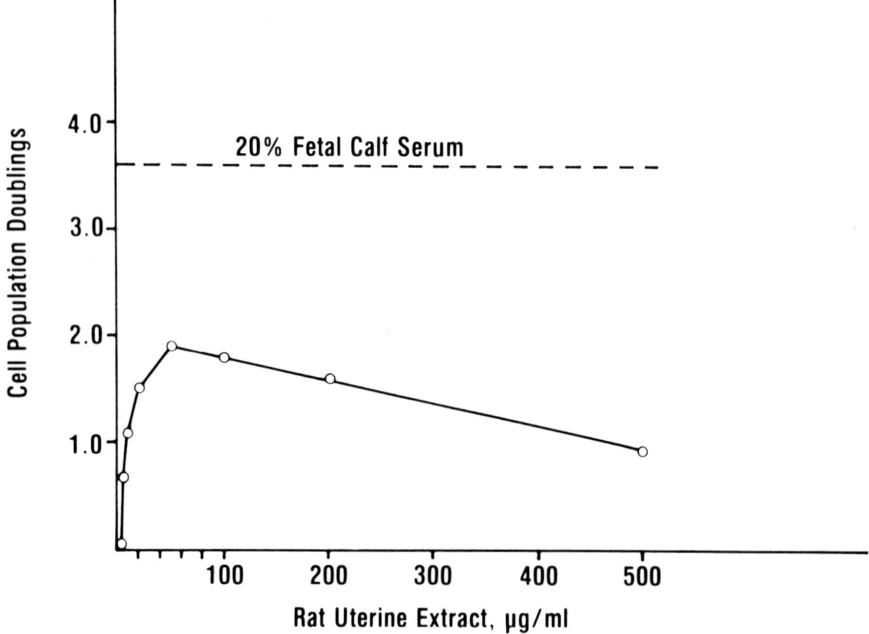


FIG. 8. Growth of the human MCF-7 breast adenocarcinoma cells in serum-free DME medium supplemented with the designated concentrations of rat uterine extract. These data are reproduced from Sirbasku and Benson (1980).

lated RAMA-25 epithelial rat mammary cells. These lines of apparently different mammary gland cell type origins were developed by Bennett *et al.* (1978) from DMBA induced rat mammary tumors, and not only show very different morphologies in culture, but also very different growth rates. Hence, the data presented in Fig. 7 are normalized to account for growth rate differences. These data indicate that the uterine activity may well have greater specificity for some types of myoepithelial cells in mammary glands or tumors than for others.

One last question we have approached is whether the rat derived uterine activity could promote the growth of mammary tumor cells derived from other species. We were particularly interested in determining if these extracts could promote the growth of the MCF-7 (Soule *et al.*, 1973) human mammary tumor cells. As shown in Fig. 8, 50% of the serum requirement for MCF-7 cells can be replaced by low concentrations of uterine extract alone in serum-free culture medium.

### C. Biochemical Properties and Partial Purification of the Uterine-Derived Activity

One of the major questions raised by the studies just presented was what are the biochemical properties of these growth factor activities? We have summarized (Sirbasku and Benson, 1979) some of the properties of the hamster liver activity for H-301 cells, but little additional work has been conducted with this activity. Instead, we have focused our attention on the rat uterine derived activity for the MTW9/PL rat mammary and GH3/C14 rat pituitary cells, feeling that work with one of these organs would provide the most direct route to a firm basis for the estromedin hypothesis. Beside this point, we knew (Shih *et al.*, 1940) that estogen-treatment of ovariectomized female rats caused the uterine horns to fill with fluid that contained secretions from the uterine cells (Wolf and Mastroianni, 1975; Meglioli, 1976). Thus, the work with uterine activity could lead relatively quickly to asking the all important question about whether estrogen-induced secretions of the uterus contain the same growth factor identified in the extracts of the washed tissues.

Our first studies were then to ask whether the uterine growth factor activity was a protein, steroid hormone, or lipidlike material. As summarized in Table V, the data all support the conclusion that the uterine derived mammary cell activity is a protein of apparent molecular weight of 70,000, and does not exhibit either steroid hormone or lipidlike properties.

The next order of business, and certainly the most important study now being conducted in our laboratory, is the purification of the rat uterine

TABLE V
SUMMARY OF THE PROPERTIES OF THE UTERINE-DERIVED MTW9/PL CELL GROWTH FACTOR ACTIVITY

| Property tested | Growth factor activity |
|---|---|
| Heat stability | 90% labile at 80°C for 10 minutes |
| Dialysis | Not dialyzable over 8 days at 4°C at pH 7.2 |
| G-100 Sephadex MW | 70,000 |
| Trypsin treatment | 100% labile in 4 to 6 hours at 37°C |
| Ammonium sulfate precipitation | 33% to 67% saturation |
| Isoelectric focusing | p*I* 4.8 to 5.2 |
| Charcoal extraction at 56°C | 100% stable |
| Chloroform/methanol extraction | Not in lipid soluble fraction |
| 50% Ethanol, acetone, or isopropanol treatment | 50% to 70% denatured |
| 6 *M* guanidine or 8 *M* urea at 37°C | 50% to 70% denatured |
| pH 2.0 treatment | 90% to 100% labile |
| pH 12.0 treatment | 80% labile |
| Repeated slow freeze/thaw cycles | Gradually labile |
| Augmentation of uterine factor growth promotion by added estrogen | No effect with estradiol added at $10^{-11}$ to $10^{-8}$ *M* |

growth factor activity for the MTW9/PL and GH3/C14 cells. At present, we are not certain whether these activities are identical, but indications are that they are very similar when derived from the rat uterus. A partial four-step purification has been developed based on our earlier (Sirbasku, 1980) studies of estromedins. A summary of the purification scheme is presented in Fig. 9. Through the first three steps, this procedure yields a 14-fold purification of the MTW9/PL or GH3/C14 cell growth activity that, in itself, still represents a crude state of purity, but, more importantly, it is the application of four separate criteria to the fractionation of the uterine activity. This approach provides information about the properties of the mitogenic activity and offers a method of at least partial comparison of the uterine tissue extract activity to activities from uterine luminal fluid (see Section III,D). In addition, we have preliminary information about seven additional steps beyond the procedures shown in Fig. 9 that, when applied sequentially, offer the promise of ultimate purification of the uterine activity.

As present, the studies with the rat kidney derived activity are just beginning, but preliminary information suggests that this activity may be similar to that of the uterus when derived from the rat, but possibly not when obtained from other sources such as the kidneys of pregnant sheep.

Purification of the uterine and kidney derived factors is now the major emphasis of our work, and it will continue until growth factors are pure enough to raise antibodies by conventional methods or are partially purified sufficiently to apply monoclonal antibody techniques to raising of a specific antiserum.

One of the major problems encountered during the purification has been that the average rat uterus obtained weighed 0.75 gm and the combined weights of the kidneys is 2.2 gm. During the past year, it has become

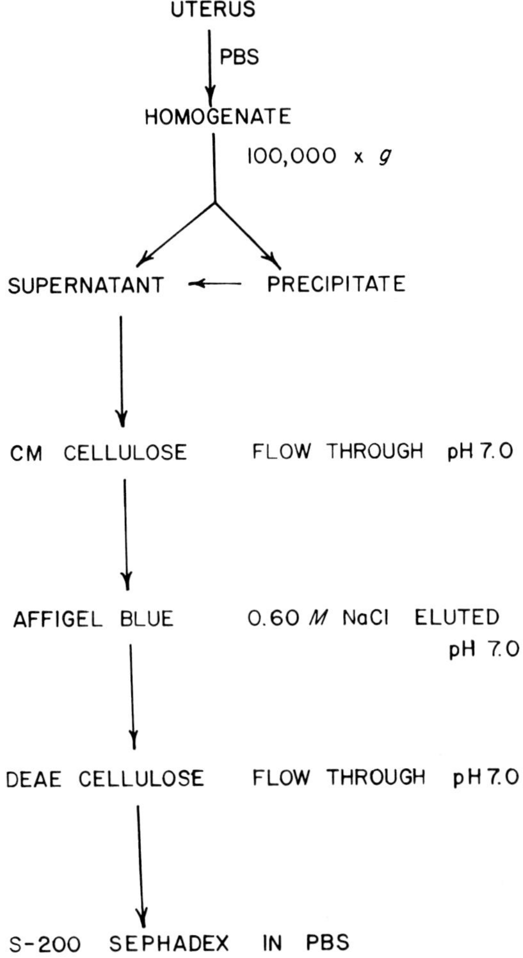


FIG. 9. Schematic representation of the partial purification method for mammary/pituitary cell mitogens in rat uterine extracts, uterine luminal fluid, female rat plasma, and MTW9/PL tumor extracts.

apparent that the use of rats as the sole source of the growth activity is very expensive, requiring many animals for the estimated 1 to 2 kg of starting tissue needed for purification of milligram amounts of growth factors. Because of this problem, we have sought the growth factors in uterine and kidney tissues of pregnant sheep and rabbits. Our results are preliminary, but it appears that the pregnant sheep tissues are a very promising source of mammary tumor cell estromedins. The experiments with pregnant rabbit are in progress.

### D. Presence in the General Circulation

When considering an endocrine estromedin mechanism, the specific measurement of the hormone in the blood and the ultimate demonstration of change in levels with estrogen status of the rats are essential parts of the concept. We intend to approach this question with a specific RIA method when antibodies are available, either raised by classical methods or monoclonal antibody methods (see Section II,C).

However, even before such antibodies are in hand, we have attempted to explore this problem by preparing serum from ovariectomized rats, estradiol-treated ovariectomized rats, and normal female rats and to compare the ability of these sera to support the growth of MTW9/PL or GH3/C14 cells in culture. Presumably, the serum from estrogen-treated animals will be a more potent growth promoter than serum prepared from control animals. To summarize, we found no differences in any of the types of serum used. This result was surprising only until Caroline Eastment of our laboratory (Eastment and Sirbasku, 1978; Eastment *et al.*, 1978; Eastment and Sirbasku, 1980) showed that platelets from human and rat (Eastment and Sirbasku, 1978) contained a very active mitogen for both of the cell types we were studying. Further, the platelet content of this different activity was not influenced by estrogens. Since, in preparation of serum, platelets release growth factors, we believe this platelet-derived activity masks the presence of other growth factors when measured by the bioassay of cell growth in culture. Hence, the need for a specific assay became more apparent.

We have now developed a procedure for preparing platelet-poor plasma from rats by aortic puncture into EDTA and siliconized tubes. This procedure will, hopefully, eliminate the platelet-derived growth factor problem, since the platelets do not aggregate, but instead, are removed by centrifugation from the plasma. The experiments are in progress to determine whether plasma from estrogen-treated rats is a better promoter of MTW9/PL and GH3/C14 cell growth than plasma from control, untreated animals. However, our search to identify a uterinelike activity in plasma has been furthered, since platelet-poor plasma from estrogen-treated ovariectomized rats was carried through the partial purification shown in Fig. 9, and it revealed only one growth activity that copurifies, at least to this point, with the activity from the uterus. The specific activity of the partially purified plasma preparation does not equal that of the uterine extract carried through the same fractionation steps.

Another approach suggested from Shih *et al.* (1940) observations mentioned above (see Section III,C) was to examine the contents of the luminal fluid accumulated in the uterine horns after 8 to 15 day estrogen treatment of castrated female rats. This fluid had previously been shown by us (Sirbasku and Benson, 1979) to contain a growth factor activity for the MTW9/PL cells. We have advanced these studies, and as summarized in Fig. 10 we have shown that the uterine luminal fluid (ULF) contains a potent mitogenic activity for both MTW9/PL and GH3/C14 cells, as well as bacterial origin inhibitors which originate from such organisms as *Pseudomonas aeruginosa* and *Proteus mirabilis*. These microorganisms invade the uterus from the vagina within 2 days after starting exogenous estrogen treatment of normal or castrated female rats (F. E. Leland, D. Kohn, and D. A. Sirbasku, manuscript in preparation). The estrogen-induced accumulation of an activity in ULF suggested that the mitogen(s) may come from uterine tissue, but much stronger evidence was obtained when the ULF was also carried through the partial purification shown in Fig. 9. The ULF activity was purified over 250-fold by this procedure, paralleling, but exceeding, the purification achieved with uterine extract using the same procedures. Further, when properties like heat and protease stability of the activity in ULF

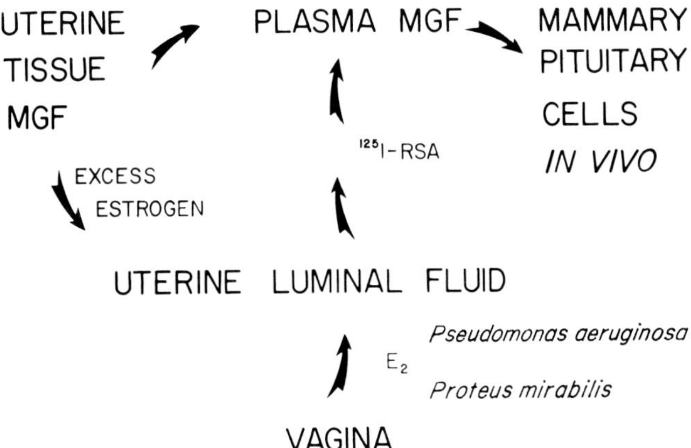


FIG. 10. Outline of the studies done to demonstrate secretion and/or circulation of the uterine derived mammary/pituitary tumor cell mitogen.

were compared to those of the uterine tissue extracts, the properties were identical. Thus, from all of our preliminary studies, including those reported by Sirbasku (1980), it appears that the fluid and tissue activities from the uterus are the same.

One further study, summarized in Fig. 10, was conducted to ask whether proteins of approximately 70,000 molecular weight could find their way from ULF into plasma. Our results have shown that $^{125}$I-labeled rat serum albumin, injected directly into the ULF of estrogen-treated, castrated females, can reach the plasma intact as both albumin monomer and possibly dimer. This suggests that if the ULF activity is a secreted form of the uterine tissue activity, and if the mitogenic activity could be transferred to plasma by the same mechanism that transferred the $^{125}$I[RSA], then further support for a uterine-derived estromedin is gained. However, as noted in Fig. 10, we are not certain that the uterine tissue derived activity is only secreted into the ULF, but may be secreted directly into the plasma as well.

## IV. EVIDENCE FOR EITHER PARACRINE OR AUTOCRINE ESTROMEDIN CONTROL *IN VIVO*

During the course of studies designed to ask whether we could identify a uterine derived growth factor activity in the general circulation, we felt that one possible proof might be the identification of the growth factor activity in extracts of target tumor cells growing *in vivo*. We knew already that optimal GH3/C14 and MTW9/PL tumor formation occurs in castrated females given exogenous estradiol (Sorrentino *et al.*, 1976a; Sirbasku, 1978b). We hoped that it would be possible to identify the growth factor in the tumor cells growing *in vivo* because their receptors would presumably be saturated with growth factor under these conditions. We have made extracts of both MTW9/PL tumors from *in vivo*, and GH3/C14 tumors from *in vivo*, and asked the question: Can these extracts support the growth of the same cell lines in serum-free medium in culture? We found first that GH3/C14 tumor extracts do not support GH3/C14 cell growth in culture (F. E. Leland and D. A. Sirbasku, unpublished), but that extracts of MTW9/PL tumors from *in vivo* supported growth of the MTW9/PL cells *in vitro* (Fig. 11). The growth activity found in the MTW9/PL tumors *in vivo* was as active as that identified in uterine extracts, and more active than seen with kidney extracts (Benson *et al.*, 1980). While we concluded that this activity could have come from the uterus (or kidney), it is equally possible that it may well be a product(s) of either the mammary cells themselves, or a product of other elements of the tumor (Benson *et al.*, 1980). One way of establishing whether the MTW9/PL tumor associated activity is like uterine growth fac-

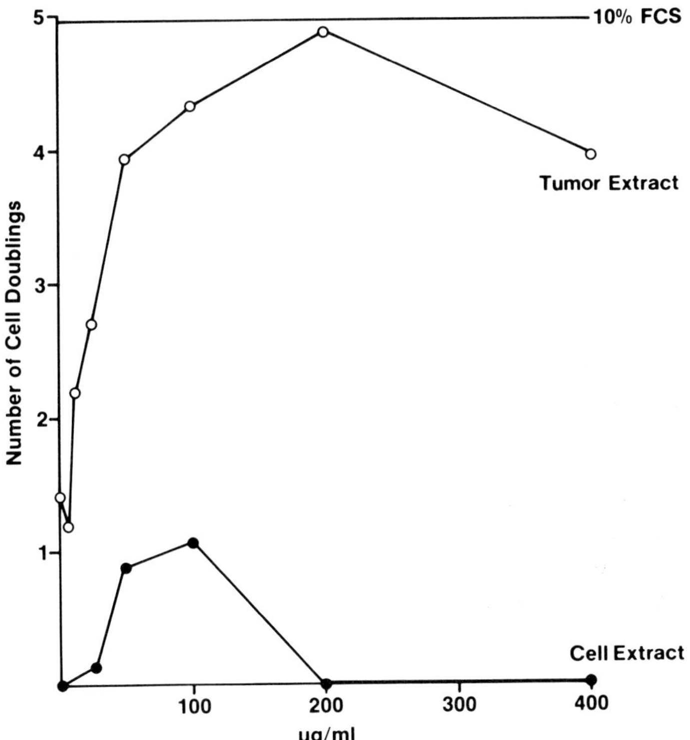


FIG. 11. Growth of MTW9/PL rat mammary tumor cells in response to crude extracts of MTW9/PL tumors growing in estrogen-treated ovariectomized rats (open circles), and in response to extracts of MTW9/PL cells growing in culture (closed circles).

tor was to conduct a partial characterization of the tumor extracted activity similar to that done with uterine extracts. To summarize our findings, when MTW9/PL tumor extract is treated under various conditions (see Table V) we found that the activity in the crude state did not compare to that found in crude uterine preparations (see Table V) or uterine luminal fluid. By any number of criteria, heat stability, protease susceptibility, stability to organic solvents, pH stability, and molecular weight estimation, we were led to conclude that this activity was different from that of the uterus.

Further, when extracts of MTW9/PL cells growing in culture were prepared, we were able to identify small, but measurable, amounts of growth activity in these extracts (Fig. 11). At present, we have not developed the procedures for testing the conditioned medium from MTW9/PL cells for growth factor production, but these experiments are planned in the near future.

One other series of experiments important to our understanding of the role of the tumor associated activity has been the partial purification (Fig. 9) conducted with MTW9/PL tumor extract. At the Affi-Gel Blue step, 50% of the growth factor activity of tumor extracts does not associate with this resin, but passes through in the running buffer. This amount of activity is not in the Affi-Gel flow through fraction of uterine extract chromatography. The remaining 50% of the tumor activity which is eluted with 0.6 *M* sodium chloride could be uterinelike in properties, but more work must be done on this point. Nevertheless, by several criteria, the activity present in MTW9/PL tumor extract is different than that extracted from uterus.

At present, we cannot distinguish between possible autocrine and paracrine controls of the tumor associated activity, although our approach to this question will be to grow the MTW9/PL cells either alone in hormonally defined media or in cocultivation with rat fibroblasts, and attempt isolation of the growth factor from the culture medium.

One more suggestion of paracrine/autocrine control of estrogen-dependent growth *in vivo* comes from the observation that Syrian hamster kidney extracts contain growth factor for the H-301 Syrian hamster kidney cells (Fig. 5). Could it be that some cells in the kidney produce activity that promotes growth of the adjacent kidney cells? This question is open to further study, but the fact that a high specific activity kidney cell factor is present in kidney extracts offers encouragement.

## V. SUMMARY OF THE RELATIONSHIP OF THE ESTROMEDIN HYPOTHESIS TO OTHER ESTROGENIC MODELS

The proposal of three new models of estrogen-promoted tumor cell growth *in vivo* represents our most current thought about growth factor involvement in estrogen-responsive tumor formation. We believe that any combination of these three mechanisms "endocrine," "paracrine," or "autocrine" (Fig. 1) could be functioning *in vivo* and that they are not necessarily mutually exclusive. Indeed, all three may be functioning in concert to cause estrogen-promoted tumor cell growth, and could even be functioning preferentially at different stages of tumor growth depending on the blood supply to the tumor tissue. We are currently conducting experiments with the goal of showing that the sustained growth of the MTW9/PL rat mammary cells in serum-free defined medium *in vitro* requires the different factors from uterus, kidney, and those extracted from the MTW9/PL *in vivo* tumors (F. E. Leland and D. A. Sirbasku, unpublished). Clearly, if this proves to be the case, it would have some implications for the *in vivo* system. It should be noted also that thus far our results with the GH3/C14 pituitary cell line are very different from those with the MTW9/PL cells. Both certainly require estrogens for optimal growth *in vivo* (see Sorrentino *et al.*, 1976a; Sirbasku, 1978b), but no growth factor activity for GH3/C14 cells can be found in extracts of GH3/C14 tumors growing in estrogen-stimulated hosts. Thus, we cannot now conclude that the paracrine/autocrine control is possible for all estrogen-dependent tumors, but it certainly seems possible for estrogen-dependent mammary tumors. We are currently planning further experiments with MCF-7 human mammary tumor cells grown in nude mice (D. Barnes and D. A. Sirbasku, experiment in progress), by preparing extracts of these tumors and determining whether the MCF-7 cells in culture grow in response to extracts of MCF-7 tumors.

In addition to our proposal of growth factor control of estrogen promoted tumor cell growth *in vivo*, Sonnenschein and colleagues (Soto and Sonnenschein, 1980; Sonnenschein *et al.*, 1980a,b) have proposed a negative indirect model of estrogen action *in vivo* involving $\alpha$-fetoprotein and estrogens as inhibitors of mammary tumor cell growth. Their proposal has merit, and it seems entirely possible that not only are positive estrogen related growth promoters involved, but that negative control may be exerted by estrogen-related inhibitors as well. Recently, Shafie (1980) has suggested that estrogen-controlled inhibitors are responsible for the estrogen-responsive growth of MCF-7 cells in athymic nude mice. However, his proposal and that of Sonnenschein and colleagues (Sonnenschein *et al.*, 1980a,b) ignore the overwhelming evidence that no cell lines are known that grow without an appropriate addition of serum containing growth factors (see Holley, 1975) or mixtures of hormones and growth factors in defined media (Barnes and Sato, 1980). From the data available, we believe that both positive and negative growth controls may exist, and that further work in these areas is required.

Beyond these points, we recognize that a large number of "estrogen-mitogenic" responses have been reported. Since we have reviewed this literature elsewhere (Sirbasku and Benson, 1980), we will only state our conclusions here. Those reports equating the incorporation of tritium-labeled thymidine into DNA with cell growth are inconclusive for all the reasons known to complicate this measure of growth (Sirbasku and Benson, 1980). Second, even the known responses fall within the 1.5- to 2.0-fold increase range, which itself is not great when considering the magnitude of the differences in tumor masses formed in estrogen-treated castrated females versus castrated females (see Table III and Sorrentino *et al.*, 1976b; Sirbasku, 1978b). The differences in actual tumor masses are difficult to understand in terms of a 1.5- to 2.0-fold estrogen-mitogenic effect, especially when these responses do not occur in 100% of the samples described in most reports, but instead, tend to occur in 50% or less of the samples (Sirbasku and Benson, 1980).

The one example of an apparent direct estrogen effect is with the human mammary tumor ZR-75-1 cells (Lippman *et al.*, 1979) that show when estrogen is removed from the medium, the cell growth rate gradually reduces, although it must be noted that even after 14 days in culture, only a 2-fold difference in cell number is seen between estradiol supplemented and unsupplemented media. We have suggested alternatives for this apparent mitogenic response which includes estrogens acting as permissive agents or promoting daughter cell survival (Sirbasku and Benson, 1980). Here again, it is important to recognize that the ZR-75-1 cells stand alone among the human mammary tumor cell lines that show an apparent direct mitogenic response to estrogen. When these data are evaluated critically (Sirbasku and Benson, 1980), it is still apparent that estrogens alone are not capable of supporting cell growth, but still require high concentrations of insulin and other growth factors. These data suggest to us that even when small or moderate estrogen-mitogenic responses are found, there remains the requirement for other mitogenic agents for the full mitogenic response. Our view is that growth factors such as the estromedins could play this role.

In summary, we have presented evidence that suggests that estrogen-related growth factors can be identified in tissue extracts, and that the studies presented, as well as those proposed for the future, should provide a basis for determining whether estromedin mechanisms are important for estrogen-related tumor cell growth *in vivo*.

## ACKNOWLEDGMENTS

The work from our laboratory reported here was supported by both an American Cancer Society grant BC-255B and a National Cancer Institute grant R01-CA26617. The authors wish to express their appreciation to Mrs. Karen Haynes for her work with the purification techniques, and to Ms. Judy Roscoe who performed all the animal studies. D.A.S. is the recipient of an American Cancer Society Faculty Research Award FRA212.

## REFERENCES

Allegra, J. L., and Lippman, M. E. (1978). *Cancer Res.* **38**, 3823–3829.
Barnes, D., and Sato, G. (1979). *Nature (London)* **281**, 388–389.
Barnes, D., and Sato, G. (1980). *Anal. Biochem.* **102**, 252–270.
Bennett, D. C., Peachey, L. A., Durbin, H., and Rudland, P. S. (1978). *Cell* **5**, 283.
Benson, R. H., Eastment, C. T., and Sirbasku, D. A. (1980). *Endocrinology, Suppl.* **106**, 273.
Bottenstein, J., Hayashi, I., Hutchings, S., Masui, S., Mather, J., McClure, D. B., Ohasa, S., Rizzino, A., Sato, G., Serrero, G., Wolf, R., and Wu, R. (1979). *Methods Enzymol.* **58**, 94.

Butler, W. B., Kirkland, W. L., Gargola, T. L., Goran, N., and Kelsey, W. H. (1980). *J. Cell Biol.* **87,** Pt. 2, 162a.

Chong, M. T., and Lippman, M. (1980). *Cancer Res.* **40,** 3172–3176.

Daughaday, W. H., Phillips, L. S., and Herington, A. C. (1975). *Adv. Metab. Disord.* **8,** 151–157.

Dulak, N. C., and Temin, H. M. (1973a). *J. Cell Physiol.* **81,** 153–160.

Dulak, N. C., and Temin, H. M. (1973b). *J. Cell Physiol.* **81,** 161–170.

Eastment, C. T., and Sirbasku, D. A. (1978). *J. Cell Physiol.* **97,** 17.

Eastment, C. T., and Sirbasku, D. A. (1980). *In Vitro* **16,** 694.

Eastment, C. T., Sorrentino, J. M., and Sirbasku, D. A. (1978). *In Vitro* **14,** 343.

Gospodarowicz, D., and Moran, J. S. (1976). *Annu. Rev. Biochem.* **45,** 531–558.

Holley, R. W. (1975). *Nature (London)* **258,** 487.

Jensen, E. V., and DeSombre, E. R. (1972). *Annu. Rev. Biochem.* **41,** 789.

Kim, U., and Depowski, M. J. (1975). *Cancer Res.* **35,** 2068–2077.

Kirkland, W. L., Sorrentino, J. M., and Sirbasku, D. A. (1976). *J. Natl. Cancer Inst.* **56,** 1159.

Lippman, M. E., Allegra, J. C., and Strobl, J. S. (1979). *In* "Hormones and Cell Culture" (G. Sato and R. Ross, eds.), Vol. 6, pp. 545–558. Cold Spring Harbor Lab., Cold Spring Harbor, New York.

McGuire, W. L., and Horwitz, K. B. (1979). *In* "Hormones and Cell Culture" (G. Sato and R. Ross, eds.), Vol. 6, pp. 937–947. Cold Spring Harbor Lab., Cold Spring Harbor, New York.

Meglioli, G. (1976). *J. Reprod. Fertil.* **46,** 395.

Meites, J., Lu, K. H., Wuttke, W., Welsch, C. W., Nagasawa, H., and Quadri, S. K. (1972). *Recent Prog. Horm. Res.* **28,** 471.

O'Malley, B. W., and Means, A. R. (1974). *Science* **183,** 610.

Pledger, W. J., Stiles, C. D., Antoniades, H., and Scher, C. D. (1978). *Proc. Natl. Acad. Sci. U.S.A.* **75,** 2839.

Rowe, J., and Kasper, S. (1980). *Endocrinology, Suppl.* **106,** 144.

Sato, G., and Reid, L. (1978). *In* "Biochemistry and Mode of Action of Hormones" (H. V. Rikenberg, ed.), Vol. II, pp. 219. Univ. Park Press, Baltimore, Maryland.

Shafie, S. M. (1980). *Science* **209,** 701.

Shih, H. E., Kennedy, J., and Huggin, C. (1940). *Am. J. Physiol.* **130,** 287.

Sirbasku, D. A. (1978a). *Proc. Natl. Acad. Sci. U.S.A.* **75,** 3786–3790.

Sirbasku, D. A. (1978b). *Cancer Res.* **38,** 1154–1165.

Sirbasku, D. A. (1980). *In* "Control Mechanisms in Animal Cells: Specific growth factors" (L. J. de Asua, R. Levi-Montalcini, R. Shields, and S. Iacobelli, eds.), pp. 293–298. Raven, New York.

Sirbasku, D. A., and Benson, R. H. (1979). *In* "Hormones and Cell Culture" (G. Sato and R. Ross, eds.), Vol. 6, pp. 479–497, Cold Spring Harbor Lab., Cold Spring Harbor, New York.

Sirbasku, D. A., and Benson, R. H. (1980). *In* "Cell Biology of Breast Cancer" (C. McGrath and M. Rich, eds.), pp. 289–314, Academic Press, New York.

Sirbasku, D. A., and Kirkland, W. L. (1976). *Endocrinology* **98,** 1260.

Skipper, J. K., and Hamilton, T. H. (1977). *Proc. Natl. Acad. Sci. U.S.A.* **74,** 2384.

Sonnenschein, C., Ucci, A. A., and Soto, A. M. (1980a). *J. Natl. Cancer Inst.* **64,** 1141.

Sonnenschein, C., Ucci, A. A., and Soto, A. M. (1980b). *J. Natl. Cancer Inst.* **64,** 1147.

Sorrentino, J. M., Kirkland, W. L., and Sirbasku, D. A. (1976a). *J. Natl. Cancer Inst.* **56,** 1149.

Sorrentino, J. M., Kirkland, W. L., and Sirbasku, D. A. (1976b). *J. Natl. Cancer Inst.* **56,** 1155.

Soto, A. M., and Sonnenschein, C. (1979). *J. Steroid Biochem.* **11,** 1185–1190.

Soto, A. M., and Sonnenschein, C. (1980). *Proc. Natl. Acad. Sci. U.S.A.* **77,** 2084–2087.

Soule, H., Vazques, J., Long, A., Albert, S., and Brennan, M. (1973). *J. Natl. Cancer Inst.* **51,** 1409.

Sporn, M. B., and Todaro, G. J. (1980). *N. E. J. Med.* **303,** 878.

Wolf, D. P., and Mastroianni, L. (1975). *Fertil. Steril.* **26,** *240.*

Wyche, J. H., and Noteboom, W. D. (1979). *Endocrinology* **104,** 1765–1773.

# CHAPTER 6

# Chemical Characterization of Nuclear Acceptors for the Avian Progesterone Receptor

*Thomas C. Spelsberg*





BIOCHEMICAL ACTIONS OF HORMONES, VOL. IX

ISBN 0-12-452809-0

## I. INTRODUCTION

Steroid hormone–target tissue systems have become attractive models for the mechanistic study of eukaryote gene expression. Steroid hormones are small hydrophobic compounds which enter a cell and bind to specific carrier proteins called receptors. This complex migrates to the nucleus and interacts with the genetic material to alter gene expression. The subject of this chapter concerns the biological and biochemical properties of these nuclear binding sites for steroid–receptor complexes. These nuclear binding sites for steroid receptors were termed "acceptor sites" by Spelsberg *et al.* (1971b). The identification and characterization of these nuclear acceptor sites for steroid receptors are important. The nuclear translocation and binding of steroid receptors immediately follows steroid receptor binding and represents the first nuclear event which precedes the steroid-induced alteration of transcription. Thus, knowledge of this process should help elucidate the mechanism action of gene regulation in eukaryotes.

This chapter is not designed as a comprehensive review of the area of steroid nuclear acceptors but focuses primarily on work performed on the progesterone–chick oviduct system. A more comprehensive review of the nuclear acceptors in other systems is presented elsewhere (Thrall *et al.*, 1978). Some discussion of the pertinent findings on nuclear acceptors in other steroid–target tissue systems is presented for comparison.

## II. GENERAL MECHANISM OF ACTION OF STEROID HORMONES

The same general theme for the mechanism of action of steroids has been identified in all steroid–target tissue systems. This is outlined in Fig. 1. For more comprehensive reviews, the readers are referred elsewhere (Jensen

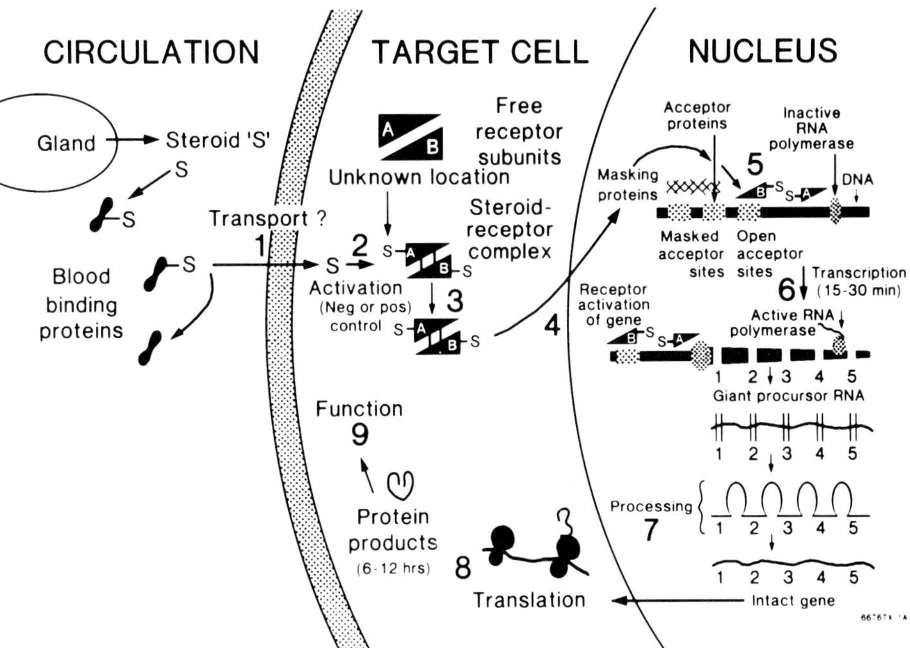


FIG. 1. Basic pathway for the action of steroid hormones in target cells. This pathway is described in the text. It represents the general mechanism of action of all steroids. Briefly, beginning on the left side of the model, the steroid (S) passes through the cell membrane and binds ot its specific receptor. The receptor is then "activated" and the complex of steroid–receptor translocates and binds to the nuclear acceptor sites. This results in changes (quantitative and qualitative) in DNA-dependent RNA synthesis. The giant precursor mRNA molecules are "processed" to small mRNA molecules which are transported out of the nucleus to the ribosomes where they code for specific steroid-induced proteins. These proteins carry out the various steroid-induced physiological responses of the target cell. In essence, the first major intracellular process which responds to the steroids is the alteration in gene transcription (RNA synthesis). This is preceded by the binding of the steroid receptor to the nuclear acceptor sites.

and DeSombre, 1972; O'Malley and Means, 1974; Spelsberg and Toft, 1976; Gorski and Gannon, 1976; Thrall *et al.*, 1978). Briefly, systemic steroids, bound or unbound to serum carrier proteins, enter target cells. Whether the transfer involves active transport or passive diffusion remains obscure (Milgrom *et al.*, 1970; Peck *et al.*, 1973; Williams and Gorski, 1974; Harrison *et al.*, 1974). Whether a steroid enters nontarget tissues is also open to question. Studies with radiolabeled steroids have suggested that they do enter nontarget cells (Jensen and Jacobson, 1962; Jensen *et al.*, 1968); however, these results may be explained by translocation of steroids from the blood compartments of organs to the "cytosol" during tissue homogenization. In any event, the steroids are retained in their target cells but not in nontarget cells for extended periods (Jensen and Jacobson, 1962; Jensen *et al.*, 1968; Stumph and Sar, 1976). This retention was found to be due to specific steroid binding proteins termed receptors which are found only in target cells (Talwar *et al.*, 1964; Toft and Gorski, 1966; Beato *et al.*, 1969; Sherman *et al.*, 1970; Swaneck *et al.*, 1970). Although the exact intracellular compartment in which unbound receptors reside remains obscure, there is some evidence that they are associated with microsomes (Little *et al.*, 1972, 1973) while others claim they might even reside in the nucleus (Sheridan *et al.*, 1979; Martin and Sheridan, 1980).

Once bound by the steroid, the receptor becomes "activated," a process that capacitates the complex to "migrate" into the nucleus and bind to nuclear acceptor sites. These processes of activation and translocation of a steroid–receptor complex into the nucleus are not well understood. For instance, exactly from what site the migration occurs in unknown. There also appear to be cytosolic factors that can induce (enhance) activation (Notides and Neilson, 1974; Yamamoto, 1974; Cake *et al.*, 1976; Thrower *et al.*, 1976; Puca *et al.*, 1977) and others that suppress activation or translocation (Milgrom *et al.*, 1973a; Chamness *et al.*, 1974; Andre and Rockefort, 1975; Simons *et al.*, 1976; Cake *et al.*, 1976; Goidl *et al.*, 1977; Bailly *et al.*, 1977). Still others have presented evidence that the native form of at least one receptor (the chick oviduct progesterone receptor) is composed of two molecular species (Sherman *et al.*, 1970; Schrader and O'Malley, 1972; Boyd and Spelsberg, 1979a). It is speculated that the two species act as subunits to a dimer which represents the active form of the receptor (Schrader *et al.*, 1975; Buller *et al.*, 1976a; Vedeckis *et al.*, 1978; Boyd and Spelsberg, 1979b). It is further speculated that this dimer then migrates to the nucleus where the two difference subunits (termed A and B) perform distinct functions. The B subunit binds the complex to specific acceptor sites on the chromatin, while A alters transcription by binding the adjacent DNA sequence. This active subunit model, however, requires further study.

Once bound to nuclear acceptor sites, the steroid–receptor complex

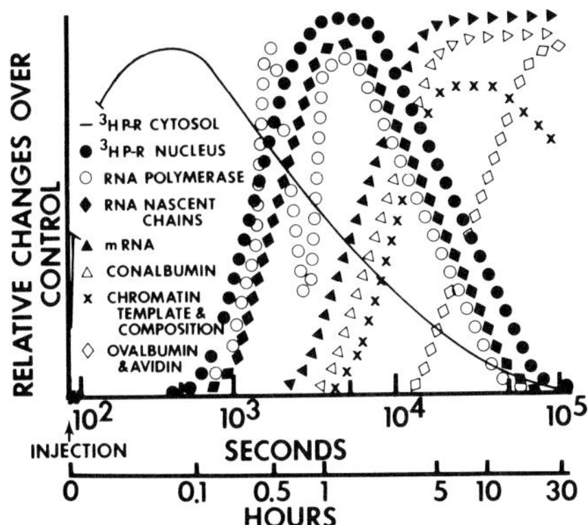


FIG. 2. Composite of the early biochemical responses of a target tissue (oviduct) to a steroid (progesterone or estradiol). The responses to progesterone were usually measured in fully developed oviducts from immature chicks injected for 2 to 4 weeks with an estrogen. The responses to estrogen and in a few instances progesterone were measured in oviducts from estrogen-treated chicks and withdrawn from estrogen for 2 to 3 weeks (——) Levels of labeled progesterone (or estrogen) receptor complex in the cytosol (O'Malley *et al.*, 1970, 1971). (●) Levels of labeled progesterone (or estrogen)–receptor complex bound to nuclear chromatin (O'Malley *et al.*, 1970, 1971; Tsai *et al.*, 1975; Kalimi *et al.*, 1976; Palmiter *et al.*, 1976; Spelsberg, 1976; Sutherland and Baulieu, 1976). (○) Activity of RNA polymerase II after injection of estradiol; the response to progesterone is chronologically the same but qualitatively different (Spelsberg and Cox, 1976). (◆) Numbers of newly synthesized nascent RNA chains in the nuclear chromatin after injection of estradiol into estrogen withdrawn chicks (Tsai *et al.*, 1975; Kalimi *et al.*, 1976). (▲) Numbers of mRNA (for ovalbumin, avidin, and conalbumin) in response to estrogen or progesterone (Chan *et al.*, 1973, 1976; Harris *et al.*, 1975; Palmiter *et al.*, 1976; Spelsberg and Cox, 1976). (△) Levels (synthesis) of conalbumin in response to estradiol in estrogen withdrawn chicks (Palmiter *et al.*, 1976). (×) Changes in chromatin composition and template capacity (for DNA-dependent RNA synthesis) in response to estrogen in estrogen withdrawn chicks (Schwartz *et al.*, 1975; Spelsberg and Cox, 1976). (◇) Levels (synthesis) ovalbumin and avidin in response to estrogen and progesterone (O'Malley *et al.*, 1969; Palmiter *et al.*, 1976). Reproduced with permission from Thrall *et al.* (1978).

markedly alters RNA synthesis (Mueller *et al.*, 1958; Hamilton *et al.*, 1968; Knowler and Smellie, 1971) and the transcription of specific genes (Chan *et al.*, 1973, 1976; Harris *et al.*, 1975; Palmiter *et al.*, 1976; Spelsberg and Cox, 1976). The subsequent effects of steroids on RNA and protein processing, if any, are poorly understood due to the few studies undertaken (Church and McCarthy, 1970).

Figure 2 shows a composite of the early biochemical responses of the chick oviduct to progesterone or estrogen. Within 1 to 2 minutes after injection of labeled progesterone into the chicks, which have been primed with estrogen, the steroid is located in the cytosol bound to its receptor. By 10 minutes postinjection, the steroid accumulates in the nucleus, followed closely by changes in RNA synthesis and chromatin template capacity. After 1 to 2 hours specific messenger RNA's appear whose coded proteins begin to accumulate within 3 to 6 hours. If only a single injection of the steroid is used, the rapid steroid-induced changes just as rapidly return to control values. At 12 hours postinjection, the radiolabeled steroids in the cytoplasm and nucleus have disappeared as have the bulk changes in RNA syntheses. The steroids are metabolized and excreted from the cells. Whether or not they are reutilzied to some degree in the steroid action pathway is unknown. The receptor, at least in part, is thought to be recycled (Clark *et al.*, 1974; Caponey and Rochefort, 1975).

Thus, the binding of the steroid–receptor complex to acceptor sites on the chromatin represents the first nuclear event which occurs before the steroid-induced changes in transcription occur. The receptor, wherever it may reside in the cell, is triggered when bound by a specific steroid to migrate into the nucleus, bind to chromatin acceptor sites, and alter transcription. The whole process is rapidly reversible to allow quick control of the target tissue by the steroid. It is the author's opinion that the steroid receptors may well represent one of the first, if not the first, intracellular gene regulators discovered in eukaryotes.

## III. STUDIES ON THE EXISTENCE AND CHEMICAL NATURE OF NUCLEAR ACCEPTOR SITES FOR MANY STEROID–TARGET TISSUE SYSTEMS

### A. Existence of High Affinity Nuclear Acceptor Sites

Studies involving autoradiography (Stumpf, 1968, 1969; Jensen *et al.*, 1969a) and cell fractionations following injections of labeled steroids into whole animals (King *et al.*, 1965a; Noteboom and Gorski, 1965; King and Gordon, 1966; Baulieu *et al.*, 1967; Gorski *et al.*, 1968; Jensen *et al.*, 1968; Arnaud *et al.*, 1971c) have demonstrated a translocation of radioactivity from the cytosol and a rather strong binding to the nucleus. Recently, Sheridan *et al.* (1979) reported that these earlier studies might involve artifacts and that the free receptors (not bound by steroids) reside in the nucleus. When the steroid binds the receptor, there is an intranuclear translocation of the complex to nuclear acceptor sites. In this instance, there is no cytoplasmic-nuclear translocation. In any event, the "nuclear localization" has been explained in terms of two mechanisms. One is the existence of high affinity nuclear acceptor sites for the steroid receptors. The references here are numerous and are listed throughout this chapter at the appropriate places. The alternative proposed mechanism is the model for a cytoplasmic exclusion hypothesis (Horowitz and Moore, 1974; Williams and Gorski, 1974).

This model is based on the idea that the steroid–receptor complex migrates to the nucleus independent of any binding phenomenon but is driven by polarity or phase differences between the cytoplasm and nucleus to achieve equilibrium between the water spaces of these two compartments. This exclusion mechanism explains nuclear localization of the steroid–receptor complex but does not explain how the complex affects transcription.

Since practically all regulatory and chemical reactions in cells occur by physical interactions between reactants involving high affinity sites and since many laboratories report high affinity nuclear "acceptor" sites for steroid–receptor complexes, the existence of such sites is strongly favored by the author.

### B. Correlations between Bound Nuclear Acceptor Sites and Biological Responses to the Steroid

There have been many attempts to correlate the nuclear binding of steroid–receptor complexes with biological responses of their target tissues. These have been reviewed in detail elsewhere (Thrall *et al.*, 1978). There is no question that steroid receptors must bind to nuclear acceptor sites before steroid-induced alterations in transcription and biological responses can occur. There are many instances where target cells lack any steroid receptor and do not respond to the steroid [e.g., androgen receptors in the testicular feminization syndrome (Bardin and Bullock, 1974), glucocorticoid receptors in lymphoid cell lines (Lippman *et al.*, 1973), and estrogen receptors in breast tumors (Horwitz *et al.*, 1975)] or have defective receptors which fail to translocate to the nucleus [glucocorticoid receptors in lymphoid-cell lines (Rosenau *et al.*, 1972; Gehring and Tomkins, 1974; Sibley and Tomkins, 1974; Yamanoto *et al.*, 1976), androgen receptors in certain androgen insensitivity syndromes in humans (Amrhein *et al.*, 1976; Griffin *et al.*, 1976; Larrea *et al.*, 1978), progesterone receptors in the chick oviduct (Boyd and Spelsberg, 1979b; Halberg and Spelsberg, 1980), and estrogen receptors in human breast tumors (Shyamala, 1972)]. Antisteroids such as antiestrogens which cause a cytoplasmic depletion of the receptors in target cells also cause the target cells to become temporarily nonresponsive to subsequent estrogen treatments. In each of these instances, the target tissues show a nonresponsiveness to the respective steroid. Thus, only if the receptor is present and only if this steroid–receptor complex can migrate and bind to nuclear acceptor sites, do biological responses induced by the steroid occur.

Lastly, there are many studies on the correlation of the number of nuclear bound steroid receptors in a target tissue with a variety of biochemical/biological responses. This has been reviewed in detail elsewhere (Clark *et al.*, 1973; Gorski and Raker, 1974; Anderson *et al.*, 1975a,b; Thrall *et al.*,

1978). In brief, among steroid–target tissue systems studied, the range of 1000 to 10,000 high affinity nuclear acceptor sites per cell has been reported. This range has been determined by (1) directly measuring for high affinity sites and transcription responses to progesterone (Buller *et al.*, 1975b; Jaffe *et al.*, 1975; Spelsberg, 1976; Pikler *et al.*, 1976) and for estrogen in the chick oviduct (Thrall *et al.*, 1978), and (2) correlating nuclear bound estrogen receptors with organ weight in the rat uterus (Clark *et al.*, 1973) or with conalbumin RNA induction in the chick oviduct (Mulvihill and Palmiter, 1977). It should be mentioned, however, that not all biochemical/biological responses correlate with the number of nuclear acceptor sites bound by a steroid–receptor complex (Clark *et al.*, 1973). The exact number of nuclear bound steroid receptors required for a biological response will be determined in part by the particular response being monitored and in part by the time after injection the analysis is made. The responses that occur at long intervals after application of the steroid require significantly greater doses of the steroid in order to maintain sustained cellular and nuclear bound levels of steroid–receptor complex throughout longer periods. Further, the nuclear binding of steroid receptors is not a static event but undergoes constant, dynamic changes as shown in Fig. 2 in the case of the oviduct system. Thus, the exact number of required nuclear bound steroid receptor measured in each study reflects not only the method used to quantitate the nuclear bound steroid but also the time after exposure of the cells to the steroid.

### C. Progress and Problems in the Chemical Characterization of Acceptor Sites

Studies on the intranuclear localization of steroid–receptor complexes for estrogen (King *et al.*, 1965a,b, 1966; Beato *et al.*, 1973; Alberga *et al.*, 1971a; Jensen and DeSombre, 1972), progesterone (O'Malley *et al.*, 1972; Spelsberg, 1974; Swaneck *et al.*, 1970; Spelsberg *et al.*, 1971b, 1975, 1976c, 1977a,b, 1979a,b; Webster *et al.*, 1976; Thrall *et al.*, 1978), dihydrotestosterone (Lebeau *et al.*, 1973), glucocorticoids (Simons *et al.*, 1976; Hamana and Iwae, 1978), and aldosterone (Swaneck *et al.*, 1970) have suggested that the cell binding occurs on the chromatin (the deoxyribonucleoprotein) in the nucleus of cells.

Identifying the component of chromatin which binds the steroid–receptor complex (acceptor sites) has been the object of much attention in the past 12 years. These studies have shown that (1) proper cell-free nuclear binding assays must be established, (2) the nuclear sites being measured are similar to those measured *in vivo*, (3) the extent of contamination of the chromatin, e.g., nuclear envelope, nuclear matrix, and cytoplasmic entities, should be measured. The latter situation raises the possibility that the nuclear acceptor sites, although associated with chromatin, may in fact represent some other cellular component.

Finally, there have been other problems in the search for steroid acceptor sites. For example, there are many reports that the nuclear acceptors must be proteins since the steroids are released by protease treatment of chromatin (Fanestil and Edelman, 1966; King and Gordon, 1967; Wagner, 1970; Swaneck *et al.*, 1970). However, the proteases are very likely degrading the receptor itself, thus releasing the steroid. Similarly, studies using deoxyribonuclease treatment of chromatin are also obscure in that some claim that the acceptor sites are destroyed (Shyamala-Harris, 1971; King and Gordon, 1972; Baxter *et al.*, 1972; Middlebrook *et al.*, 1975) while others claim that the sites are not destroyed (Musliner and Chader, 1972; Buller *et al.*, 1975a). Even the nuclease induced release of a bound steroid does not prove that DNA is the sole acceptor site since the DNA may represent only a part (coacceptor) of the acceptor site and since the nuclease may cause the release of intact "acceptor" sites (e.g., proteins) from the chromatin. As a result of these problems, most investigators began studying the cell-free nuclear binding of steroid–receptor complexes to chromatin acceptor sites. However, there are also several obstacles inherent within cell free binding assays which will be discussed in Section IV,B.

Considering these problems, a variety of nuclear components have been identified as the acceptor sites for a variety of steroid hormones, the nuclear envelope (Jackson and Chalkley, 1974a,b), histones (Sekeris and Lang, 1965; Sluyser, 1966, 1969; King and Gordon, 1967), nonhistone basic proteins (Puca *et al.*, 1974, 1975; Mainwaring *et al.*, 1976), nonhistones acidic proteins and nonhistone-protein DNA complexes (Sluyser, 1966, 1969; Alberga *et al.*, 1971b; Spelsberg *et al.*, 1971b, 1972, 1975, 1976a,c, 1977a,b; Tymoczko and Liao, 1971; Baxter *et al.*, 1972; King and Gordon, 1972; Liang and Liao, 1972; Liao *et al.*, 1972; (O'Malley *et al.*, 1972; Schrader *et al.*, 1972; Lebeau *et al.*, 1973; Defer *et al.*, 1974; Gschwendt, 1976; Klyzsejko-Stefanowicz *et al.*, 1976; Webster *et al.*, 1976; Klyzesejko-Stefanowicz *et al.*, 1976; Thrall *et al.*, 1978; Perry and Lopez, 1978; Hamana and Iwai, 1978), pure DNA (Harris and Shyamala, 1971; Baxter *et al.*, 1972; Clemens and Kleinsmith, 1972; King and Gordon, 1972; Musliner and Chader, 1972; Toft, 1972; Yamamoto and Alberts, 1972, 1973, 1975, 1976; Higgens *et al.*, 1973a,b,c; Andre and Rochefort, 1975; Yamamoto *et al.*, 1974; Rousseau *et al.*, 1975; Simons *et al.*, 1976), ribonucleoproteins (Liao *et al.*, 1973), and finally the nuclear matrix (Barrack *et al.*, 1977; Barrack and Coffey, 1980).

Current evidence in our laboratory strongly supports the role of specific nonhistone proteins and DNA sequences which together comprise the acceptor site and act as coacceptors for the chick oviduct progesterone receptor. This evidence is presented in Sections VI,B and VII. Nuclear acceptors with similar properties to that described for the avian oviduct progesterone receptor have been subsequently reported for other steroid–target tissue systems using some of the same technology. These studies are brifely discussed in Section VIII.

## IV. CELL-FREE NUCLEAR BINDING ASSAYS AS PROBES FOR THE NUCLEAR ACCEPTOR SITES

### A. Limitations of the *In Vivo* Approach

Although the study of the nuclear binding *in vivo* has the main advantage of maintaining true biological conditions, many problems have been identified. First, only a fraction of the radioactive steroid injected into whole animals localizes in the target organs. This has two disadvantages: (1) Large amounts of expensive radiolabeled hormones are required to achieve measurable nuclear binding. (2) It is difficult if not impossible to saturate the nuclear acceptor sites (Jensen and DeSombre, 1972; Spelsberg, 1976; Thrall *et al.*, 1978). Second, during standard nuclei isolation procedures, large portions of the nuclear bound steroid–receptor complexes are dissociated from the nuclei (Spelsberg, 1976). This resulted from the use of buffers containing monovalent (0.05 *M*) and divalent (.005 to .01 *M*) salt concentrations sufficient to dissociate well over half of the endogenous or the cell-free nuclear bound complexes. Nonionic detergents also cause considerable losses. In addition to losing acceptor bound radiolabeled steroid receptors, there is always the added concern that the dissociated steroid–receptor complexes will reassociate under nonideal conditions to nonbiological sites. These problems can be partly solved by eliminating detergent washes and by using buffers with low salt concentrations ($< 0.1\ M$ monovalent and $< 5\ mM$ divalent cations) while adding additional steps to the isolation procedure to maintain equivalent purity of nuclei (Spelsberg, 1976).

One should also consider that the binding of a steroid–receptor complex to the nuclear acceptor sites *in vivo* may not be a one step event, e.g., there may be an initial binding to the acceptor sites followed by a translocation to secondary sites involved in the regulation of gene expression (Schrader and O'Malley, 1972; Schrader *et al.*, 1975; Boyd and Spelsberg, 1979b). Therefore, most of the *in vivo* nuclear bound receptor would not be isolated as complexes with the acceptor sites, i.e., those sites that initially bind the steroid–receptor complex. Finally, the approach of using steroid–receptor complexes bound to nuclear acceptor sites *in vivo* to determine the chemical composition of the acceptor has not been feasible. Besides the complexity involved in interpreting the results of protease and nuclease treatments of chromatin, the steroid–receptor complexes are bound to acceptor sites via relatively weak ionic interactions and are readily dissociated from chromatin long before any chromosomal proteins are dissociated from the DNA (Spelsberg, 1976; Thrall *et al.*, 1978). Attempts to covalently attach the receptor to the "acceptor" sites using bifunctional alkylating agents have failed due to the minute amounts of steroid-receptor complexes bound to large amounts of chromatin and to instability of the receptor binding over the lengthy periods required to cross link these complexes (T. C. Spelsberg, unpublished results).

### B. Factors Affecting the Cell-Free Nuclear Binding Assays

The cell-free nuclear binding assays eliminate many of the obstacles in the *in vivo* assays as discussed in the section above. It allows the chemical characterization of the acceptor sites by the selective dissociation of certain chromatin components followed by the binding of the steroid–receptor complex. The cell-free assay, however, has variables and artifacts, some intrinsic to the assay and some to the receptor and nuclei/chromatin preparations.

#### 1. *Protease and Nuclease Activities in the Chromatin and Receptor Preparations*

Both chromatin (Dounce and Umana, 1962; Furland and Jericijo, 1967; Panyin *et al.*, 1968; Panyim and Chalkley, 1969; Spelsberg *et al.*, 1971a; Webster and Spelsberg, 1979) and the receptor preparations (especially, the crude cytosols) (Sherman *et al.*, 1976, 1978; Sherman and Diaz, 1977; Webster and Spelsberg, 1979; Vedeckis *et al.*, 1978, 1980) contain nuclease and protease activities. The proteases can degrade the steroid–receptor complexes and prevent binding to nuclear acceptor sites (Sherman *et al.*, 1976; Sherman and Diaz, 1977; Vedeckis *et al.*, 1980). Partial purification of the avian oviduct progesterone receptor removes most, if not all, of the protease activity, resulting in a better maintenance of the integrity of the receptor (and chromatin, if incubated together) (Sherman *et al.*, 1976, 1978; Sherman and Diaz, 1977; Schrader *et al.*, 1977a,b; Vedeckis *et al.*, 1978, 1980).

Figure 3 shows that mild protease action on oviduct chromatin will cause an increase in the number of chromatin acceptor sites for the progesterone–receptor complex (P-R), whereas severe protease action will cause a marked

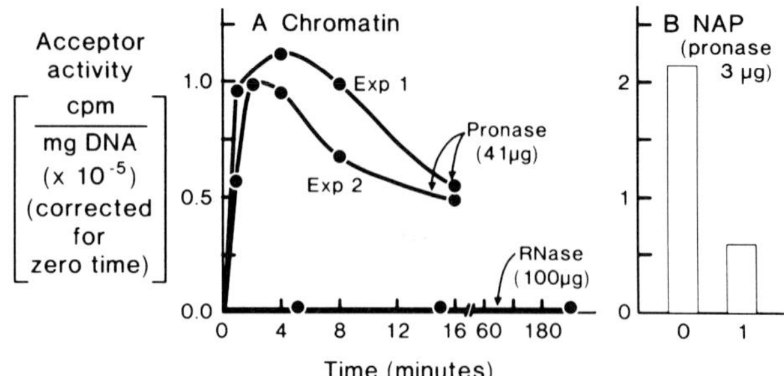


FIG. 3. Effects of proteolytic action on oviduct chromatin and its consequences on the binding of the oviduct progesterone receptor (P-R). Oviduct chromatin (A) and oviduct nucleoacidic protein (NAP) (B) were treated with pronase at a ratio of pronase to DNA (w/w) of .05 at 4°C in dilute Tris buffer (pH 7.5). At various intervals, the aliquots were removed, diluted 10-fold with buffer, and centrifuged at $10^5$ *g* for 12 hours. The DNA-residual protein pellets were resuspended in dilute buffer and assayed for acceptor activity (P-R binding). In (A) (●) P-R binding to the pronase- or ribonuclease-treated chromatins is indicated. The ribonuclease/DNA (w/w) was 0.2. The mean of four replicate binding assays are presented for each value. In (B) the bar graph indicates the P-R binding. From G. Martin-Dani and T. C. Spelsberg (in preparation).

decrease in the number of acceptor sites. The increase in acceptor sites with mild protease action is due to the destruction of masking proteins which cover many acceptor sites in target tissues and all acceptor sites in nontarget tissues (Spelsberg *et al.*, 1976a, 1977a,b; Thrall *et al.*, 1978; G. Martin-Dani and T. C. Spelsberg, in preparation). This masking is discussed further in Section VI. If measures are not taken to minimize protease activity, increased binding to both target and nontarget tissue chromatins will occur, producing an apparent lack of saturable binding to nuclear sites (Chamness *et al.*, 1974; Milgrom and Atger, 1975) as well as a loss of tissue specific nuclear binding (Clark and Gorski, 1969; Chamness *et al.*, 1973; Higgens *et al.*, 1973b). This will be discussed in greater detail in Sections VI,F and G. Thus, assay conditions should be established to reduce protease action by using low temperatures (4°C), previously activated receptors, partially purified receptor preparations, high ionic strength, and clean chromatin (Thrall *et al.*, 1978; Webster and Spelsberg, 1979).

Nucleases have also been shown to degrade the chromatin DNA during cell-free nuclear binding assays under certain conditions. The binding to isolated chromatin can be enhanced or decreased as a result of mild or extensive nuclease action respectively (Webster and Spelsberg, 1979). Therefore, the conditions for the cell-free binding assay should include those which also minimize the nuclease activity. Fortunately, many of these conditions are the same as those required to minimize protease activity (Webster and Spelsberg, 1979).

### 2. *Use of High Ionic Conditions to Identify High Affinity Nuclear Acceptor Sites*

It has been shown that the ionic condition in the cell-free binding assay has a marked influence on the saturability and level of binding of the P-R to oviduct nuclear acceptor sites (Pikler *et al.*, 1976; Webster *et al.*, 1976; Spelsberg *et al.*, 1976b). Figure 4 shows the effects of using a low (0.05 *M* KCl) and a high (0.15 *M* KCl) salt concentration on the cell-free binding of labeled progesterone receptor to oviduct chromatin. At the higher salt concentrations, i.e., physiological levels or higher (including Langendorf's media which has, quantitatively and qualitatively, the equivalent ions as the nucleus), only the high affinity class of nuclear binding sites is detectable for the chick oviduct progesterone receptor. Using lower ionic conditions, a nonspecific nonsaturable binding is observed (Spelsberg *et al.*, 1976b). As discussed later, the ionic factor together with the proteolysis factor explain in part the reported lack of saturable nuclear binding using cell-free assays in certain laboratories. Therefore, the ionic conditions of 0.15 to 0.18 *M* KCl are recommended for the cell-free binding assays.

### 3. *Variations in the Levels and Biological Activity of the Receptors*

We have recently reported that the chick oviduct progesterone receptor varies at different times of the year both in quantity and in biological activity,

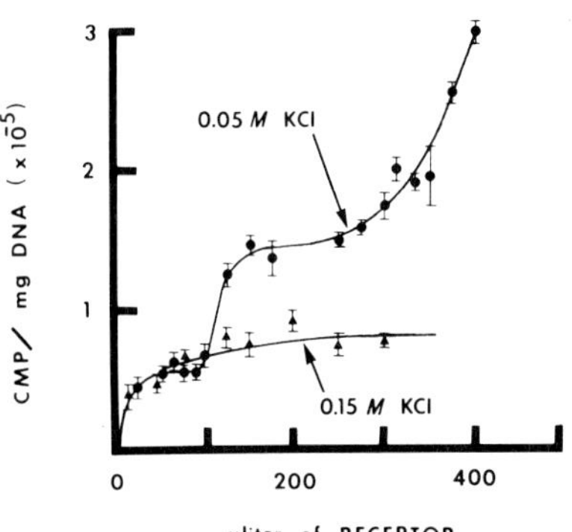


FIG. 4. Detection of multiple classes of nuclear binding sites *in vitro* in the hen oviduct; effects of ionic strength. These experiments were performed with the oviducts from mature hens as described elsewhere (Pikler *et al.*, 1976; Spelsberg *et al.*, 1976b). The assay mixtures contained either (●) 0.05 *M* KCl or (▲) 0.15M KCl (final concentration). The assays were performed using 25 μg of DNA per assay and the standard assay method. The range and average of three replicates of analyses for each receptor concentration are shown. Reproduced with permission from Pikler *et al.* (1976).

i.e., nuclear binding and alteration of transcription (Boyd and Spelsberg, 1979b; Spelsberg and Halberg, 1980). In the winter the progesterone receptor decreases to its normal level and loses biological activity. Similar seasonal effects are seen in the estrogen receptor (O. L. Kon and T. C. Spelsberg, in preparation). These studies also revealed a seasonal variation in the nuclear binding of the chick oviduct progesterone and estrogen receptors using both *in vivo* and *in vitro* binding assays. These results are presented and discussed further in Section IV,D. Other studies have shown that the progesterone receptors from the immature oviduct, from estrogen withdrawn chicks, or from molting hens are also not capable of nuclear translocation and binding (P. A. Boyd and T. C. Spelsberg, in preparation). Apparently estrogen administered to the immature chick regulates a "binding factor" which in turn regulates the capacity of the progesterone receptor to bind to the nuclear acceptor sites (T. C. Spelsberg, in preparation). Thus, the progesterone receptors of the chick oviduct are not always constant in levels or biological activity, a factor that must be considered when performing cell-free assays. Whether such events occur in other animals remains to be determined.

As discussed earlier (Section II), the cytosol of many target tissues contains small and/or large molecules which appear to regulate the receptor activation and nuclear binding. The cytosols also contain proteases and nucleases as discussed in Section IV,B,1. Partial purification of the receptors by ammonium sulfate precipitation appears to separate some of the regulatory factors as well as the proteases from steroid receptors (Milgrom and Atger, 1975; Cake *et al.*, 1976; Schrader *et al.*, 1977a,b; Vedeckis *et al.*, 1978, 1980). Therefore, it is recommended that cell-free binding assays utilize partially purified receptor preparations to reduce variability. Other studies have shown that the titration of crude steroid–receptor complexes with constant amounts of chromatin to determine saturation of nuclear acceptor sites may involve an artifact due to other proteins in the cytosol. While the use of partially purified receptors may alleviate nonspecific protein interference with acceptor site saturation analysis, this problem should be further examined. The cell-free assays can be organized to keep the cytosol protein constant and vary the nuclear acceptor sites. Alternately, one could titrate with increasing target cell cytosol and maintain equivalent protein in the assay by adding albumin or the cytosol protein from nontarget tissues containing no receptor.

The studies discussed in this section demonstrate that the physiological state of the animal may have a large impact on the reproducibility of cell-free binding assays and the estimation of the number of nuclear acceptor sites. To identify such variations of steroid receptors, extensive analysis of the nuclear binding of the steroid–receptor complex is required.

### 4. *Problems with Different Steroids*

Chick oviduct estrogen and progesterone receptors, when used for nuclear acceptor site analysis, revealed marked differences in the adsorption of the free radiolabeled steroids to nuclei and nuclear components (Kon *et al.*, 1980). Estrogen displayed as much as 5- to 10-fold greater nonspecific adsorption than does progesterone. Therefore, in order to demonstrate a receptor dependent, specific binding to nuclear acceptor sites, cell-free nuclear binding assays with the estrogen receptor had to be developed using modifications (Kon *et al.*, 1980) of the method used for the progesterone receptor sites (Pikler *et al.*, 1976; Spelsberg *et al.*, 1977a,b). Further problems are encountered when using other steroids such as androgens which can interact with the receptors of other steroids and corticosteroids which can have significant amounts of serum binding protein.

## C. Development of a Cell-Free Nuclear Binding for the Chick Oviduct Progesterone Receptor: Discriminating for High Affinity Sites While Minimizing Proteolytic Activity

The basic procedure for performing cell-free nuclear binding studies is to incubate a labeled steroid receptor preparation with isolated nuclei or nuclear component, and then measure bound versus free steroid receptor. The numerous reports involving such studies utilize some variation of this approach. These variations include the level of purification of the receptor, the method of "activation" of the steroid–receptor complex (e.g., salt treatment, dilution, partial purification, or heat activation), the experimental design used in analyzing nuclear uptake (e.g., varying the receptor levels, varying the nuclear levels), the conditions of the cell-free assay (e.g., temperature of incubation, ionic strength), and the method of removing unbound or nonspecifically bound steroid–receptor complex from the nuclear components. Consideration for the selection of each of these parameters to achieve optimal conditions for nativelike binding is discussed above (Section IV,B).

Using the considerations described in Section IV,B, a cell-free nuclear binding assay for the progesterone receptor in the chick oviduct was developed. This is outlined in Fig. 5 for both whole nuclei/chromatin as well as for various soluble nuclear components which require special handling. Since the free steroid–receptor complexes are soluble but the nuclei and chromatin are not, it is easy to separate the bound from unbound receptors when using these intact cell constituents. The partially deproteinized chromatins, however, are soluble and thus are more difficult to separate

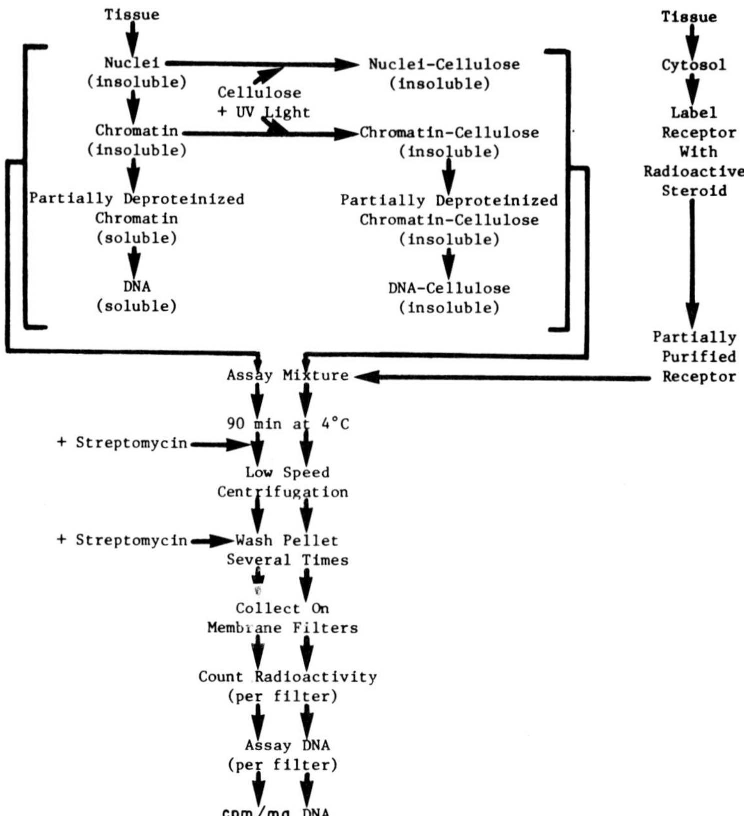


FIG. 5. Outline of basic procedure for the cell-free assay of [$^3$H]P-R binding to nuclear acceptor sites. These methods are described in detail elsewhere (Webster *et al.*, 1976; Spelsberg *et al.*, 1976c, 1977a, 1979a,b; Webster and Spelsberg, 1979; Spelsberg and Halbert, 1980). These methods were selected on the basis of achieving saturable binding to the highest affinity class of sites and for maintenance of the integrity of the steroid–receptor complex, the chromatin protein, and its DNA (see text). Reproduced with permission from Thrall *et al.* (1978).

from the soluble receptors. Long periods of centrifugation were initially used to separate these two soluble entities, but low recovery, degradation, and limited sample numbers present problems (Spelsberg *et al.*, 1971b, 1972). A better approach is to render the soluble nucleoproteins insoluble. This is accomplished in either of two ways and is outlined in Fig. 5. First, the chromatin can be attached to an insoluble resin such as cellulose or acrylamide and the various protein fractions removed leaving residual DNA or DNA–protein complex attached to the resins in an insoluble state. These can then be used in the binding assays. Alternately, the soluble chromatin fractions can be rendered insoluble after the hormone binding using streptomycin sulfate to precipate the nucleoprotein with bound steroid receptors. In each method, the complexes of DNA and steroid receptor are washed several times to remove traces of the unbound steroid receptor. The washed complexes are then transfered to Millipore filters and the bound radioactivity counted. The DNA per filter is quantitated and the cpm per mg DNA or molecules of bound P-R per cell are calculated as described elsewhere (Pikler *et al.*, 1976; Webster *et al.*, 1976). These methods are detailed elsewhere (Thrall *et al.*, 1978).

The assay conditions utilize a partially purified receptor (20-fold purification) which is preactivated (Lohmar and Toft, 1975; Pikler *et al.*, 1976), a low temperature (4°C), a 90 minute incubation period, and varying ratios of receptor/nuclear DNA with 30 to 100 $\mu$g DNA (as nuclei or nuclear components) per assays. The time of incubation was selected to allow equilibrium between acceptor bound and the free progesterone receptor in the range of receptor concentrations used. As shown in Fig. 4, these conditions allow a saturable binding in a short period of time using increasing amounts of the receptor with constant amounts of nuclear components. Figure 6 demonstrates that saturation is also observed when the nuclear components are varied with constant amounts of receptor. We have found that 90% of the progesterone receptor remains intact throughout the assay (Pikler *et al.*, 1976; Thrall *et al.*, 1978), the chromatin proteins and DNA show relatively little damage (Webster and Spelsberg, 1979), and about 60 to 80% of the chromatin DNA is recovered on the filters after the binding, washing, and transfer. Further, when [$^{14}$C]ovalbumin is added to the binding assays and

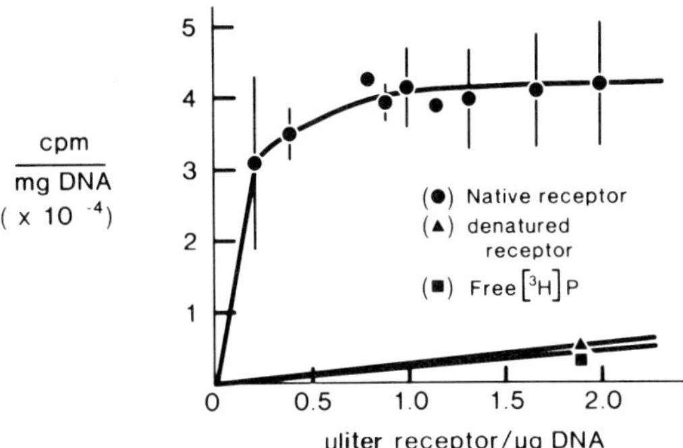


FIG. 6. Titration of P-R binding to hen oviduct chromatin. The cell-free nuclear binding of (●) native P-R, (▲) P-R denatured by heating at 50°C for 1 hour and (■) free steroid to oviduct chromatin was performed as described elsewhere (Pikler *et al.*, 1976) except that the levels of chromatin were varied with the P-R concentrations constant. The mean and standard deviation of four replicate binding assays to the native receptor are presented. From T. C. Spelsberg (unpublished results).

then assayed by SDS polyacryalmide gel electrophoresis, less than 10% of the ovalbumin is damaged (T. C. Spelsberg, unpublished results). In contrast, when the cell-free binding assays are performed under conditions of higher temperature (25°C), for longer periods or with crude cytosol, significant proteolytic damage to the [$^{14}$C]ovalbumin is observed. This proteolytic activity is accompanied by increases in binding of the progesterone receptor to nuclear acceptor sites, as discussed in Section II,A and Fig. 3. When more extensive proteolysis occurs, damage to the receptor and to the nuclear acceptor sites are detected with marked losses in nuclear binding (Fig. 3) (G. Martin-Dani and T. C. Spelsberg, in preparation). The use of mild protease inhibitors such as phenylmethyl sulfonyl fluoride offer additional protection. However, it should be warned that potent protease inhibitors often damage the receptors and prevent nuclear binding.

### D. Biological Relevance of the Cell-Free Nuclear Binding of the Progesterone Receptor

Before discussing the isolation and characterization of the nuclear acceptors, a brief discussion of the biological relevance of the cell-free assays should be made. Table I outlines the nativeness of cell-free nuclear binding assays reported from many laboratories for many steroid receptor–target tissue systems. Many of these laboratories have concluded that the cell-free nuclear binding assays do identify the native nuclear acceptor sites in their systems (Raynaud-Jammet and Baulieu, 1969; Beziat *et al.*, 1970; Arnaud *et al.*, 1971a,b; Mohla *et al.*, 1972; Jensen *et al.*, 1973, 1974; Buller *et al.*, 1976a,b; Schwartz *et al.*, 1976a,b). These studies do support the nativeness of the cell-free nuclear binding assays. Unfortunately, these studies have not been pursued, so whether these responses *in vitro* occur by the same mechanism(s) as occurs *in vivo* remains to be determined.

Several additional lines of evidence support the view that the cell-free nuclear binding in the progesterone receptor-avian oviduct system represents the native (endogenous) binding sites. It has been reported using whole cell and cell-free studies that multiple classes of nuclear binding sites exist for P-R (Spelsberg *et al.*, 1975, 1976c, 1977a,b; Pikler *et al.*, 1976; Spelsberg, 1976; Webster *et al.*, 1976). The binding to the highest affinity class of sites occurs when physiological levels of the steroid in the plasma are achieved (Spelsberg, 1976; Spelsberg *et al.*, 1977a,b). Second, there is a marked correlation between the binding of P-R to the high affinity nuclear binding sites *in vivo* and the progesterone-induced alteration of transcription in the oviduct of estrogen-primed chicks. Binding to the lower affinity sites *in vivo* shows no correlation with the steroid-induced changes in tran-

TABLE I

"NATIVENESS" OF THE CELL-FREE NUCLEAR BINDING OF STEROID RECEPTORS[a]

1. The receptor binds the steroid under cell-free conditions with the same affinity and apparent specificity as measured under whole cell conditions (1–14)[b]
2. The steroid–receptor complex formed under cell-free conditions has the same physicochemical properties (molecular weight, hydrodynamic properties, etc.) as that complex formed in intact cells (1–11, 13–16)
3. Requirements for nuclear uptake and binding in cell-free assays (e.g., steroid bound to a receptor, receptor activation, etc.) are the same as those for the whole cell (1,4,6–14,17–21)
4. Conditions required for activation of the receptor, a prerequisite for nuclear uptake and binding, are the same for both cell-free and whole cell systems (1,4,6–14,21,22)
5. Under proper conditions, the cell-free binding results in a similar pattern and the level of nuclear binding as does the whole cell binding (1,4,6–14,17–21,23,24). Levels of both cell-free and whole cell nuclear bound steroid correlate with physiological responses (23–27)
6. The properties of the triplex of steroid–receptor–chromatin formed under cell-free conditions closely resembles that formed under whole cell conditions with respect to dissociation by salt, certain divalent ions, and detergents, etc. The dissociated radioactive steroids are still complexed to the receptor (1,3,4,6–14,17,18,21,28)
7. The interaction of an isolated steroid–receptor complex with isolated nuclei has been reported to alter RNA polymerase activity and transcription of selected genes in a pattern similar to that which occurs in the intact cell (29–38)
8. Conditions and/or periods *in vivo* in which the steroid receptor fails to translocate and bind to nuclear acceptor sites and alter transcription (e.g., seasonal rhythms in the mature avian oviduct, the immature oviduct, or in the oviduct of molting hens) also have been demonstrated in the cell-free assays (39–41).
9. Receptor specific nuclear acceptor sites demonstrated *in vivo* between two different steroids are also displayed in the cell-free assays (19,42)

[a]Taken from Thrall *et al.* (1978).

[b]*Key to references:* 1. Raspe (1971); 2. Sherman *et al.* (1970); 3. O'Malley *et al.* (1971); 4. Jensen and DeSombre (1972); 5. Schrader and O'Malley (1972); 6. Jensen *et al.* (1974); 7. King and Mainwaring (1974); 8. O'Malley and Means (1974); 9. Spelsberg (1974); 10. Gorski and Gannon (1976); 11. Pasqualini (1976); 12. Pikler *et al.* (1976); 13. Spelsberg and Toft (1976); 14. Yamamoto and Alberts (1976); 15. Kuhn *et al.* (1977); 16. Schrader *et al.* (1977a); 17,18,19. Higgins *et al.* (1973a,b,c); 20. Simons *et al.* (1976); 21. Webster *et al.* (1976); 22. Schrader *et al.* (1972); 23,24. Spelsberg *et al.* (1977a,b); 25. Tomkins (1970). 26. Clark *et al.* (1973); 27. Spelsberg (1976); 28. Spelsberg *et al.* (1971b); 29. Raynaud-Jammet and Baulieu (1969); 30. Beziat *et al.* (1970); 31,32. Arnaud *et al.* (1971a,b); 33. Mohla *et al.* (1972); 34. Jensen *et al.* (1973); 35, 36. Buller *et al.* (1976a,b); 37, 38. Schwartz *et al.* (1976)a,b); 39. Boyd and Spelsberg (1979b); 40. Spelsberg and Halberg (1980); 41. P. A. Boyd and T. C. Spelsberg (in preparation); 42. O. L. Kon and T. C. Spelsberg (in preparation)

scription. Consequently, these high affinity sites, representing 6000 P-R binding sites per oviduct cell and an equilibrium dissociation constant between the receptor and the acceptor sites of $K_d \sim 10^{-9}M$, appear to be the ones directly involved in transcription and thus in the physiological response. Third, as shown in Fig. 4, these high affinity sites, but not the low affinity sites, survive conditions of physiological ionic strengths in the cell-

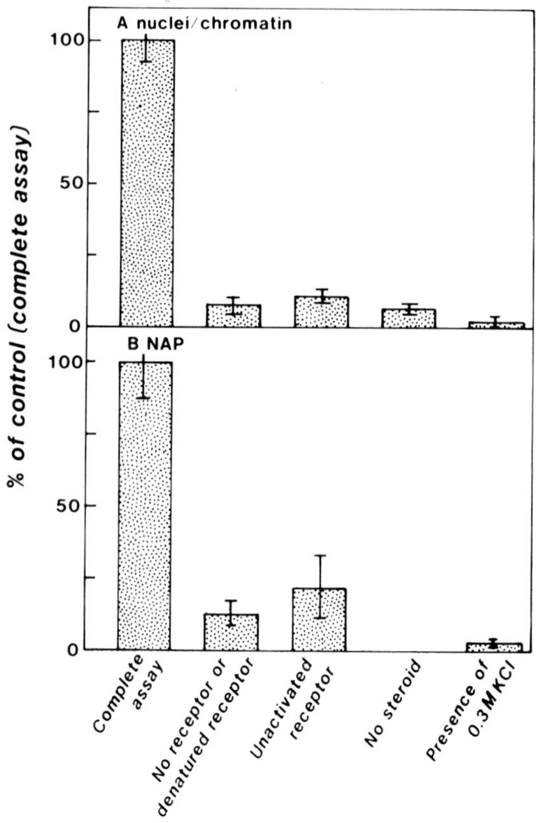


FIG. 7. Summary of the cell-free binding of P-R to nuclear acceptor sites. (A) The level of P-R binding to oviduct nuclei or chromatin under the varying conditions listed. (B) The levels of P-R binding to oviduct NAP under similar conditions. The cell-free P-R nuclear binding was performed as described elsewhere (Webster *et al.*, 1976). From T. C. Spelsberg (unpublished results).

free binding assay (Spelsberg *et al.*, 1975, 1976b, 1977a,b; Pikler *et al.*, 1976; Webster *et al.*, 1976). The fourth supporting fact is that the high affinity sites measured in the cell-free binding assays resemble those measured *in vivo* in requiring an intact activated receptor which is bound with a steroid and in the dissociation of the steroid–receptor complex by 0.3 *M* KCl (Pikler *et al.*, 1976; Webster *et al.*, 1976). These data are summarized in Fig. 7A. The fifth supporting evidence is that the cell-free binding sites quantitatively resemble those measured *in vivo* which, as stated above, correlates with biological responses and serum levels of the steroid.

Under conditions specifying binding of P-R to the high affinity nuclear sites, a receptor specificity for these sites is observed. Recently, the estrogen receptor from the chick/hen oviduct was isolated, partially purified, and sufficiently stabilized for use in a cell-free binding assay (Kon *et al.*, 1980). Figure 8 shows that using competitive binding studies in the cell-free assay described here for P-R, the unlabeled estrogen receptor effectively competes with the radiolabeled estrogen receptor but not with the radiolabeled P-R (O. L. Kon and T. C. Spelsberg, in preparation). Studies *in vivo* support the cell-free binding assays in that the progesterone does not compete with [$^3$H]estrogen for nuclear binding and vice versa (Kon, O. L. and Spelsberg, T. C., in preparation). These studies support those of Higgens *et al.* (1973c) who reported receptor specific acceptors for estrogen and dexamethasone in the rat uerus and HTC cells. The observation that the cell-free assay demonstrates receptor-specific acceptor sites, a specificity observed *in vivo*, provides yet further support for the nativeness of these assays.

Finally, recent studies in the author's laboratory revealed unexpected but confirmatory support for a nativelike cell-free binding. In this instance, a marked correlation between the cell-free and endogenous nuclear bindings were observed at different periods of the year. Every winter for a 4 year period a loss of nuclear binding capacity of P-R to whole oviduct chromatin and NAP was demonstrated (Boyd and Spelsberg, 1979b; Spelsberg and

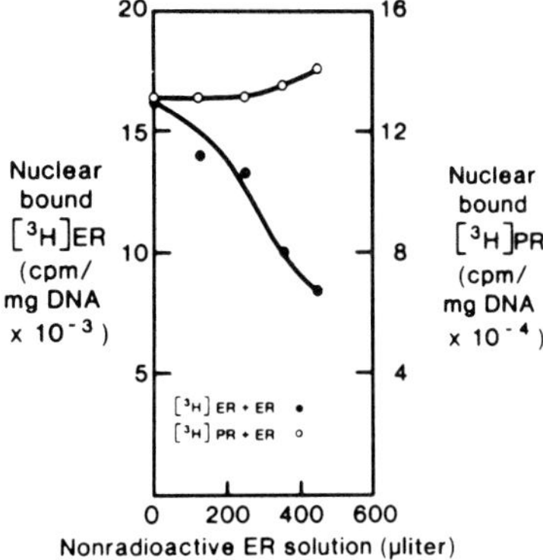


FIG. 8. Competition of nonradioactive ER for binding of [$^3$H]ER and [$^3$H]PR to isolated oviduct nuclei. A constant volume (400 $\mu$l) of [$^3$H]PR prepared as previously described (Pikler *et al.*, 1976) or of [$^3$H]ER prepared as previously described (Kon *et al.*, 1980) with an additional heparin agarose chromatography was added to the cell-free nuclear binding assays. Increasing amounts of unlabeled ER was then added. In order to maintain constant protein concentration in all incubations, the volume of each incubation was brought to 1 ml with redissolv d ammonium sulfate precipitate (35% saturation) of spleen cytosol prepared in a similar manner as ER. The ratio of [$^3$H]receptor complex to nuclei employed in this experiment was saturating, as previously determined. (●), Nuclear bound [$^3$H]ER in the presence of nonradioactive ER; (○), nuclear bound [$^3$H]PR in the presence of nonradioactive ER. Each value is the mean of triplicate determinations. From O. L. Kon and T. C. Spelsberg (in preparation).

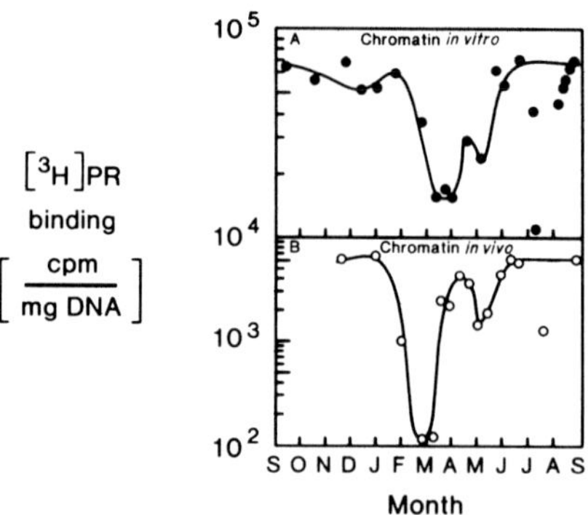


FIG. 9. Seasonal variations in the capacity of [$^3$H]PR to bind to chromatin acceptor sites in vivo and in vitro. (A) The *in vitro* binding to whole chromatin performed within one week in June, using [$^3$H]P-R isolated at various periods of the year. The receptor preparations and the nuclear binding assays were conducted as described elsewhere (Pikler *et al.*, 1976; Spelsberg *et al.*, 1976c; Boyd and Spelsberg, 1979b). Saturating levels of [$^3$H]P-R (300 μl/assay) for 60 μg/DNA assay were used in the binding assays. Each point represents the mean of four replicate analyses of the binding of [$^3$H]P-R to chromatin. The receptor preparations were isolated at specific times during the year, stored at −80°C as ammonium sulfate precipitates, and resuspended on the day of the binding assay. The chromatin represented two preparations which were stored similarly and used upon demand. (B) The in vivo binding of [$^3$H]P-R to nuclear chromatin in fully developed oviducts of immature chicks conducted at various periods of the year. DES-treated chicks were injected with 200 μCi of [$^3$H]P in 50 μl of ethanol–$H_20$ (1:1) into the wing vein. Evans Blue dye was included as a marker for the accuracy of the injection. One-half hour after injection, the birds were sacrificed and oviducts quickly excised. The nuclear chromatin was immediately isolated and quantitated for DNA and assayed for nuclear binding. The nuclear bound [$^3$H]P was extracted with 0.3 *M* KCl and found to be bound to a 4 S sedimenting macromolecule in sucrose. The blood was collected and the radioactivity per 50 ml did not change. The data are plotted as cpm per mg DNA for the nuclear binding versus the date on which [$^3$H]P was injected. Data reproduced with permission from Boyd and Spelsberg (1979b).

Halberg, 1980). Figure 9 shows the binding of P-R to oviduct chromatin *in vitro* and *in vivo*. Clearly, a seasonal variation in the pattern of binding is observed with a decrease or loss in binding occurring in the winter. These results are further supported by a similar seasonal pattern in the effects of progesterone on RNA polymerase II activity (transcription), representing the first nuclear response to the binding of the steroid–receptor complex to nuclear acceptor sites (Boyd and Spelsberg, 1979b; Spelsberg and Halberg, 1980). These circannual rhythms are also accompanied by similar rhythms in the oviduct weights and cytosol protein. These rhythms were subsequently found to be based on regulations via the progesterone receptor (Boyd and Spelsberg 1979b; Spelsberg and Halberg, 1980). In any case, the cell-free bindings mimic those *in vivo* which in turn correlate with the subsequent transcriptional response to the steroid. Reciprocally when the steroid–

receptor complex fails to translocate and bind to nuclear acceptor sites *in vivo*, the receptor isolated at the same period fails to bind in the cell-free assays using the conditions selected in Section IV,C. At a period when the complex does bind to nuclear acceptor sites *in vivo*, the receptor isolated at this time shows marked nuclear binding in the cell-free assay.

## V. THE APPROACH TO THE CHEMICAL CHARACTERIZATION OF THE CHROMATIN ACCEPTOR SITES FOR THE PROGESTERONE RECEPTOR IN THE HEN OVIDUCT

Some laboratories have selected a certain component of chromatin, such as DNA, as the nuclear acceptor for a particular steroid without examining the whole chromatin or other components of chromatin. In the approach to characterize an acceptor site, comparisons should first be made between the nuclear binding of a steroid receptor *in vivo* and *in vitro*. When the cell-free binding assay with nativelike properties has been established, the various components of chromatin should then be examined. Since the acceptor may be a protein, RNA, DNA, or combinations of these, it is recommended that the first approach involve selective removal of components from the isolated chromatin and monitoring the acceptor activity in the residual deoxyribonucleoproteins. This study would then be followed by one examining the dissociated components. During the dissociation of components from chromatin, an increase in activity which remains until all proteins are removed indicates that DNA is the acceptor. If a loss of activity occurs during protein removal, a chromatin protein fraction should be considered as the acceptor. In the latter case, one should collect that fraction which when removed from the chromatin (DNA) causes a loss in acceptor activity. This fraction should then be tested for acceptor activity alone, as well as reconstituted (reannealed) to DNA. It should be mentioned that denaturants are often required to remove proteins from the chromatin DNA. Therefore, methods used to renature protein structure and enzyme activities should be applied to these components in hopes of renaturing the acceptor activity. These same methods can then be used to reanneal the acceptor proteins to DNA should a combination of protein and DNA represent the acceptor. This is discussed in detail in Section VII,A.

Further purification of the acceptor factor(s) can be achieved via standard fractionation techniques for proteins (or RNA). The properties of the acceptor which are characteristic of those found in whole chromatin and nuclei such as the affinity, tissue specificity, and requirement for activated receptor should be examined with the purified acceptor. The next two major sections

(VI and VII) on isolating and characterizing the acceptor for the avian oviduct progesterone receptor follow just this approach.

The majority of laboratories have reported that the high affinity nuclear acceptor sites reside on chromatin (King *et al.*, 1965a,b; Mauer and Chalkley, 1976; Puca and Bresciani, 1968; Teng and Hamilton, 1968;

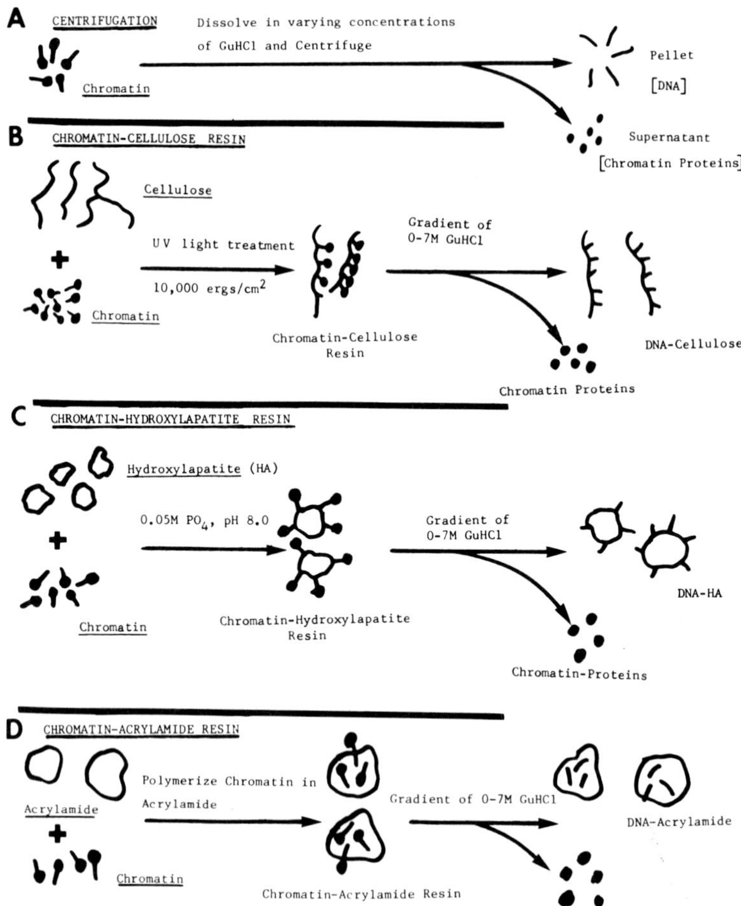


FIG. 10. Outlines of the methods for selectively removing proteins from chromatin. Using solutions of 1 to 8 *M* GuHCl or other solvents as described in the text the proteins of chromatin can be selectively dissociated from the DNA. At any stage of the deproteinization, the residual deoxyribonucleoproteins can be washed and assayed for acceptor activity (P-R binding). This is described in greater detail in the text. Reproduced with permission from Spelsberg *et al.* (1977b).

Swaneck *et al.*, 1970; Alberga *et al.*, 1971a,b; Spelsberg *et al.*, 1971b, 1976a,c, 1977a; Jensen and DeSombre, 1972; Lebeau *et al.*, 1973 Webster *et al.*, 1976; Socher *et al.*, 1976; Sala-Trepat *et al.*, 1977; Hemminki and Vauhkonen, 1977; Thrall *et al.*, 1978). Therefore, the initial step in examining the chemical nature of the nuclear acceptor sites utilizes chromatin isolated from purified nuclei as the starting material. It should be mentioned again that nuclear and even cytoplasmic entities of a nonchromatin nature may be associated with isolated chromatin; therefore, chromatin "acceptor" sites may in reality not be chromatin associated in the intact cell.

Figure 10 outlines several methods to selectively dissociate and fractionate proteins and RNA from chromatin. In Fig. 10A the aliquots of hen oviduct chromatin are placed in solutions containing increasing concentrations of guanidine hydrochloride (GuHCl) or some other dissociating reagent. These solutions are centrifuged 36 hours at $10^5$ $g$ to sediment the nucleoprotein, leaving the dissociated protein and RNA in the supernatant. Alternatively, the chromatin is bound to an insoluble resin as cellulose using uv light (Fig. 10B), to hydroxylapatite through adsorption of the DNA phosphates to the resin (Fig. 10C), or to acrylamide via trapping of chromatin DNA in the resin (Fig. 10D). These resins are then subjected to the increasing molarities of dissociating reagent (e.g., GuHCl) to remove selective fractions from the chromatin. The centrifugation (Fig. 10A), cellulose (Fig. 10B), and acrylamide (Fig. 10D) methods are well suited for analysis of the acceptors remaining on residual nucleoprotein after selective removal of components from the DNA. The cellulose (Fig. 10B), hydroxylapatite (Fig. 10C), and the acrylamide (Fig. 10D) methods are well suited for analysis of the dissociated material. It was hoped that through this approach any combination of protein and DNA, protein and RNA, or RNA and DNA alone which may display acceptor activity might readily be identified.

## VI. EVIDENCE FOR MASKING THE MAJORITY OF PROGESTERONE ACCEPTOR SITES IN THE AVIAN OVIDUCT CHROMATIN: ROLE OF CHROMATIN NONHISTONE PROTEINS

Initial studies on the effects of protein dissociation from the chromatin on the acceptor activity met with unexpected results. In the procedure of selectively removing proteins beginning with whole chromatin and ending with pure DNA, the extent of steroid receptor binding first markedly increases followed by an even greater decrease to a level of almost no binding. This is described below.

### A. Role of Chromatin Protein Fraction 2 (CP-2) in the Masking of Nuclear Acceptor Sites

In the early studies, bulk fractions of the chromatin proteins were removed from chromatin either free or attached to cellulose followed by an analysis of the acceptor activity on the residual protein–DNA complexes (Webster *et al.*, 1976; Spelsberg *et al.*, 1976b). Table II presents an outline of these fractions, how they were dissociated from chromatin, and the proportion of total chromatin protein they represented. The terminology of the residual deoxyribonucleoprotein after removal of each of the protein fractions from the chromatin is also given. Figure 11 shows the acceptor activity in chromatin (attached to cellulose) from which the histones (CP-1), then the bulk of the nonhistone proteins (CP-2), and finally the remainder of the nonhistone protein tightly bound to the DNA (CP-3) were removed to yield pure DNA (Spelsberg *et al.*, 1976b; Webster *et al.*, 1976). Figure 11A shows that the removal of the CP-1 fraction from oviduct chromatin causes little change in the binding of P-R to the residual nucleoprotein (dehistonized chromatin). When fraction CP-2 (representing the bulk of the nonhistone protein) is removed, however, the binding by the P-R is markedly increased (Spelsberg *et al.*, 1971b, 1976a, 1977a,b; Webster *et al.*, 1976; Thrall *et al.*, 1978). Finally, the removal of the CP-3 fraction yields pure DNA which displays a marked decrease in binding. Table III shows the extent of masking in oviduct chromatin with regard to the number of molecules of the P-R bound to nuclear acceptor sites per cell.

TABLE II
Crude Fractionation of Proteins from the Avian Oviduct Chromatin[a]

| Residual complex of deoxyribonucleoprotein (after removal of fraction) | Solvent used to extract protein | Protein fractions removed | Abbreviated name of fractions | Quantity of fraction in chromatin (mg/mg DNA) |
|---|---|---|---|---|
| Chromatin | None | None | None | — |
| Dehistonized chromatin | 3.0 *M* NaCl pH 6.0 | All histones 10% nonhistone | CP-I | 1.2 |
| Nucleoacidic protein (NAP) | 4.0 *M* GuHCl pH 6.0 | 75% of nonhistone protein | CP-II (masking proteins) | 1.4 |
| DNA | 7.0 *M* GuHCl pH 6.0 | 15% of nonhistone protein | CP-III (acceptor proteins) | 0.2 |

[a]Taken from Webster *et al.* (1976); Spelsberg *et al.* (1976a,b, 1977a,b, 1979a,b).

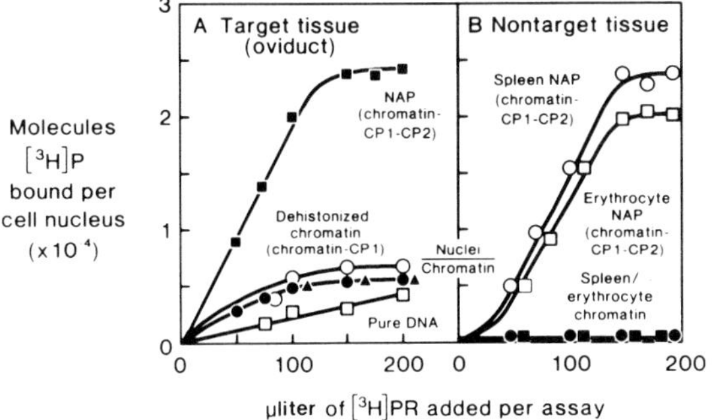


FIG. 11. Binding of [$^3$H]P-R to high affinity sites in the nuclear material of chick tissues. The *in vitro* binding of [$^3$H]P-R to the soluble DNA or DNA–protein complexes was performed using the cellulose method. The high affinity binding in vitro was assayed in 0.15 *M* KCl using 0 to 200 $\mu$l of labeled receptor and 50 $\mu$g DNA (as chromatin or protein–DNA complexes). The removal of total histones (CP-1), the first group of nonhistone proteins (CP-2), or the remaining nonhistone protein (CP-3) has been described elsewhere (Spelsberg *et al.*, 1976a, 1977■). The efficiency of removing these fractions from chromatin DNA and the integrity of the nuclear components were assayed by polyacrylamide gel electrophoresis and estimation of the protein–DNA ratio. (A) The symbols represent binding to the following for each tissue: (▲) nuclei; (●) whole chromatin; (○) chromatin deficient of histone (CP-1); (■) chromatin deficient of CP-1 and CP-2; and (□) chromatin deficient of total protein (pure DNA). From the [$^3$H]P-R bound per mg DNA was calculated the molecules of nuclear bound P-R per cell. (B) (●) spleen chromatin, (■) mature erythrocyte chromatin, (○) spleen NAP, and (□) erythrocyte NAP which represent chromatins devoid of CP-1 and CP-2. Reproduced with permission from Spelsberg *et al.* (1976a).

Following lengthy studies of this phenomenon (discussed further in the following sections), the increase in binding was termed an "unmasking" of acceptor sites with the CP-2 fraction assumed to contain the masking factor(s). As shown in Table II, the residual DNA-CP-3 complex containing the high capacity binding has been termed "nucleoacidic protein" or NAP. The decrease in binding of the progesterone receptor with the removal of the CP-3 fraction suggested that this fraction contains the acceptor component(s). This CP-3 fraction is discussed in Section VII.

Interestingly, the nontarget tissue chromatins such as spleen and erythrocyte show little or no binding by the P-R (Fig. 11B) (Webster *et al.*, 1976; Spelsberg *et al.*, 1971b, 1975, 1976a,b, 1977a,b). When the CP-1 and CP-2 fractions are removed from these chromatins, the resulting NAP's display marked binding, equivalent to the NAP obtained from the target tissue chromatin. Table III shows the extent of masking to these nontarget tissue chromatins based on the number of steroid–receptor complexes bound to nuclear acceptor sites per cell. When the NAP's from these chromatins are completely deproteinized, the resulting pure DNA's show the same low level of binding as the DNA from oviduct. Thus, the chromosomal material

TABLE III
EXTENT OF MASKING OF HIGH AFFINITY SITES[a]

| Source | Level of binding at saturation (molecules/cell) | Percentage of total sites masked |
|---|---|---|
| 1. Oviduct nuclei *in vivo* | 10,600 | 58 |
| 2. Oviduct nuclei *in vitro* | 5,951 | 76 |
| 3. Oviduct chromatin *in vitro* | 7,441 | 71 |
| 4. Oviduct chromatin in minus histone (CP-1) | 9,278 | 58 |
| 5. Oviduct chromatin in minus histone (CP-1) and CP-2 | 25,290 | 0 |
| 6. DNA | 2,055 | — |
| 1. Spleen nuclei | 60 | 100 |
| 2. Spleen chromatin | 48 | 100 |
| 3. Spleen chromatin minus histone (CP-1) and CP-2 | 24,106 | 0 |
| 1. Erythrocyte nuclei | 357 | 100 |
| 2. Erythrocyte chromatin | 416 | 100 |
| 3. Erythrocyte chromatin minus histone (CP-1) and CP-2 | 15,018 | 0 |

[a]The number of binding sites measured in each of the chromatin minus histone (CP-1) and CP-2 preparations was assumed to represent the total sites in the respective chromatin, and thus each of these preparations was assigned 0% masking. The values at saturation for each preparation were taken at 100 $\mu$g of injected hormone for the *in vivo* binding and 200 $\mu$l labeled receptor preparation for the *in vitro* binding. The preparations of the nuclear components as well as the hormone binding assays were performed as described elsewhere (Webster *et al.*, 1976). Reproduced with permission from Spelsberg *et al.* (1976c).

of many tissues of the bird appear to contain the same number of acceptor sites for progesterone but most of these (and in nontarget tissues all of them) are "masked" in chromatin. Similar findings have subsequently been reported in other steroid target tissue systems, as discussed in Section VIII.

Chytil and Spelsberg (1971) successfully prepared rabbit antisera to the chick oviduct CP-3 protein fraction. Using a complement fixation assay, these investigators demonstrated that the majority of the antigenic sites of the CP-3 fraction were "masked" in whole oviduct chromatin. Removal of the CP-2 fraction unmasked ~ 80% of the antigenic sites. These results obtained with the complement fixation assays using antisera to CP-3 closely mimic those obtained with the cell-free assays of P-R binding to nuclear acceptor sites with regard to the "masking" of the CP-3. In order to examine the significance of these findings, the biological relevance of these masked sites was examined. Comparisons between the binding of the progesterone receptor to the oviduct NAP (in which all acceptor sites are exposed) in cell-free assays and the binding to whole chromatin (in which only a fraction of the sites are exposed) in both cell-free and *in vivo* assays were performed.

## B. RELATIONSHIP BETWEEN THE UNMASKED AND MASKED ACCEPTOR SITES IN OVIDUCT CHROMATIN

Figure 7B shows that the binding of the progesterone receptor to acceptor sites on the oviduct NAP, containing all acceptor sites including many which normally are masked in whole chromatin, requires an intact, activated receptor as found with whole chromatin. The receptor is dissociated from the NAP with higher salt. Figure 11 shows that the binding to these sites on the NAP are saturable. Previous studies showed similar affinities of binding of the P-R to both the masked and unmasked sites with a $K_d \sim 10^{-8}$ to $10^{-9}$ $M$ (Webster *et al.*, 1976). Thus these properties show a marked similarity between the acceptor sites expressed in intact chromatin (i.e., part of the sites expressed) and the sites in NAP (i.e., all sites expressed).

The receptor preparations showing seasonal rhythms in nuclear binding as described in Section IV,D and Fig. 9 were then used to analyze these unmasked sites. Figure 12 shows that cell-free binding of the progesterone receptor to the NAP (all sites unmasked) reflects the same seasonal rhythm as does the *in vivo* binding to whole chromatin (20% sites unmasked). This represents another level of similarity between the masked and unmasked sites. Other studies were performed using the estrogen-induced oviduct

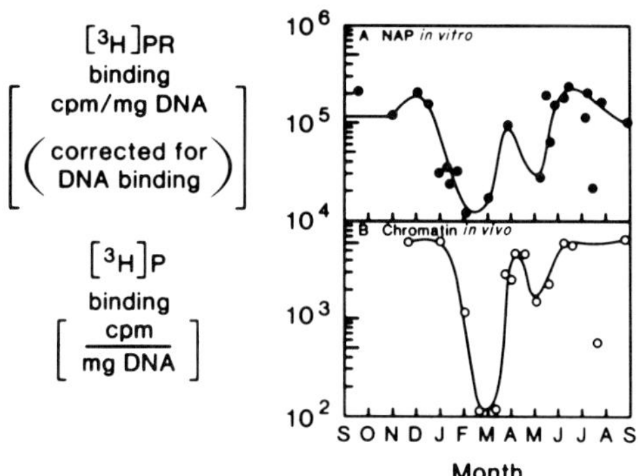


FIG. 12. Seasonal rhythms in P-R binding to nuclear acceptor sites in the chick oviduct. The binding of P-R to isolated NAP *in vitro* and chromatin *in vivo* using receptors isolated at various times of the year has been described in the legend of Fig. 9 and elsewhere (Boyd and Spelsberg, 1979b; Spelsberg and Halberg, 1980). (A) The seasonal binding by P-R to NAP *in vitro*. (B) The seasonal binding to oviduct chromatin *in vivo*. Reproduced with permission from Boyd and Spelsberg (1979b).

development system. As shown in Fig. 13, in the early stages of the oviduct development, the P-R is incapable of translocating and binding to nuclear acceptor sites *in vivo* and altering transcription. As development progresses, the receptor acquires the capacity for nuclear binding (P. A. Boyd and T. C. Spelsberg, in preparation). Interestingly, the P-R isolated from the undeveloped oviduct also shows little or no cell-free binding to NAP. As development progresses, these isolated receptors gradually gain the capacity for binding to NAP in the cell-free assays. Since the NAP used in these studies was from the same group of mature oviducts, the pattern of binding was not due to the nuclear acceptor site. Thus, the cell-free binding to NAP mimics the binding to chromatin *in vivo*.

It can be seen that the normally masked sites appear to have many properties in common with the normally exposed sites on the chromatin. The similarities include dependency on an intact, activated receptor, the affinity of binding, the concentration of salt required to dissociate the steroid–receptor complex, and the patterns of binding observed during oviduct development and during the year in the mature oviduct. Absolute proof of identical sites between masked and normally unmasked sites will require purification of the acceptor proteins and comparison of various properties as peptide maps and antigenic properties.

### C. Possible Biological Function of the Masking Phenomenon: Regulation of Acceptor Site Expression

The question arises as to the biological role of the masking phenomenon. Why do the nontarget tissues contain an equivalent number of acceptor sites as the target tissue but all are masked? One possible function may be that the masking regulates which genes will respond to the P-R or, on a broader scale, regulates a multitude of genes (i.e., as repressors), and we are detecting only those masking steroid-regulated genes. The regulation of which genes will respond to a steroid would explain a heretofore unexplained but important dilemma in endrocrinology: why different target tissues of the same organism with presumably the same type of receptor display markedly different responses with regard to gene expression to the same steroid. In short, different genes seem to be regulated by the same steroid–receptor complex in different tissues. Recent evidence indicating that the steroid receptors are antigenically related in different tissues of the same animal minimize the regulatory role of the receptors themselves (Green *et al.*, 1977, 1980; Eisen, 1980).

In short, those genes that are masked in the oviduct chromatin may represent either genes which are currently expressed (unmasked) in other proges-

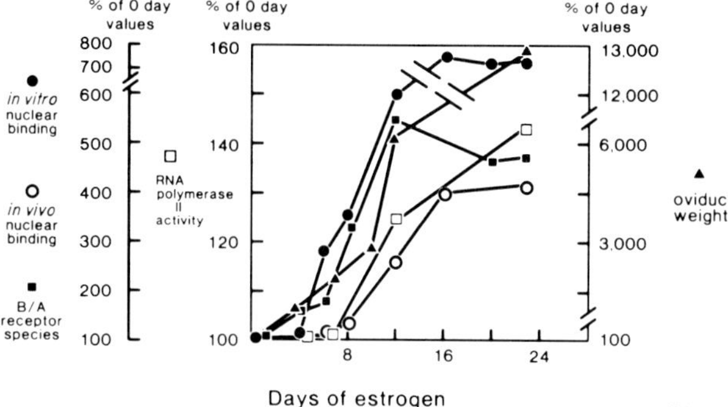


FIG. 13. Composite of functions of progesterone receptor during oviduct development. The undeveloped oviducts of immature chicks were induced to full development with daily injections of estrogens. Changes in the (▲) oviduct weight, (●) cell-free NAP binding by the isolated P-R, (■) ratio of the quantity of the B species and the A species of the P-R, (○) nuclear binding *in vivo*, and (□) RNA polymerase II responses to injected progesterone were analyzed. The methods are described elsewhere (Boyd and Spelsberg, 1979b). It can be seen that a nonfunctioning P-R occurs in the immature oviduct, explaining the nonresponsiveness of the organ to progesterone. From P. A. Boyd and T. C. Spelsberg (in preparation).

terone target tissues or genes which were expressed at an earlier stage of development in that organ. In organs that are nontarget tissues and do not possess steroid receptors and thus do not require genes that respond to steroids, all such steroid-regulated genes would be masked. This is supported in Fig. 11B wherein all acceptor sites appear to be masked in nontarget tissues. This concept is further supported by studies on the developing oviduct. During the development of a target organ such as oviduct, quantitative and qualitative changes in the masking activity might be expected as different cell types appear or change in proportions and different genes are found to respond to the same steroid such as estrogen (O'Malley *et al.*, 1969). The total number of acceptor sites (masked and unmasked) would not be expected to change but the masking of the binding sites presumably would change. Figure 14 shows that quantitative changes in masking and total number of acceptor sites during oviduct development is observed (G. Martin-Dani and T. C. Spelsberg, in preparation). The total number of sites (NAP binding) does not change throughout the estrogen-induced development but the extent of masking changes considerably. Indications that the masking during organ development may be qualitatively changing was suggested by antigenic analysis of the CP-3 fraction during rat liver development. Using the complement fixation assay with antisera prepared against the CP-3 fraction of the adult rat liver chromatin, as discussed earlier with the chick oviduct (Chytil and Spelsberg, 1971), an indication of possible changes in masking during the development of the rat liver was observed

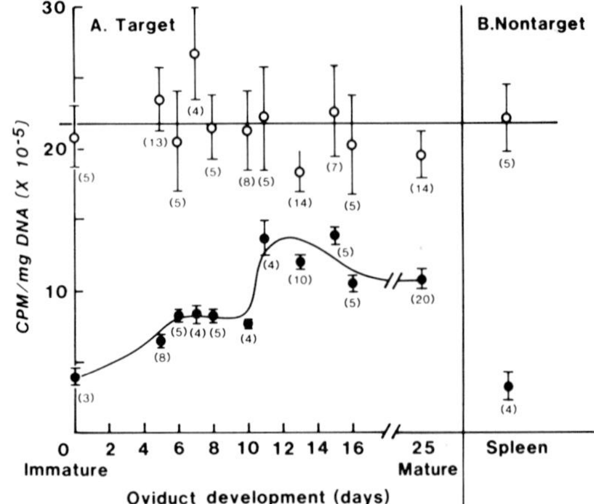


FIG. 14. Differential masking of progesterone acceptor sites during oviduct cytodifferentiation. (A) The acceptor levels for P-R (at saturation) in (●) whole chromatin or (○) NAP during oviduct development using a cell-free binding of P-R as described elsewhere (Webster *et al.*, 1976; Boyd and Spelsberg, 1979b). (B) The same values for spleen, a nontarget tissue for progesterone removed at the 25 day of estrogen treatment. The mean and standard deviation of multiple replicate analyses of the binding (the number shown in parentheses) are presented. These experiments are described in greater detail in the text. From G. Martin-Dani and T. C. Spelsberg (in preparation).

(Chytil *et al.*, 1974). This suggests that the masking of different fractions of the CP-3 proteins is occurring on the chromatin during organ development. Therefore, the masking phenomenon may well represent the means by which steroid-regulated genes are differentially expressed in different target tissues. At present this model of masking remains to be verified. Evidence that masking exists in other steroid target tissue system (see Section VIII) lends support to its existence. The evidence of total masking of the steroid receptor binding sites in nontarget tissues is interesting but the rationale for it is obscure since these tissues do not contain receptors anyway.

### D. A Hypothetical Model for the Masking Process

Figure 15 shows a model of chromatin with its nucleosomes containing the bulk of the histones, a suggested position for the H1 histone and expressed (unmasked) acceptor sites (the square blocks) as well as the masked acceptor sites (square blocks covered with the cylinders). The acceptor sites denoted as blocks are bound to specific DNA sequences. The removal of the CP-1 fraction (or histones) with 3 *M* NaCl does not remove the masking proteins. The removal of the CP-2 fraction (represented by the cylinders) with 4 *M*

GuHCl to yield the NAP does remove the masking proteins (and other proteins) and causes a marked enhancement in binding of the P-R by exposing many additional acceptor sites. During cytodifferentiation, the masking components (the cylinders) would be shifted from one acceptor site to another, thereby preventing some while allowing others to respond to incoming steroid receptors.

### E. Reconstitution of the Masking Activity: Evidence for Specific Nonhistone Proteins with Masking Activity

Recently, the CP-2 proteins were reannealed to the NAP (the DNA–CP-3 complex) using a regressing concave gradient from 6 *M* GuHCl to 0 *M* GuHCl in specially designed chambers (G. Martin-Dani and T. C. Spelsberg, in preparation). Since it was originally designed for the acceptor proteins, this method is described in more detail in Section VII,A. In any event a remasking of a similar quantity of sites as measured in the original intact chromatin was achieved. The CP-2 fraction was then subfractionated

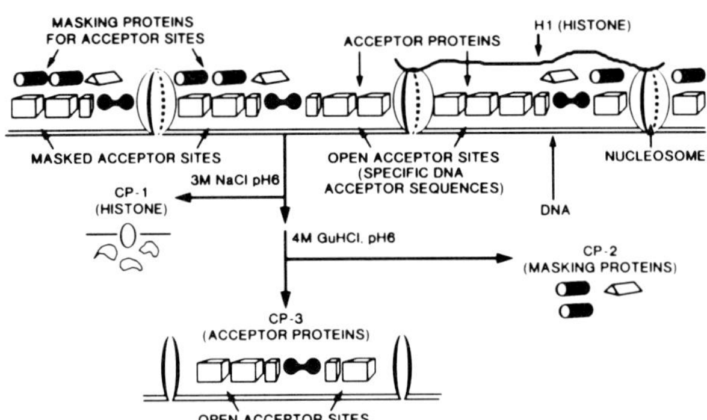


FIG. 15. Model of the oviduct chromatin with regard to steroid receptor action. This model depicts the DNA wrapping in and around the nucleosomes (Nu bodies) which contain all of the histones (CP-1 fraction) except the H1 histone species. The multitude of different nonhistone species are represented in large groups as symbols, i.e., one symbol represents many species. The cylinders represent masking proteins which are a part of the CP-2 fraction which masks the squares (i.e., the acceptor proteins). The squares which represent the acceptor proteins are a part of the CP-3 fraction. These acceptor proteins in turn sit on specific DNA sequences. Positions on the intact chromatin where the cylinders do not cover the squares represent the "open acceptor" sites for P-R; those with cylinders covering them represent masked sites. The model also depicts the removal of the CP-1 fraction with 3 *M* NaCl and the CP-2 fraction with 4 *M* GuHCl. The latter causes an unmasking of all acceptor sites, as depicted in the figure. From T. C. Spelsberg (unpublished data).

into three fractions, CP-2a, CP-2b, and CP-2c. As shown in Fig. 16, when a variety of proteins are reannealed to NAP, only one fraction, the CP-2b, representing only 10% of the CP-2 fraction, displayed the masking activity, i.e., markedly lowered the extent of binding of the P-R. The CP-2a fraction, ovalbumin and histones, display no masking activity. The increase in binding observed with the ovalbumin was observed occasionally and found to be caused by a protection of the acceptor sites from proteolytic activity occurring toward the end of the reconstitution. Since proteolytic but not nucleolytic action on chromatin can cause an unmasking of sites (see Fig. 3), protein(s) are believed to represent the masking factors (G. Martin-Dani and T. C. Spelsberg, in preparation). Since the CP-2b fraction dissociates from chromatin long after the histones and since the histones do not mask the acceptor sites, it is speculated that the masking activity is a specific class of nonhistone proteins. Preliminary analysis by molecular sieve chromatography using CL-Sepharose 6B in 6 *M* GuHCl (pH 6.0) suggest a very

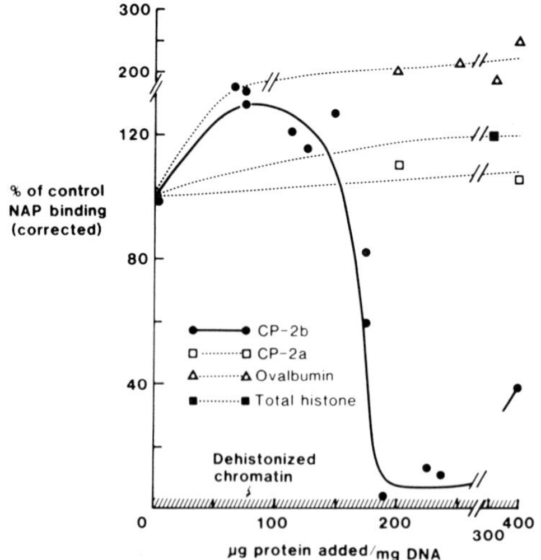


FIG. 16. Reconstitution of chromatin components which mask nuclear acceptor sites for progesterone. The CP-2 fraction of the chromatin proteins was subfractionated into several groups: CP-2a, CP-2b, and CP-2c, representing 10%, 6%, and 33% of the total chromatin protein, respectively. Two of these fractions, as well as standard ovalbumin and total histone, were reannealed to the NAP at increasing ratios of protein to DNA using methods described previously (Spelsberg *et al.*, 1976c, 1977a,b; Thrall *et al.*, 1978). After reconstruction, the DNA bound protein was separated from the unbound protein and the former assayed for P-R binding using the streptomycin assay (Webster *et al.*, 1976). The values are corrected for DNA binding. (●) CP-2b, (□) CP-2a, (△) ovalbumin, and (■) histone. The hatched area on the abscissa represents values for P-R binding to the dehistonized chromatin. From G. Martin-Dani and T. C. Spelsberg (in preparation).

heterogeneous population of masking "proteins" with monomer molecular weights ranging from 60,000 to 130,000 and possibly larger (G. Martin-Dani and T. C. Spelsberg, in preparation).

### F. The Role of Masking in the Controversy over Tissue-Specific Acceptor Sites

It is uncertain whether or not there is tissue specificity with respect to the nuclear acceptor sites for steroid receptors on chromatin. Since nontarget tissues do not have cytoplasmic receptors for the respective steroids, whether or not their chromatin contains acceptor sites for the steroid is, biologically speaking, of no consequence. The question arose from studies of cell-free binding assays wherein hybrid situations could be generated using nontarget cell chromatin and steroid receptors from target cells. Numerous laboratories reported that a variety of target cell nuclei for a variety of steroids contain markedly more acceptor sites than nontarget cell nuclei using cell-free binding assays (Brecher *et al.*, 1967; Jensen *et al.*, 1969b; Musliner *et al.*, 1970; King *et al.*, 1971; Mainwaring and Peterkin, 1971; O'Malley *et al.*, 1971, 1972; Spelsberg *et al.*, 1971b, 1972, 1976c, 1977a, 1979b; Steggles *et al.*, 1971; Gschwendt and Hamilton, 1972; King and Gordon, 1972; O'Malley *et al.*, 1972; Schrader and O'Malley, 1972; Schrader *et al.*, 1972; Higgins *et al.*, 1973a,c; Kalimi *et al.*, 1973; Buller *et al.*, 1975a,b; Jaffe *et al.*, 1975; Pikler *et al.*, 1976; Saffran *et al.*, 1976; Webster *et al.*, 1976). Many of these reports did not state that nontarget cell nuclei lacked any acceptor sites, but that they contained fewer numbers of them. Others reported a total lack of acceptor sites in certain nontarget cell chromatin (Webster *et al.*, 1976; Spelsberg *et al.*, 1976b). The term "tissue-specific" nuclear binding may be misleading an "enhanced" binding in target tissue nuclei may be more appropriate.

In contrast, a few laboratories have reported that they observed no difference in nuclear binding between the chromatin of target and nontarget cells (Clark and Gorski, 1969; Chamness *et al.*, 1973; Higgins *et al.*, 1973c). In these studies, different steroid–target tissue systems and different binding conditions were used. These factors probably explain the discrepancy. First of all, the properties of the steroid and the ionic conditions can play a significant role in the extent of the cell-free binding to a particular chromatin, as discussed in Sections IV,B,2 and 4. The masking of a multitude of acceptor sites, however, may also explain the discrepancy in the reports on tissue-specific acceptor sites. Sections IV,B,1, VI,E, and Fig. 3 have revealed that mild protease treatment of chromatin results in the unmasking of acceptor sites (G. Martin-Dani and T. C. Spelsberg, in preparation). Since proteolytic activity is detected in both steroid receptor preparations and in the nuclei or chromatin (see Section IV,B,1), it is very possible that some studies were performed under conditions allowing mild proteolysis to occur. Indeed, as discussed in Section IV,B,1, when [$^{14}$C]ovalbumin is incubated in the cell-free assay and subsequently analyzed on SDS-polyacrylamide gel electrophoresis, proteolytic breakdown of the ovalbumin is observed under certain conditions (T. C. Spelsberg, unpublished results). Many of the conditions that enhance proteolysis such as use of crude cytosol, temperatures above 4°C, and long periods of incubation were used in some studies reporting a lack of tissue specific acceptor sites on chromatin (Clark and Gorski, 1969; Chamness *et al.*, 1973; Higgens *et al.*, 1973c). Thus, the chromatin from nontarget tissues, which normally may display no steroid receptor binding (i.e., no exposed acceptor sites), when subjected to mild proteolysis during cell-free binding do generate significant binding of the steroid receptor. In this instance, a lack of tissue-specific acceptor sites is observed.

### G. Role of Masking in the Controversy over Saturable Binding of Acceptor Sites in Cell-Free Binding Assays

Unsaturable binding to nuclear acceptor sites has been reported for a couple of steroid–target tissue systems using the cell-free binding assays. While some of these studies can be explained by low ionic conditions (Spelsberg *et al.*, 1976b), other studies using estradiol (Chamness *et al.*, 1974) and glucocorticoids (Milgrom and Atger, 1975) included adequate ion concentrations to achieve saturable binding. As discussed in Section IV,C,4, recent studies in this laboratory revealed that the high adsorptivity of certain steroids such as estrogen causes significant nonspecific, nonsaturable binding to nuclei in cell-free assays (Kon *et al.*, 1980). The evidence for proteins masking acceptor sites and the action of proteases on this masking gives an alternative explanation for the apparent nonsaturable binding in the cell-free assays.

As shown in Fig. 3, very mild proteolytic action on oviduct chromatin causes a rise in the binding of the P-R. Based on the evidence discussed in Section VI,E, the protease is degrading the masking proteins. As discussed above, analysis for proteolytic activity in cell-free nuclear binding assays reveals minimal activity in assays incubated for 90 minutes at 4°C using partially purified receptor preparations. Incubations for periods longer than 90 minutes, or under higher temperatures, or in the presence of a crude receptor preparation results in significant proteolytic activity and actually causes an increase in P-R binding (G. Martin-Dani and T. C. Spelsberg, in preparation). Therefore, the conditions in a cell-free binding assay can readily cause an increase (i.e., an unmasking) of acceptor sites to create the appearance of a nonsaturable binding to nuclear acceptor sites.

## VII. CHEMICAL CHARACTERIZATION OF THE NUCLEAR ACCEPTOR SITES FOR THE AVIAN OVIDUCT PROGESTERONE RECEPTOR

### A. Role of Chromatin Protein Fraction 3 (CP-3) and DNA in the Nuclear Acceptor Sites

#### 1. *Reconstitution of Proteins to DNA*

It is necessary to establish methods to assay for the acceptor as it is being purified as well as methods for fractionating the chromatin proteins. Two unique approaches have been developed using different hormone systems. Puca *et al.* (1974, 1975) pioneered the use of nuclear protein immobilization on activated Sepharose and the measurement of the affinity of binding of the steroid receptor (crude and purified) to this matrix to identify the high affinity acceptor among nuclear fractions. The other approach, used mainly by the author, utilizes acceptor protein either natively bound to DNA or reconstituted back to DNA. It is apparent that different assumptions are being made by the respective groups. In the first case, it is assumed that a steroid–receptor complex will interact with the isolated protein alone, while in the second it is reasoned that either the protein or a DNA–protein complex is a more native state for the interaction.

Evidence will be presented below which supports that the reconstitution of the acceptor proteins to DNA does renature the acceptor sites for the avian oviduct progesterone receptor–acceptor system with properties similar to those of the undissociated acceptor sites.

*a. Reconstitution of Chromatin Proteins to DNA.* The removal of the components from the DNA in chromatin requires the use of denaturing agents. Solvents containing a high concentration of salt (e.g., 2..0 *M* NaCl) do not quantitatively remove all chromosomal proteins from DNA. In past years, chaotropic agents [such as urea (Bekhor *et al.*, 1969; Gilmour and Paul, 1969, 1970; Huang and Huang, 1969; Elgin and Bonner, 1970; MacGillivray *et al.*, 1972; Monahan and Hall, 1973), GuHCl (Hill *et al.*, 1971; Arnold and Young, 1972; Levy *et al.*, 1972; Spelsberg *et al.*, 1976a,c, 1977a, 1979a,b; Thrall *et al.*, 1978)], formic acid (Elgin and Bonner, 1970), and detergents such as sodium dodecyl sulfate (SDS) (Shirey and Huang, 1969; Wilson and Spelsberg, 1973) have been used in place of, or in addition to, high salt for complete dissociation of proteins from the DNA. The possibility of denaturing "acceptor" activity, especially if it is a protein, is likely. The only recourse at this point is to renature the activity by (1) methods used to refold denatured enzymes and proteins to their biologically active forms (Tanford, 1968; Teipel and Kochland, 1971; Weber and Kuter, 1971; Teipel, 1972; Yazgan and Henkens, 1972; Carlsson *et al.*, 1973; Ahmad and Salahuddin, 1976; Lykins *et al.*, 1977), and (2) recombining proteins and DNA by methods for the reconstruction of nativelike deoxyribonucleoproteins (Spelsberg and Hnilica, 1970; Spelsberg *et al.*, 1971a, 1972, 1976c 1979b; Paul *et al.*, 1973; Axel *et al.*, 1974; Barrett *et al.*, 1974; Stein *et al.*, 1974, 1975; Chae, 1975; Gadski and Chae, 1976; Woodcock, 1977, Thrall *et al.*, 1978). The methods and conditions used to reconstruct nucleoproteins are similar to those used to renature proteins so when performing the former one may achieve the latter as well.

In short, if the acceptor activity is identified as DNA, there is less concern over denaturing this activity with the agents used to dissociate proteins. If it is identified with a protein or nucleoprotein, then such macromolecules will probably require refolding and reannealing to restore nuclear binding (acceptor) activity. If the acceptor is a small protein, like ribonuclease, with no quaternary structure and a relatively simple tertiary structure, it may refold spontaneously. Larger molecules or protein–DNA complexes require more involved procedures to renature the activity.

*b. Method of Reconstituting the Acceptor Activity on DNA.* The procedure for reannealing the isolated acceptor proteins to pure DNA was developed in part empirically and in part from the literature published over the

TABLE IV

IMPORTANT CONSIDERATIONS IN THE RECONSTITUTION OF THE ACCEPTOR "ACTIVITY" OF THE AVIAN OVIDUCT PROGESTERONE RECEPTOR[a]

1. A special chamber is used. The chamber contains inlet and outlet valves. The dialysis bags with the reconstitution mixture are placed in the chamber which sits on a rocking platform. The 6 *M* GuHCl in the chamber is gradually replaced by buffer using a peristaltic pump while the chamber is being rocked. Air bubbles perform the mixing both inside and outside the dialysis bags.
2. The following conditions were found to markedly affect the success of the reconstitution.
   a. The concentration of the DNA (0.5 mg/ml is best)
   b. The ratio of the protein and DNA (discussed in Section VI,B)
   c. The pH of the solvents (pH 6.0 is best)
   d. The period of the reverse gradient (10 hours)
   e. The removal of unbound protein and DNA from the reconstituted nucleoacidic protein
3. Other conditions such as the presence of small concentrations of reducing agent and EDTA were found to play only a moderate effect on a successful reconstitution

[a]Reproduced from T. C. Spelsberg and H. Toyoda, in preparation.

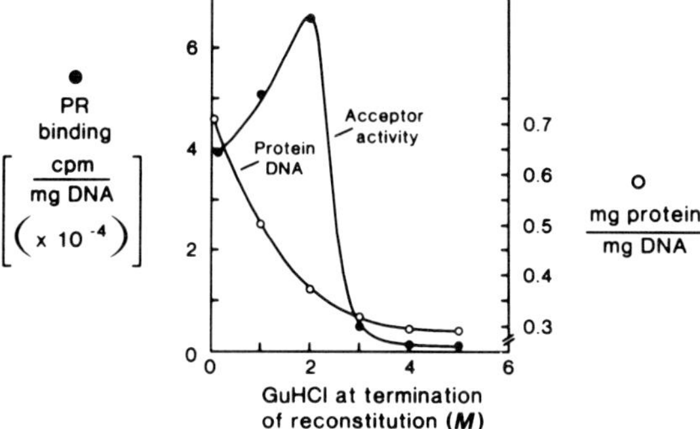


FIG. 17. Reconstitution of acceptor activity at various concentrations of GuHCl. The CP-3 fraction was reannealed to pure DNA using methods described in the text and elsewhere (Spelsberg *et al.*, 1976c, 1977a,b; Thrall *et al.*, 1978). When various concentrations of the GuHCl were reached (from the starting 6 *M* GuHCl), representative reconstitution assays were removed and the DNA (with bound protein) sedimented at $10^5$ *g* for 48 hours. The pellets were resuspended in dilute buffer, dialyzed, and analyzed for (○) protein to DNA ratio and (●) P-R binding (acceptor activity). From T. C. Spelsberg and H. Toyoda (in preparation).

past 20 years. Since the isolated chromatin proteins are hydrophobic, the proteins were originally reannealed to DNA to render a more soluble complex with which to assay acceptor activity. Later it was found that the DNA is critical for acceptor activity (see Section VII,C). Since NaCl–urea and GuHCl were used to dissociate the acceptor activity from the DNA, a method was developed following the classic reverse gradient techniques (Spelsberg and Hnilica, 1970; Spelsberg *et al.*, 1971a, 1972, 1977a,b; Paul *et al.*, 1973; Axel *et al.*, 1974; Barrett *et al.*, 1974; Stein *et al.*, 1974, 1975; Chae, 1975; Gadski and Chae, 1976; Woodcock, 1977; Woodcock *et al.*, 1980). The method was modified for achieving optimal amounts of active acceptor sites (Spelsberg *et al.*, 1976c, 1977a,b, 1979b; Thrall *et al.*, 1978; Spelsberg and Halberg, 1980) and several conditions were found to be critical. These are outlined in Table IV. Details of the method are described elsewhere (T. C. Spelsberg and H. Toyoda, in preparation). This method allows the monitoring of the acceptor activity for P-R as it dissociates from the chromatin and as it is being characterized and purified. Figure 17 shows that, during the reannealing of the CP-3 fraction to pure DNA, the acceptor activity is reconstituted to the DNA when the GuHCl concentration decreases from 6 *M* to 2 *M* GuHCl. At the lower concentrations of GuHCl, the activity decreases to some extent. This may be due to a blockade of some acceptor sites by "other proteins" and/or the action of proteases when GuHCl concentrations reach 0.5 *M* or less. In any case, the acceptor activity can be reconstituted on the DNA and the method can be used during further purfication steps to identify the acceptor activity.

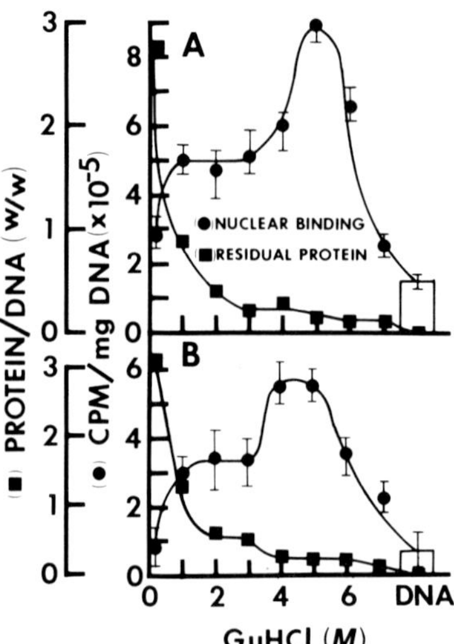


FIG. 18. Binding of [$^3$H]P-R to nuclear acceptor sites on residual deoxyribonucleoprotein after GuHCl extractions of chromatin. Binding of [$^3$H]P-R to hen oviduct chromatin–cellulose in (A) treated with GuHCl or unattached hen oviduct chromatin in (B) treated with GuHCl and centrifuged. In these experiments, portions of chromatin–cellulose or unattached chromatin were washed twice in 20 volumes of solutions with various concentrations of GuHCl buffered at pH 6.0. The cellulose resins were then washed in dilute Tris-EDTA buffer several times, frozen, and lyophilized. The free chromatin samples in various concentrations of GuHCl were centrifuged at $10^5$ *g* for 36 hours. The pellets of residual deoxyribonucleoproteins were resuspended in dilute Tris buffer at 1 mg DNA/ml and dialyzed versus the buffer. The residual material was tested for (■) protein and (●) acceptor activity using saturating levels of the P-R. The binding assays were performed essentially as described by Webster *et al.* (1976). The average and range of three replicate analyses for each assay of the hormone binding are shown. (A) Reproduced with permission from Spelsberg *et al.* (1975). (B) Reproduced with permission from Thrall *et al.* (1978).

### 2. *Identification of the Acceptor Activity with Specific Protein Fraction*

Figure 18 shows the acceptor activity remaining on the protein–DNA complexes after the oviduct chromatin was treated with various concentrations GuHCl. In Fig. 18A the chromatin was attached to cellulose while it was unattached in Fig. 18B. After each extraction of the chromatin–cellulose resin in Fig. 18A, the resin is washed with dilute buffers to remove traces of guanidine. The free chromatin (Fig. 18B) is first sedimented by ultracentrifugation to separate it from the dissociated protein. In each case, the residual nucleoprotein is resuspended in dilute buffer and dialyzed against the same buffer to remove traces of GuHCl. Acceptor sites are unmasked on the residual deoxyribonucleoprotein with the various extractions of GuHCl up to 4.0 *M*.

The level of unmasking achieved with the 4 *M* GuHCl (pH 6.0) is identical with that achieved using the 2 *M* NaCl–5 *M* urea (pH 6.0) shown in Fig. 11. As shown in Fig. 18, when the chromatin is extracted with 6 to 7 *M* GuHCl (or treated with phenol–chloroform or pronase as seen in Fig. 3B), the acceptor activity markedly decreases to levels found with pure DNA. The 7 *M* GuHCl treatment thus dissociates the CP-3 fraction which contains the "acceptor activity" from the DNA.

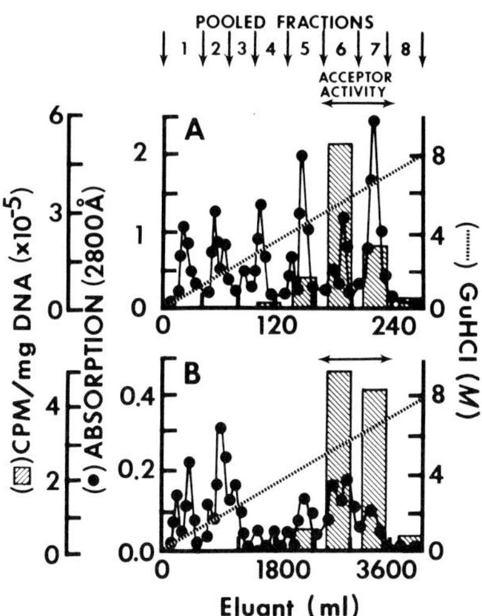


FIG. 19. Selective dissociation of proteins and acceptor activity from chromatin–cellulose and chromatin–hydroxylapatite resins. (A) Hen oviduct chromatin–cellulose resin was prepared as described elsewhere (Spelsberg *et al.*, 1975; Webster *et al.*, 1976). Briefly, 20 gm of this resin containing approximately 60 mg DNA as chromatin were resuspended in 100 ml cold phosphate buffer (pH 6.0) and allowed to hydrate for 2–6 hours with gentle stirring at 4°C. The resin was collected in a column and a gradient of 0–8 *M* GuHCl in phosphate buffer (pH 6.0) passed through the column with a 4 hour period. (B) Resins of chromatin–hydroxylapatite were prepared in the presence of 0.05 *M* $KPO_4$, pH 6.0. The resin containing 100 mg chromatin DNA and 100 gm hydroxylapatite was placed on the column and 4 ml fractions were collected under a 0–7 *M* GuHCl gradient. Tubes were monitored by absorption at 280 nm. Fractions were also monitored for conductivity as well as refractive index, and the gradient level of GuHCl plotted. Fractions from both resins were pooled according to their elution with each unit of concentration of GuHCl (1, 2, 3 *M*, etc.). Pooled samples were then dialyzed thoroughly against water and lyophilized. The lyophilized materials were resuspended in a small volume of water, homogenized in a Teflon pestle glass homogenizer, assayed for protein, and reannealed to pure hen organ DNA using a reverse gradient of 0 *M* GuHCl, as described in the text. The nucleoproteins were analyzed for acceptor activity by the streptomycin method (Webster *et al.*, 1976), subtracting the values obtained with pure DNA. This activity is presented as bar graphs. Total recoverable protein after dialysis and lyophilization was estimated to be 50% of the total protein placed on the column as chromatin–cellulose or chromatin–hydroxylapatite. (A) Reproduced with permission from Spelsberg *et al.* (1975). (B) Reproduced with permission from Spelsberg *et al.* (1977b).

The proteins dissociated from the chromatin DNA by the chromatin–cellulose and the chromatin–hydroxylapatite were then examined for acceptor activity. As depicted in Fig. 19, the fractions eluting from these resins were pooled according to the molarities of GuHCl in the eluants. These pooled samples were reconstituted to DNA and assayed for acceptor activity, i.e., progesterone receptor binding. Figure 19 shows that in both methods of fractionating the chromosomal proteins, the fractions dissociating from DNA between 4 and 6 *M* GuHCl contained the acceptor activity. Thus, only fraction CP-3 appears to contain this activity. The acceptor activity appears in the eluant when it disappears from the chromatin (see Fig. 18). The 4–7 *M* GuHCl fraction of the chromatin hydroxylapatite resin was subsequently used as a source of the acceptor activity and subjected to a series of analyses, first in the reconstitution assays and second as the starting point in the purification and chemical characterization of the acceptor activity.

### B. Nativeness of the Reconstituted Acceptor Sites

The binding of the P-R to the reconstituted NAP displays the same requirements (shown in Fig. 7) as was determined for the native (undissociated) NAP and chromatin. Further, as shown in Fig. 20, the receptor preparations isolated at various periods of the year display a seasonal rhythm in binding to the same preparation of reconstituted NAP as is observed for the native NAP and whole chromatin (refer to Figs. 9 and 12). These results indicate that the reconstituted NAP is very similar to the native NAP which in turn displays the same seasonal pattern of nuclear binding as found *in vivo*

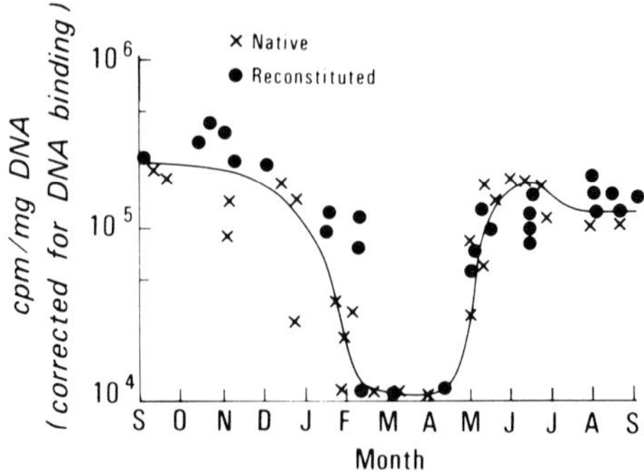


Fig. 20. Comparison of acceptor activities in native (undissociated) and reconstituted NAP. The binding of P-R isolated at various periods of the year to native (undissociated) NAP and reconstituted NAP were performed essentially as described in the legends of Figs. 9 and 12A. Reproduced with permission from Spelsberg and Halberg (1980).

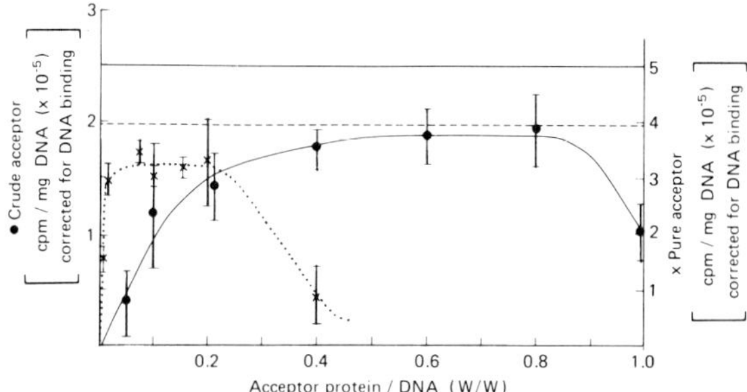


FIG. 21. Effects of varying quantities of the acceptor protein added to DNA on the acceptor activity of the reconstituted NAP. The acceptor proteins were obtained from the 4–7 *M* GuHCl extract from hydroxylapatite–hen oviduct chromatin resin. These were reannealed to the hen DNA in varying quantities using a reverse gradient of 6 to 0 *M* GuHCl, as described in the text. The DNA concentration was 0.2 mg/ml. After reconstitution the pelleted DNA-protein was resuspended in the dilute Tris buffer (0.5 mg DNA/ml) and analyzed for DNA and P-R binding. Pure DNA was also analyzed for hormone binding and the values subtracted from those obtained from the protein-DNA. (×) Reconstitution of acceptor proteins purified further by molecular sieve chromatography (agarose - 1.5 *M*). (---) Average binding levels of P-R to native NAP. Reproduced with permission from Spelsberg (1977b).

(see Fig. 12). The following section describing the quantitative titration of the acceptor activity on the DNA gives further support to the reconstitution of native acceptor sites on pure DNA.

## C. EVIDENCE FOR SPECIFIC DNA SEQUENCE(S) FOR THE ACCEPTOR SITES

Figure 21 shows the reconstitution of the acceptor activity (binding of the progesterone receptor activity) as a function of the ratio of the CP-3 protein to DNA. Two interesting aspects arose from these studies. First, the reconstitution of the acceptor activity to pure DNA is saturable. Second, the level of progesterone receptor binding at this saturation is approximately the same level measured in native (undissociated) NAP (see broken line in Fig. 21). These results suggest a DNA sequence specificity for the acceptor "factor" which is detectable by the reconstitution methods described earlier.

To further analyze this possibility, the CP-3 fraction was reannealed to DNA from different sources containing different sequences. As shown in Fig. 22A, when the CP-3 is reannealed to bacterial or salmon sperm DNA or to poly(dG-C)(dC-G) little or no acceptor activity (corrected for the respective pure DNA binding) is detected. When reannealed to poly(dA-T)(dT-A), however, a marked level of binding is achieved. There is little difference in the bindings of the progesterone receptor to the pure DNA from various

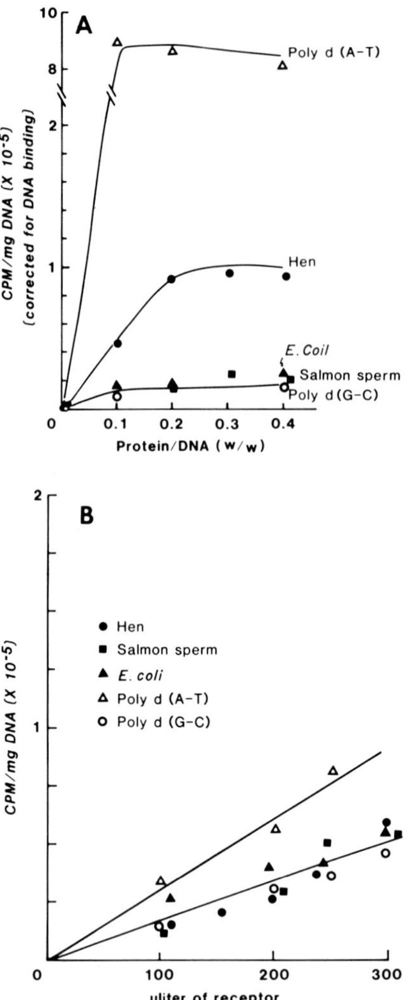


FIG. 22. Binding of [$^3$H]P-R to reconstituted NAP and various DNA's. (A) The binding of [$^3$H]P-R to reconstituted NAP containing DNA from various sources. The NAP's were reconstituted using the various DNA's and increasing levels of hen oviduct acceptor protein (CP-3 fraction). The bindings were performed at a saturating receptor level. The various reconstituted NAPs contained (●) hen DNA; (■) Salmon sperm DNA; (▲) *E. coli* DNA; (○) poly d(G-C); (△) poly d(A-T). The binding values to the various pure DNA preparations were subtracted from the corresponding DNA reconstituted as NAP. (This gives the "corrected for DNA binding.") (B) The binding of P-R to the pure DNA isolated or obtained from different species or sources. Various DNA's except hen DNA are purchased from PL Biochemicals (Milwaukee, WI.). The DNA's are further purified to less than 1% (w/w) protein and RNA. The mean of four replicate analyses of each receptor level for each DNA is presented in each panel. From H. Toyoda and T. C. Spelsberg (in preparation).

sources (Fig. 22B). Thus, not only does DNA seem to be required for acceptor activity but specific sequences of DNA may be essential.

These studies are currently being pursued using nuclease and restriction enzyme fragments of the undissociated NAP. Preliminary studies indicate that the DNA sequence bound by the CP-3 proteins are of the intermediate repetitive to highly repetitive sequences and spread throughout the genome of chickens (H. Toyoda, C. D. Liarakos, M. J. Getz, and T. C. Spelsberg, in preparation).

### D. Specific Class of Nonhistone Chromatin Proteins with Acceptor Activity: Chemical Characterization

#### 1. *The Acceptor Factor as a Protein*

Two early studies were performed to determine whether or not the acceptor activity was due to protein(s). Figure 3B shows that when the NAP is treated with pronase, most of the acceptor activity is lost. Figure 23 shows that, when isolated CP-3 is subjected to increasing degrees of proteolysis and then reannealed to DNA, a loss in the acceptor function occurs. No such loss in acceptor function is observed when the CP-3 protein is subjected to ribonuclease action (T. C. Spelsberg, unpublished data).

A more physical chemical approach was used to show the proteinaceous property of the acceptor activity. Figure 24 shows the patterns of isopycnic centrifugation of the DNA-free acceptor "activity." Standards for protein, RNA, and DNA were also applied to similar gradients. The gradients consisted of 6 *M* GuHCl with increasing concentrations of $CsCl_2$ and run at 5°C for 72 hours. This method was developed for application to hydrophobic proteins (T. C. Spelsberg, unpublished results). Fractions from the gradient were collected, pooled as shown in the figure, reannealed to the DNA at varying protein to DNA ratios, and the reconstituted NAP assayed for acceptor activity. All acceptor activity bands in the density region of proteins. Thus, the acceptor factor behaves as a protein with regard to proteolytic destruction and density. The acceptor will be termed acceptor protein in subsequent discussion.

#### 2. *Some Chemical Properties of the Acceptor Proteins*

For these studies, the CP-3 fraction containing the acceptor protein was isolated by chromatin–hydroxylapatite chromatography. Briefly, histones (CP-1) are removed by 3 *M* NaCl (pH 6.0). The CP-2 fraction (containing the masking activity) is removed with 4 *M* GuHCl (pH 6.0). The CP-3 fraction (containing the acceptor activity) is then removed with 7 *M* GuHCl (pH 6.0). The CP-3 fraction is then concentrated in an Amicon hollow fiber dialyzer/

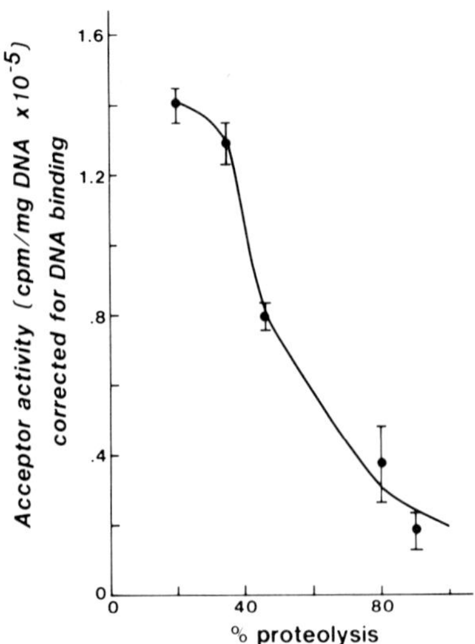


FIG. 23. Effects of proteolysis on the CP-3 fraction on the P-R acceptor activity. The CP-3 fraction in dilute buffer was subjected to endogenous proteolytic action by incubations at 4°C over a 4 day period. [$^{14}$C]Ovalbumin was included in the incubation solutions to serve as an indicator of proteolysis. Part of the solutions were applied to SDS-polyacrylamide gel electrophoresis, the gels sliced, and counted. The percent of the total gel radioactivity that is measured in the ovalbumin migration zone is used to calculate the percent proteolysis. The other portion of the incubation solution is reannealed to pure DNA and analyzed for P-R binding. The P-R binding is plotted against the percent proteolysis. The mean and standard deviation of four replicate binding analyses is shown. From T. C. Spelsberg (unpublished results).

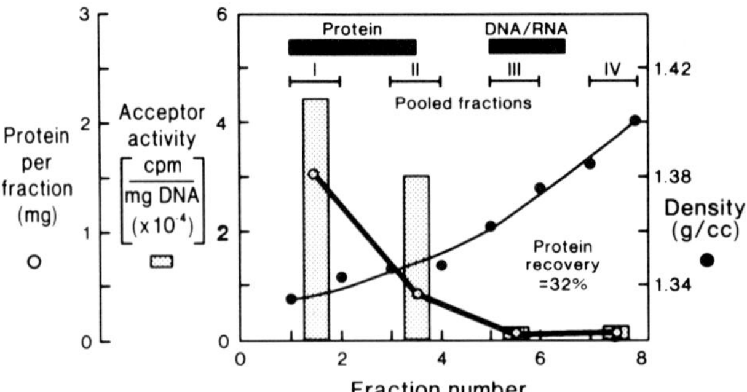


FIG. 24. The CP-3 protein fraction was placed in 6 *M* GuHCl buffered at pH 6.0 and the solution layered over a gradient of 10 to 50% $CsCl_2$ in 6 *M* GuHCl in SW 50.1 rotor tubes. The tubes were centrifuged for 72 hours at 100,000 *g*. Some tubes contained standard DNA, RNA, or protein. Fractions of the gradients were collected and the (●) density determined. The fractions were then pooled as depicted in the figure, and the (○) protein content quantitated. These fractions were reannealed to pure DNA and the reconstituted NAP assessed for P-R binding (acceptor activity) as illustrated by the bars. Values for DNA binding were subtracted from the respective NAP binding values. From T. C. Spelsberg (unpublished results).

concentrator, dialyzed against water, lyophilized, and stored as a lyophilized powder at room temperature. It is this stock CP-3 fraction that was used in the following analysis and those in Figs. 25 through 27.

Figure 25 shows the elution of total protein and the acceptor activity from a 5 × 100 cm column of CL-Sepharose 6B using 6 *M* GuHCl buffered at pH 6.0 as the solute. The fractions were pooled into six large groups (as shown in the figure) and each fraction reannealed to DNA and assayed for receptor binding. Although some of the activity elutes near the void volume, the bulk of the acceptor elutes near the inclusion volume of the column in the molecular weight range of 14,000 and 18,000. When resins with exclusion sizes, e.g., Sephadex G-200 or agarose 0.5 *M* were used with 6 *M* GuHCl, the activity eluted near or at the void volumes.

Figure 26 shows the focusing pattern of acceptor activity and total protein using the LKB flat bed gel apparatus with Superfine G-60 Sephadex in 6 *M* urea and ampholines for a 3 to 10 pH range. After focusing the fractions were pooled according to pH range and reconstituted to DNA. Two primary peaks with acceptor activity are observed, one focusing around pH 5.0 and the other over a broader range of pH 6 to 7.5. These proteins clearly are not histones since they elute from the DNA at much higher GuHCl concentrations than histones and they focus in acidic pH range while histones focus at the extreme basic pH range. The broad range of the one peak of activity on the gel suggests more than one species.

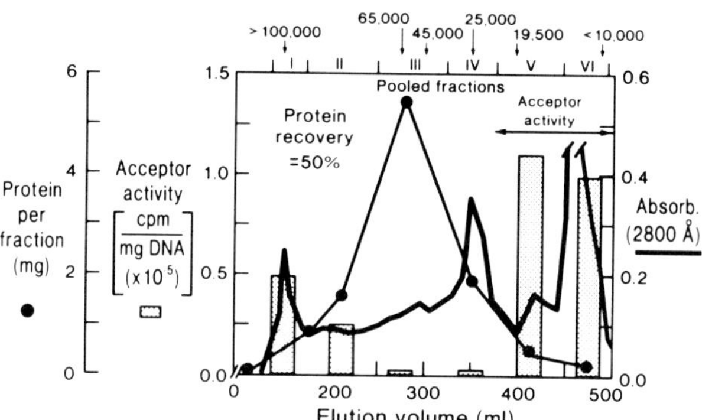


FIG. 25. CL-Sepharose 6-B molecular sieve chromatography of the CP-3 and acceptor activity. The CP-3 protein fraction was resuspended in a 6 *M* GuHCl solution at 2 mg protein/ml. This protein solution was clarified by centrifugation at 20,000 *g* for 10 minutes and then applied to a 2.6 × 94 cm column of the resin. The eluted fractions were pooled according to the absorbing peaks (——) as shown in the figure. The pooled fractions were quantitated for (●) protein and then reannealed to DNA and assayed for "acceptor" activity (as illustrated by the bars) using the streptomycin assay (Webster *et al.*, 1976). Values for DNA binding were subtracted from respective values obtained with nucleoprotein. The average of four replicates of the binding analysis are shown. From T. C. Spelsberg (unpublished results).

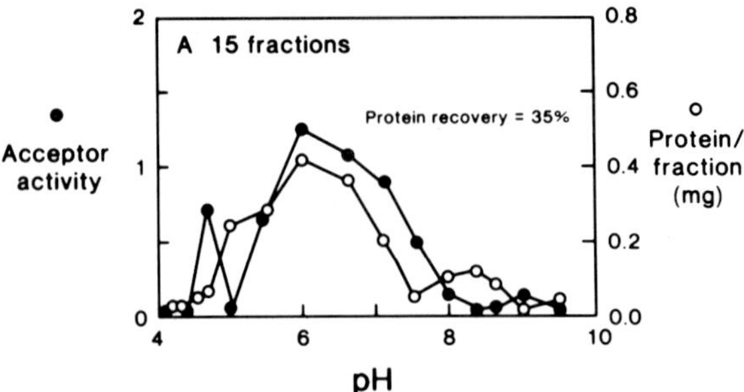


FIG. 26. Isoelectric focusing of acceptor activity in Sephadex resin and 6 *M* urea. The CP-3 fraction of chromatin proteins was applied to isoelectric focusing on flat beds containing ultrafine Sephadex G-60. The resins contained pH 3–10 ampholines and 6 *M* urea. After 12 hours of focusing, the resin was sectioned, the sections tested for pH and placed in columns, and the protein eluted by 6 *M* GuHCl. The fractions were dialyzed, lyophilized, and the (○) protein quantitated, the proteins reannealed to pure DNA and the (●) acceptor activity (P-R binding) measured. From T. C. Spelsberg (unpublished results).

That two or more species exist is supported in Fig. 27 where the elution of acceptor activity from octyl Sepharose using various concentrations of methanol and then 6 *M* GuHCl reveals two major peaks of activity. When other eluting solvents such as ethylene glycol and chaotropic salts (Na perchlorate, etc.) are used, two peaks of activity are also detected. The major peak of activity consistently elutes only at the higher concentrations of GuHCl or chaotropic salts suggesting the acceptor protein(s) are very hydrophobic. This in turn suggests that the proteins might lie in one of the two grooves of the DNA to interact with the hydrophobic base pairs in the center of the helix. Alternatively, the proteins might interact with each other in clusters on the DNA.

In any event, the acceptor activity probably is composed of two or more nonhistone proteins bound to specific sequences of the DNA. The proteins appear to be slightly acidic and of low molecular weight. The actual heterogeneity is not presently known since the extent of proteolytic degradation is difficult to determine. Attempts are now in progress to further purify these proteins from bulk quantities of chromatin.

Most studies on the quantitative nuclear binding of steroids estimate between 1000 and 10,000 biologically important nuclear acceptor sites per cell for a variety of steroid–target tissue systems (see Section III,B). If the masked sites are the same as the unmasked sites in the hen oviduct chromatin, then about 25,000 acceptor sites per cell are estimated (Table IV). Assuming that there is one P-R per one acceptor protein, that the acceptor proteins average about 15,000 in molecular weight, and using the facts that avian DNA contains $2.5 \times 10^{-12}$ gm DNA per diploid cell and that 1 mg chromatin DNA can be isolated from 1 gm of oviduct, it can be calculated that 10 kg of oviduct should yield 2.5 mg acceptor protein at 100% recovery. If the above assumptions are in reality close to the actual state, the purification of the acceptor protein(s) is feasible.

## E. Hypothetical Function(s) of the Acceptor Proteins

Figure 28 presents a hypothetical model of the functioning of the acceptor protein(s) and their DNA sequences(s). The model shows one of the two possible species of the steroid receptor (the B species) binding to the acceptor protein in the chromatin acceptor sites with the A species binding to the DNA to somehow activate transcription. This two subunit receptor theory was devised somewhat empirically based on the nuclear binding properties of the two receptor species (Schrader *et al.*, 1972; Buller *et al.*, 1976a; Vedeckis *et al.*, 1978). It should be mentioned, however, that the exact mechanism of binding of the receptors to the nuclear acceptor sites remains to be determined. The biological function of the A and B subunits of the chick oviduct progesterone receptor are obscure. It is not even known whether the steroid–receptor complex binds directly to the acceptor protein(s) or to the DNA in the vicinity of the acceptor protein–DNA sequence. The stoichometric relationship between the number of receptors and the number of acceptor proteins as well as the number of receptors bound to one

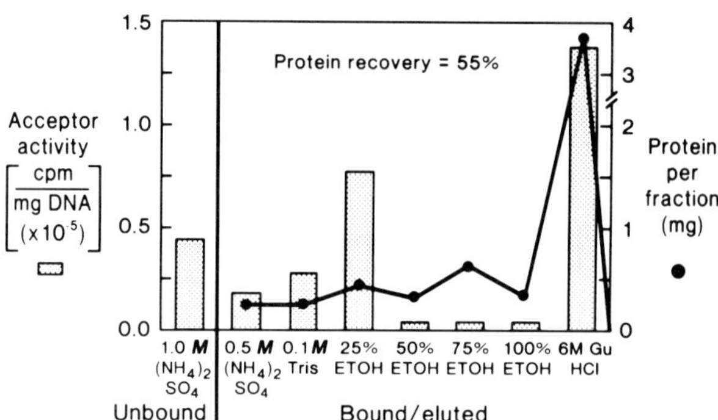


FIG. 27. Hydrophobic chromatography of the acceptor activity on octyl Sepharose. The lyophilized CP-3 fraction of chromatin was resuspended in 6 *M* GuHCl (pH 6.0) for several hours. The solution was dialyzed against 1 *M* $(NH_2)_2SO_4$ and the retentate clarified by centrifugation. The supernatant was applied to the octyl Sepharose column. Two to three column volumes of each of the listed solvents were passed through the resin and each collected. Each fraction was (●) quantitated for protein, reconstituted to DNA, and reconstituted NAP's were tested for P-R binding (acceptor activity), as depicted by the bars. From T. C. Spelsberg (unpublished results).

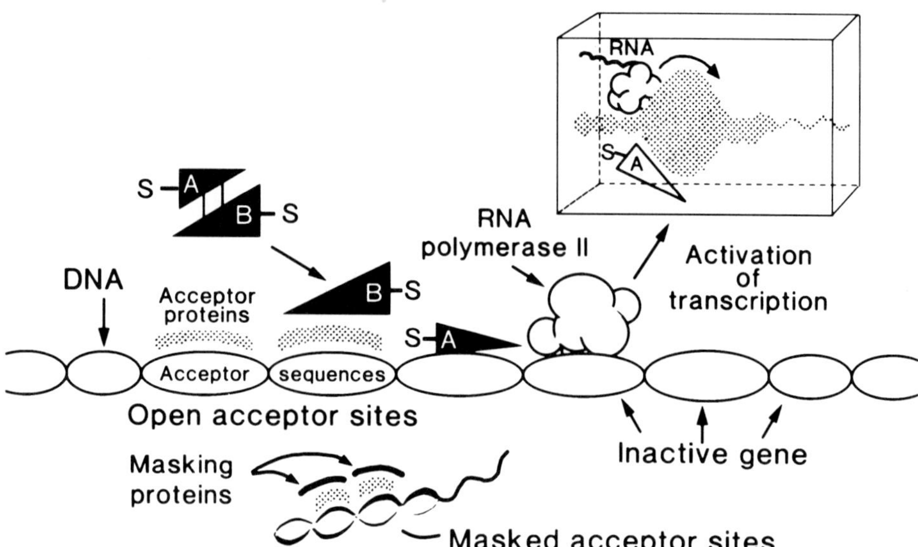


FIG. 28. Model of possible mechanism of action of steroids on transcription. In this scheme, the steroid–receptor complex enters the nucleus and binds to the acceptor sites, either directly to the acceptor proteins or to the adjacent DNA or both. The receptor would then activate transcription by modulating the DNA structure or affecting the polymerase itself. The acceptor proteins in this instance would serve either as a direct binding site for the steroid receptor or would perturb the DNA structure to allow the steroid–receptor complex to bind to the DNA. In this model, one of the two subunits of the P-R (the B species) binds to the protein, the A species binds to the adjacent DNA to activate transcription. The lower figure depicts "masked" acceptor sites and the upper figure, the unwinding of the DNA to initiate transcription.

functional sequence of the genome is not known. Lastly, if the receptor binds to the DNA, the mechanism by which the acceptor proteins function to enhance this binding is unknown. These and many other questions must first await the elucidation of the exact chemical nature of the acceptor sites, the isolation of the components, and the reconstruction of the acceptor sites with these components.

## VIII. RELATED FINDINGS IN OTHER STEROID–TARGET TISSUE SYSTEMS

Since the steroid receptors have very similar properties and the same basic functions in practically all systems, it is logical to assume that the fundamental properties and functions of the nuclear acceptor sites for all steroids will be similar (but not necessarily identical). Using similar methods as described above and elsewhere (Spelsberg *et al.*, 1971b, 1972, 1976c,

1977a,b, 1979b; Spelsberg, 1974; Pickler *et al.*, 1976; Webster *et al.*, 1976; Thrall *et al.*, 1978), the high affinity binding to chromatin in cell-free assays, the masking phenomenon, and the high affinity saturable binding to the unmasked sites on NAP have been reported for other steroid target tissue systems. These are androgens in the rat prostate (Klyzesejko-Stefanowicz *et al.*, 1976), estrogens and progesterone in the sheep brain (Perry and Lopez, 1978), glucocorticoids in the rat liver (Hamana and Iwai, 1978), estrogens in the calf uterus (Ruh *et al.*, 1981), and progesterone in the guinea pig uterus (W. Leavitt, the Worcester Foundation, personal communication.) The basic results of these studies in general are very similar to those described in this chapter for the avian oviduct progesterone receptor and so will not be discussed here.

## IX. A BRIEF EXAMINATION OF SOME OTHER TYPES OF ACCEPTOR SITES

### A. Protein Acceptors

Of the many chemically characterized nuclear acceptor sites for steroid receptors described this past decade, only the pure DNA will be discussed in detail. Puca *et al.* (1974, 1975) and Mainwaring (1976) described a basic protein with a molecular weight of 60,000 which appeared to have high affinity for the estrogen receptor in the calf uterus and androgen receptor in rat prostate, respectively. The binding occurred in the absence of DNA. Since other nonchromatin basic proteins demonstrated similar estrogen receptor binding (Puca *et al.*, 1974, 1975), and since no further reports for these acceptors have been published in the past 6 years, these will not be discussed further. There have recently been two reports on the localization of a nuclear acceptor for the estrogen receptor in the nuclear matrix with minimal amounts of DNA. Since these studies are more anatomic than biochemical, they will be discussed in Section X.

### B. DNA Acceptors

It is undisputed that under cell-free conditions steroid receptors bind to DNA. Many laboratories have reported that a variety of steroid–receptor complexes bind to DNA (Baxter *et al.*, 1972; Clemens and Kleinsmith, 1972; King and Gordon, 1972; Musliner and Chader, 1972; Spelsberg *et al.*, 1971b, 1976c, 1977a,b, 1979a; Toft, 1972; Yamamoto and Alberts, 1974,

1975; Sluyser *et al.*, 1974; Andre and Rochefort, 1975; Rousseau *et al.*, 1975; Webster *et al.*, 1976; Thrower *et al.*, 1976; Alberga *et al.*, 1976; Simons *et al.*, 1976; Bugany and Beato, 1977; Simons, 1977; Cidlowski and Munck, 1978; Thanki *et al.*, 1978; Kallos and Hollander, 1978; Kallos *et al.*, 1978; Thrall and Spelsberg, 1980).

The binding of the receptor to DNA appears to be in part electrostatic interaction, decreasing with increasing ionic strength (King and Gordon, 1972; Toft, 1973; Yamamoto, 1974; Yamamoto and Alberts, 1974; Rousseau *et al.*, 1975; Yamamoto *et al.*, 1976; Spelsberg *et al.*, 1976b). The same is true of receptor binding to nuclei and chromatin (Pikler *et al.*, 1976; Webster *et al.*, 1976) but DNA binding, however, is reduced to a greater extent than chromatin or nuclei binding at higher ionic strengths (Spelsberg *et al.*, 1976b). The interaction apparently is not completely electrostatic in nature, however, as evidenced by the inhibitory effect of the intercalating drugs, ethidium bromide and 9-hydroxyellipticine, on receptor binding to DNA (Andre *et al.*, 1976). These compounds significantly reduced receptor binding to a double-stranded DNA-cellulose, but not to phosphocellulose or polyadenylic acid–cellulose.

The exact physiological significance of steroid receptor–DNA interactions remains to be demonstrated. One indication that DNA binding may have physiological significance has been reported by Yamamoto *et al.* (1976), who found that the response of mutant clones of cultured mouse lymphoma cells to glucocorticoids is paralleled by the DNA affinity of the receptor *in vitro*. Further, there have been reports of pseudospecific interactions in terms of preferences of steroid receptors for substituted over unsubstituted DNA's (Kallos *et al.*, 1978), for native over denatured DNA's (Andre *et al.*, 1976; Kallos and Hollander, 1978), for poly(dA-T) (Sluyser *et al.*, 1974; Kallos and Hollander, 1978), oligo(dT) or oligo(dC) (Thrower *et al.*, 1976; Thanki *et al.*, 1978) over other synthetic polydeoxyribonucleotides, for eukaryotic over prokaryotic DNA (Clemens and Klensmith, 1972), and finally for native DNA over RNA (Toft, 1972; Yamamoto and Alberts, 1974; Rousseau *et al.*, 1975).

The fact that DNase treatment of nuclei will reduce receptor binding or release previously bound receptor in a variety of steroid-target tissue systems supports the notion that DNA might play a role in acceptor activity (Harris, 1971; King and Gordon, 1972; Baxter *et al.*, 1972; Higgins *et al.*, 1973a,b,c; Buller *et al.*, 1975a). That this role may be an important one is implied by the analysis of the nuclear acceptor for the avian oviduct progesterone receptor described in Sections VII,A–C. These results suggest that the receptor binds either to DNA sites altered by chromosomal protein interaction or to protein sites modified by DNA interaction.

Other properties of the cell-free binding of steroid receptor to pure DNA, however, cast doubt on the notion that the DNA alone is representative of the nuclear acceptor sites *in vivo*. Tfhe affinity of the progesterone receptor for the DNA is significantly lower than that of the receptor for nuclei and chromatin, in the chick oviduct (Buller and O'Malley, 1976). Furthermore, the differences in binding of the steroid receptors to different DNA sequences are relatively small. In fact, many laboratories have found no differences in the binding of steroid–receptor complexes to the native DNA's of a variety of sources (Yamamoto and Alberts, 1974; Rousseau *et al.*, 1975; Alberga *et al.*, 1976; Simons, 1977; Kallos and Hollander, 1978). In most instances, the binding to pure DNA is not saturable, suggesting a nonspecific interaction (Sluyser *et al.*, 1974; Yamamoto and Alberts, 1974; Andre and Rochefort, 1975; Rousseau *et al.*, 1975; Buller and O'Malley, 1976; Alberga *et al.*, 1976; Simons *et al.*, 1976; Spelsberg *et al.*, 1976b; Webster *et al.*, 1976; Thanki *et al.*, 1978; Thrall and Spelsberg, 1980). It should be mentioned that this lack of DNA specificity could be due to the inability to detect a few specific sites among an overwhelming number of slightly lower affinity, nonspecific sites (Yamamoto and Alberts, 1975, 1976). Proof for these few specific sites, however, has yet to be reported.

Recent studies by Thrall and Spelsberg (1980) indicate that the binding of P-R to DNA does not correlate with the binding measured *in vivo* and reveal specific artifacts in the DNA-binding assays. The interaction of the chick oviduct P-R with various nuclear components displays a variable, nonsaturable binding of P-R to DNA whereas a saturable binding is observed with NAP. Three factors are identified which affected the binding of P-R to the DNA: (1) the conditions of the binding assay, (2) the properties of the receptor, and (3) the state of the DNA. The conditions in the binding assay which affect DNA binding are the choice of the blanks, the salt concentration, and the pH of the assay. The receptor preparations display their own characteristic levels of binding to native DNA. The basis of this DNA binding capacity by each preparation is unknown. Lastly, the purity and the integrity of the DNA also determines the level of binding of the P-R. Protein impurities, moderate degradation of the DNA by enzymatic or physical fragmentation, and ultraviolet light treatment greatly enhance the receptor binding to the DNA. The extent of binding to DNA depended on the degree of damage. Interestingly, totally denatured (single-stranded) DNA displays little or no binding of the P-R. As shown in Fig. 29, seasonal differences which are observed for the binding of P-R to chromatin *in vivo* and *in vitro* and to NAP *in vitro* do not occur with DNA. Thrall and Spelsberg (1980) concluded from their studies that under controlled conditions and by using DNA preparations as native as possible, minimal binding of P-R to pure DNA occurs.

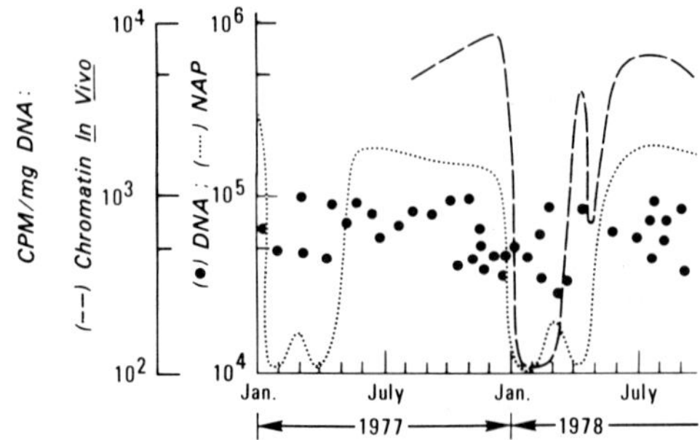


FIG. 29. Seasonal binding of various [$^3$H]P-R preparations to the same isolated DNA sample and NAP sample *in vitro* and to chromatin *in vivo*. Bindings were performed by the streptomycin method using saturating amounts of receptor, equivalent amounts of either DNA and NAP as described in the legend of Fig. 9. Results are plotted by the date on which each particular receptor was isolated. P-R binding is expressed on a logarithmic scale. (●) The means of four replicate analyses for DNA binding with each receptor preparation. (· · ·) Binding to the NAP *in vitro*, corrected for pure DNA binding. (---) Chromatin binding *in vitro*. Reproduced with permission from Thrall and Spelsberg (1980).

The numerous reports in the literature describing marked binding of the steroid–receptor complex to DNA may well be due to one of the three classes of conditions listed above. Further native or partially degraded DNA alone does not appear to represent the native nuclear acceptor sites for the chick oviduct P-R (Thrall and Spelsberg, 1980). In contrast, the DNA–nonhistone protein (acceptor protein) complexes did show characteristics of the nativelike acceptor sites.

## X. INTRANUCLEAR LOCALIZATION OF THE ACCEPTOR SITES

The intranuclear localization of acceptor sites for steroid receptors has not received much attention. As mentioned above, the DNA sequences involved in the nuclear acceptor sites for P-R in the chick oviduct involve at best 5% of the total cellular DNA and probably represent much less. The CP-3 fraction represents about 10% of the total chromatin protein but the more purified subfractions of CP-3 represent much less than 1.0% of the total chromatin protein. The localization of the acceptor proteins and their DNA sequences for the progesterone receptor in the chick oviduct have been investigated indirectly. Antisera to the CP-3 fraction was used in an immunofluorescent assay on oviduct sections to localize the CP-3 antigens (Chytil, 1975). Figure 30 shows sections with control antisera on the left and antisera to CP-3 fraction on the right. The antigenic sites are localized in the interior of the nuclei and not on the envelope nor in the cytoplasm. Therefore, the crude fraction containing the acceptor activity of the progesterone receptor appears to be of nuclear origin (at least this applies to the major antigenic sites) and not a cytological contaminant or structurally close to the nuclear envelope. The exact nuclear compartment on which this acceptor resides is still unclear.

There have been some direct studies on the intranuclear localization for acceptor sites of other steroid receptors. The intranuclear location of the estrogen receptors from bovine endometrial tissue (Jackson and Chalkley, 1974a,b) and androgen receptors from the rat ventral prostate (Lefebvre and Novosad, 1980) has been reported to be localized on the nuclear envelopes of those respective tissues. Unfortunately, only an indirect binding assay, i.e., binding of the free steroid, to the nuclear envelope, possibly involving exchange with nuclear bound receptors, was used to detect these sites. These "nuclear bound receptors" survived 0.4 *M* KCl and Triton X-100 treatments, conditions that cause a total dissociation of the progesterone receptor from the nuclear sites *in vivo* (Spelsberg, 1976) and *in vitro* (Pikler *et al.*, 1976; Thrall *et al.*, 1978).

Barrack and co-workers (1977, 1980) have reported that as much as 67% of the total nuclear bound dihydrotestosterone receptor and 100% of the salt resistant nuclear receptors are localized in the nuclear matrix of the rat ventral prostate. Similar results were obtained with estrogen in the chicken liver. Structurally, this nuclear matrix is composed of a residual nuclear

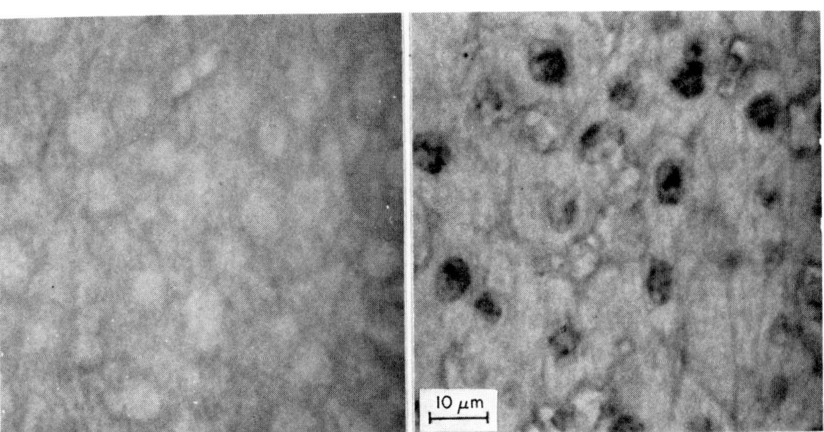


FIG. 30. Intracellular localization of CP-3 complexes in rat liver slices using antisera to the CP-3-DNA in the peroxidase bridge analysis. (Left) Adult rat liver slices incubated with control serum. (Right) Rat liver slices with anti-liver CP-3 protein antibody. The CP-3 was isolated according to Spelsberg *et al.* (1972) and antisera were prepared against the CP-3 according to Chytil and Spelsberg (1971). Reproduced with permission from Chytil (1975).

envelope with pore complexes, remnants of an internal fibrogranular network, and the residual nucleoli. Chemically, it contains 7% of the total nuclear protein and 2% of the total cellular DNA. They further found that a subfraction of the nuclear matrix, the internal ribonucleoprotein network, involving the internal network but not the peripheral lamina, contained the majority of the androgen receptors associated with the whole matrix (Barrack and Coffey, 1980). Interestingly, these sites displayed expected quantitative changes under different endocrine states of the animals. Unfortunately, these studies also involved an indirect binding assay, i.e., steroid exchange. As mentioned by these authors, the chemical nature of these binding sites remains obscure. These sites (receptors) survived 2 *M* NaCl extractions. The binding sites for the steroids, however, did display many properties characteristic of steroid receptors, including saturability, steroid specificity, high affinity, and low capacity.

The exact chemical characterization of the nuclear acceptor sites identified with the nuclear matrix awaits further investigation. It is interesting that the sites appear to be destroyed by a combination of DNase treatments, RNase, and dithiothreitol. It is possible that the acceptor sites for the avian oviduct progesterone receptor may reside in the nuclear matrix. The small amounts of DNA and protein located in the nuclear matrix could well contain the acceptor sites for the oviduct progesterone receptor as described above and in Section VII,C. The confusing aspect is that the estrogen and androgen "receptors" which are bound to the nuclear matrices survive 2 *M* NaCl extraction, a phenomenon not observed with the progesterone receptor in the avian oviduct and many other systems. It is possible that there are more than one type (class) of acceptor sites in the nucleus, one dissociable by high salt and one not (Barrack and Coffey, 1980). It is also possible, however, that there is only one class of acceptor site but there also exists secondary binding sites which are occupied after the receptors bind to the original acceptor site. These secondary sites may be functional sites for regulating gene transcription.

## XI. CONCLUSIONS

This chapter has dealt with the problems and progress in the chemical characterization of the nuclear acceptor sites for steroid receptors with major emphasis on the progesterone receptor of the avian oviduct. In regard to the latter, major effort is presently underway to purify to homogeneity the acceptor proteins, to prepare antisera (whole animal and monoclonal) against these proteins, and to use these antibodies to examine the masked and unmasked acceptor sites, the tissue and species specificity of the acceptor proteins, and to assist in the isolation of the specific DNA sequences bound by acceptor proteins.

It is this author's opinion that steroid receptors represent one class of intracellular gene regulators in eukaryotes. The nuclear acceptor sites may reside in or near structural genes or more distant at regulatory genes. The acceptor proteins and their specific DNA sequences may function only as recognition (binding) sites or may be involved in the regulation of transcription of these genes. Since there are thousands of nuclear acceptor sites, the DNA component may be a class of repetitive sequences (intermediate or highly repetitive), residing in many locations throughout the genome. These sequences may not necessarily be close to the steroid-regulated structural genes, but they or their neighboring sequences could transcribe products which in turn regulate these structural genes.

## REFERENCES


Ahmad, F., and Salahuddin, A. (1976). *Biochemistry* **15,** 5168–5175.

Alberga, A., Jung, I., Massol, N., Raynaud, J.-P., Raynaud-Jammet, C., Rochefort, H., Truong, H., and Baulieu, E.-E. (1971a). *Adv. Biosci.* **7,** 45–74.

Alberga, A., Massol, N., Raynaud, J.-P., and Baulieu, E.-E. (1971b). *Biochemistry* **10,** 3835–3843.

Alberga, A., Ferrez, M., and Baulieu, E.-E. (1976). *FEBS Lett.* **61,** 223–226.

Amrhein, J. A., Meyer, W. J., Jones, H. W., and Migeon, C. J. (1976). *Proc. Natl. Acad. Sci.* **73,** 891–894.

Anderson, J. N., Peck, E. J., and Clark, J. H. (1975a). *Endocrinology* **92,** 1488–1495.

Anderson, J. N., Peck, E. J., and Clark, J. H. (1975b). *Endocrinology* **96,** 160–167.

Andre, J., and Rochefort, H. (1975). *FEBS Lett.* **50,** 319–323.

Andre, J., Pfeiffer, A., and Rochefort, H. (1976). *Biochemistry* **15,** 2964–2969.

Arnaud, M., Beziat, Y., Guilleux, J. C., Hough, A., Hough, D., and Mousseron-Canet, M. (1971a). *Biochim. Biophys. Acta* **232,** 117–131.

Arnaud, M., Beziat, Y., Borgna, J. L., Guilleux, J. C., and Mousseron-Canet, M., (1971b). *Biochim. Biophys. Acta* **254,** 241–254.

Arnaud, M., Beziat, Y., Guilleux, J. C., and Mousseron-Canet, M. (1971c). *C. R. Acad. Sci.* **D272,** 635–638.

Arnold, E. A., and Young, K. E. (1972). *Biochim. Biophys. Acta* **157,** 482–496.

Axel, R., Melchoir, W., Sollner-Webb, B., and Felsenfeld, G. (1974). *Proc. Natl. Acad. Sci.* **71,** 4101–4105.

Bailly, A., Sallas, N., and Milgrom, E. (1977). *J. Biol. Chem.* **252,** 858–863.

Bardin, C. W., and Bullock, L. P. (1974). *J. Invest. Dermatol.* **63,** 75–84.

Barrack, E. R., and Coffey, D. S. (1980). *J. Biol. Chem.* **255,** 7265–7275.

Barrack, E. R., Hawkins, E. F., Allen, S. L., Hicks, L. L., and Coffey, D. S. (1977). *Biochem. Biophys. Res. Commun.* **79,** 829–836.

Barrett, T., Maryanka, D., Hamlyn, P. H., and Gould, H. J. (1974). *Proc. Natl. Acad. Sci.* **71,** 5057–5061.

Baulieu, E.-E., Alberga, A., and Jung, I. (1967). *C. R. Acad. Sci.* **D265,** 454–457.

Baxter, J. D., Rousseau, G. G., Bensen, M. C., Garcea, R. L., Ito, J., and Tomkins, G. M. (1972). *Proc. Natl. Acad. Sci.* **69**, 1892–1896.

Beato, M., Biesewig, D., Brindle, W., and Sekeris, C. E. (1969). *Biochim. Biophys. Acta* **192**, 494–507.

Beato, M., Kalimi, M., Konstam, M., and Feigelson, P. (1973). *Biochemistry* **12**, 3372–3378.

Bekhor, I., Kung, G. M., and Bonner, J. (1969). *J. Mol. Biol.* **39**, 351–364.

Beziat, Y., Guilleux, J. C., and Mousseron-Canet, M. (1970). *C. R. Acad. Sci.* **D270**, 1620–1623.

Boyd, P. A., and Spelsberg, T. C. (1979a). *Biochemistry* **18**, 3679–3685.

Boyd, P. A., and Spelsberg, T. C. (1979b). *Biochemistry* **18**, 3685–3690.

Brecher, P. I., Vigerski, R., and Wotiz, H. S. (1967). *Steroids* **10**, 635–651.

Bugany, H., and Beato, M. (1977). *Mol. Cell. Endocrin.* **7**, 49–66.

Buller, R. E., and O'Malley, B. W. (1976). *Biochem. Pharmacol.* **25**, 1–12.

Buller, R. E., Toft, D. O., Schrader, W. T., and O'Malley, B. W. (1975a). *J. Biol. Chem.* **250**, 801–808.

Buller, R. E., Schrader, W. T., and O'Malley, B. W. (1975b). *J. Biol. Chem.* **250**, 809–818.

Buller, R. E., Schwartz, R. J., Schrader, W. T., and O'Malley, B. W. (1976a). *J. Biol. Chem.* **251**, 5178–5186.

Buller, R. E., Schwartz, R. J., and O'Malley, B. W. (1976b). *Biochem. Biophys. Res. Commun.* **69**, 106–113.

Cake, M. H., Goidl, J. A., Parchman, L. G., and Litwack, G. (1976). *Biochem. Biophys. Res. Commun.* **71**, 45–52.

Capony, F., and Rochefort, H. (1975). *Mol. Cell. Endocrin.* **3**, 233–251.

Carlsson, U., Henderson, L. E., and Lindskog, S. (1973). *Biochim. Biophys. Acta* **310**, 367–387.

Chae, C. B. (1975). *Biochemistry* **14**, 900–906.

Chamness, G. C., Jennings, A. W., and McGuire, W. L. (1973). *Nature (London), New Biol.* **241**, 458–460.

Chamness, G. C., Jennings, A. W., and McGuire, W. L. (1974). *Biochemistry* **13**, 327–331.

Chan, L., Means, A. R., and O'Malley, B. W. (1973). *Proc. Natl. Acad. Sci.* **70**, 1870–1874.

Chan, L., Jackson, R. L., O'Malley, B. W., and Means, A. R. (1976). *J. Clin. Invest.* **58**, 368–379.

Church, R. B., and McCarthy, B. J. (1970). *Biochim. Biophys. Acta* **199**, 103–114.

Chytil, F. (1975). *Methods Enzymol.* **40**, 191–198.

Chytil, F., and Spelsberg, T. C. (1971) *Nature (London), New Biol.* **233**, 215–218.

Chytil, F., Glasser, S. R., and Spelsberg, T. C. (1974). *Dev. Biol.* **37**, 295–305.

Cidlowski, J. A., and Munck, A. (1978). *Biochim. Biophys. Acta* **543**, 545–555.

Clark, J. H., and Gorski, J. (1969). *Biochem. Biophys. Acta* **192**, 508–515.

Clark, J. H., Anderson, J. N., and Peck, E. J. (1973). *Adv. Exp. Biol. Med.* **36**, 15–59.

Clark, J. H., Peck, E. J., and Anderson, J. N. (1974). *Nature (London)* **251**, 446–448.

Clemens, L. E., and Kleinsmith, L. J. (1972). *Nature (London), New Biol.* **237**, 204–206.

Defer, N., Dastugue, B., and Kruh, J. (1974). *Biochimie Physiol. Pflanz.* **56**, 559–566.

Dounce, A. L., and Umana, R. (1962). *Biochemistry* **1**, 811–819.

Eisen, H. J. (1980). *Proc. Natl. Acad. Sci. U.S.A.* **77**, 3893–3897.

Elgin, S. C. R., and Bonner, J. (1970). *Biochemistry* **9**, 4440–4447.

Fanestil, D. D., and Edelman, I. S. (1966). *Proc. Natl. Acad. Sci.* **56**, 872–879.

Furlan, M., and Jericijo, M. (1967). *Biochim. Biophys. Acta* **147**, 145–153.

Gadski, R. A., and Chae, C. B. (1976). *Biochemistry* **15**, 3812–3817.

Gehring, U., and Tomkins, G. M. (1974). *Cell* **3**, 301–306.

Gilmour, R. S., and Paul, J. (1969). *J. Mol. Biol.* **40**, 137–139.

Gilmour, R. S., and Paul, J. (1970). *FEBS Lett.* **9**, 242–244.

Goidl, J. A., Cake, M. H., Dolan, K. P., Parchman, L. G., and Litwack, G. (1977). *Biochemistry* **16**, 2125–2130.

Gorski, J., and Gannon, F. (1976). *Annu. Rev. Physiol.* **38**, 425–450.

Gorski, J., and Raker, B. (1974). *Gynecol. Oncol.* **2**, 249–258.

Gorski, J., Toft, D. O., Shyamala, D., Smith, A., and Notides, A. (1968). *Recent Prog. Horm. Res.* **24**, 45–80.

Green, G. L., Closs, D. E., Fleming, H., DeSombre, E. R., and Jensen, E. V. (1977). *Proc. Natl. Acad. Sci. U.S.A.* **74**, 3681–3685.

Greene, G. L., Nolan, C., Engler, J. P., and Jensen, E. V. (1980). *Proc. Natl. Acad. Sci. U.S.A.* **77**, 5115–5119.

Griffin, J. E., Punyashthiti, K., and Wilson, J. D. (1976). *J. Clin. Invest.* **57**, 1342–1351.

Gschwendt, M. (1976). *Eur. J. Biochem.* **67**, 411–419.

Gschwendt, M., and Hamilton, T. H. (1972). *Biochem. J.* **128**, 611–616.

Hamana, K., and Iwai, K. (1978). *J. Biochem. (Toyko)* **83**, 279–286.

Hamilton, T. H., Teng, C. S., and Means, A. R. (1968). *Proc. Natl. Acad. Sci.* **59**, 1265–1272.

Harris, S. E., Rosen, J. M., Means, A. R., and O'Malley, B. W. (1975). *Biochemistry* **14**, 2071–2081.

Harrison, R. W., Fairfield, S., and Orth, D. N. (1974). *Biochem. Biophys. Res. Commun.* **61**, 1262–1267.

Hemminki, K., and Vauhkonen, M. (1977). *Biochim. Biophys. Acta* **474**, 109–116.

Higgins, S. J., Rousseau, G. G., Baxter, J. D., and Tomkins, G. M. (1973a). *Proc. Natl. Acad. Sci.* **70**, 3415–3418.

Higgins, S. J., Rousseau, G. G., Baxter, J. D., and Tomkins, G. M. (1973b). *J. Biol. Chem.* **248**, 5866–5872.

Higgins, S. J., Rousseau, G. G., Baxter, D. D., and Tomkins, G. M. (1973c). *J. Biol. Chem.* **248**, 5873–5879.

Hill, R. J., Poccia, D. L., and Doty, P. (1971). *J. Mol. Biol.* **61**, 445–462.

Horowitz, S. B., and Moore, L. C. (1974). *J. Cell Biol.* **60**, 405–415.

Horwitz, K. B., McGuire, W. L., Pearson, O. H., and Segaloff, A. (1975). *Science* **189**, 726–727.

Huang, R. C. C., and Huang, P. C. (1969). *J. Mol. Biol.* **39**, 365–378.

Jackson, V., and Chalkley, R. (1974a). *J. Biol. Chem.* **249**, 1615–1626.

Jackson, V., and Chalkley, R. (1974b). *J. Biol. Chem.* **249**, 1627–1636.

Jaffe, R. C., Socher, S. H., and O'Malley, B. W. (1975). *Biochim, Biophys Acta* **399**, 403–419.

Jensen, E. V., and DeSombre, E. R. (1972). *Annu. Rev. Biochem.* **41**, 203–230.

Jensen, E. V., and Jacobson, H. I. (1962). *Recent Prog. Horm. Res.* **18**, 387–414.

Jensen, E. V., Suzuki, T., Kawashima, T., Stumpf, W. E., Jungblut, P. W., and DeSombre, E. R. (1968). *Proc. Natl. Acad. Sci.* **59**, 632–638.

Jensen, E. V., DeSombre, E. R., Jungblut, P. W., Stumpf, W. E., and Roth, L. J. (1969a). *In* "Autoradiography of Diffusible Substances" (L. J. Roth and W. E. Stumpf, eds.), pp. 81–97. Academic Press, New York.

Jensen, E. V., Numata, M., Smith, S., Suzuki, T., Brecher, P. I., and DeSombre, E. R. (1969b). *Dev. Biol., Suppl.* **3** 151–171.

Jensen, E. V., Brecher, P. I., Numata, M., Mohla, S., and DeSombre, E. R. (1973). *Adv. Enzyme Regul.* **11**, 1–16.

Jensen, E. V., Mohla, S., Gorell, T. A., and DeSombre, E. R. (1974). *Vit. Horm. (N.Y.)* **32**, 89–127.

Kalimi, M., Beato, M., and Feigelson, P. (1973). *Biochemistry* **12**, 3365–3371.

Kalimi, M., Tsai, S. Y., Tsai, M. J., Clark, J. H., and O'Malley, B. W. (1976). *J. Biol. Chem.* **251**, 516–523.

Kallos, J., and Hollander, V. (1978). *Nature (London)* **272**, 177–179.

Kallos, J., Fasy, T., Hollander, V., and Beck, M. (1978). *Proc. Natl. Acad. Sci. U.S.A.* **75**, 4896–4900.

King, R. J. B., and Gordon, J. (1966). *J. Endocrinol.* **34**, 431–437.

King, R. J. B., and Gordon, J. (1967). *J. Endocrinol.* **39**, 533–542.

King, R. J. B., and Gordon, J. (1972). *Nature (London), New Biol.* **240**, 185–187.

King, R. J. B., Gordon, J., and Inman, D. R. (1965a). *J. Endocrinol.* **32**, 9–15.

King, R. J. B., Gordon, J., and Martin, L. (1965b). *Biochem. J.* **97**, 28P.

King, R. J. B., Gordon, J., Cowan, D. M., and Inman, D. R. (1966). *J. Endocrinol.* **36**, 139–150.

King, R. J. B., Beard, V., Gordon, J., Pooley, A. S., Smith, J. A., Steggles, A. W., and Vertes, M. (1971). *Adv. Biosci.* **7**, 21–44.

King, R. J. B., and Mainwaring, W. I. P. (1974) *In* "Steroid Cell Interactions." Univ. Park Press, Baltimore, Maryland.

Klyzsejko-Stefanowicz, L., Chui, J. F., Tsai, Y. H., and Hnilica, L. S., (1976). *Proc. Natl. Acad. Sci.* **73**, 1954–1958.

Knowler, J. T., and Smellie, R. M. S. (1971). *Biochem. J.* **125**, 605–614.

Kon, O. L., Webster, R. A., and Spelsberg, T. C. (1980). *Endocrinology* **107**, 1182–1191.

Kuhn, R. W., Schrader, W. T., Coty, W. A., Conn, P. M., and O'Malley, B. W. (1977). *J. Biol. Chem.* **252**, 308–317.

Larrea, F., Benavides, G., Scaglia, H., Hofman-Alfaro, S., Ferrusca, E., Medina, M., and Perez-Palacros, G. (1978). *J. Clin. Endocrin. Metab.* **46**, 961–970.

Lebeau, M. C., Maisol, N., and Baulieu, E.-E. (1973). *Eur. J. Biochem.* **36**, 294–300.

Lefebvre, Y. A., and Novosad, Z. (1980). *Biochem. J.* **186**, 641–647.

Levy, S., Simpson, R. T., and Sober, H. A. (1972). *Biochemistry* **11**, 1547–1554.

Liang, T., and Liao, S. (1972). *Biochim. Biophys. Acta* **277**, 590–594.

Liao, S., Liang, T., and Tymoczko, J. L. (1972). *J. Steroid Biochem.* **3**, 401–408.

Liao, S., Liang, T., and Tymoczko, J. L. (1973). *Nature (London), New Biol.* **241**, 211–213.

Lippman, M., Hallerman, R., Perry, S., Levanthal, B., and Thompson, E. B. (1973). *Nature (London)* **242**, 157–158.

Little, M., Rosenfeld, G. C., and Jungblut, P. W. (1972). *Hoppe-Seylers Z. Physiol. Chem.* **53**, 231–242.

Little, M., Szendro, P. I., and Jungblut, P. W. (1973). *Hoppe-Seylers Z. Physiol. Chem.* **354**, 1599–1610.

Lohmar, P. H., and Toft, D. O. (1975). *Biochem. Biophys. Res. Commun.* **67**, 8–15.

Lykins, L. F., Akey, C. W., Christian, E. G., Duval, G. E., and Topham, R. W. (1977). *Biochemistry* **16**, 693–698.

MacGillivray, A. J., Camerson, A., Krauze, R. J., Rickwood, D., and Paul, J. (1972). *Biochim. Biophys. Acta* **277**, 384–402.

Mainwaring, W. I. P., and Peterkin, B. M. (1971). *Biochem. J.* **125**, 285–295.

Mainwaring, W. I. P., Symes, E. K., and Higgins, S. J. (1976). *Biochem. J.* **156**, 129–141.

Martin, P. M., and Sheridan, P. J. (1980). *Experientia* **36**, 620–622.

Maurer, H. R., and Chalkley, G. R. (1967). *J. Mol. Biol.* **27**, 431–441.

Middlebrook, J. L., Wong, M. D., Ishii, D. N., and Aronow, L. (1975). *Biochemistry* **14**, 180–186.

Milgrom, E., and Atger, M. (1975). *J. Steroid Biochem.* **6**, 487–492.

Milgrom, E., Atger, M., Baulieu, E.-E. (1970). *Steroids* **167**, 741–754.

Milgrom, E., Atger, M., and Baulieu, E.-E. (1973a). *Biochemistry* **12**, 5198–5205.

Mohla, S., DeSombre, E. R., and Jensen, E. V. (1972). *Biochem. Biophys. Res. Commun.* **46,** 661–667.

Monahan, J. J., and Hall, R. H. (1973). *Can. J. Biochem.* **51,** 709–720.

Mueller, G. C., Herranen, A. M., Jervell, K. J. (1958). *Recent Prog. Horm. Res.* **14,** 95–139.

Mulvihill, E. R., and Palmiter, R. D. (1977). *J. Biol. Chem.* **252,** 2060–2068.

Musliner, T. A., and Chader, G. J. (1972). *Biochim. Biophys. Acta* **262,** 256–263.

Musliner, T. A., Chader, G. J., and Villee, C. A. (1970). *Biochemistry* **9,** 4448–4453.

Noteboom, W. D., and Gorski, J. (1965). *Arch. Biochem. Biophys.* **111,** 559–568.

Notides, A. C., and Nielsen, S. (1974). *J. Biol. Chem.* **249,** 1866–1873.

O'Malley, B. W., and Means, A. R. (1974). *Science* **183,** 610–620.

O'Malley, B. W., McGuire, W. L., Kohler, P. O., and Korenman, S. G. (1969). *Recent Prog. Horm. Res.* **25,** 105–160.

O'Malley, B. W., Sherman, M. R., and Toft, D. O. (1970). *Proc. Natl. Acad. Sci. U.S.A.* **67,** 501–508.

O'Malley, B. W., Toft, D. O., and Sherman, M. R. (1971). *J. Biol. Chem.* **246,** 1117–1122.

O'Malley, B. W., Spelsberg, T. C., Schrader, W. T., Chytil, F., and Steggles, A. W. (1972). *Nature (London)* **235,** 141–144.

Palmiter, R. D., Moore, P. B., Mulvihil, E. R., and Emtage, S. (1976). *Cell* **8,** 557–572.

Panyim, S., Jensen, R. H., and Chalkley, R. (1968). *Biochim. Biophys. Acta* **160,** 252–255.

Panyim, S., and Chalkley, R. (1969). *Arch. Biochem. Biophys.* **130,** 337–346.

Pasqualini, J. R. (1976). *In* "Receptors and Mechanism of Action of Steroid Hormones," Parts I and II. Dekker, New York.

Paul, J., Gilmour, R. S., Birnie, G. D., Marrison, B. P., Hell, A., Humpheries, S., Windase, J., and Young, B. (1973). *Cold Spring Harbor Symp. Quant. Biol.* **38,** 885–890.

Peck, E. J., Burgner, J., and Clark, J. H. (1973). *Biochemistry* **12,** 4596–4603.

Perry, B. N., and Lopez, A. (1978). *Biochem. J.* **176,** 873–883.

Pikler, G. M., Webster, R. A., and Spelsberg, T. C. (1976). *Biochem. J.* **156,** 399–408.

Puca, G. A., and Bresciani, F. (1968). *Nature (London)* **218,** 967–969.

Puca, G. A., Sica, V., and Nola, E. (1974). *Proc. Natl. Acad. Sci.* **71,** 979–983.

Puca, G. A., Nola, E., Hibner, U., Cicala, G., and Sica, V. (1975). *J. Biol. Chem.* **250,** 6452–6459.

Puca, G. A., Nola, E., Sica, V., and Bresciani, F. (1977). *J. Biol. Chem.* **252,** 1358–1366.

Raspe, G. (1971). *Adv. Biosci.* **7,** 5–400.

Raynaud-Jammet, C., and Baulieu, E.-E. (1969). *C. R. Acad. Sci.* **D268,** 3211–3214.

Rosenau, W., Baxter, J. D., Rosseau, G. G., and Tomkins, G. M. (1972). *Nature (London), New Biol.* **237,** 20–24.

Rousseau, G. G., Higgins, S., Baxter, J. D., Gelfand, D., and Tomkins, G. M. (1975). *J. Biol. Chem.* **250,** 6015–6022.

Ruh, T. S., Ross, Jr., P., Wood, D. M., and Keene, J. L. (1981). *Biochem. J.* **200,** 133–142.

Saffran, J., Loeser, B. K., Bohnett, S. A., and Faber, L. E. (1976). *J. Biol. Chem.* **251,** 5607–5613.

Sala-Trepat, J. M., Hibner, U., and Vallet-Strouve, C. (1977). *Nucleic Acid Res.* **4,** 649–662.

Schrader, W. T., and O'Malley, B. W. (1972). *J. Biol. Chem.* **247,** 51–59.

Schrader, W. T., Toft, D. O., and O'Malley, B. W. (1972). *J. Biol. Chem.* **247,** 2401–2407.

Schrader, W. T., Heuer, S. S., and O'Malley, B. W. (1975). *Biology of Reproduction* **12,** 134–142.

Schrader, W. T., Coty, W. A., Smith, R. G., and O'Malley, B. W. (1977a). *Ann. N.Y. Acad. Sci.* **286,** 64–80.

Schrader, W. T., Kuhn, R. W., O'Malley, B. W. (1977b). *J. Biol. Chem.* **252,** 299–307.

Schwartz, R. J., Tsai, M. J., Tsai, S. Y., and O'Malley, B. W. (1975). *J. Biol. Chem.* **250,** 5175–5182.

Schwartz, R. J., Kuhn, R. W., Buller, R. E., Schrader, W. T., and O'Malley, B. W. (1976a). *J. Biol. Chem.* **251,** 5166–5177.

Schwartz, R. J., Schrader, W. T., and O'Malley, B. W. (1976b). *In* "Juvenile Hormones" (L. Gilbert, ed.), pp. 530–557. Plenum, New York.

Sekeris, C. E., and Lang, N. (1965). *Hoppe-Seyler's Z. Physiol. Chem.* **340,** 92–94.

Sheridan, P. J., Buchannon, J. M., Anselmo, V. C., Martin, P. M. (1979). *Nature (London)* **282,** 579–582.

Sherman, M. R., and Diaz, S. C. (1977). *Ann. N.Y. Acad. Sci.* **286,** 81–86.

Sherman, M. R., Corvol, P. L., and O'Malley, B. W. (1970). *J. Biol. Chem.* **245,** 6085–6096.

Sherman, M. R., Tuazon, F. B., Diaz, S. C., and Miller, L. K. (1976). *Biochemistry* **15,** 980–989.

Sherman, M. R., Pickering, L. A., Rollwagen, F. M., and Miller, L. K. (1978). *Fed. Proc. Fed. Am. Soc. Exp. Biol.* **37,** 167–173.

Shirey, T., and Huang, R. C. C. (1969). *Biochemistry* **8,** 4138–4148.

Shyamala, G. (1972). *Biochem. Biophys. Res. Commun.* **46,** 1623–1630.

Shyamala-Harris, G. (1971). *Nature New Biol.* **231,** 246–248.

Sibley, C. H., and Tomkins, G. M. (1974). *Cell* **2,** 221–227.

Simons, S. S. (1977). *Biochim. Biophys. Acta* **496,** 349–358.

Simons, S. S., Martinez, H. M., Gracea, R. L., Baxter, J. D., and Tomkins, G. M. (1976). *J. Biol. Chem.* **251,** 334–343.

Sluyser, M. (1966). *J. Mol. Biol.* **19,** 591–595.

Sluyser, M. (1969). *Biochim. Biophys. Acta* **182,** 235–244.

Sluyser, M., Evers, S. G., and Nijssen, T. (1974). *Biochem Biophys. Res. Commun.* **61,** 380–387.

Socher, S. H., Krall, J. F., Jaffe, R. C., and O'Malley, B. W. (1976). *Endocrinology* **99,** 891–900.

Spelsberg, T. C. (1974). *In* "Acidic Proteins of the Nucleus" (I. L. Cameron and J. R. Jeter, Jr., eds.), pp. 249–296. Academic Press, New York.

Spelsberg, T. C. (1976). *Biochem. J.* **156,** 391–398.

Spelsberg, T. C., and Hnilica, L. S. (1970). *Biochem J.* **120,** 435–437.

Spelsberg, T. C., and Cox, R. F. (1976). *Biochim. Biophys. Acta* **435,** 376–370.

Spelsberg, T. C., and Halberg, F. (1980). *Endocrinology* **107,** 1234–1244.

Spelsberg, T. C., and Toft, D. O. (1976). *In* "Receptors and the Mechanism of Action of Steroid Hormones" (J. R. Pasqualini, ed.), Part I, pp. 262–309. Dekker, New York.

Spelsberg, T. C., Hnilica, L. S., and Ansevin, A. T. (1971a). *Biochem. Biophys. Acta* **228,** 550–562.

Spelsberg, T. C., Steggles, A. W., and O'Malley, B. W. (1971b). *J. Biol. Chem.* **246,** 4188–4197.

Spelsberg, T. C., Steggles, A. W., Chytil, F., and O'Malley, B. W. (1972). *J. Biol. Chem.* **247,** 1368–1374.

Spelsberg, T. C., Webster, R. A., and Pikler, G. M. (1975). *In* "Chromosomal Proteins and Their Role in Gene Expression" (G. Stein and L. Kleinsmith, eds.), pp. 153–186. Academic Press, New York.

Spelsberg, T. C., Webster, R. A., and Pikler, G. M. (1976a). *Nature (London)* **262,** 65–67.

Spelsberg, T. C., Pikler, G. M., and Webster, R. A. (1976b) *Science* **194,** 197–199.

Spelsberg, T. C., Webster, R., Pikler, G., Thrall, C., and Wells, D. (1976c). *J. Steroid Biochem.* **7,** 1091–1101.

Spelsberg, T. C., Webster, R., Pikler, G., Thrall, C., and Wells, D. (1977a). *Ann. N.Y. Acad. Sci.* **286**, 43–63.

Spelsberg, T. C., Thrall, C. L., Webster, R. A., and Pikler, G. M. (1977b). *J. Toxicol. Environ. Health* **3**, 309–337.

Spelsberg, T. C., Knowler, J., Boyd, P. A., Thrall, C. L., and Martin-Dani, G. (1979a). *J. Steroid Biochem.* **11**, 373–388.

Spelsberg, T. C., Thrall, C. L., Martin-Dani, G., Webster, R. A., and Boyd, P. A. (1979b). *In* "Ontogeny of Receptor and Reproductive Hormone Action" (T. H. Hamilton, J. H. Clark, and W. A. Sadler, eds.), pp. 31–63. Raven, New York.

Steggles, A. W., Spelsberg, T. C., Glasser, S. R., and O'Malley, B. W. (1971). *Proc. Natl. Acad. Sci.* **68**, 1479–1482.

Stein, G. S., Spelsberg, T. C., and Kleinsmith, L. J. (1974). *Science* **183**, 817–824.

Stein, G. S., Mans, R. J., Gabbay, E. J., Stein, J. L., Davis, J., and Adawadkar, P. D. (1975). *Biochemistry* **14**, 1859–1866.

Stumpf, W. E. (1968). *Endocrinology* **83**, 777–782.

Stumpf, W. E. (1969). *Endocrinology* **85**, 31–37.

Stumpf, W. E., and Sar, M. (1976). *In* "Receptors and Mechanisms of Action of Steroid Hormones" (J. R. Pasqualini, ed.) Part I, pp. 41–84. Dekker, New York.

Sutherland, R. L., and Baulieu, E. E. (1976). *Eur. J. Biochem.* **70**, 531–541.

Swaneck, G. E., Chu, L. L. H., and Edelman, I. S. (1970). *J. Biol. Chem.* **245**, 5282–5389.

Talwar, G. P., Segal, J. J., Evans, A., and Davidson, O. W. (1964). *Proc. Natl. Acad. Sci.* **52**, 1059–1066.

Tanford, C. (1968). *Adv. Protein Chem.* **23**, 122–282.

Teipel, J. W. (1972). *Biochemistry* **11**, 4100–4107.

Teipel, J. W., and Kochland, D. E. (1971). *Biochemistry* **10**, 782–798.

Teng, C. S., and Hamilton, T. H. (1968). *Proc. Natl. Acad. Sci.* **60**, 1410–1417.

Thanki, K., Beach, T., and Dickerman, H. (1978). *J. Biol. Chem.* **253**, 7744–7750.

Thrall, T. C., and Spelsberg, T. C. (1980). *Biochemistry* **19**, 4130–4138.

Thrall, C., Webster, R. A., and Spelsberg, T. C. (1978). *In* "The Cell Nucleus" (H. Busch, ed.), Vol. VI, Part 1, pp. 461–529. Academic Press, New York.

Thrower, S., Hall, C., Lim, L., and Davidson, A. N. (1976). *Biochem. J.* **160**, 271–280.

Toft, D. O. (1972). *J. Steroid Biochem.* **3**, 515–522.

Toft, D. O. (1973). *In* "Receptors for Reproductive Hormones" (B. W. O'Malley and A. R. Means, eds.), pp. 85–96. Plenum, New York.

Toft, D. O., and Gorski, J. (1966). *Proc. Natl. Acad. Sci.* **55**, 1574–1581.

Tomkins, G. M. (1970). *Cold Springs Harbor Symp. Quant. Biol.* **35**, 635–640.

Tsai, S. Y., Tsai, M. J., Schwartz, R., Kalimi, M., Clark, J. H., and O'Malley, B. W. (1975). *Proc. Natl. Acad. Sci. U.S.A.* **72**, 4228–4232.

Tymoczko, J. L., and Liao, S. (1971). *Biochim. Biophys. Acta* **252**, 607–611.

Vedeckis, W. V., Schrader, W. T., and O'Malley, B. W. (1978). *In* "Biochemical Actions of Hormones" (G. Litwack, ed.), Vol. V, pp. 321–372. Academic Press, New York.

Vedeckis, W. V., Freeman, M. R., Schrader, W. T., and O'Malley, B. W. (1980). *Biochemistry* **19**, 335–343.

Wagner, T. E. (1970). *Biochem. Biophys. Res. Commun.* **38**, 890–893.

Weber, K., and Kuter, D. J. (1971). *J. Biol. Chem.* **246**, 4504–4509.

Webster, R. A., and Spelsberg, T. C. (1979). *J. Steroid Biochem.* **10**, 343–351.

Webster, R. A., Pikler, G. M., and Spelsberg, T. C. (1976). *Biochem. J.* **156**, 409–419.

Williams, D., and Gorski, J. (1974). *Biochemistry* **13**, 5537–5542.

Wilson, E., and Spelsberg, T. C. (1973). *Biochim. Biophys. Acta* **322**, 145–154.

Woodcock, C. L. F. (1977). *Science* **195**, 1350–1352.

Woodcock, C.L.F., Frado, L. L. Y., and Wall, J. S. (1980). *Proc. Natl. Acad. Sci.* **77**, 4181–4822.

Yamamoto, K. R. (1974). *J. Biol. Chem.* **249**, 7068–7075.

Yamamoto, K. R., and Alberts, B. M. (1972). *Proc. Natl. Acad. Sci.* **69**, 2105–2109.

Yamamoto, K. R., and Alberts, B. M. (1974). *J. Biol. Chem.* **249**, 7076–7086.

Yamamoto, K. R., and Alberts, B. M. (1975). *Cell* **4**, 301–310.

Yamamoto, K. R., and Alberts, B. M. (1976). *Annu. Rev. Biochem.* **45**, 722–746.

Yamamoto, K. R., Stampfer, M. R., and Tomkins, G. M. (1974). *Proc. Natl. Acad. Sci.* **71**, 3901–3905.

Yamamoto, K. R., Gehring, U., Stampfer, M. R., and Sibley, C. H. (1976). *Recent Prog. Horm. Res.* **32**, 3–32.

Yazgan, A., and Henkens, R. W. (1972). *Biochemistry* **11**, 1314–1318.

# CHAPTER 7

# The Use of Pyridoxal 5-Phosphate as a Tool in the Study of Steroid Receptors

*Dennis M. DiSorbo and Gerald Litwack*



## I. INTRODUCTION

Our understanding of the mechanism of action of steroid hormones has grown steadily since the initial reports by Jensen *et al.* (1968) and Gorski *et al.* (1968) of a specific intracellular estrogen binding protein and by Litwack *et al.* (1965) of glucocorticoid binding proteins. Present knowledge of steroid receptors has enabled investigators to pursue a multidirectional approach in an attempt to elucidate the chain of events involved in hormone action. These events begin with the entry of the steroid into the cell, the association of the steroid with a cytoplasmic receptor molecule, and finally the translocation of the steroid-receptor complex to the nucleus culminating in the induction of specific mRNAs. The penultimate event, the translocation of the



BIOCHEMICAL ACTIONS OF HORMONES, VOL. IX

ISBN 0-12-452809-0

receptor complex to the nucleus, may be mediated by an "activation" or a conformational change in the steroid–receptor complex enabling it to associate with the genome. The object of this chapter is to examine the data dealing with the "activation" of the steroid–receptor complex and how our understanding of the process of the "activation" step has been facilitated by the use of the chemical reagent pyridoxal 5′-phosphate.

## II. PYRIDOXAL 5′-PHOSPHATE AND SCHIFF BASE FORMATION

It is appropriate to review briefly the interactions of pyridoxal 5′-phosphate and amino acids. Knowledge of this interaction explains the use of the $B_6$ vitamer as a chemical probe of steroid receptors.

Pyridoxal 5′-phosphate has been shown to inhibit the activity of several enzymes (Johnson and Deal, 1970; Kopelovich and Wolfe, 1977; Anai *et al.*, 1979). The mechanism of the inhibitory action of pyridoxal 5′-phosphate in this context involves the formation of a Schiff base with an amino group localized at the active site of the enzyme. The amino group usually has been found to be the ε-amino group of a lysine residue as in the case of glutamate dehydrogenase (Anderson *et al.*, 1966; Piszkiewicz and Smith, 1971), hexokinase (Grillo, 1968), glutamic-aspartic transaminase (Hughes *et al.*, 1962), muscle pyruvate kinase (Johnson and Deal, 1979), and bovine plasma albumin (Dempsey and Christensen, 1962). However, pyridoxal 5′-phosphate can react with primary amines such as the N-terminal amino group of a protein. The overall mechanism of the reaction is depicted in Fig. 1. The interaction of pyridoxal 5′-phosphate with an amino group generates an imine complex. The reaction is readily reversible but can be made irreversible by reacting it with a reducing agent, such as sodium borohydride ($NaBH_4$). The reduction of the pyridoxal 5′-phosphate–protein complex by $NaBH_4$ produces a stable pyridoxal 5′-phosphate–protein derivative.

## III. THE USE OF PYRIDOXAL 5′-PHOSPHATE TO ELUCIDATE THE MECHANISM OF ACTION OF THE GLUCOCORTICOID RECEPTOR

Initial reports by Litwack *et al.* (1963, 1965) and later by Beato *et al.* (1969) demonstrated that upon *in vivo* administration of [$^3$H]cortisol the radioactive ligand was bound to a cytoplasmic macromolecule in liver. Subsequently, radioactivity was found in the nucleus 20 minutes after the injection of [$^3$H]cortisol. The data implied that the transport of cortisol to the

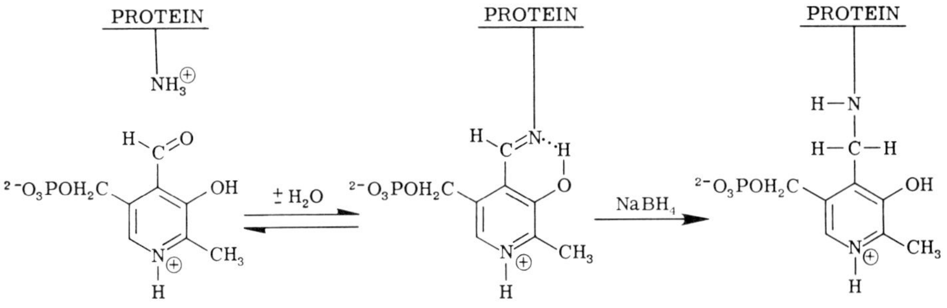

FIG. 1. Interaction of pyridoxal 5′-phosphate with either a primary amino acid residue or an ε-amino group of a lysine residue forming a Schiff base. Irreversible reduction is achieved with $NaBH_4$.

nucleus was involved in the mechanism of action of the hormone. Later studies by Baxter *et al.* (1972) demonstrated, in a cell-free system, that the binding of cytoplasmic glucocorticoid receptors to isolated nuclei and DNA occurred. The reaction required a temperature-dependent modification of the receptor.

The increased affinity of cytoplasmic receptors for DNA upon heat "activation" (25°C for 30 minutes) prompted speculation that the receptor existed in two forms, unactivated and "activated." In 1973, Milgrom *et al.* showed that the heat "activated" hepatic glucocorticoid–receptor complex, but not the unactivated receptor complex, could bind to nuclei, DNA, and a variety of other polyanions. It was concluded that the receptor exists in two forms and the "activated" form of the receptor probably undergoes a conformational change exposing positive charges on the surface of the molecule thus increasing its affinity for polyanions. Additional studies have shown that "activation" of the receptor can occur at low temperatures (4°C) by increasing the ionic strength of the medium (Higgins *et al.*, 1973; Milgrom *et al.*, 1973; Kalimi *et al.*, 1975) or by the addition of calcium ions (Kalimi *et al.*, 1975). Gel filtration of cytosol was another means to accomplish activation (Cake *et al.*, 1976; Goidl *et al.*, 1977). Furthermore, Parchman *et al.* (1977) showed that the "activation" of the hepatic glucocorticoid receptor is stimulated by the addition to the cytosol of the basic amino acids, lysine, arginine, and histidine, but not by other amino acids.

The observations, cited above, provided two important pieces of information. The functionalities of the "activated" receptor in binding to DNA-cellulose, nuclei, and other polyanions suggested that the "activation" step resulted in the exposure of positive charges on the surface of the receptor.

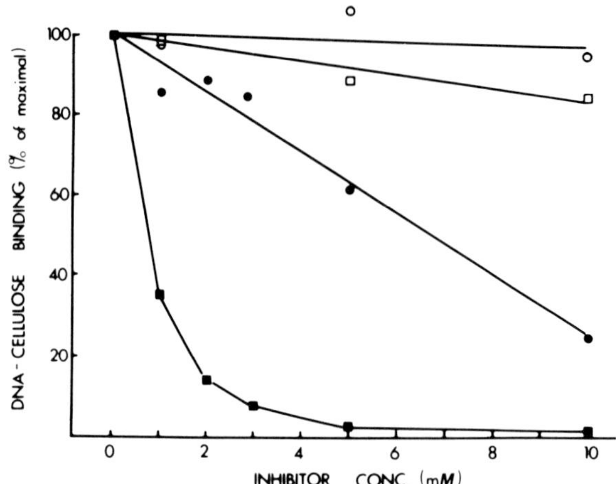


FIG. 2. Specificity of the effect of pyridoxal 5′-phosphate. A rat liver cytosol (1 gm of liver + 7 ml of buffer BSM) was incubated with 30 n*M* [$^3$H]dexamethasone and the steroid receptor complexes activated by heating at 25°C for 30 minutes. At this point the indicated concentrations of pyridoxal 5′-phosphate (■), and pyridoxal (●), pyridoxamine 5′-phosphate (□), and pyridoxamine (○) were added and incubation continued for a further 20 minutes. The binding of the complexes to DNA-cellulose were determined and results are expressed as the percentage of maximal binding. From Cake *et al.* (1978) with permission.

Second, the observation that rat liver cytosol, incubated at 4°C with [$^3$H]-triamcinolone acetonide, could be activated by separating micromolecular components from receptor (Cake *et al.*, 1976) inferred that a small molecule was involved in the "activation" mechanism. Assuming that the positive charges resulted from the exposure of basic amino acid residues, Litwack and Cake (1977) examined the DNA-binding property of the receptor in the presence of pyridoxal 5′-phosphate. The results of this study indicated that pyridoxal 5′-phosphate could prevent the binding of the activated glucocorticoid–receptor complex to DNA-cellulose. The authors suggested that pyridoxal 5′-phosphate acted by forming a Schiff base with the $\epsilon$-$NH_2$ group of a lysine residue which was one of the required basic residues functioning in the DNA-binding site of the "activated" steroid–receptor complex. Subsequent work by Cake *et al.* (1978) showed that the pyridoxal 5′-phosphate effect was concentration dependent and specific for pyridoxal 5′-phosphate (Fig. 2). These data correlated with the ability of pyridoxal 5′-phosphate to form a Schiff base with proteins and primary amines (Snell and DiMari, 1970). Pyridoxal 5′-phosphate proved to be a competitive inhibitor of DNA binding with respect to the concentration of DNA. Consequently, it follows that the inhibition of DNA binding should be the result of direct interaction of pyridoxal phosphate and the DNA binding site of the receptor (Fig. 3). Use of the reducing agent, sodium borohydride ($NaBH_4$), confirmed that pyridoxal 5′-phosphate is binding to a site that becomes exposed as a result of the activation process. When pyridoxal 5′-phosphate and sodium borohydride were added in the cold, prior to heat activation, the inhibitory effect of pyridoxal 5′-phosphate was abolished indicating that the site to which pyridoxal 5′-phosphate binds is unavailable in the unactivated state of the receptor.

To date there is only one published report on the regulation of the glucocorticoid receptor by pyridoxal 5′-phosphate *in vivo* (DiSorbo *et al.*, 1980a). The hepatic glucocorticoid receptor from control and vitamin $B_6$-deficient animals was assayed for its ability to bind to DNA-cellulose. After 15 minutes of incubation at 25°C, the cytosol prepared from the $B_6$-deficient animals had 3.3 times more receptor molecules bound to DNA-cellulose than the cytosol prepared from control animals (Fig. 4). A reduction in the cellular level of pyridoxal 5′-phosphate, confirmed by the tyrosine aminotransferase holoenzyme:apoenzyme ratio, facilitates an increase in the number of receptor molecules capable of binding to DNA-cellulose.

After an intraperitoneal injection of [$^3$H]triamcinolone acetonide vitamin $B_6$-deficient animals took up and retained less radioactive steroid in their

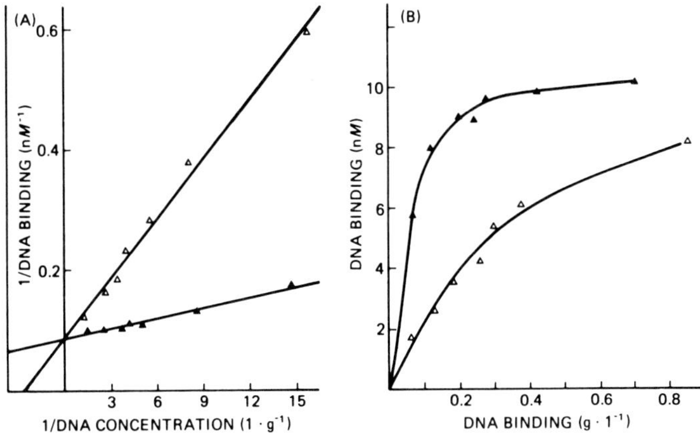


FIG. 3. Kinetics of pyridoxal 5′-phosphate inhibition. [$^3$H]Dexamethasone-labeled cytosol (1 gm of liver + 1 ml of buffer BSM) was heat-activated by incubation at 25°C for 45 minutes. Half was then exposed to 2.5 m$M$ pyridoxal 5′-phosphate at 0°-4°C for an additional 30 minutes. Aliquots of each fraction, heat activated and then not exposed (▲) or exposed (△) to pyridoxal 5′-phosphate, were then incubated with increasing concentrations of DNA-cellulose for 4 hours at 0°–4°C. After thorough washing, specific binding of the steroid–receptor complexes to DNA-cellulose was determined. Results are expressed as a double reciprocal plot (A) or as a standard plot of DNA binding versus the DNA concentration (B). Maximal binding to DNA-cellulose of the specifically bound radioactivity is 35% in these experiments. From Cake *et al.* (1978) with permission.

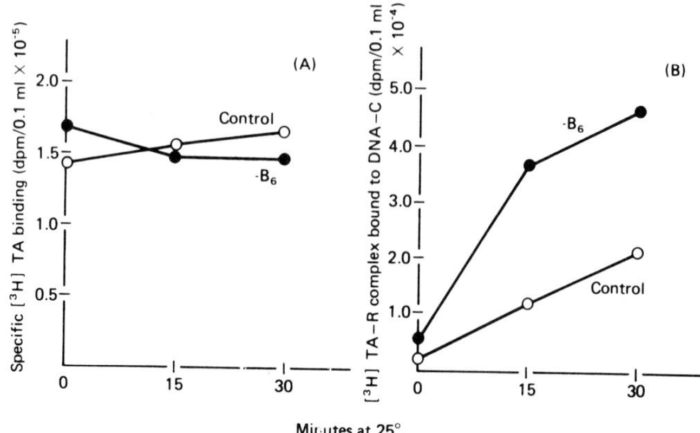


FIG. 4. Analysis of specific [$^3$H]triamcinolone acetonide binding to receptor and binding of activated receptor complexes to DNA-cellulose in cytosol prepared from control (○), and pyridoxine-deficient animals (●). Liver cytosol that had been previously incubated at 4°C with 30 n$M$ [$^3$H]triamcinolone acetonide alone or with 1000-fold excess unlabeled triamcinolone acetonide was placed in a 25°C water bath. At the time intervals indicated aliquots were removed and assayed for specific steroid binding (A) and binding of activated receptor complex to DNA-cellulose (B) as described under "Materials and Methods." The data represent the means of three experiments. From DiSorbo *et al.* (1980a) with permission.

livers than control animals. In spite of the lowered concentration of [$^3$H]-steroid in the livers of the vitamin $B_6$-deficient animals, the amount of radioactive steroid associated with nuclei from both control and deficient animals was approximately the same (Fig. 5). Thus, the amount of steroid needed to translocate the glucocorticoid receptor complex to the nucleus in vitamin $B_6$-deficient animals is substantially less than that needed to translocate an equivalent number of receptor molecules from vitamin $B_6$-sufficient animals.

In addition to using pyridoxal 5′-phosphate as a probe for the DNA-binding site of the receptor, Dolan and Litwack (1978) and Cidlowski and Thanassi (1978) showed that pyridoxal 5′-phosphate could elute the receptor complex from DNA-cellulose and nuclei. This activity was predicted from the finding (see above) that pyridoxal 5′-phosphate is a competitive inhibitor of DNA binding by the activated glucocorticoid–receptor complex with respect to DNA concentration. It was reported later that the pyridoxal 5′-phosphate-eluted receptor complex was less prone to aggregation at low ionic strength and more stable with respect to steroid binding than receptor complexes eluted with 0.45 $M$ NaCl (Dolan *et al.*, 1980). These findings could help to explain an earlier report by Cidlowski and Thanassi (1979) concerning an apparent conversion of the inactivated dexamethasone–receptor complex (7–8 S) to a form that has a sedimentation profile similar to the "activated" complex (4–5 S) after incubation with pyridoxal 5′-phosphate. This apparent conversion could be due solely to the disaggregation of receptor complexes by pyridoxal 5′-phosphate. However, recent reports by Kalimi and Love (1980) and Cidlowski (1980) have shown that when the glucocorticoid receptor was incubated with pyridoxal 5′-phosphate, the size of the receptor was altered. Kalimi and Love (1980) theorized that pyridoxal 5′-phosphate stimulates the degradation of the receptor into three fragments, one of which (peak III) binds poorly to nuclei. According to these authors, the fragmentation of the receptor by the action of pyridoxal 5′-phosphate is the mechanism by which the coenzyme inhibits binding of receptor to DNA. Along similar lines of investigation Cidlowski (1980) presented evidence showing that pyridoxal 5′-phosphate caused an alteration in the size of the thymus glucocorticoid receptor. When pyridoxal 5′-phosphate was incubated with cytosol at 3°C for 2 hours followed by reduction with $NaBH_4$, a shift in the molecular weight of the receptor was observed (250,000 $M_r$ to 110,000 $M_r$). An extended period of incubation (16 hours) of the receptor with pyridoxal 5′-phosphate followed by $NaBH_4$ reduction produced an even smaller receptor species (55,000 $M_r$) which the author claims is not the meroreceptor. This report indicated that pyridoxal 5′-phosphate

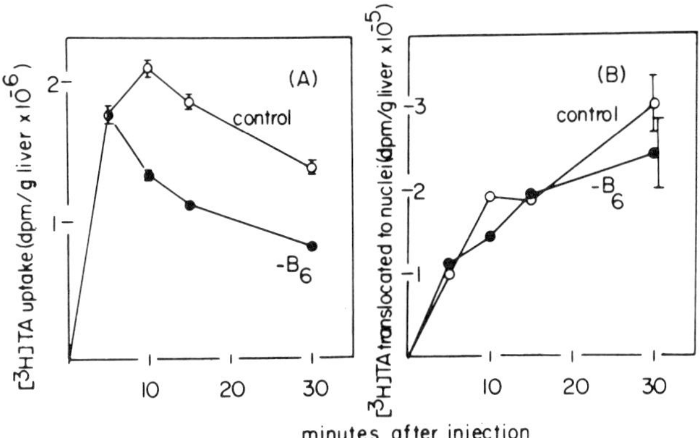


FIG. 5. Intraperitoneal injection of [$^3$H]triamcinolone acetonide (25 $\mu$Ci/100 gm of body weight) to control and pyridoxine-deficient animals. Animals were sacrificed at the indicated time intervals and livers removed and analyzed for [$^3$H]steroid uptake into the liver (controls, ○; pyridoxine deficient, ●) and for localization of radioactivity in the nucleus (control, ○, pyridoxine deficient, ●). Each data point represents the means ± SD of four to five animals. Where the SD was too small to be indicated in the figure, the results are as follows. (A) 15- and 30-minute time points for pyridoxine-deficient animals: 1,119,426 ± 9,466 and 808,970 ± 128,895 dpm/gm liver respectively. (B) 5-, 10-, and 15-minute time points for controls: 108,582 ± 15,996, 192,440 ± 48,287, and 189,664 ± 43,681 dpm/gm liver, respectively; pyridoxine-deficient animals for the same time points, 114,034 ± 12,164, 144,668 ± 28,676, and 190,640 ± 45,208 dpm/gm liver, respectively. From DiSorbo *et al.* (1980a) with permission.

alters the proteolysis of the thymus glucocorticoid receptor. However, some caution must be used in the interpretation of the above findings. One must question the inordinate length of time that pyridoxal 5′-phosphate was incubated with thymus cytosol. The initial studies demonstrating the inhibitory action of pyridoxal 5′-phosphate on receptor binding to DNA-cellulose employed a 30 minute incubation period with the coenzyme (Cake *et al.*, 1978; DiSorbo *et al.*, 1980a). Additional studies by Howard Eisen at the National Institutes of Health (personal communication) report no fragmentation of the hepatic glucocorticoid receptor upon incubation with pyridoxal 5′-phosphate.

In addition to an extended incubation time with the coenzyme, Cidlowski (1980) also carried out these studies on dilute cytosols prepared under low ionic strength conditions. Since these experimental conditions deviate substantially from those carried out on the hepatic glucocorticoid receptor, one must question the validity of the results obtained under such nonphysiological conditions.

The stabilization of the glucocorticoid–receptor complex by pyridoxal 5′-phosphate coupled with its ability to elute the receptor complex from DNA-cellulose has facilitated the purification of the receptor. Wrange *et al.* (1979) used pyridoxal 5′-phosphate to elute the receptor complex from DNA-cellulose columns. The authors reported that the elution of the

TABLE I

EFFECT OF $B_6$ ANALOGS ON THE BINDING OF [$^3$H]TA TO THE RECEPTOR[a]

| Compound | Temp. (°C) | Specific binding (pmol/mg protein) | Amount bound (%) | Temp. (°C) | Specific binding (pmol/mg protein) | Amount bound (%) |
|---|---|---|---|---|---|---|
| Control | 0 | 0.196 ± 0.014 | 100 | 25 | 0.114 ± 0.005 | 100 |
| Pyridoxal | 0 | 0.137 ± 0.012 | 70 | 25 | 0.013 ± 0.002 | 11 |
| Pyridoxal-P | 0 | 0.198 ± 0.018 | 100 | 25 | 0.008 ± 0.001 | 7 |
| Pyridoxamine-P | 0 | 0.219 ± 0.004 | 112 | 25 | 0.115 ± 0.003 | 100 |
| Pyridoxine | 0 | 0.264 ± 0.014 | 135 | 25 | 0.157 ± 0.006 | 138 |
| 4-Deoxypyridoxine | 0 | 0.229 ± 0.005 | 117 | 25 | 0.129 ± 0.004 | 113 |

[a]Liver cytosol (105,000 *g* supernatant fraction) was placed into test tubes containing buffer or a $B_6$ analog (final concentration, 10 m*M*) and incubated for 15 minutes at either 0° or 25°C. At the end of the preincubation period, all tubes were placed at 0°C and 30 n*M* [$^3$H]TA were added to all tubes. For determination of nonspecific binding, a 1000-fold excess of unlabeled TA was added to a control tube. After the addition of radioactive steroid, the incubation was continued for 2 hours at 0°C. The charcoal adsorption method was used to determine specifically bound steroid (expressed as picomoles per mg protein). Results are the means of four experiments ± SD. From DiSorbo *et al.* (1980b) with permission.

glucocorticoid receptor from the affinity column with pyridoxal 5′-phosphate is superior to the elution with NaCl. With the pyridoxal 5′-phosphate procedure, the receptor can be obtained at about 95% purity in good yield.

Up to this point, the discussion has concerned the DNA binding site of the receptor. However, a recent study has indicated that pyridoxal 5′-phosphate also can interfere with steroid binding to the receptor. When the receptor was preincubated with vitamin $B_6$ analogs at 25°C followed by incubation with [$^3$H]triamcinolone acetonide at 0°C, pyridoxal and pyridoxal 5′-phosphate prevent subsequent steroid binding to receptor (DiSorbo *et al.*, 1980b) (Table I). At 0°C, pyridoxal 5′-phosphate has no effect on steroid binding while pyridoxal inhibits this binding by 30%. Therefore, a lysine residue(s) may be localized at or near the steroid binding site of the receptor. This lysine residue also may be buried partially or localized in an environment which prevents the binding of pyridoxal 5′-phosphate at 0°C.

## IV. PYRIDOXAL 5′-PHOSPHATE AS A PROBE OF OTHER STEROID RECEPTORS

### A. Estrogen

Pyridoxal 5′-phosphate is being used currently as a reagent to probe the mechanism of action of other steroid receptors. Two laboratories have contributed information on the estrogen receptor. Müller *et al.* (1980) demonstrated that pyridoxal 5′-phosphate had no effect on either estradiol binding to the receptor or on the stability of the estradiol–receptor complex. However, like the glucocorticoid receptor, pyridoxal 5′-phosphate inhibited nuclear binding of the heat "activated" estrogen–receptor complexes. Similar findings were reported by Muldoon and Cidlowski (1980) for the inhibition of receptor binding to DNA-cellulose by pyridoxal 5′-phosphate. The inhibition has been shown to be reversible by reacting pyridoxal 5′-phosphate treated cytosol with Tris, lysine, ethylenediamine, or dithiothreitol. However, if the pyridoxal 5′-phosphate treated cytosol is first subjected to the action of the reducing agent, $NaBH_4$, these agents could not reverse the inhibitory action of pyridoxal 5′-phosphate. These findings are consistent with the formation of a Schiff base between pyridoxal 5′-phosphate and a lysine residue(s) on the surface of the receptor.

The inhibition of the estrogen receptor binding to either DNA-cellulose or nuclei by pyridoxal 5′-phosphate appears to involve more than just the binding of pyridoxal 5′-phosphate to the DNA-binding site of the receptor. Experiments by Traish *et al.* (1980) and Muldoon and Cidlowski (1980) indicate

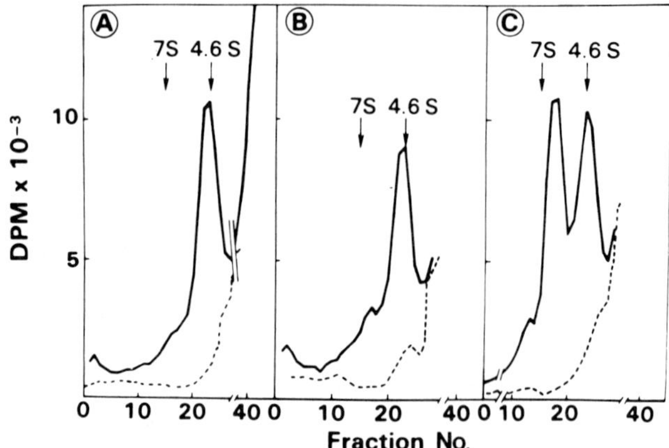


FIG. 6. Pyridoxal 5′-phosphate inhibition of $R \cdot E_2$ activation. Unactivated $R \cdot E_2$ (2.4 mg of protein/ml) was incubated for 30 minutes at 0°C with an equal volume of buffer BSM containing 40 m*M* pyridoxal 5′-phosphate. Aliquots (A) were kept at 0°C, or heat activated (B), and subjected to centrifugation on BSMK, 20 m*M* pyridoxal 5′-phosphate 10 to 30% sucrose gradients. (C) A mixture of unactivated and activated, untreated $R \cdot E_2$ (1:1, v/v) was centrifuged on BSMK gradients without pyridoxal 5′-phosphate. From Traish *et al.* (1980) with permission.

that the "activation" or transformation step, i.e., 4.5 S to 6 S shift, is blocked by pyridoxal 5′-phosphate (Fig. 6). Thus, pyridoxal 5′-phosphate appears to inhibit "activation" of the estrogen–receptor complex. This could be a major target for the coenzyme in producing the inhibition of estrogen receptor binding to nuclei. On the other hand, a recent report has raised the possibility that the transformation step (4.5 S to 6 S) may be distinct from the activation of the estrogen receptor (Bailly *et al.*, 1980). While exposure to 0.4 *M* KCl at 0°C resulted in estrogen receptor complexes bound to DNA-cellulose, examination of these complexes by sucrose gradient centrifugation showed them to sediment in the 4 S form with only a small percentage in the 5 S region. Thus, the activation of the estrogen receptor may be a separate phenomenon from 4 S to 5 S transformation. In the light of this report, the exact mechanism by which pyridoxal 5′-phosphate interacts with and modulates the estrogen receptor remains to be established.

### B. PROGESTIN

The initial work on the interaction of pyridoxal 5′-phosphate with the progesterone receptor has been carried out by Nishigori *et al.* (1978). Their results indicated that incubation of the progesterone receptor with pyridoxal 5′-phosphate prevented subsequent binding of the receptor complex to an

ATP-Sepharose column. At a pyridoxal 5′-phosphate concentration of 2.5 m*M*, complete inhibition of progesterone receptor binding to ATP-Sepharose was observed. This effect was specific for pyridoxal 5′-phosphate as pyridoxal, pyridoxine, pyridoxamine, and pyridoxamine 5′-phosphate showed little inhibition. The above findings suggested that the altered binding to ATP-Sepharose was due to a change in the charge of the receptor molecule.

In an attempt to elucidate the mechanism by which pyridoxal 5′-phosphate interacted with the progesterone receptor, Nishigori and Toft (1979) carried out a series of experiments to characterize the physical properties of the receptor after treatment with this reagent. Initial studies showed that pyridoxal 5′-phosphate could prevent aggregation of the receptor on sucrose density gradient centrifugation performed in low salt concentration (0.01 *M* KCl). In addition to maintaining the receptor in a disaggregated state, pyridoxal 5′-phosphate stabilized the progesterone receptor. When the progesterone receptor was incubated at 37°C in the absence of pyridoxal 5′-phosphate, a rapid loss of [$^3$H]progesterone binding to receptor ensued (Fig. 7). In the presence of pyridoxal 5′-phosphate, the steroid–receptor complex was stable for up to 2 hours. The stabilization of the

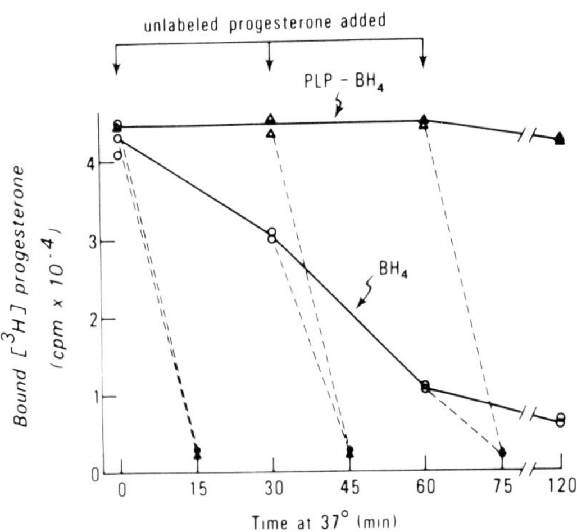


FIG. 7. Temperature stability of control and pyridoxal-P-modified receptor. Control ($NaBH_4$ treated; $BH_4$) and pyridoxal-P-modified (PLP-$BH_4$) receptor were prepared. Aliquots (0.2 ml) were incubated at 37°C for the times indicated. They were then chilled in ice and bound [$^3$H]progesterone was determined by charcoal adsorption. As a measure of binding exchangeability, a 1000-fold excess of unlabeled progesterone was added to some samples for a 15-minute period at 37°C. The resulting loss of [$^3$H]progesterone binding is indicated by the broken line and closed symbols. From Nishigori and Toft (1979) with permission.

progesterone receptor by pyridoxal 5′-phosphate should prove useful in its purification.

Characterization and partial purification of the progesterone receptor from chick oviduct (Sherman *et al.*, 1970; Schrader and O'Malley, 1972; Clark *et al.*, 1976) have shown the receptor to consist of two 4 S subunits designated A and B. The A and B subunits can be separated on DEAE-cellulose chromatography. Treatment of the receptor with pyridoxal 5′-phosphate followed by chromatography on DEAE-cellulose, modifies the separation (Nishigori and Toft, 1979) (Fig. 8). The most prominent difference was the stabilization of the A and B subunits. The first peak, representing the A subunit, was distinctly resolved in the pyridoxal 5′-phosphate treated sample compared to a shoulder in the control preparation. A second difference in the elution profile was the increase in acidity of the A and B subunits as characterized by the increased salt concentration required to elute them from the column. Pyridoxal 5′-phosphate was concluded to bind to a basic region on the surface of the receptor which is involved in the binding of the receptor complex to DNA. The contribution of a phosphate group from each pyridoxal 5′-phosphate attached, coupled with neutralization of one ionizable amino group on the receptor, was probably responsible for the increased acidity of the A and B subunits.

A more recent report by Grody *et al.* (1980) supports the conclusion that pyridoxal 5′-phosphate interacts with the A and B subunits of the proges-

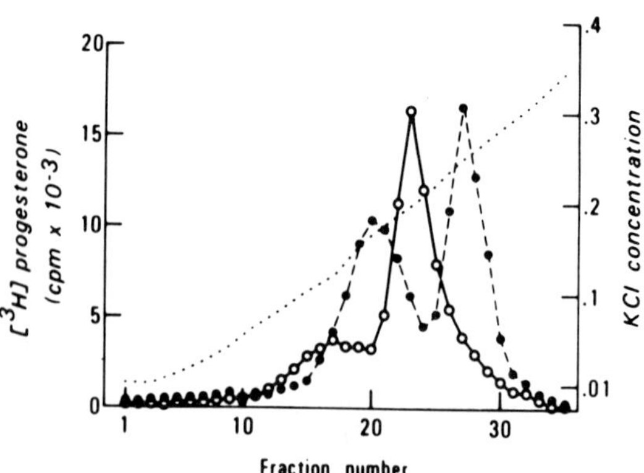


FIG. 8. Analysis of pyridoxal-P-modified receptor by DEAE-cellulose chromatography. Control (○) and pyridoxal-P-modified (●) preparations of [$^3$H]progesterone–receptor complex (1.5 ml each) were chromatographed on identical 5-ml columns of DEAE-cellulose. The columns were first washed with 60 ml of Tris buffer II plus 0.01 *M* KCl and then with a gradient of 0.01 to 0.4 *M* KCl. Aliquots (50 μl) from each 2-ml fraction were analyzed for [$^3$H]progesterone content. Only the gradient elution of adsorbed receptor is illustrated. The KCl concentration of each fraction was determined by conductivity and is indicated by the dotted line. From Nishigori and Toft (1979) with permission.

terone receptor. These investigators showed that the addition of 5 m*M* pyridoxal 5′-phosphate to [$^3$H]progesterone labeled cytosol (0°C) dissociates receptor aggregates to monomers as assayed by the appearance of a 4 S peak after sucrose density gradient centrifugation. Removal of pyridoxal 5′-phosphate from the 4 S monomers (addition of 50 m*M* ethanolamine dissociates pyridoxal 5′-phosphate from the receptor subunit by formation of a Schiff base with the amino group of ethanolamine) caused their recombination to form a 6 S dimer. The authors suggested that pyridoxal 5′-phosphate interacts at a site on one or both subunits and this site is critical in holding the dimer together. This information, together with reports previously cited, indicate that pyridoxal 5′-phosphate binds at a site localized at or near the DNA-binding site of the progesterone receptor.

### C. Androgen

There has been only one report demonstrating an interaction between pyridoxal 5′-phosphate and the androgen receptor. Experiments by Hiipakka and Liao (1980) showed that pyridoxal 5′-phosphate interacts with the androgen receptor in a manner similar to that previously described for other steroid hormone receptors. The binding of the androgen–receptor complex to DNA-cellulose can be inhibited by preincubation with pyridoxal 5′-phosphate; pyridoxal, pyridoxine, pyridoxamine, and pyridoxamine phosphate are without effect. The data are consistent with the formation of a Schiff base with pyridoxal 5′-phosphate and a lysine residue(s) at or near the DNA-binding site of the receptor.

## V. SUMMARY

Pyridoxal 5′-phosphate has shown to be a useful tool in studying the physicochemical properties of steroid receptors. The present data suggest that pyridoxal 5′-phosphate interacts with a basic region, probably a lysine residue, at or near the DNA-binding site of the receptor. The blockage of these positive charges on the receptor molecule appears to be at least one mechanism for inhibiting its binding to both DNA-cellulose and nuclei. However, in the case of the estrogen receptor, Traish *et al.* (1980) have indicated that pyridoxal 5′-phosphate also prevents the "activation" or transformation of the 4.5 S to 6 S receptor complex. Thus, it appears that pyridoxal 5′-phosphate interacts at more than one locus on the surface of the estrogen receptor producing physical changes unique to that protein.

The physiological role of pyridoxal 5′-phosphate as a regulator of steroid action is still an open question. To date there have been two reports suggesting that pyridoxal 5′-phosphate modulates steroid receptors. With respect to the estrogen receptor, Müller *et al.* (1980) demonstrated that incubation of uterine tissue with pyridoxal 5′-phosphate for 30 minutes at 37°C inhibited nuclear translocation of the estrogen receptor. A more intensive study on the modulation of the glucocorticoid receptor by pyridoxal 5′-phosphate has been reported by DiSorbo *et al.* (1980a). These investigators, using vitamin $B_6$ deficient animals, clearly showed that a reduction in the intracellular level of pyridoxal 5′-phosphate resulted in a marked increase in receptor binding to either DNA-cellulose or nuclei. These results are consistent with an earlier report by Puskar and Tryfiates (1974) that hydrocortisone induced the hepatic enzyme, tyrosine aminotransferase, between 3½ and 6 hours after treatment in vitamin $B_6$-deficient animals while peak enzyme activity in control animals occurred after 6 hours of hormonal treatment. Thus, the earlier peak of enzyme activity in the vitamin $B_6$-deficient animals could be due to either an increase in the number of glucocorticoid receptors translocated to the nucleus or to a more efficient rate of translocation of receptor molecules to the nucleus. Whichever the case may be, the reduced intracellular levels of pyridoxal 5′-phosphate are associated with an increase in receptor activity both *in vitro* and *in vivo*.

The ability of pyridoxal 5′-phosphate to stabilize steroid–receptor complexes already has proved useful in the purification of the glucocorticoid receptor. Since pyridoxal 5′-phosphate not only stabilizes the receptor complex but also elutes receptors prebound to DNA-cellulose, its use in the purification of other steroid receptors seems imminent.

## ACKNOWLEDGMENTS

The research of this laboratory is supported by research grants AM13531 and AG00939 from the National Institutes of Health; PCM 782567 from the National Science Foundation; BC-361 from the American Cancer Society; and CA 12227 from the National Cancer Institute to the Fels Research Institute. We thank Sherry Battaglia for typing the manuscript.

## REFERENCES

Anai, M., Fujiyoshi, T., Nakayama, J., and Takagi, Y. (1979). *J. Biol. Chem.* **254**, 10853–10856.

Anderson, B. M., Anderson, C. D., and Churchich, J. E. (1966). *Biochemistry* **5**, 2893.

Bailly, A., LeFevre, B., Savouret, J. F., and Milgrom, E. (1980). *J. Biol. Chem.* **255**, 2729–2734.

Baxter, J. D., Rousseau, G. G., Benson, M. C., Garcea, R. L., Ito, J., and Tomkins, G. M. (1972). *Proc. Natl. Acad. Sci. U.S.A.* **69**, 1892–1896.

Beato, M., Biesewig, D., Braendle, W., and Sekeris, C. E. (1969). *Biochem. Biophys. Acta* **192**, 494.

Cake, M. H., Goidl, J. A., Parchman, L. G., and Litwack, G. (1976). *Biochem. Biophys. Res. Commun.* **71**, 45–52.

Cake, M. H., DiSorbo, D. M., and Litwack, G. (1978). *J. Biol. Chem.* **253**, 4886–4891.

Cidlowski, J. A. (1980). *Biochemistry* **19**, 6162–6170.

Cidlowski, J. A., and Thanassi, J. W. (1978). *Biochem. Biophys. Res. Commun.* **82**, 1140–1146.

Cidlowski, J. A., and Thanassi, J. W. (1979). *Biochemistry* **18**, 2378–2384.

Clark, J. C., Peck, E. J., Schrader, W. T., and O'Malley, B. W. (1976). *Methods Cancer Res.* **12**, 367.

Dempsey, W. B., and Christensen, H. N. (1962). *J. Biol. Chem.* **237**, 1113.

DiSorbo, D. M., Phelps, D. S., Ohl, V. S., and Litwack, G. (1980a). *J. Biol. Chem.* **255**, 3866–3870.

DiSorbo, D. M., Phelps, D. S., and Litwack, G. (1980b). *Endocrinology* **106**, 922–929.

Dolan, K. P., and Litwack, G. (1978). *Proc. Endocr. Soc. (Miami)* **131**, 308.

Dolan, K. P., Diaz-Gil, J. J., and Litwack, G. (1980). *Arch. Biochem. Biophys.* **201**, 476–485.

Goidl, J. A., Cake, M. H., Dolan, K. P., Parchman, L. G., and Litwack, G. (1977). *Biochemistry* **16**, 2125–2130.

Gorski, J., Toft, D., Shyamala, G., Smith, D., and Notides, A. (1968). *Recent Progr. Horm. Res.* **24**, 45.

Grillo, M. A. (1968). *Enzymologia* **34**, 7.

Grody, W. W., Schrader, W. T., and O'Malley, B. W. (1980). *62nd Annu. Meet. Endocr. Soc.* p. 76.

Higgins, S. J., Rousseau, G. G., Baxter, J. D., and Tomkins, G. M. (1973). *J. Biol. Chem.* **248**, 5866–5872.

Hiipakka, R. A., and Liao, S. (1980). *J. Steroid Biochem.* **13**, 841–846.

Hughes, R. C., Jenkins, W. T., and Fischer, E. H. (1962). *Proc. Natl. Acad. Sci. U.S.A.* **48**, 1615–1618.

Jensen, E., Suzuki, T., Kawashima, T., Stumpf, W. E., Jungblut, P. W., and DeSombre, E. R. (1968). *Proc. Natl. Acad. Sci.* **59**, 632.

Johnson, G. S., and Deal, W. C., Jr. (1970). *J. Biol. Chem.* **245**, 238–245.

Kalimi, M., and Love, K. (1980). *J. Biol. Chem.* **255**, 4687–4690.

Kalimi, M., Colman, P., and Feigelson, P. (1975). *J. Biol. Chem.* **250**, 1080–1086.

Kopelovich, L., and Wolfe, G. (1977). *Biochemistry* **16**, 3721–3726.

Litwack, G., and Cake, M. H. (1977). *Fed. Proc. Fed. Am. Soc. Exp. Biol.* **36**, 911.

Litwack, G., Sears, M. L., and Diamondstone, T. I. (1963). *J. Biol. Chem.* **238**, 302–305.

Litwack, G., Fiala, E. S., and Filosa, R. J. (1965). *Biochem. Biophys. Acta* **111**, 569–571.

Milgrom, E., Atger, M., and Baulieu, E. E. (1973). *Biochemistry* **12**, 5198–5208.

Muldoon, T. G., and Cidlowski, J. A. (1980). *J. Biol. Chem.* **255**, 3100–3107.

Müller, R. E., Traish, A., and Wotiz, H. H. (1980). *J. Biol. Chem.* **255**, 40624062–4067.

Nishigori, H., and Toft, D. (1979). *J. Biol. Chem.* **254**, 9155–9161.

Nishigori, H., Moudgil, V. K., and Toft, D. (1978). *Biochem. Biophsy. Res. Commun.* **80**, 112–118.

Parchman, L. G., Goidl, J. A., and Litwack, G. (1977). *FEBS Lett.* **79**, 25–28.

Piszkiewicz, D., and Smith, E. L. (1971). *Biochemistry* **10**, 4544–4552.

Puskar, T., and Tryfiates, G. P. (1974). J. Nutr. **104**, 1407–1415.

Schrader, W. T., and O'Malley, B. W. (1972). *J. Biol. Chem.* **247**, 51–59.

Sherman, M. R., Corvol, P. L., and O'Malley, B. W. (1970). *J. Biol. Chem.* **245**, 6085–6096.

Snell, E. E., and DiMari, S. J. (1970). *In* "The Enzymes" (P.D. Boyer, ed.), Student Edition, Vol. II, pp. 335–370. Academic Press, New York.

Traish, A., Müller, R. E., and Wotiz, H. H. (1980). *J. Biol. Chem.* **255**, 4068–4072.

Wrange, Ö., Carlstedt-Duke, J., and Gustafsson, J.-A. (1979). *J. Biol. Chem.* **254**, 9284–9290.

# CHAPTER 8

# Affinity Labeling of Glucocorticoid Receptors: New Methods in Affinity Labeling

*S. Stoney Simons, Jr. and E. Brad Thompson*



## I. Introduction*

The utility of affinity labeling is well documented in several recent reviews (Jakoby and Wilchek, 1977; Katzenellenbogen, 1977; Chowdhry and West-

*Abbreviations: dexamethasone, 9-fluoro-11$\beta$,17,21-trihydroxy-16$\alpha$-methylpregna-1,4-diene-3,20-dione; triamcinolone acetonide, 9-fluoro-11$\beta$,16$\alpha$,17,21-tetrahydroxypregna-1,4-



BIOCHEMICAL ACTIONS OF HORMONES, VOL. IX

ISBN 0-12-452809-0

heimer, 1979). In this chapter, we discuss the existing methods of affinity labeling that have been tried, and some of the general problems encountered in the quest for a covalent glucocorticoid receptor–steroid complex. One major problem appears to be that the variety of methods of affinity labeling in general use is rather limited. Thus, the bulk of this paper is devoted to new approaches that we have taken for the affinity labeling of glucocorticoid receptors and to chemical reaction sequences that we feel could prove to be new, general methods of affinity labeling for various binding macromolecules including glucocorticoid receptors. It is possible that these and other new methods will result in success from the sheer variety of chemical specificities embodied by these new reactions. In fact, our initial results with one new affinity labeling functional group indicate that the glucocorticoid receptor has finally been covalently labeled. As an added benefit, these new methods have certain unique advantages and potentially can yield information that cannot be obtained by the currently available methods of affinity labeling. Efforts to affinity label other steroid receptors are mentioned when relevant.

## A. Utility of Affinity Labeling of Steroid Receptors

Affinity labeling is, in principle, a very powerful technique. The high affinity and selectivity of a ligand for its binding site is used to direct a suitably modified ligand to the combining site of its unique binding macromolecule, where a chemical reaction occurs to give a covalent ligand–macromolecule complex. In principle, covalent complexes are formed only with the appropriate binding macromolecule due to the specificity embodied in the modified ligand. Affinity labeling studies have almost always been conducted in cell-free systems, but there is no theoretical reason why whole-cell, and whole-animal, studies cannot also be performed. This scenario is obviously oversimplified, but it does explain the special appeal of

---

diene-3,20-dione cyclic 16,17-acetal with acetone; cortisol, 11β,17,21-trihydroxypregn-4-ene-3,20-dione; progesterone, pregn-4-ene-3,20-dione; hexestrol, 4,4′-(1,2-diethylethylene)diphenol; R5020, 17α,21-dimethyl-19-norpregn-4,9-diene-3,20-dione; deacylcortivazol, 11β,17,21-trihydroxy-6,16α-dimethyl-2′-phenyl-2′*H*-pregna-2,4,6-trieno[3,2-*c*]pyrazol-20-one; OPTA, *o*-phthalaldehyde; FCAL, fluorescent chemoaffinity labeling; HTC, rat hepatoma tissue culture; DBB, *syn*-dibromobimane, 3,7-dimethyl-4,6-bis(bromomethyl)-1,5-diazabicyclo[3,3,0]octo-3,6-diene-2,8-dione; estradiol, 17β-estradiol; $BBE_2M$, 2,4-bis(bromomethyl)estradiol-17β 3-methyl ether; glucose-6-phosphate dehydrogenase, D-glucose-6-phosphate:NADP oxidoreductase (EC 1.1.1.49); CM, cortisol 21-methanesulfonate; DM, dexamethasone 21-methane sulfonate; TAT, tyrosine aminotransferase, L-tyrosine:2-oxoglutarate aminotransferase (EC 2.6.1.5).

affinity labeling to people studying macromolecules, such as steroid receptors, which are present in very low concentrations and which have no apparent activity except when combined with their specific ligand. Thus, an ideal steroidal affinity label would ferret out the few receptor molecules among the myriad of cellular proteins and form a covalent complex, thereby transforming the inherently inactive receptor macromolecule into a readily and permanently identifiable species. Dissociation of the receptor–steroid complex—the bane of those working with steroid receptors—would no longer be a problem, and numerous experiments would become possible for the first time. Purification of the receptor would be dramatically simplified, thus enabling an investigation of the chemical groups involved in steroid–receptor binding and a straightforward approach to the design of new steroid hormones. The raising of antibodies to intact receptor–steroid complexes would become possible. The protein biochemistry of receptors during cell development, tissue differentiation and evolution, and following acquired steroid resistance could be studied more readily and thoroughly than is now possible. Subtle differences in receptors between steroid-sensitive and steroid-resistant tissues, tumors, and leukemias could be sought. Finally, covalent receptor–steroid complexes would make feasible numerous whole-cell and perhaps even whole-animal experiments on the synthesis, turnover, and intracellular localization of receptors and on the mechanism of action of agonist, and antagonist, steroid hormones. Affinity labeling steroids might also reveal the existence of as yet unsuspected classes of receptors or other important but scarce binding molecules.

## B. General Problems with Affinity Labeling of Steroid Receptors

### 1. *Limitations of Screening Procedures*

While the theory of affinity labeling is simple, it has proved very difficult in practice to realize the potential of affinity labeled receptors. Part of this problem may derive from the screening procedures used to detect potential affinity labels. A failure to be aware of the limitations of these assays can lead one to discard what could later prove to be a bona fide steroidal affinity label. Since the synthesis of radioactively labeled, derivatized steroids is time consuming and costly, indirect assays with nonradioactively labeled steroids are required. The first such assay is generally a cell-free competition assay used to determine the affinity ($K_a$) of the potential affinity label for the receptor. If the steroid in question does not have a high $K_a$ for receptors, it is usually ignored on the assumption that its binding to and labeling of non-receptor proteins will be too large. In fact, most modifications of steroids do result in a decrease in $K_a$ of the steroid for its receptor (Rousseau *et al.*, 1972, 1979; Failla *et al.*, 1975; El Masry *et al.*, 1977; Simons *et al.*, 1979a, 1980a). However, the results of competition assays with potential affinity labels can be misleading. Because a chemically reactive affinity label will form covalent bonds and thus cannot give the equilibrium conditions required for a true $K_a$ determination, the incubation time of the assay can be important. For reversibly binding steroids, the rates of association are quite similar; it is the slow rates of dissociation of receptor–steroid complexes that determine the affinities of steroids (Pratt *et al.*, 1975). For an affinity labeling steroid, the situation is more complex. If the rate constants for the binding reactions shown in Eq. (1) are such that $k_3 < k_1$, or $k_4 > k_2$ and $k_5$, then a competition binding assay of short duration could cause an underestimation of the apparent $K_a$ and lead to rejection of the potential affinity labeling steroid. This problem is compounded since the dissociation rates of the $^3$H-labeled steroids often used ([$^3$H]dexamethasone or [$^3$H]triamcinolone acetonide) are so slow that even a 20 hour assay at 0°C does not allow the system to achieve equilibrium (Pratt *et al.*, 1975; Simons *et al.*, 1979b; Yeakley *et al.*, 1980). Thus, the $K_a$ derived from a cell-free competition assay is of interest for later comparison but should not be used to rule out the utility of a potential affinity labeling steroid, as will be seen below (i.e., Section III,E,2).

$$\left.\begin{array}{c}[^3\text{H}]\text{steroid}\\ + \\ \text{receptor} \\ + \\ \text{Affinity labeling}\\ \text{steroid}\end{array}\right\} \begin{array}{l} \underset{k_2}{\overset{k_1}{\rightleftharpoons}} \ \text{receptor–}[^3\text{H}]\text{steroid} \\ \\ \underset{k_4}{\overset{k_3}{\rightleftharpoons}} \ \begin{array}{l}\text{receptor–affinity}\\ \text{labeling steroid}\\ \text{(noncovalent)}\end{array} \xrightarrow{k_5} \begin{array}{l}\text{receptor–affinity}\\ \text{labeling steroid}\\ \text{(covalent)}\end{array}\end{array} \qquad (1)$$

A more reliable screening assay for use with nonradioactively labeled candidates for affinity labeling steroids is a receptor exchange binding assay (Simons *et al.*, 1980a, 1980b). This assay involves preincubating the receptor with the potential affinity label, or cortisol, and then determining the amount of a standard [$^3$H]steroid that can exchange bind to the preformed receptor–steroid complexes. The decrease in specific binding of the subsequently added [$^3$H]steroid, relative to the cortisol control, is a measure of possible covalent receptor–steroid complexes. These nonexchanging complexes are candidates for binding-site affinity labeled complexes if the decrease in [$^3$H]steroid exchange binding can be prevented by the presence of a large excess of competing steroid during the preincubation with affinity labeling steroid. Unfortunately even these protection experiments are not infallible in identifying binding-site affinity labels. Specific destruction of the steroid binding activity of receptors can occur without covalent attachment of the affinity label. This phenomenon has been proposed to explain the results of the potential photoaffinity label 4-azidoestradiol with $\alpha$-fetoprotein (Payne *et al.*, 1980). On a molecular level, the loss of binding activity of $\Delta^5$-3-ketosteroid isomerase after attempted photoaffinity labeling with 17$\beta$-hydroxyandrosta-1,4,6-triene-3-one appeared to be due to a loss of one protein —SH group, via a transformation of cysteine to glycine (Smith and Benisek, 1980). A similar mechanism was postulated (Smith and Benisek, 1980) to account for the results of another $\alpha,\beta$-unsaturated ketone photoaffinity label (i.e. 6-oxoestradiol) with the estrogen receptor (Katzenellenbogen, 1977). Thus, the above screening procedure can give false positives for prospective affinity labels which would not be detected until the radioactively labeled affinity labeling steroids are synthesized and used.

Cell-free screening assays usually are performed at 0°C and are thus limited, since they could miss entire classes of affinity labeling steroids such as those steroids which require higher temperatures for covalent coupling to receptors or which yield covalent complexes only after temperature-dependent transformations (such as activation to the nuclear binding form) of the initial, noncovalent receptor–steroid complex. We have found that the most complete, albeit time consuming, screening procedure involves both cell-free competition and "receptor exchange binding" assays (to look directly at unactivated receptors at 0°C) and whole-cell biological activity and competition of biological activity assays at 37°C (to look at effects that might be manifested only at higher temperatures) (Simons *et al.*, 1980b; Simons and Thompson, 1981; Simons, 1981).

*2. Nonspecific Labeling*

A major problem in identifying steroidal affinity labels is certainly that of nonspecific labeling. Steroid receptors constitute only about 0.005% of the crude cytosol proteins. Even if the remaining proteins had no affinity for the affinity label, they contain such a large excess of functional groups (e.g., $—NH_2$, —COOH, —OH, —SH) able to react with the affinity labeling functional group that most of the affinity labeling steroid could be consumed before it ever reached the receptor. In fact, there probably are many low affinity binders of steroid hormones which go undetected in the standard binding assays with [$^3$H]steroid because the low affinity complexes are dissociated by the "work-up" conditions of the assays. However, if radiolabeled affinity ligands are used, the $^3$H-affinity labeling steroids can react with some of these low affinity binders to produce covalent complexes. The result is much higher backgrounds, even if the "binding specificity" of the affinity labeling steroid were identical to that of the standard, noncovalently binding steroid. Finally, for relatively stable affinity labels, it may be difficult to determine the actual amount of specific covalent labeling. In order to demonstrate specific labeling, one assumes that the addition of a noncovalently binding steroid can block the formation of a covalent receptor–affinity labeling steroid complex. However, because of competing reversible and nonreversible reactions, some of the authentic, covalent receptor–steroid complex may appear as "noncompetable," or non-specific, labeling. Thus, even the receptors initially blocked with non-covalently bound steroid will dissociate and can end up covalently labeled if the incubation time is long enough. This can be a much larger problem if a rapidly reversible complex is initially formed in the binding reaction [i.e., RS′ of Eq. (2), as has been postulated by Pratt *et al.* (1975) for glucocorticoid receptors] and if this RS′ complex can also react to give a covalent complex. In this situation, just the formation of very small amounts of the noncovalent, receptor–affinity label complex could, with time, result in the formation of large amounts of covalent RS′ and thus reduce the amount of protected, noncovalent RS′. For this reason, much larger concentrations of the rapidly dissociating, noncovalently binding steroid might be required to prevent the formation of covalent receptor–steroid complexes. Even then it might be very difficult to detect specific affinity labeling since now nonspecific labeling might also be depressed, which would cause artificially high levels of specific labeling.

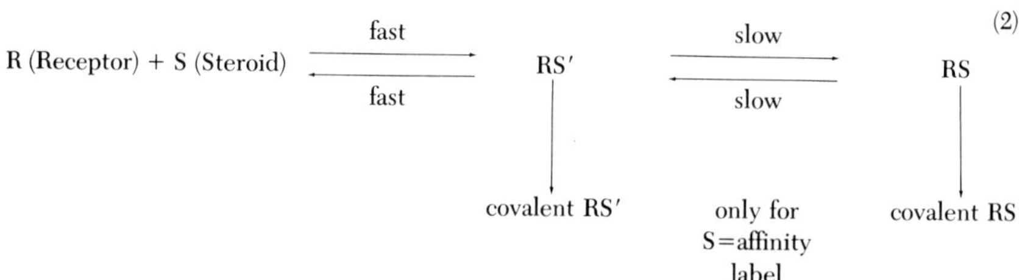


Some methods of affinity labeling can reduce nonspecific labeling more effectively than others. The specificity of affinity labeling of enzymes was increased by the development of "suicide inactivators," in which the normal enzymatic processes convert a modified substrate into the actual affinity label (Abeles and Maycock, 1976). Thus, the affinity label is initially present only in the active site of the enzyme and nonspecific labeling can occur only if the rate of dissociation of the generated affinity label from the enzyme is competitive with the rate of affinity labeling of the enzyme. Unfortunately, this precise approach cannot be used with steroid receptors since they do not appear to cause any chemical transformations of steroids. However, it is possible that similar methods could be developed to increase the specific labeling of molecules devoid of enzyme activity, such as glucocorticoid receptors.

### C. Generally Available Methods of Affinity Labeling

A survey of the literature (e.g., Jakoby and Wilchek, 1977) indicates that virtually all affinity labeling studies to date have employed either electrophilic affinity labeling or photoaffinity labeling (see below). Furthermore, the vast majority of affinity labels contain one of a very limited selection of affinity labeling functional groups. Most electrophilic affinity labels have been $\alpha$-halo-ketones or -esters, sulfonyl halides, or nitrogen mustards. Photoaffinity labeling has usually employed azides, diazo-ketones or -esters, or $\alpha,\beta$-unsaturated carbonyl compounds. This restricted repertoire has been sufficient for the labeling of numerous enzymes (Jakoby and Wilchek, 1977), nonreceptor steroid binding proteins (Pons *et al.*, 1976; Khan and Rosner, 1977; Bhatnager *et al.*, 1978), and, it appears, even several neuroendocrine receptors (Caruso *et al.*, 1979; Portoghese *et al.*, 1979; Rice *et al.*, 1979; Costall *et al.*, 1980). In contrast, this limited arsenal has afforded little success in the affinity labeling of steroid receptors (see Section III). While these established methods might work with purified receptors (Govindan and Sekeris, 1978; Eisen and Glinsmann, 1978; Wrange *et al.*, 1979) once they become available, it is our feeling that the development of new methods of affinity labeling and new affinity labeling functional groups are needed to increase the prospects of obtaining covalent, affinity labeled steroid receptors, and in particular glucocorticoid receptors.

## II. DESCRIPTION OF VARIOUS METHODS OF AFFINITY LABELING

### A. Basic Chemical Principles of Affinity Labeling

The chemistry of affinity labeling is defined by the general classes of organic reactions: nucleophilic, electrophilic, free-radical, and excited-state reactions. Since biological systems contain high concentrations of nucleophiles (e.g., $H_2O$, $—NH_2$, —SH, $—COO^-$) which react with electrophiles, the few naturally occurring reactive electrophiles [e.g., epoxides, —N=C=S, $C=S^+—O^-$ (Block *et al.*, 1980) $—\overset{+}{N}\equiv\overset{-}{C}$] are rare and often short-lived. Thus, the use of nucleophilic steroids is not a promising method for affinity labeling receptors. Free-radical and excited-state species are highly reactive and, for purposes of affinity labeling, are most conveniently generated *in situ* while complexed with the binding macromolecule.

Affinity labeling methods are of two general types: those in which all of the reactants are added at the same time (Type I) and those where an essential component is added at a later time (Type II). Only with the latter type is it possible to control the timing of covalent bond formation. In view of the above discussion of the chemistry of affinity labeling, only electrophilic reagents appear to be of general use for Type I affinity labeling of receptors. Of the various possible added components in Type II affinity labeling, we will consider only light and chemicals (Fig. 1).

Type I

1. ELECTROPHILIC AFFINITY LABELING

$$A-X + HNuc-B \xrightarrow[-H^+]{-X'} A-Nuc-B$$

Type II

2. PHOTOAFFINITY LABELING (Photoactivated affinity labelling)

$$A-Z + B \xrightarrow{h\nu} A-Z^{\cdot} + B \longrightarrow A-Z'-B$$

3. CHEMOAFFINITY LABELING (Chemically activated affinity labelling)

$$A-M + N-B \xrightarrow{O} A-M'-O'-N'-B$$

FIG. 1. General classes of affinity labeling methods.

## B. ELECTROPHILIC AFFINITY LABELING (TYPE I LABELING)

Electrophilic affinity labeling describes the labeling of a macromolecule B with a ligand A containing an electrophilic functional group X (Baker *et al.*, 1961; Jakoby and Wilchek, 1977) (Fig. 1). This method requires the presence of a nucleophile (HNuc) in the binding cavity of the macromolecule B which can attack the chemically reactive group X (e.g., an $\alpha$-halocarbonyl group), often with the subsequent deplacement of a fragment X′. The functional group X usually is stable and reacts with a limited variety of nucleophiles so that high yields of reaction to give A-Nuc-B are possible even for slow reactions. It is not possible to control the timing of reaction, and the level of nonspecific labeling is high, but the derived product A-Nuc-B usually contains only one or two labeled amino acids (Pons *et al.*, 1976; Khan and Rosner, 1977; Bhatnager *et al.*, 1978).

### C. Photoaffinity Labeling (Type II Labeling)

Light is the added essential component in the Type II labeling process called photoaffinity labeling (Fig. 1) (Singh *et al.*, 1962; Jakoby and Wilchek, 1977; Chowdhry and Westheimer, 1979). Photolysis converts a group Z (such as an azide, diazo-ketone, or $\alpha,\beta$-unsaturated carbonyl) into a highly reactive group Z* which will combine with almost any amino acid of B, thus ensuring the formation of some A—Z′—B. The reaction is almost instantaneous but occurs only after irradiation, thereby permitting control over the moment of covalent labeling and reduction of nonspecific labeling by removing excess A—Z before adding light. Unfortunately the yields of A—Z′—B are uniformly low, apparently because of nonproductive side reactions of A—Z* with itself and with solvent. The labeling of B can involve many amino acids at different positions, which complicates the identification of products. Furthermore, photolytic generation of electrophilic (or nucleophilic) affinity labels can result in "pseudophotoaffinity labeling" (Ruoho *et al.*, 1973; Payne *et al.*, 1980), in which case more than one type of affinity labeling process is occurring.

### D. Chemoaffinity Labeling (Type II Labeling)

Chemoaffinity labeling is the term we introduced to describe Type II labeling wherein the added essential component is a chemical O which initiates the formation of a covalent linkage between specific functional groups M and N found on the ligand A and the macromolecule B respectively (Fig. 1) (Simons *et al.*, 1979a). Only certain combinations are possible for M, N, and O; however, since all of the components are relatively stable, high yields of A—M′—O′—N′—B are possible even for slow reactions. Since no reaction is possible in Type II labeling procedures before adding the essential component (e.g., the chemical O), the timing of covalent attachment can be controlled and the levels of nonspecific labeling with ligand A can be reduced.

The specific differences between these Type II labeling procedures (i.e., chemo- and photoaffinity labeling) will depend somewhat on the individual examples. In general, however, chemoaffinity labeling can give high yields of reaction with a limited number of functional groups while photoaffinity labels react with almost all functional groups but usually in low overall yield (see Section III).

## III. PROGRESS AND POSSIBILITIES WITH VARIOUS AFFINITY LABEL METHODS IN YIELDING COVALENT GLUCOCORTICOID RECEPTOR–STEROID COMPLEXES

### A. Photoaffinity Labeling

Two studies have appeared concerning 21-diazo-substituted corticosteroids as photoaffinity labels for human corticosteroid binding globulin (Marver *et al.*, 1976) and potential photoaffinity labels for mineralocorticoid receptors (Wolff *et al.*, 1975). Preliminary results have appeared on the synthesis and affinity labeling activity of 21-diazodexamethasone (Manz and Govindan, 1980; Govindan and Manz, 1980). This derivative has some of the required properties of a photoaffinity label. However, due to discrepancies in the positions on SDS gels of affinity labeled protein and supposed receptor, it is not yet possible to determine if 21-diazo-dexamethasone actually can be used to form a covalent glucocorticoid receptor–steroid complex (Govindan and Manz, 1980).

Katzenellenbogen has extensively investigated the photoaffinity labeling of estrogen receptors and, using an aryl azide derivative of hexestrol, was the first to succeed in obtaining a photoaffinity labeled receptor (Katzenellenbogen *et al.*, 1977; Katzenellenbogen, 1977). More recently, the synthetic progestin R5020 was used to photoaffinity label the progesterone receptor by virtue of an excited $\pi^*$ state of the $\alpha,\beta,\gamma,\delta$-diene-one system of R5020 (Dure *et al.*, 1980). In both cases the yield of labeled material was low (10–20%) which is characteristic of photoaffinity labels in general. Recently an approximately 50% inactivation of benzodiazepine receptor binding activity was reported but this was achieved with only ~ 15% covalent labeling as shown by use of the tritiated photoaffinity label (Möhler *et al.*, 1980). The only exception of which we are aware to low yields with conventional photoaffinity labeling groups is the recent report of Kerlavage and Taylor (1980) where ~ 44% of the initially bound 8-azido-cAMP was covalently linked to the regulatory subunit of cAMP-dependent protein kinase II, with > 90% of the covalent attachment being to a single tyrosine in the peptide chain.

Several new photolabeling groups have recently been developed which could be especially useful in affinity labeling receptors. Diazerines can give as much as 30% labeling efficiency (Standring and Knowles, 1980). Unlike most photoaffinity label functional groups, photoexcited aromatic nitro groups do not decompose in the absence of reaction with nucleophiles (Jelenc *et al.*, 1978; Möhler *et al.*, 1980) and photoactivated nitrophenyl ethers specifically react with thiols, amines, and acids (Jelenc *et al.*, 1978). Bifunctional photoaffinity labels (Henkin, 1977; Jelenc *et al.*, 1978) could be used as photoaffinity cross-linkers. A bifunctional nitrophenyl ether gave 80% cross-linking of hemoglobin (Jelenc *et al.*, 1978). Most of these photolabeling groups are attached to aromatic rings and thus could readily be incorporated into deacylcortivazol (Fried *et al.*, 1963), which we found is an extremely potent glucocorticoid with high affinity for receptors (Simons *et al.*, 1979b; Harmon *et al.*, 1981). One or two other steroids containing aromatic rings have been reported to possess glucocorticoid activity (Steelman and Hirschmann, 1967) and might also be derivatized, although it has not yet been determined that they can bind to receptors.

Increased selectivity appears possible with a new procedure called energy transfer photoaffinity labeling in which photolabeling occurs only with those affinity labels that are activated by energy transfer from nearby excited tryptophan groups (Goeldner and Hirth, 1980).

### B. Chemoaffinity Labeling

Basically any bifunctional cross-linker (Peters and Richards, 1977; Henkin, 1977; Jelenc *et al.*, 1978) can be used as the added essential component in what we call chemoaffinity labeling (Simons *et al.*, 1979a; Simons, 1981). Depending on the size of the added chemical and the fit of the receptor–steroid complex, it may not be possible for chemoaffinity labeling to occur in the steroid binding site. In this case, a bridging arm would be used to give, via exo affinity labeling (Cory *et al.*, 1977), a complex where the actual covalent bond is removed from the steroid binding site. In either case, however, the utility of chemoaffinity labeling will be greatest if the cross-linker is very specific in its reactions.

#### 1. *With Enzymes as the Added Chemical*

Enzymes are probably the most specific reagents available. Transglutaminases have been used to couple bifunctional primary amines to the $\gamma$-carboxamide group of glutamine residues in proteins (Gorman and Folk, 1980, and references cited). Due to the extreme bulk of the enzyme, this method would be limited to affinity labeling with those ligands that are not buried in the macromolecule or to those ligands which contained a long bridging arm. There are no known examples of this method in the affinity labeling of receptors.

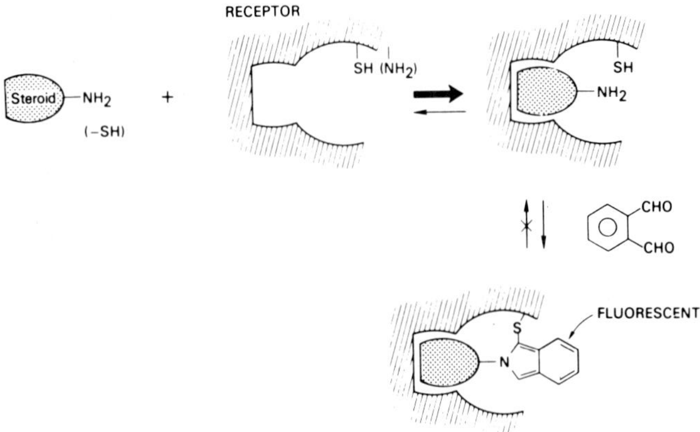


FIG. 2. Model of fluorescent chemoaffinity labeling (FCAL) as applied to glucocorticoid receptors.

## 2. *With* o-*Phthalaldehyde (OPTA) as the Added Chemical*

We have determined that OPTA specifically and rapidly reacts with thiols and primary amines to give isoindoles (Simons and Johnson, 1976, 1977a, 1978a). We thus investigated the use of appropriately derivatized steroids and OPTA to form isoindole-linked receptor–steroid complexes (Fig. 2) (Simons *et al.*, 1979a). An added advantage of the choice of OPTA is that almost all of these isoindoles are intensely fluorescent (Simons and Johnson, 1976, 1977b, 1978b; Simons *et al.*, 1979a). Thus this particular example of chemoaffinity labeling is called fluorescent chemoaffinity labeling, or FCAL (Simons *et al.*, 1979a). The formation of a covalent fluorescent receptor–steroid complex would be especially useful since fluorescence studies can give much information that is not accessible with radioactively labeled covalent complexes (e.g., polarity of the binding site and accessibility of solvent, mobility of the ligand, and conformational changes of the receptor).

OPTA also reacts with just primary and secondary amines in the absence of thiols but these products are barely fluorescent, if at all. High concentrations of amines and elevated temperatures cause dimers and polymers (Do Minh *et al.*, 1977), but neither of these conditions would be used to label glucocorticoid receptors by FCAL. Thus, undesired reactions with amines will reduce the available concentration of OPTA but should not produce extraneous fluorescence or cross-linking.

Nonspecific fluorescent products, formed by the reaction of OPTA with endogenous thiols and primary amines in the absence of the modified steroid, are a major problem in the fluorescent chemoaffinity labeling of very impure molecules such as glucocorticoid receptors in crude cell extracts (Simons *et al.*, 1979a). These "nonspecific," or non-steroid-containing, fluorescent isoindoles are most likely due to the intramolecular cross-linking of —$NH_2$ and —SH groups in proteins. This "nonspecific fluorescence" can be eliminated by prior treatment of the protein with thiol reagents like *N*-ethylmaleimide (Weidekamm *et al.*, 1973) but this may also alter the glucocorticoid receptor, which is sensitive to thiol reagents (Baxter and Tomkins, 1971; Simons, 1979; Kalimi and Love, 1980). Alternatively, amine blocking groups could be used except that glucocorticoid receptors also appear to be affected by amine-specific reagents (DiSorbo *et al.*, 1980). Thus, the best way to reduce "nonspecific fluorescence" in FCAL studies of the glucocorticoid receptor would be to purify the receptor–steroid complex either before or after the addition of OPTA. This could be most easily achieved by using radioactively labeled steroids to follow the receptor–steroid complex until the "nonspecific fluorescence" was low enough to permit spectroscopic observation of the fluorescent, covalent receptor–steroid complex.

Nonspecific cross-linking of the ligand occurs with FCAL as in all affinity labeling procedures. However, this is less of a problem with Type II affinity labeling methods, such as chemoaffinity labeling, where the free (and some nonspecifically bound) ligand can be removed before OPTA is added to initiate the formation of covalent receptor–steroid complexes. The stability of isoindoles varies with the amine and thiol substituents (Simons and Johnson, 1977b, 1978b; Svedas *et al.*, 1980) and with pH and solvent polarity (Simons and Johnson, 1977b, 1978b); but covalent, isoindole–protein complexes formed under FCAL conditions appear to be relatively stable (Chen *et al.*, 1979) with 50% of the initial fluorescence remaining after 13 days at 0°C (Simons *et al.*, 1979a).

One of the theoretical advantages of FCAL with OPTA is that the isoindoles could participate in energy transfer from excited tryptophan residues. Given the sensitivity of energy transfer to the distance between the two chromophores, energy transfer constitutes a very sensitive probe for protein conformational changes. As shown in Fig. 3, when isoindole cross-linked proteins from rat hepatoma tissue culture (HTC) cells are irradiated at the $\lambda_{excit}$ of tryptophan (i.e., 286 nm), there is an efficient quenching of tryptophan fluorescence at $\sim$ 330 nm by the isoindoles [$\lambda_{excit} \simeq 340$ nm (Simons and Johnson, 1978b)] which results in the characteristic blue-shifted fluorescence of OPTA cross-linked proteins at $\sim$ 415 nm (Weidekamm *et al.*, 1973). As expected the magnitude of energy transfer is proportional to the concentration of isoindoles (Fig. 3).

Our studies have not yet progressed far enough to be able to demonstrate a covalent fluorescent steroid–isoindole–receptor complex, but numerous derivatives of dexamethasone have been prepared which have high affinity for HTC cell receptors and are good substrates in the FCAL reaction (Si-

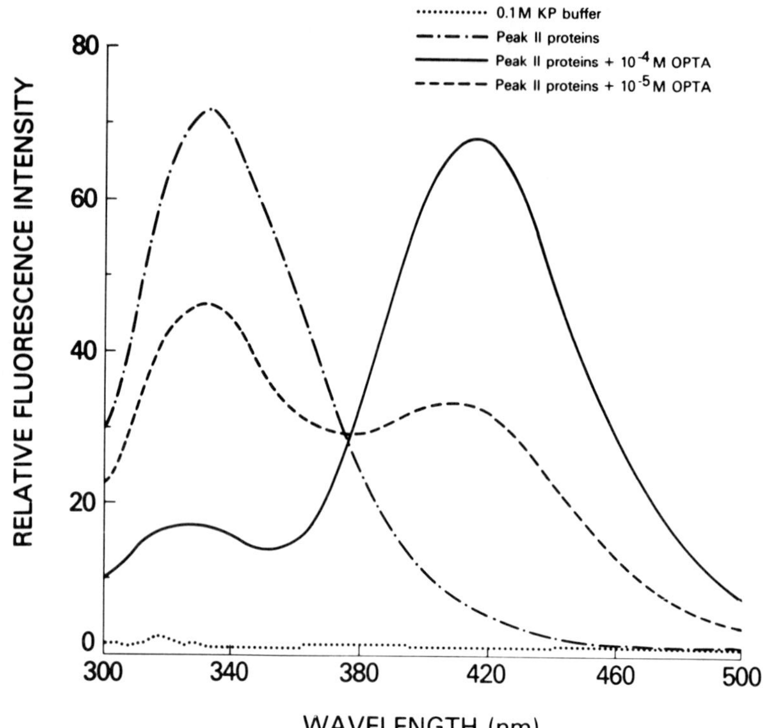


FIG. 3. Energy transfer from tryptophan to isoindole in OPTA cross-linked HTC cell proteins. Crude HTC cell, steroid-free glucocorticoid receptors (Simons *et al.*, 1979b) were chromatographed on Sephadex G-25 and eluted from a DEAE-cellulose column with 0.3 *M* potassium phosphate buffer (pH 7.8 at 0°C) to yield a "peak II" protein fraction that, in the presence of steroid, would contain receptor–steroid complexes (Sakaue and Thompson, 1977). This peak II material was diluted 1:3 with water and then treated at 0°C with 150× concentrated solutions of OPTA in 95% EtOH to give a final concentration of OPTA equal to $10^{-4}$ *M*, or $10^{-5}$ *M*. After 2 hours at 0°C, the fluorescence emission spectra of the 1:3 diluted phosphate buffer (····), peak II proteins (–·–·), peak II proteins + $10^{-5}$ *M* OPTA (----), and peak II protein + $10^{-4}$ *M* OPTA (——) were recorded ($\lambda_{excit}$ = 286 nm, temp. = 2.8°C). The fluorescence emission of isoindoles excited directly at 286 nm is very low (Simons and Johnson, 1978b).

mons *et al.*, 1979a; M. Pons, E. B. Thompson, and S. S. Simons, Jr., manuscript in preparation). In a model experiment, a covalent, fluorescent steroid–isoindole–protein complex was readily demonstrated using bovine serum albumin in place of the receptor (M. Pons, E. B. Thompson, and S. S. Simons, Jr., manuscript in preparation).

### 3. *With* syn*-Dibromobimane (DBB) as the Added Chemical*

DBB is another bifunctional chemical which, like OPTA, could be added to give fluorescent chemoaffinity labeling of the glucocorticoid receptor.

DBB itself is not fluorescent but highly fluorescent products are formed upon reaction with nucleophiles (Kosower *et al.*, 1979, 1980). Thiols react preferentially with DBB (Kosower *et al.*, 1979, 1980) but amines, alcohols, and carboxylates also appear to react (Kosower *et al.*, 1980). Although the reaction specificity of DBB is not as high as might be desired, the products are very stable. DBB has not yet been used in conjunction with the affinity labeling of receptors.

*4. With Sodium Borohydride ($NaBH_4$) as the Added Chemical*

High concentrations (1–10 m*M*) of pyridoxal phosphate and pyridoxal have been observed to interact with glucocorticoid receptors and to reduce the affinity of activated receptor–steroid complexes for nuclei and DNA (Cake *et al.*, 1978; Cidlowski and Thanassi, 1979; Di Sorbo *et al.*, 1980). In each case, the effects of pyridoxal phosphate were observed to be reversible, but the addition of a strong reducing agent (i.e., $NaBH_4$) rendered the effects of pyridoxal phosphate irreversible. Similar results have been reported for progesterone (Nishigori *et al.*, 1978) and estrogen (Müller *et al.*, 1980; Muldoon and Cidlowski, 1980) receptors. These results have been explained by the known chemistry of pyridoxal phosphate which readily reacts with primary amines to form hydrolyzable imines (Schiff bases) which, in turn, can be reduced to give stable, nonhydrolyzable secondary amines [Eq. (3)].

$$\text{R-CHO} + \text{H}_2\text{N-R}^1 \underset{\text{H}_2\text{O}}{\overset{-\text{H}_2\text{O}}{\rightleftharpoons}} \text{R-CH}=\text{N-R}^1 \underset{\times}{\overset{\text{NaBH}_4}{\rightleftharpoons}} \text{R-CH}_2\text{-NH-R}^1 \tag{3}$$

This particular example of chemoaffinity labeling involves the attack of a nucleophile as a zero-length cross-linker to stabilize an otherwise reversible chemical bond. We previously argued that nucleophilic groups would not be suitable for the affinity labeling of biological systems due to the scarcity of naturally occurring electrophiles and the abundance of nucleophiles (see Section II,A). The success of the above labeling reaction [Eq. (3)] is an exception due to the use of a strong nucleophile to react with a functional group not found among naturally occuring amino acids and formed only under special conditions in biological systems. In the present case, an exogenous aldehyde is used to form the electrophilic imine group.

In view of the relatively high concentrations (1–10 m*M*) of pyridoxal phosphate that are used and the abundance of amines in receptor containing solutions, it is unlikely that this particular example of chemoaffinity labeling is very specific for receptors. There is some evidence that pyridoxal phosphate can also compete for steroid binding to the receptor (DiSorbo *et al.*, 1980), in which case more specific chemoaffinity labeling of the receptor might be achieved with a derivatized glucocorticoid containing an aldehyde group.

The utility of this type of chemoaffinity labeling should be greatly extended by the use of sodium cyanoborohydride ($NaCNBH_3$) instead of $NaBH_4$. The advantages of $NaCNBH_3$ are that it is more stable than $NaBH_4$ in aqueous solutions and, at pH 6–8, $NaCNBH_3$ will readily reduce imines but not aldehydes (Lane, 1975). Thus, the use of $NaCNBH_3$ to chemoaffinity label receptors with a glucocorticoid aldehyde would involve two stable components which would not react with each other. This feature would be very important if steroid–receptor imine formation was slow or readily reversible.

### 5. *With Dimethyl Sulfate and Sodium Borohydride ($NaBH_4$) as the Added Chemicals*

A somewhat more complicated potential method for chemoaffinity labeling utilizes the method that Mirzabekov *et al.* (1978) have developed to cross-link chromosomal proteins to DNA. First, dimethyl sulfate is added to generate one of the reactants (a sugar aldehyde) via hydrolytic elimination of the methylated purine bases [Eq. (4)]. Reaction with a primary amine, followed by $\beta$-elimination gives an $\alpha,\beta$-unsaturated imine which, as in Section III,B,4., is reduced to a stable secondary amine by the addition of $NaBH_4$. It is unlikely that this approach will be of use for forming covalent steroid–protein bonds but it should be especially suited for investigating steroid–DNA and receptor–steroid complex–DNA interactions.

## C. Electrophilic Transfer Affinity Labeling

As far as we are aware, all examples of affinity labeling with modified ligands involve the displacement of a small leaving group (X′) and the covalent attachment of the ligand (A) to the binding macromolecule (B) (Fig. 1). In most cases, the resulting ligand–macromolecule complexes are devoid of biological activity (Marver *et al.*, 1976; Jakoby and Wilchek, 1977; Katzenellenbogen, 1977). In one case, the labeled enzyme could use the covalently attached ligand as a substrate but the entry of other substrates into the enzyme binding site was blocked by the covalently bound ligand (Groman *et al.*, 1975). A logical approach to circumventing this problem is to reverse the polarity of the reactive chemical bond of the affinity labeling ligand so that the ligand becomes the leaving group after transferring a smaller group to the macromolecule. With this procedure, one might be able to obtain a functionally active, covalently labeled macromolecule (or receptor).

We have synthesized the thiol acetate (**I**) and xanthate (**II**) derivatives of

(4)

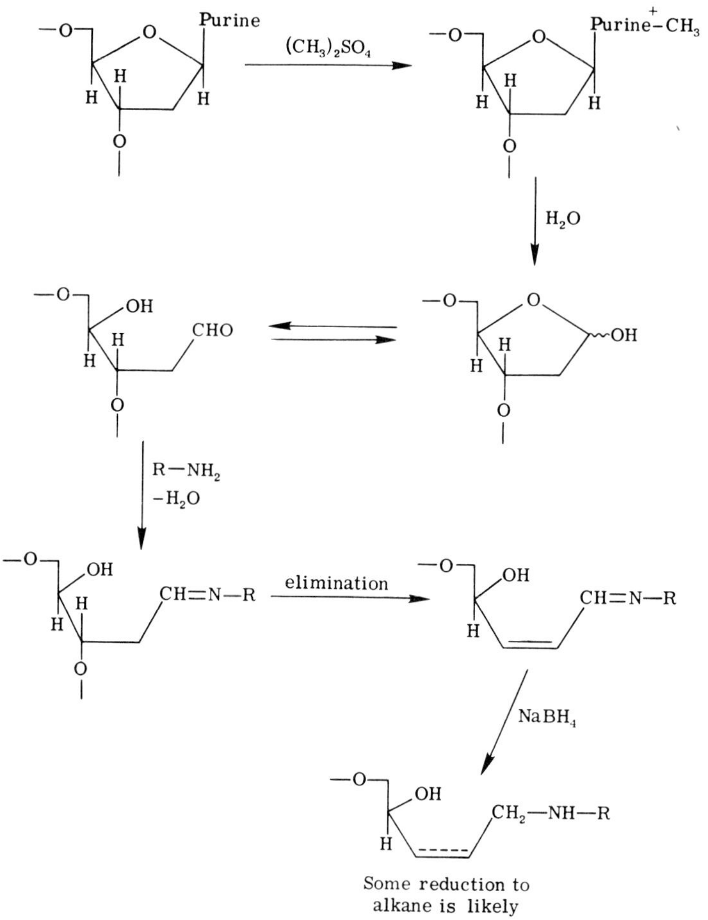

$(CH_3)_2SO_4$ — Purine → $\overset{+}{\text{Purine}}-CH_3$

$H_2O$

$R-NH_2$, $-H_2O$

elimination

$NaBH_4$

CHO; CH=N—R; $CH_2$—NH—R; OH

Some reduction to alkane is likely

cortisol to investigate this approach to the affinity labeling of glucocorticoid receptors (Simons *et al.*, 1980a; Simons, 1981). Both derivatives react rapidly with amines, and the xanthate (**II**) reacts with thiol anions, to cleave the thiol–acyl (S—X) bond to generate cortisol thiol (**III**). We envisaged that the xanthate (or thiol acetate) would bind to glucocorticoid receptors

$CH_2-S-X$; $C=O$; OH; HO; O

**I**: $X = \overset{O}{\overset{\|}{C}}-CH_3$

**II**: $X = \overset{S}{\overset{\|}{C}}-O-CH_2-CH_3$

**III**: X = H

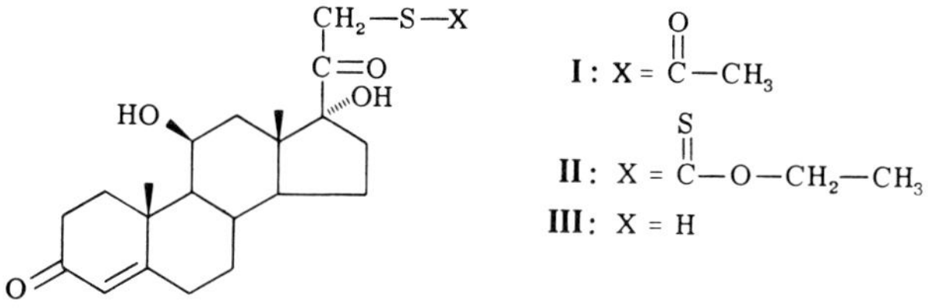

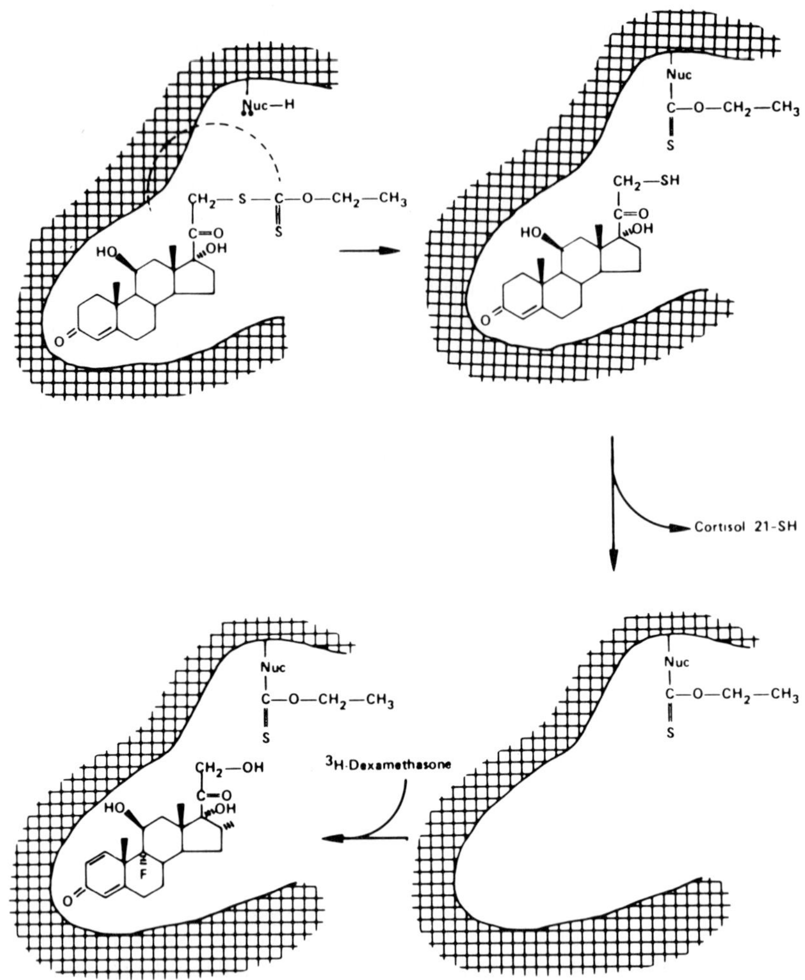


FIG. 4. Model of electrophilic transfer affinity labeling of the glucocorticoid receptor with cortisol 21-xanthate (**II**) to yield cortisol 21-thiol (**III**) and a functionally active, covalently labeled receptor.

with high affinity and react with a suitably placed nucleophile in the steroid binding site thus yielding a noncovalently bound receptor–cortisol–thiol (**III**) complex and a covalently labeled receptor (Fig. 4). Since there has been virtually no net change in the steric interactions in the binding site between the steroid and the receptor, it is reasonable to expect that the complex of modified receptor and noncovalently bound cortisol–thiol (**III**) would dissociate to give a steroid-free, covalently labeled receptor. This labeled receptor should still be functionally active and could rebind added steroid (Fig. 4). Such a covalently labeled receptor would be especially useful in "pulse labeling" active receptors so that the intracellular distribution of receptors under various conditions could be examined. For example, nuclear bound receptor–steroid complexes could be followed after their effects on gene transcription were completed. Antibodies to glucocorticoid receptors have been prepared (Govindan and Sekeris, 1978; Eisen, 1980) and will permit a classical measurement of a specific protein, in this case, the glucocorticoid receptor. However as long as the antigenic site is intact, antibodies can not discriminate between "pro-receptors," active receptors, and once active (or partially degraded) receptors. In contrast, transfer affinity labels would detect only active and once active (or partially degraded) receptors. Double-label techniques using radioactive steroids could distinguish between these two groups.

Our results with the thiol acetate (**I**) and the xanthate (**II**) are consistent with, but do not prove, electrophilic transfer affinity labeling of glucocorticoid receptors (Simons *et al.*, 1980a). Both steroids have a slightly higher apparent affinity for receptors than does the thiol **III.** However, after taking into account the lability of the easily oxidized thiol of cortisol–thiol **III**, it appears that all three steroids (**I–III**) have a threefold higher affinity for cell-free receptors than does the parent steroid cortisol. This was completely unexpected since the steric differences of the substituents in **I–III** would be predicted to influence the affinity of these steroids for receptors (Rousseau *et al.*, 1972, 1979; Failla *et al.*, 1975; El Masry *et al.*, 1977; Simons *et al.*, 1979a, 1980a; Simons and Thompson, 1981; Eisen *et al.*, 1981). The identical cell-free affinities, combined with the identical but very low whole cell biological activities of **I–III**, suggest that each compound is acting via a common steroid, i.e., the thiol **III.** One could then neatly explain the higher *apparent* cell-free receptor affinity of thiol acetate (**I**) and xanthate (**II**) versus thiol (**III**) by the hypothesis that the thiol acetate, or xanthate, was reacting in the steroid binding site of the receptor to give the thiol **III** and a covalent acyl–receptor via electrophilic transfer affinity labeling (Fig. 4). The thiol **III** formed from the thiol acetate, or xanthate, in the steroid binding site would be partially protected from oxidation and thus would exhibit a higher apparent affinity for receptors than does the thiol **III** when added directly to receptor solutions.

Receptors preincubated with thiol acetate (**I**) or xanthate (**II**) are still functionally active, as shown by their ability to rebind [$^3$H]dexamethasone (Simons *et al.*, 1980a). This is again consistent with reaction of the thiol acetate, or xanthate, to give functionally active, covalently labeled receptors. Radiolabeled acetate or thionocarbethoxy groups are required, however, to confirm this attractive hypothesis.

## D. Equilibrium Electrophilic Affinity Labeling

Bifunctional cross-linkers (Peters and Richards, 1977) such as OPTA can be used as chemoaffinity cross-linking agents to give irreversibly bound complexes (see Section III,B). Recently, a new type of cross-linker has been described which is capable of undergoing *reversible* Michael reactions. While these reversible reactions can be stopped at any point by the addition of sodium dithionite, the products formed at equilibrium will be the thermodynamically most stable products (Mitra and Lawton, 1979) [Eq. (5)].

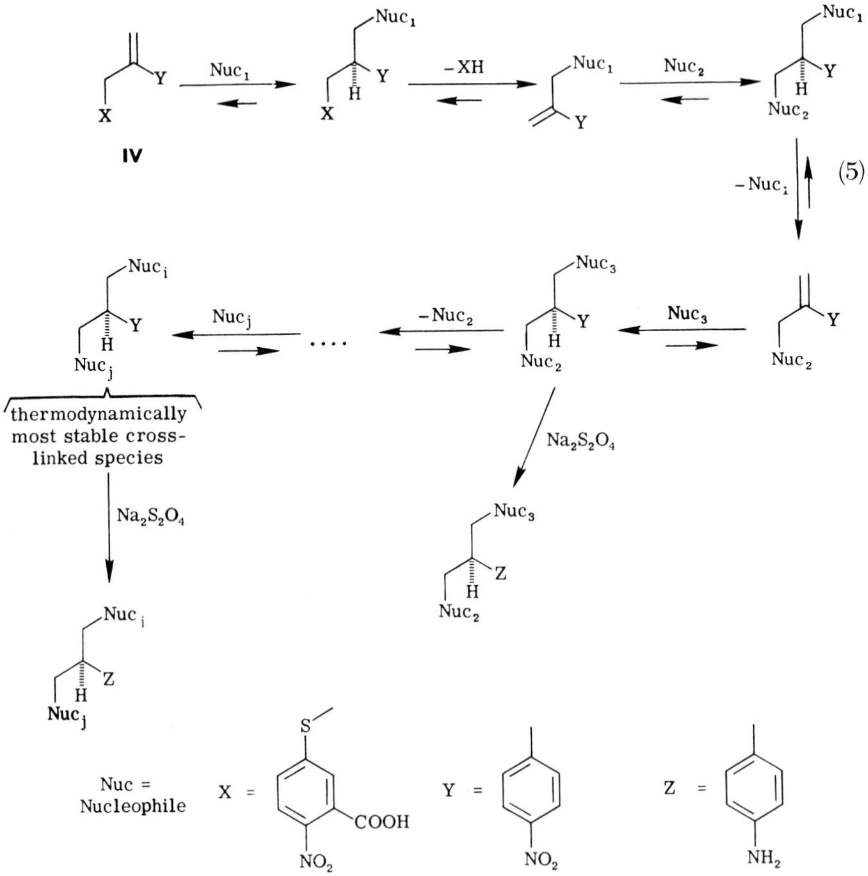

IV

Nuc₁ / −XH / Nuc₂ / −Nuc₁ (5)

Nuc₃ / −Nuc₂ / Nucⱼ

thermodynamically most stable cross-linked species

$Na_2S_2O_4$

Nuc = Nucleophile X = (2-nitro-5-thio-benzoic acid: S, COOH, $NO_2$) Y = ($p$-nitrophenyl, $NO_2$) Z = ($p$-aminophenyl, $NH_2$)

So far this approach has been used only with ribonuclease (Mitra and Lawton, 1979); but, the reversible nature of the labeling makes it very appealing for use with steroid receptors, since it would be possible to distinguish between affinity-labeled products that were formed under kinetic versus thermodynamic control. A monofunctional steroid derivative of **IV** where X is a glucocorticoid (or a bifunctional derivative where Y could be a *m*-steroidal *p*-nitrophenyl group) would form covalent complexes with receptors and nonspecific binders. Covalent complexes with the nonspecific binders would probably be the kinetically determined products. With time, however, the high affinity binding of the steroid should direct the formation of thermodynamically stable covalent receptor–steroid complexes. The nonspecifically labeled proteins would probably be kinetically labile and might be susceptible to selective destruction if a large excess of small molecular weight nucleophile, such as β-mercaptoethanol, were added before adding the dithionite.

Another theoretical advantage of this approach to affinity labeling is that it could be used to probe different forms of the receptor. It is possible that the functional groups labeled before and after activation or nuclear binding, or by agonist versus antagonist derivatives, would be different due to conformational changes in the receptor.

## E. Electrophilic Affinity Labeling

### 1. *Previous Studies*

Basically, any reactive electrophilic functional group is a potential affinity labeling group. Given the wide assortment of such functional groups in organic chemistry, it is surprising that more variety has not appeared in the choice of electrophilic affinity labeling functional groups (Jakoby and Wilchek, 1977). One infrequently used functional group is the organomercurials. These groups are very specific in their reaction with thiols. Unfortunately the mercury–sulfur bond is relatively labile in that other thiols can easily displace the original thiol from the initial complex. This feature is probably the reason for the lack of popularity of organomercurials as electrophilic affinity labels. Nevertheless, the first evidence for a covalent receptor–steroid complex involved a mercury derivative of estradiol (Muldoon and Warren, 1969; Muldoon, 1971, 1980). 4-Mercuri-17β-estradiol exhibits certain types of estrogenic activity in whole animals for at least 60 hours (Muldoon and Warren, 1969; Muldoon, 1980) and forms a covalent receptor–steroid complex (Muldoon, 1971, 1980), but this receptor–steroid complex does not translocate into the nucleus (Muldoon, 1980). It would thus be interesting to see if 4-mercuriestradiol also exhibits the long-term effects of active estrogens, such as cellular hypertrophy plus hyperplasia, which have been linked to long-term nuclear retention of estrogen receptor–steroid complexes (Clark *et al.*, 1978). At the moment, however, there is no ready explanation of how 4-mercuriestradiol induces an estrogenic effect (i.e., induction of glucose-6-phosphate dehydrogenase activity) while acting as an anti-estrogen by preventing the expected nuclear translocation of receptor–steroid complexes. It thus appears either that 4-mercuriestradiol can induce the dehydrogenase activity via a non-receptor-mediated pathway or that nuclear translocation of receptor–steroid complexes is not required for the expression of steroid hormone action, which is contrary to most current models of steroid hormone action (O'Malley and Birnbaumer 1978; Baxter and Rousseau, 1979; see also Discussion in Thompson and Lippman, 1974).

Another infrequently used electrophilic affinity label functional group is the benzyl bromide. This group was incorporated into estradiol to give 2,4-bis(bromomethyl)estradiol-17$\beta$ 3-methyl ether ($BBE_2M$), which exhibits persistent whole animal estrogenic activity (i.e., induction of glucose-6-phosphate dehydrogenase activity) and appears to covalently bind to estrogen receptors (Kanamarlapudi and Warren, 1975). It would thus appear that $BBE_2M$ is a potential irreversible agonist. In light of the above results with 4-mercuriestradiol (Muldoon, 1980), however, further interpretation of the activity of $BBE_2M$ requires a more definitive identification of the postulated $BBE_2M$ labeled receptors [e.g., via cross-reaction with antibodies to $E_2$ receptors (Green *et al.*, 1977)] and a quantitation of the nuclear translocation of $BBE_2M$ labeled receptors.

Few studies have appeared on electrophilic affinity labeling of glucocorticoid receptors (El Masry *et al.*, 1977; Simons *et al.*, 1980a,b). The nitrogen mustards of triamcinolone acetonide and cortisol 21-carbonates exhibit a decreased affinity with receptors, compared to the parent steroids (El Masry *et al.*, 1977). Both the interaction with receptors and the whole-cell biological activity of these nitrogen mustards was reversible (El Masry *et al.*, 1977), perhaps because of excessive deactivation of the nitrogen mustard group due to amide–imine resonance forms and the resulting very low basicity of the carbonate nitrogen atom. The C-21 $\alpha$-bromoacetate and acrylate esters of cortisol show little promise as effective affinity labels in view of the instability of the $\alpha$-bromoacetate toward solvolysis and the apparent facile conversion of both derivatives to cortisol in whole cell systems (Simons *et al.*, 1980a).

### 2. *Studies with New Functional Groups*

The most promising results so far on the affinity labeling of glucocorticoid receptors seem to have come from our studies with a new electrophilic affinity label group: the $\alpha$-keto mesylate (Simons *et al.*, 1980,a,b,c; Simons and Thompson, 1981; Eisen *et al.*, 1981; S. S. Simons, Jr. and E. B. Thompson, manuscript in preparation). Derivatized glucocorticoids have been prepared which exhibit irreversible cell-free and whole-cell properties and which form specific, covalent bonds with glucocorticoid receptors.

$\alpha$-Keto mesylates react extremely rapidly with thiol anions while the reactions with amines and carboxylate anions are at least three orders of magnitude slower and no reaction is observed with imidazole or alcohols (Simons *et al.*, 1980c). Two affinity labels incorporating the $\alpha$-keto mesylate group have been synthesized and studied: cortisol–mesylate (CM) (**V**) (Simons *et al.*, 1980a,b,c) and dexamethasone–mesylate (DM) (**VI**) (Simons and Thompson, 1981; Eisen *et al.*, 1981; S. S. Simons, Jr., R. E. Schleenbaker, and H. J. Eisen, manuscript in preparation). Even though CM has a very low apparent affinity for glucocorticoid receptors and virtually no biological activity in the cell systems tested thus far (Simons *et al.*, 1980a,b), further studies with HTC cells revealed that it irreversibly inhibits the cell-free binding of [$^3$H]dexamethasone to receptors and the whole-cell induction of tyrosine aminotransferase (TAT) activity by dexamethasone (Fig. 5) (Simons *et al.*, 1980b). These results illustrate, as was pointed out in Section I,B,1, the danger of relying on determinations of the affinity of synthetic steroids for receptors as a means of screening potential affinity labels; by this criterion we would have discarded CM long ago.

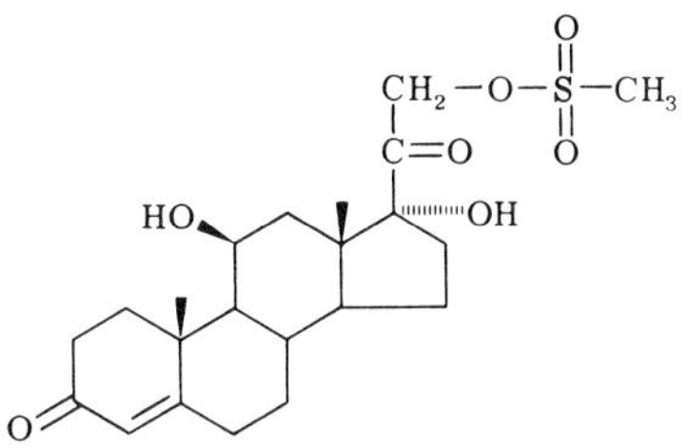

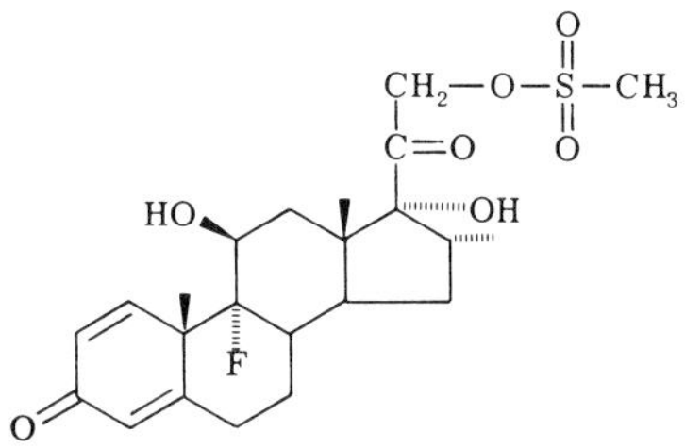

If CM is actually interacting with the receptor in an irreversible manner, a determination of the $K_a$ of CM for receptors is impossible, unless one is interested in the $K_a$ of a potential, reversible receptor–steroid complex that exists as an intermediate before the final covalent complex is formed. A rough estimate of an *apparent* $K_a$ of CM for whole cell receptors can be obtained from a whole cell competition experiment where the induction of TAT after 16 hours of dexamethasone plus increasing concentrations of CM is determined. In such an experiment, about a 6-fold excess of CM produced a 50% reduction in the induction of TAT by dexamethasone (Fig. 6) (Simons *et al.*, 1980b). This indicates that CM is much more active than would be expected from its *apparent* cell-free affinity for receptors, which is ~ 75-fold less than that of dexamethasone. A whole-cell experiment looking at the kinetics of CM inhibition of TAT induction by dexamethasone (Fig. 7) confirms the results of the above competition experiment and shows that the

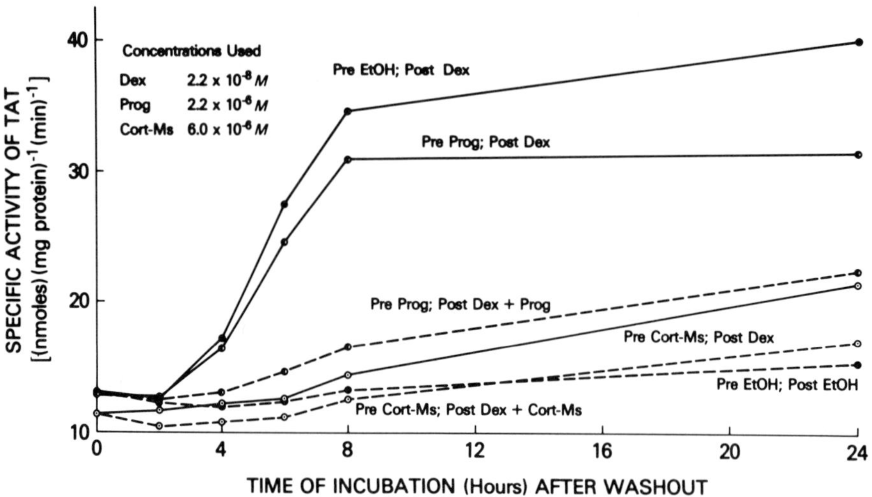


FIG. 5. TAT induction after EtOH, progesterone or CM pretreatment of HTC cells. Spinner cultures containing 200 ml of HTC cells (Thompson *et al.*, 1966; Thompson, 1979) at $2 \times 10^5$/ml were treated with 0.938 ml of EtOH $\pm$ $4.69 \times 10^{-4}$ *M* progesterone or $1.28 \times 10^{-3}$ *M* CM. After incubation at 37°C for 15½ hours, ~ $6 \times 10^7$ cells were centrifuged at 600 *g* for 10 minutes at 22°C and resuspended in 200 ml of "conditioned" medium that also had been held at 37°C for 15½ hours. After a second centrifugation, each cell pellet was again resuspended in 210 ml of "conditioned" medium. Duplicate aliquots (3 ml) were removed for 0 time protein and TAT determinations, and duplicate 50 ml aliquots were placed in 100 ml Wheaton bottles containing 300μl of EtOH $\pm$ $3.67 \times 10^{-6}$ *M* dexamethasone for the EtOH preincubated cells and 300μl of EtOH solutions of $3.67 \times 10^{-6}$ *M* dexamethasone $\pm$ $3.67 \times 10^{-4}$ *M* progesterone (for the progesterone pretreated cells) or $\pm$ $1.0 \times 10^{-3}$ *M* CM (for the CM pretreated cells). The cells in Wheaton bottles were incubated in a rotating water bath (37°C at 175 rpm) with 3 ml aliquots being removed at various time points for protein and TAT determinations in the usual manner (Gopalakrishnan and Thompson, 1977). The specific enzyme activity of TAT was then plotted against the length of incubation after the addition of steroid to washed cells for EtOH pretreated cells treated postwashout with dexamethasone (—●—) or EtOH (---●---); for progesterone pretreated cells treated postwashout with dexamethasone (—◐—) or dexamethasone + progesterone (---◐---); and for CM pretreated cells treated postwashout with dexamethasone (—○—) or dexamethasone + CM (---○---). Reprinted from Simons *et al.*, (1980b).

inhibition of TAT induction by CM at 16 hours is probably the maximal effect. The data of Figs. 5 and 7 also show the surprising result that CM is active at 37°C in the presence of growth medium containing fetal calf serum (10%) and whole cells for at least 16 hours. Thus CM appears reactive enough to form covalent bonds with components required for the induction of TAT but not so reactive that all of the CM is consumed before it can react with these essential components. This balance of reactivity is probably mandatory if an electrophilic affinity label is going to be active in whole cells.

Encouraged by the stability and low toxicity of CM in HTC cells, we

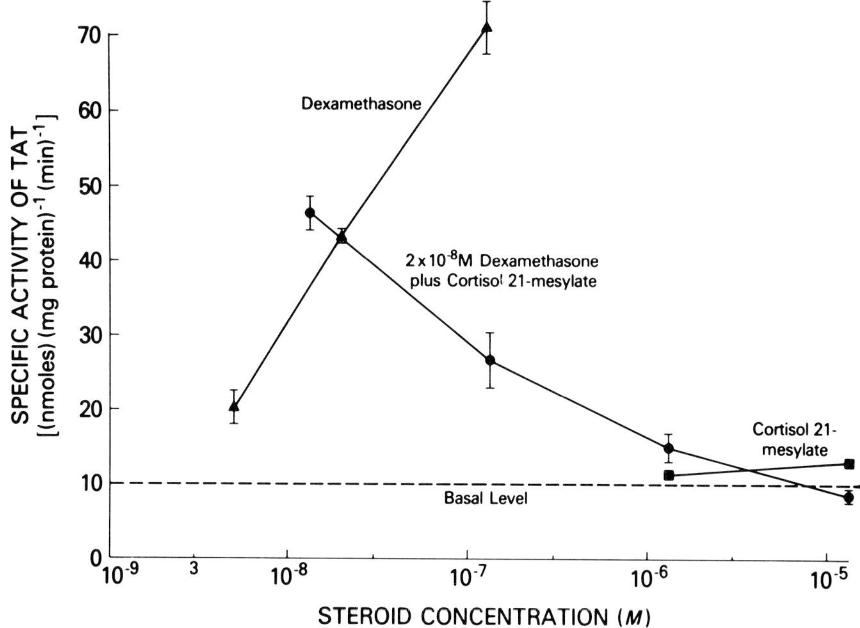


FIG. 6. Inhibition of dexamethasone induction of TAT activity in whole HTC cells by CM. Duplicate monolayer plates of HTC cells were treated with medium containing 1% EtOH ± dexamethasone (▲) or CM (■) as controls and $2 \times 10^{-8}$ $M$ dexamethasone + varying concentrations of CM (●). After incubation for 18 hours at 37°C, the specific enzyme activity of TAT in cell extracts (Gopalakrishnan and Thompson, 1977) was plotted against the concentration of that steroid present in varying amounts. The range of each duplicate determination is shown by error bars when it exceeds the area of the data points. The basal level of TAT activity is indicated by the dashed line. Reprinted from Simons *et al.* (1980b).

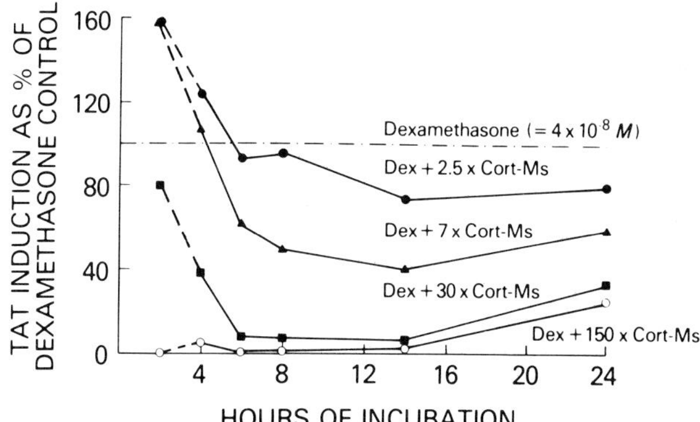


FIG. 7. Kinetics of CM inhibition of TAT induction by dexamethasone in HTC cells. Duplicate 50 ml samples of HTC cells in suspension ($3.1 \times 10^5$ cells/ml) were treated with 300 $\mu$l of EtOH with no steroid (blank), with $4 \times 10^{-8}$ $M$ dexamethasone (control), or with $4 \times 10^{-8}$ $M$ dexamethasone and varying amounts of CM. The cells were incubated in a rotating water bath at 37°C (Simons *et al.*, 1980b) for the indicated time, at which point the specific enzyme activity of TAT in cell extracts was determined (Gopalakrishnan and Thompson, 1977) and plotted as percent of the dexamethasone control. The values at short times of incubation (i.e., 0–4 hours) are of questionable significance due to the low levels of TAT induction at these times.

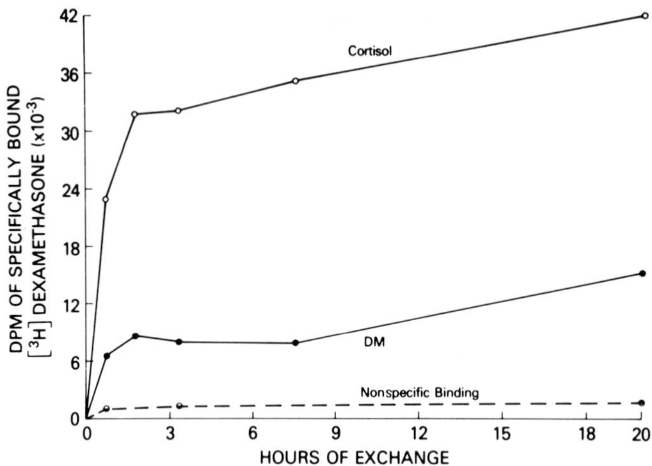


FIG. 8. Irreversible cell-free binding of DM to HTC cell receptors. Crude HTC cell glucocorticoid receptors (1.28 ml) were added to 2.24 ml of homogenization buffer (Simons *et al.*, 1979b) containing steroid to give a final concentration of $6 \times 10^{-8}$ *M* cortisol or $7.1 \times 10^{-8}$ *M* DM. After a 3 hour incubation at 0°C, 0.425 ml of activated charcoal was added to remove free steroid and to inactivate steroid-free receptors (Simons *et al.*, 1980a). The supernatants were adjusted to $1.9 \times 10^{-8}$ [$^3$H]dexamethasone ± $1.1 \times 10^{-5}$ *M* [$^1$H]dexamethasone and incubated for various times before the amount of specifically bound [$^3$H]dexamethasone in cortisol pretreated (—○—) or DM pretreated (—●—) cytosols was determined by the usual activated charcoal procedure (Simons *et al.*, 1980a). For comparison, the amount of nonspecific exchange binding in both pretreated cytosols is shown (- - -○- - -,- - -●- - -).

looked at CM in intact animals. Whole rat experiments with CM were promising in that partial antagonism of dexamethasone activity was observed. However this antiglucocorticoid activity tended to diminish with larger doses of CM, perhaps due to the toxicity of CM ($LD_{50}$ = 15–20 mg) (Chrousos *et al.*, 1981).

The results of experiments with the dexamethasone derivative DM (**VI**) (Simons and Thompson, 1981) were very similar to those obtained with CM. Thus the *apparent* affinity of DM for HTC cell glucocorticoid receptors is less than that of the parent steroid dexamethasone; however, the half-maximal inhibitory effect of DM on whole-cell induction of TAT by dexamethasone occurs at a DM concentration that is less than that expected from the relative cell-free affinity of DM for receptors. Preincubation of crude cell-free receptors with DM inhibits the subsequent ability of these receptors to bind [$^3$H]dexamethasone by ~ 70% (Fig. 8). Thus, DM, like CM, exhibits cell-free antiglucocorticoid properties. This effect is not a nonspecific alkylating effect of CM or DM since a 19-fold lower concentration of DM is just as effective as CM in inhibiting the binding of

[$^3$H]dexamethasone to pretreated receptors. Thus, the relative cell-free potency of CM and DM parallels their *apparent* relative cell-free affinities for receptors and appears to be steroid mediated (Simons and Thompson, 1981).

Synthesis of $^3$H-labeled DM allowed a direct assessment of the covalent labeling properties of DM. The results of an SDS-polyacrylamide gel of TCA precipitated proteins of crude HTC cell cytosol labeled with $^3$H-DM clearly show that $^3$H-DM is reacting to yield covalent steroid-macromolecule complexes (Fig. 9). As is usually observed with electrophilic affinity labeling, there is a large amount of nonspecific covalent labeling of the cytosol; ~ 40% of the total covalent labeling is found in a nonspecifically labeled molecule(s) of molecular weight ~ 25,500 (fractions 23–28). It is not clear what this species is but it is extensively labeled under our conditions. The total amount of specific, or competable, covalent labeling in Fig. 9 is low and extends over a wide range of molecular weights. However, a peak of specific

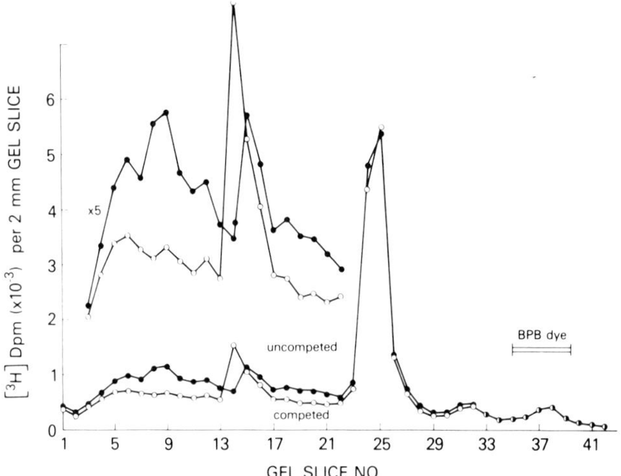


FIG. 9. SDS-polyacrylamide gels of HTC cell cytosol labeled with $^3$H–DM. Crude HTC cell receptors (Simons *et al.*, 1979b) were incubated with $1.35 \times 10^{-7}$ *M* $^3$H–DM ± $10^{-5}$ *M* $^1$H-dexamethasone, treated with activated charcoal to remove free steroid and precipitated with 10% trichloroacetic acid at 0°C. The TCA pellets were dissolved in a minimum volume of 1 *N* NaOH at room temperature, adjusted to contain 1% sodium dodecylsulfate (SDS), 1% β-mercaptoethanol, 0.48 *M* sucrose, and 0.0024% bromophenyl blue, heated for 5 minutes at 100°C, and then applied to 7.5% polyacrylamide–1% SDS–0.1 *M* sodium phosphate (pH 7.2 at room temperature) tube gels. After 4.5 hours of electrophoresis, the gels were sliced (2 mm slices), digested overnight in NCS, and then counted in toluene/POP/POPOP. A 5× magnification of the uncompeted (●) and competed (○) binding in the top half of the gel is shown in the insert.

labeling is found around fractions 8–9 (see insert of Fig. 9). The molecular weight of proteins found in this region of the gel is ~ 85,000 which is very similar to the 89,000–90,000 molecular weight form of the glucocorticoid receptor that has been observed by others (Govindan and Sekeris, 1978; Wrange *et al.*, 1979). These promising results strongly suggest, but do not prove, that CM and DM are true electrophilic affinity labels of the glucocorticoid receptor. The presence of competable $^{3}$H-DM labeling spread over other molecular weights could be due to low affinity binders (see Section I,C,2) or to proteolysis, to which glucocorticoid receptors are very susceptible (Carlstedt-Duke *et al.*, 1979; Wrange *et al.*, 1979).

At the moment the yields of specific covalent labeling are low but, considering the very low relative abundance of receptors, it is encouraging that we are able to see any specific labeling at all. Recent results indicate that partial purification, either before or after labeling with $^{3}$H-DM, yields preparations in which the specific labeling of the ~ 85,000 molecular weight species is unambiguous (Simons and Thompson, 1981; Eisen *et al.*, 1981). It thus appears that CM and DM represent the first affinity labels of glucocorticoid receptors.

If we are correct in concluding that CM and DM are forming specific, covalent receptor–steroid complexes, the data of Figs. 5 and 7 pose two interesting questions. The first question is whether the rate of appearance of steroid binding activity of receptors is controlled by the existing concentration of receptors or by steroids. Unfortunately we can not look at the rate of synthesis of total receptor proteins because there appears to be at least one form of "proreceptor" which does not bind steroids (Nielsen *et al.*, 1977; Leach *et al.*, 1979) and consequently can not yet be quantified. Thus, when quantitating receptor levels, most people report as receptors only those receptor proteins that specifically bind steroid with high affinity. We follow this convention here but realize that a complete analysis of receptor *protein* synthesis and turnover requires techniques which measure not merely receptor binding of steroids but actual receptor protein. With this limitation in mind, the number of glucocorticoid receptors in HeLa cells (Cidlowski and Michaels, 1977) and lymphocytes (Crabtree *et al.*, 1980) is reported to double during S phase. The appearance of new receptors seems to occur at the same rate as general protein synthesis (Crabtree *et al.*, 1980). The data of Figure 5 suggest that when most of the available receptors in HTC cells are inactivated by an irreversible antiglucocorticoid, the reappearance of new receptors (and thus the restoration of TAT inducibility) is relatively slow and does not rapidly return to the normal level. The effect of reversibly binding steroids on glucocorticoid receptor levels is unclear. In human lymphocytes, there is some evidence that exposure to glucocorticoids alters the number of receptors and/or their affinity for such steroids (Shipman *et al.*, 1979a,b; Schlechte *et al.*, 1980); and, adrenalectomy may cause an increase in the number of rat kidney (Claire *et al.*, 1981) and rat heart and liver glucocorticoid receptors (Gregory, 1976). In contrast, the concentration of receptors in leukocytes in whole animals (Murakami *et al.*, 1980) and in HTC cells (Bloom *et al.*, 1980) is not affected by glucocorticoids. Estrogen and progesterone receptors (O'Malley and Birnbaumer, 1978) may be under control of the homologous steroid, but each of these steroids may also affect the appearance and function of the other receptor (Evans and Leavitt, 1980). Aldosterone appears to decrease the number of rat kidney mineralocorticoid receptors (Claire *et al.*, 1981). Whether glucocorticoids, or their receptors, control the level of steroid binding activity of glucocorticoid receptors is not yet resolved, but the affinity-labeling steroids we are utilizing seem well suited to answer this question because they provide a means of selectively inactivating receptors.

The second question posed by the data of Figs. 5–7 is why CM and DM are antiglucocorticoids. The answer is an integral part of the mechanism of formation, and chemical nature, of the covalent receptor–steroid complex. An attractive hypothesis is that the covalent binding of CM or DM to the unactivated receptor prevents a conformational change that is necessary for activation of the receptor–steroid complex. We plan to examine this possibility.

The nature of the chemical bond in the suspected covalent receptor–steroid complex is not yet known. However, in view of the well-known effect of thiol reagents on glucocorticoid receptors (Baxter and Tomkins, 1971; Simons, 1979; Kalimi and Love, 1980), the selective reactivity of the $\alpha$-keto mesylate group of CM and DM with thiol anions (Simons *et al.*, 1980c) and the special interaction of thiols with the C-20 carbonyl of glucocorticoids which has been invoked to help explain the absolute requirement of a C-20 carbonyl for the high affinity binding of glucocorticoids (Simons *et al.*, 1979a), it is possible that a cysteine is intimately involved in both the binding of glucocorticoids to receptors and the covalent binding of CM and DM (Fig. 10). Normally, glucocorticoids would initially bind noncovalently to the receptor (*1*) and then form a reversible hemithioketal (*2*). Hemithioketals are known to be formed in certain ligand/enzyme complexes and in some cases the hemithioketal is even irreversible (Paech *et al.*, 1980, and references cited). The formation of the steroid–receptor hemithioketal (*2*) would be reversible even in the case of the mesylate ($X = OSO_2CH_3$). However, the thiol involved in the hemithioketal could also react to displace methanesulfonic acid anion from the adjacent C-21 carbon to give an irreversible receptor–steroid complex linked by a thioether (*3* of Fig. 10).

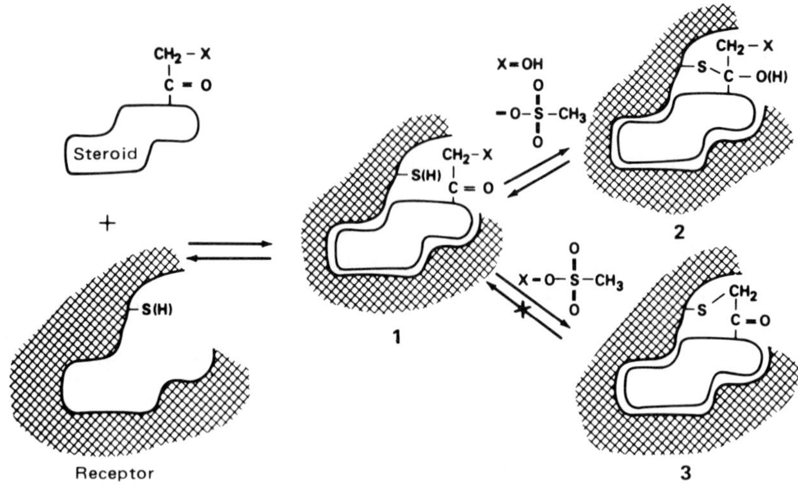


FIG. 10. Proposed mechanism for formation of a covalent glucocorticoid receptor–steroid complex with CM or DM. Reprinted from Simons and Thompson (1981).

## IV. CONCLUSIONS

The major advantage of a covalent complex with the steroid linked to the glucocorticoid receptor in the high affinity binding site would be that the receptor–steroid complex could not dissociate. Such a complex would aid purification studies, would permit mechanistic studies that are uncomplicated by the competing dissociation of receptor–steroid complexes, and would facilitate localization of the nuclear binding. In short, a covalent complex would allow receptor–steroid complexes to be treated as a unique, single entity. Finally, covalent complexes formed in whole cells could easily possess long-term, relatively irreversible, agonist (Kanamarlapudi and Warren, 1975; Caruso *et al.*, 1979; Muldoon, 1980; Brandenburg *et al.*, 1980) or antagonist (Portoghese *et al.*, 1979; Rice *et al.*, 1979; Simons *et al.*, 1980b; Costall *et al.*, 1980; Simons and Thompson, 1981) properties which could eventually be of clinical use.

Affinity labeling appears to be the simplest method for preparing a covalent receptor–steroid complex and yet there has been limited success in identifying potential steroidal affinity labels, not to mention isolating an affinity labeled receptor. Preliminary evidence for a covalent complex has been reported with estrogen (Muldoon, 1971; Kanamarlapudi and Warren, 1975; Katzenellenbogen *et al.*, 1977) and progesterone (Dure *et al.*, 1980) receptors. Our results with CM (Simons *et al.*, 1980b) and DM (Simons and Thompson, 1981; Eisen *et al.*, 1981; S. S. Simons, Jr., R. E. Schleenbaker, and H. J. Eisen, manuscript in preparation) appear to provide the first conclusive evidence for a covalent glucocorticoid receptor–steroid complex.

The difficulties that have been encountered in the affinity labeling of receptors seem to be (1) the high levels of nonspecific labeling, (2) screening procedures which can give false negatives, and (3) a restricted number of approaches to affinity labeling. We have briefly touched on the first two problems and discussed some of the solutions. Nonspecific labeling can best be reduced by partial purification of the receptor before or after affinity labeling or by employing some other, yet unknown, property of receptors which would increase the specificity of steroid–receptor interactions. Screening procedures based only on the relative cell-free affinity and whole-cell biological activity of synthetic steroids are not as accurate as assays which look at the ability of the synthetic steroid to inhibit cell-free and whole-cell glucocorticoid responses.

The main emphasis of this chapter has been on the third problem confronting those working on the affinity labeling of receptors, i.e., the limited available methods. We have discussed new approaches, some of which are yet untried with glucocorticoid, or any other, steroid receptor. These approaches involve new functional groups to be used with existing methods and new methods, some of which (e.g., electrophilic transfer affinity labeling, equilibrium electrophilic affinity labeling, and fluorescent chemoaffinity labeling) can give hitherto unobtainable information. In fact, our two new affinity labeling steroids (the C-21 mesylates of cortisol and dexamethasone) have yielded data indicating that these steroids do indeed form covalent complexes with the glucocorticoid receptor (see Section III,E,2). It is hoped that with such new approaches, success in the affinity labeling of glucocorticoid receptors will become more common and productive.

NOTE ADDED IN PROOF: Two articles have recently appeared which describe the photo-affinity labeling of cell-free glucocorticoid receptors. R5020 has been used to photolabel HTC and S49 cell receptors, both of which displayed a molecular weight of ~87,000 (Nordeen, S. K., Lan, N. C., Showers, M. O., and Baxter, J. D. (1981) *J. Biol. Chem.*, **256,** 10503–10508). Photolysis of partially purified, activated rat liver receptor–triamcinolone acetonide complexes yielded a labeled molecule of smaller molecular weight, i.e., 40,000 (Westphal, H. M., Fleischmann, G., and Beato, M. (1981) *Eur. J. Biochem.*, **119,** 101–106).

## REFERENCES

Abeles, R. H., and Maycock, A. L. (1976). *Acc. Chem. Res.* **9,** 313–319.

Baker, B. R., Lee, W. W., Tong, E., and Ross, L. O. (1961). *J. Am. Chem. Soc.* **83,** 3713–3714.

Baxter, J. D., and Rousseau, G. G., eds. (1979). "Glucocorticoid Hormone Action." Springer-Verlag, Berlin and New York.

Baxter, J. D., and Tomkins, G. M. (1971). *Proc. Natl. Acad. Sci. U.S.A.* **68,** 932–937.

Bhatnager, Y. M., Chin, C.-C., and Warren, J. C. (1978). *J. Biol. Chem.* **253,** 811–815.

Block, E., Bazzi, A. A., and Revelle, L. K. (1980). *J. Am. Chem. Soc.* **102,** 2490–2491.

Bloom, E., Matulich, D. T., Lan, N. C., Higgins, S. J., Simons, S. S., Jr., and Baxter, J. D. (1980). *J. Steroid Biochem.* **12,** 175–184.

Brandenburg, D., Diaconescu, C., Saunders, D., and Thamm, P. (1980). *Nature (London)* **286,** 821–822.

Cake, M. H., Di Sorbo, D. M., and Litwack, G. (1978). *J. Biol. Chem.* **253,** 4886–4891.

Carlstedt-Duke, J., Wrange, Ö., Dahlberg, E., Gustafsson, J.-A., and Högberg, B. (1979). *J. Biol. Chem.* **254,** 1537–1539.

Caruso, T. P., Takemori, A. E., Larson, D. L., and Portoghese, P. S. (1979). *Science* **204,** 316–318.

Chen, R. F., Scott, C., and Trepman, E. (1979). *Biochim. Biophys. Acta.* **576,** 440–455.

Chowdhry, V., and Westheimer, F. H. (1979). *Annu. Rev. Biochem.* **48,** 293–325.

Chrousos, G. P., Cutler, G. B., Jr., Simons, S. S., Jr., Pons, M., John, L. S., Moriarty, R. M., and Loriaux, D. L. (1981). In "Progress in Research and Clinical Applications of Corticosteroids" (H. J. Lee and T. J. Fitzgerald, eds.). Heyden and Son, Phila., in press.

Cidlowski, J. A., and Michaels, G. A. (1977). *Nature (London)* **266,** 643–645.

Cidlowski, J. A., and Thanassi, J. W. (1979). *Biochemistry* **18,** 2378–2384.

Clair, M., Oblin, M.-E., Steimer, J.-L., Nakane, H., Misumi, J., Michaud, A., and Corvol, P. (1981). *J. Biol. Chem.* **256,** 142–147.

Clark, J. H., Peck, E. J., Jr., Hardin, J. W., and Eriksson, H. (1978). *In* "Receptors and Hormone Action" (B. W. O'Malley and L. Birnbaumer, eds.), Vol. II, pp. 1–31. Academic Press, New York.

Cory, M., Andrews, J. M., and Bing, D. H. (1977). *Methods Enzymol.* **46,** 115–130.

Costall, B., Fortune, D. H., Law, S-J., Naylor, R. J., Neumeyer, J. L., and Nohria, V. (1980). *Nature (London)* **285,** 571–573.

Crabtree, G. R., Munck, A., and Smith, K. A. (1980). *J. Immunol.* **125,** 13–17.

Di Sorbo, D. M., Phelps, D. S., and Litwack, G. (1980). *Endocrinology* **106,** 922–929.

Do Minh, T., Johnson, A. L., Jones, J. E., and Senise, P. P., Jr. (1977). *J. Org. Chem.* **42,** 4217–4221.

Dure, L. S., IV, Schrader, W. T., and O'Malley, B. W. (1980). *Nature (London)* **283,** 784–786.

Eisen, H. J. and Glinsmann, W. H. (1978). *Biochem. J.* **171,** 177–183.

Eisen, H. J. (1980). *Proc. Natl. Acad. Sci. U.S.A.* **77,** 3893–3897.

Eisen, H. J., Schleenbaker, R. E., and Simons, S. S., Jr. (1981). *J. Biol. Chem.*, in press.

El Masry, A. H., Braun, V. C., Nielsen, C. J., and Pratt, W. B. (1977). *J. Med. Chem.* **20,** 1134–1139.

Evans, R. W., and Leavitt, W. W. (1980). *Proc. Natl. Acad. Sci. U.S.A.* **77,** 5856–5860.

Failla, D., Tomkins, G. M., and Santi, D. V. (1975). *Proc. Natl. Acad. Sci. U.S.A.* **72,** 3849–3852.

Fried, J. H., Mrozik, H., Arth, G. E., Bry, T. S., Steinberg, N. G., Tishler, M. Hirschmann, R., and Steelman, S. L. (1963). *J. Am. Chem. Soc.* **85,** 236–238.

Goeldner, M. P., and Hirth, C. G. (1980). *Proc. Natl. Acad. Sci. U.S.A.* **77,** 6439–6442.

Gorman, J. J., and Folk, J. E. (1980). *J. Biol. Chem.* **255,** 1175–1180.

Gopalakrishnan, T. V., and Thompson, E. B. (1977). *J. Biol. Chem.* **252,** 2717–2725.

Govindan, M. V., and Manz, B. (1980). *Allergologie* **4,** 204–213.

Govindan, M. V., and Sekeris, C. E. (1978). *Eur. J. Biochem.* **89,** 95–104.

Green, G. L., Closs, D. E., Fleming, H., De Sombre, E. R., and Jensen, E. V. (1977). *Proc. Natl. Acad. Sci. U.S.A.* **74,** 3681–3685.

Gregory, M. C., Duval, D., and Meyer, P. (1976). *Clin. Sci. Mol. Med.* **51,** 487–493.

Groman, E. V., Schultz, R. M., and Engle, L. L. (1975). *J. Biol. Chem.* **250,** 5450–5454.

Harmon, J. M., Schmidt, T. J., and Thompson, E. B. (1981). *J. Steroid Biochem.* **14,** 273–279.

Henkin, J. (1977). *J. Biol. Chem.* **252,** 4293–4297.

Jakoby, W. B., and Wilchek, M., eds. (1977). *Methods Enzymol.* **46.**

Jelenc, P. C., Cantor, C. R., and Simon, S. R. (1978). *Proc. Natl. Acad. Sci. U.S.A.* **75,** 3564–3568.

Kalimi, M., and Love, K. (1980). *J. Biol. Chem.* **255,** 4687–4690.

Kanamarlapudi, N. R., and Warren, J. C. (1975). *J. Biol. Chem.* **250,** 6484–6487.

Katzenellenbogen, J. A. (1977). *In* "Biochemical Actions of Hormones" (G. Litwack, ed.), Vol. 4, pp. 1–84. Academic Press, New York.

Katzenellenbogen, J. A., Carlson, K. E., Johnson, H. J., Jr., and Myers, H. N. (1977). *Biochemistry* **16,** 1970–1976.

Kerlavage, A. R., and Taylor, S. S. (1980). *J. Biol. Chem.* **255,** 8483–8488.

Khan, M. S., and Rosner, W. (1977). *J. Biol. Chem.* **252,** 1895–1900.

Kosower, N. S., Kosower, E. M., Newton, G. L., and Ranney, H. M. (1979). *Proc. Natl. Acad. Sci. U.S.A.* **76,** 3382–3386.

Kosower, N. S., Newtown, G. L., Kosower, E. M., and Ranney, H. M. (1980). *Biochim. Biophys. Acta* **622,** 201–209.

Lane, C. F. (1975). Synthesis, 135–146.

Leach, K. L., Dahmer, M. K., Hammond, N. D., Sando, J. J., and Pratt, W. B. (1979). *J. Biol. Chem.* **254,** 11884–11890.

Manz, B., and Govindan, M. V. (1980). *Hoppe-Seyler's Z. Physiol. Chem.* **361,** 953–957.

Marver, D., Chiu, W.-H., Wolff, M. E., and Edelman, I. S. (1976). *Proc. Natl. Acad. Sci. U.S.A.* **73,** 4462–4466.

Mirzabekov, A. D., Shick, V. V., Belyavsky, A. V., and Bavykin, S. G. (1978). *Proc. Natl. Acad. Sci. U.S.A.* **75,** 4184–4188.

Mitra, S., and Lawton, R. G. (1979). *J. Am. Chem. Soc.* **101,** 3097–3110.

Möhler, H., Battersby, M. K., and Richards, J. G. (1980). *Proc. Natl. Acad. Sci. U.S.A.* **77,** 1666–1670.

Muldoon, T. G. (1971). *Biochemistry* **10,** 3780–3784.

Muldoon, T. G. (1980). *J. Biol. Chem.* **255,** 1358–1366.

Muldoon, T. G., and Cidlowski, J. A. (1980). *J. Biol. Chem.* **255,** 3100–3107.

Muldoon, T. G., and Warren, J. C. (1969). *J. Biol. Chem.* **244,** 5430–5435.

Müller, R. E., Traish, A., and Wotiz, H. H. (1980). *J. Biol. Chem.* **255,** 4062–4067.

Murakami, T., Brandon, D. D., Loriaux, D. L., and Lipsett, M. B. (1980). *J. Steroid Biochem.* **13,** 1125–1127.

Nielsen, C. J., Sando, J. J., Vogel, W. M., and Pratt, W. B. (1977). *J. Biol. Chem.* **252,** 7568–7578.

Nishigori, H., Moudgil, V. K., and Toft, D. (1978). *Biochem. Biophys. Res. Commun.* **80,** 112–118.

O'Malley, B. W., and Birnbaumer, L., eds. (1978). "Receptors and Hormone Action," Vol. II, Academic Press, New York.

Paech, C., Salach, J. I., and Singer, T. P. (1980). *J. Biol. Chem.* **255,** 2700–2704.

Payne, D. W., Katzenellenbogen, J. A., and Carlson, K. E. (1980). *J. Biol. Chem.* **255,** 10359–10367.

Peters, K., and Richards, F. M. (1977). *Annu. Rev. Biochem.* **46,** 523–551.

Pons, M., Nicolas, J.-C. Boussioux, A.-M. Descomps, B., and Crastes de Paulet, A. (1976). *Eur. J. Biochem.* **68,** 385–394.

Portoghese, P. S., Larson, D. L., Jiang, J. B., Caruso, T. P., and Takemori, A. E. (1979). *J. Med. Chem.* **22,** 168–173.

Pratt, W. B., Kaine, J. L., and Pratt, D. V. (1975). *J. Biol. Chem.* **250,** 4584–4591.

Rice, K. C., Brossi, A., Tallman, J., Paul, S. M., and Skolnick, P. (1979). *Nature (London)* **278,** 854–855.

Rousseau, G. G., Baxter, J. D., and Tomkins, G. M. (1972). *J. Mol. Biol.* **67,** 99–115.

Rousseau, G. G., Kirchhoff, J., Formstecher, P. and Lustenberger, P. (1979). *Nature (London)* **279,** 158–160.

Ruoho, A. E., Kiefer, H., Roeder, P. E., and Singer, S. J. (1973). *Proc. Natl. Acad. Sci.* **70,** 2567–2571.

Sakaue, Y., and Thompson, E. B. (1977). *Biochem. Biophys. Res. Commun.* **77,** 533–541.

Schlechte, J., Sherman, B., and Ginsberg, B. (1980). *Clin. Res.* **18,** 266A.

Shipman, G. F., Bloomfield, C. D., Smith, K. A., Peterson, B. A., and Munck, A. (1979a). *Clin. Res.* **27,** 690A.

Shipman, G. F., Bloomfield, C. D., Smith, K. A., Peterson, B. A., and Munck, A. (1979b). *Blood, Suppl.* 1, **54,** 209A.

Simons, S. S., Jr. (1979). *In* "Glucocorticoid Hormone Action" (J. D. Baxter and G. G. Rousseau, eds.), pp. 161–187. Springer-Verlag, Berlin and New York.

Simons, S. S., Jr. (1981). *In* "Progress in Research and Clinical Application of Corticosteroids," (H. J. Lee and T. J. Fitzgerald, eds.) Heyden and Son, Phila., in press.

Simons, S. S., Jr., and Johnson, D. F. (1976). *J. Am. Chem. Soc.* **98,** 7098–7099.

Simons, S. S., Jr., and Johnson, D. F. (1977a). *J. Chem. Soc., Chem. Commun.*, 374–375.

Simons, S. S., Jr., and Johnson, D. F. (1977b). *Anal. Biochem.* **82,** 250–254.

Simons, S. S., Jr., and Johnson, D. F. (1978a). *J. Org. Chem.* **43,** 2886–2891.

Simons, S. S., Jr., and Johnson, D. F. (1978b). *Anal. Biochem.* **90,** 705–725.

Simons, S. S., Jr. and Thompson, E. B. (1981). *Proc. Natl. Acad. Sci. U.S.A.* **78,** 3541–3545.

Simons, S. S., Jr., Thompson, E. B., and Johnson, D. F. (1979a). *Biochemistry* **18,** 4915–4922.

Simons, S. S., Jr., Thompson, E. B., and Johnson, D. F. (1979b). *Biochem. Biophys. Res. Commun.* **86,** 793–800.

Simons, S. S., Jr., Thompson, E. B., Merchlinsky, M. J., and Johnson, D. F. (1980a). *J. Steroid Biochem.* **13,** 311–322.

Simons, S. S., Jr., Thompson, E. B., and Johnson, D. F. (1980b). *Proc. Natl. Acad. Sci. U.S.A.* **77,** 5167–5171.

Simons, S. S., Jr., Pons, M., and Johnson, D. F. (1980c). *J. Org. Chem.* **45,** 3084–3088.

Singh, A., Thornton, E. R., and Westheimer, F. H. (1962). *J. Biol. Chem.* **237,** 3006–3008.

Smith, S. B., and Benisek, W. F. (1980). *J. Biol. Chem.* **255,** 2690–2693.

Standring, D. N., and Knowles, J. R. (1980). *Biochemistry* **19,** 2811–2816.

Steelman, S. L., and Hirschmann, R. (1967). *In* "The Adrenal Cortex" (A. B. Eisenstein, ed.), pp. 345–383. Little, Brown, Boston, Massachusetts.

Svedas, V.-J., Galaev, I. J., Borisov, I. L., and Berezin, I. V. (1980). *Anal. Biochem.* **101,** 188–195.

Thompson, E. B. (1979). *In* "Glucocorticoid Hormone Action" (J.D. Baxter and G. G. Rousseau, eds.), pp. 203–217. Springer-Verlag, Berlin and New York.

Thompson, E. B., and Lippman, M. E. (1974). *Metab. Clin. Exp.* **23,** 159–202.

Thompson, E. B., Tomkins, G. M., and Curran, J. F. (1966). *Proc. Natl. Acad. Sci. U.S.A.* **56,** 296–303.

Weidekamm, E., Wallach, D. F. H., and Flükiger, R. (1973). *Anal. Biochem.* **54,** 102–114.

Wolff, M. E., Feldman, D., Catsoulacos, P., Funder, J. W., Hancock, C., Amano, Y., and Edelman, I. S. (1975). *Biochemistry* **14,** 1750–1759.

Wrange, Ö., Carlstedt-Duke, J., and Gustafsson, J.-A. (1979). *J. Biol. Chem.* **254,** 9284–9290.

Yeakley, J. M., Balasubramanian, K., and Harrison, R. W. (1980). *J. Biol. Chem.* **255,** 4182–4186.

# CHAPTER 9

# Immunochemical Approaches to the Study of Glucocorticoid Receptors

*Howard J. Eisen*



## I. INTRODUCTION

Specific and sensitive antisera are essential for research in many areas of endocrinology. Although antisera to most steroid hormones and their metabolites are currently available, antisera to steroid hormone receptors have been produced only during the past few years (Greene *et al.*, 1977; Govindan and Sekeris, 1978; Eisen, 1980). These antisera may help to resolve many of the difficult analytical problems encountered in the study of steroid hormone receptors.

We have recently developed a procedure for purifying highly the



BIOCHEMICAL ACTIONS OF HORMONES, VOL. IX

ISBN 0-12-452809-0

glucocorticoid receptor from rat liver (Eisen and Glinsmann, 1978). This partially purified preparation was used to immunize rabbits. In the initial series of immunizations, one rabbit developed antibodies (immunoglobulin G) to the glucocorticoid receptor (Eisen, 1980). In a second series of immunizations, three of five rabbits developed similar antibodies. The methods used to detect and characterize these anti-glucocorticoid receptor antibodies are discussed in this chapter. These antibodies form soluble complexes with the glucocorticoid receptor apparently without affecting the steroid ligand-binding site; many of the methods that are suitable for detecting such soluble complexes were described first by Green *et al.* (1977).

## II. PARTIAL PURIFICATION OF THE [$^3$H]TRIAMCINOLONE–RECEPTOR COMPLEX FOR USE AS AN ANTIGEN

When the [$^3$H]triamcinolone–receptor complex is formed at low temperature (4°C), the complex does not bind to isolated nuclei or DNA. The [$^3$H]triamcinolone–receptor complex can be "activated" by exposure to elevated temperature (e.g., 20°C for 30 minutes) or increased ionic strength. The activated form of the [$^3$H]triamcinolone–receptor complex is taken up by nuclei *in vitro* and binds to DNA (Rousseau *et al.*, 1975). Immobilized DNA can be used as an affinity ligand for the purification of the activated form of the [$^3$H]triamcinolone–receptor complex. However, a relatively large proportion of other cytosol proteins are adsorbed by materials such as DNA-cellulose, and it is necessary to separate the receptor from these proteins in order to achieve any reasonable degree of purification.

A two-stage procedure can be used to separate the glucocorticoid receptor from the other DNA-binding proteins (Eisen and Glinsmann, 1978; Colman and Feigelson, 1976; Simons *et al.*, 1976). In the first step, cytosol containing the unactivated form of the [$^3$H]triamcinolone–receptor complex is passed through a large column of DNA-cellulose. Although the receptor is not adsorbed, the DNA-binding proteins are adsorbed by the column. The "drop through" fractions are heated to activate the [$^3$H]triamcinolone–receptor complex, and then are chromatographed on a second DNA-cellulose column. The activated form of the [$^3$H]triamcinolone–receptor complex can be eluted with 0.45 *M* NaCl (Eisen and Glinsmann, 1978) or with pyridoxal phosphate (Dolan and Litwack, 1978; Wrange *et al.*, 1979).

Under carefully defined experimental conditions, small amounts of the [$^3$H]triamcinolone–receptor complex can be purified 5000- to 10,000-fold (Eisen and Glinsmann, 1978). These preparations (20–30 $\mu$g of receptor) were estimated to be 20–30% pure. The preparations were mixed with

Freund's complete adjuvant and injected at multiple sites into the gluteal muscles of two New Zealand white rabbits. The rabbits received a second set of injections 1 month later. One of these rabbits developed serum components that reacted with the glucocorticoid receptor (Eisen, 1980).

The receptor preparations used for a second series of immunizations were prepared as previously described, except that 10 m$M$ pyridoxal phosphate was used to elute the [$^3$H]triamcinolone–receptor complex from the second DNA-cellulose column. The receptor preparations were mixed with Freund's complete adjuvant and injected subcutaneously at multiple sites into the backs of five New Zealand white rabbits. Each rabbit received approximately 90 pmol (9 $\mu$g) of [$^3$H]triamcinolone–receptor complex. The rabbits received a second similar set of injections 1 month later.

## III. DETECTION OF ANTI-GLUCOCORTICOID RECEPTOR ANTIBODIES

Sera from the immunized rabbits did not cause precipitation of the [$^3$H]triamcinolone–receptor complex and did not produce precipitin bands (Ouchterlony immunodiffusion) against rat liver cytosol. Since the anti-estrogen receptor antibodies described by Greene *et al.* (1977) do not produce classical immunoprecipitation reactions, however, it was important to test for soluble forms of immunoglobulin–glucocorticoid receptor complexes. Two general approaches can be used to detect such complexes: (1) alterations in the apparent size of the receptor can be determined by methods such as gel permeation chromatography or sucrose density gradient centrifugation; and (2) the immunoglobulin components of such complexes can be precipitated with specific reagents such as staphylococcal protein A and antibodies to rabbit immunoglobulins.

As shown in Fig. 1, the addition of immune serum to crude rat liver cytosol labeled with [$^3$H]triamcinolone resulted in an increase in the Stokes radius ($R_s$) of the [$^3$H]triamcinolone–receptor complex. Control serum did not affect the $R_s$ (55–60 Å) of the receptor. Thus, immune serum appeared to contain factor(s) that altered the hydrodynamic properties of the [$^3$H]-triamcinolone–receptor complex.

Crude immunoglobulin fractions of immune serum were found to contain the active components. Rabbit immunoglobulin G is quantitatively adsorbed by protein A-Sepharose, and this matrix was used to purify the IgG to near homogeneity according to the method of Goding (1976). In a typical purification experiment, 15 ml of rabbit serum was passed through a column (3.5 ml) of protein A-Sepharose. The adsorbed IgG was eluted with 0.1 $M$ acetic acid and then dialyzed against phosphate buffered saline. The IgG-depleted

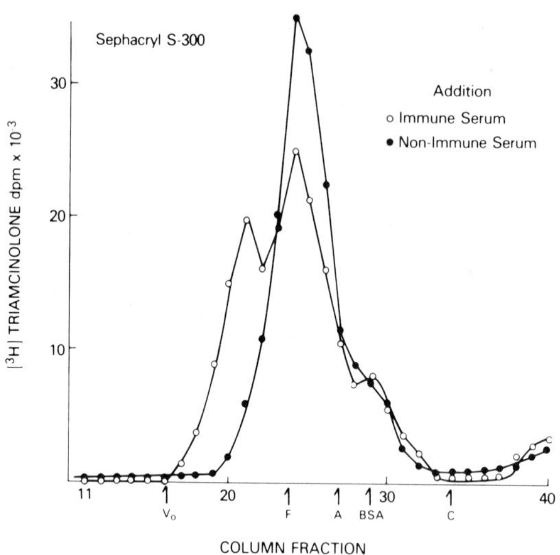


FIG. 1. Gel permeation chromatography of the rat liver [$^3$H]triamcinolone–receptor complex: effect of immune and control sera. Cytosol was prepared in HEDG buffer (10 m*M* HEPES, 1 m*M* EDTA, 1 m*M* dithiothreitol, 10% v/v glycerol, 0.1 *M* NaCl; pH 7.6) containing 50 nmol [$^3$H]triamcinolone. Cytosol (0.4 ml) and 0.1 ml of immune (○) or control (●) serum were mixed and incubated for 2 hours at 4°C. After the NaCl concentration was increased to 0.5 *M* by addition of 2.5 *M* NaCl in HEDG buffer, 0.4 ml was chromatographed on a column of Sephacryl S-300. Fractions (0.8 ml) were collected and radioactivity was determined (expressed as total dpm per fraction). $V_0$, void volume determined with blue dextran; F, ferritin (Stokes radius 65 Å); A, aldolase (51 Å); BSA, bovine serum albumin (37 Å); C, cytochrome *c* (17 Å) (Eisen, 1980).

serum did not affect the sedimentation properties of the receptor (data not shown), whereas the purified IgG resulted in sedimentation of the [$^3$H]triamcinolone–receptor complex to the bottom of the gradient (Fig. 2). In other experiments, sheep antibodies to rabbit immunoglobulin G were found to precipitate the soluble immune complexes. This evidence demonstrates that immunoglobulin G in immume serum forms complexes that involve the [$^3$H]triamcinolone–receptor complex.

Gel permeation chromatography and sucrose density gradient analysis are not suitable for rapid or multiple assays. Various preparations of immobilized staphylococcal protein A were found to be suitable for screening serum samples for the presence of anti-receptor antibodies. Staphylococcal protein A binds to the $F_c$ portion of the IgG molecule and does not interfere with the antigen-combining regions (Goding, 1976). A preparation of formalin-fixed staphylococci (Pansorbin, Calbiochem) that contained protein A (Fig. 3) was used to titrate an antiserum obtained from the second series of immunized rabbits. The [$^3$H]triamcinolone–receptor complex was mixed with immune of preimmune IgG for 2 hours at 4°C. Pansorbin was then added in excess of the amount needed to precipitate all of the IgG in the reaction mixture. Approximately 75% of the [$^3$H]triamcinolone receptor complex was precipitated at the highest concentration of immune IgG; preimmune IgG did not result in significant precipitation of the receptor. IgG–receptor complexes can also be adsorbed by chromatography on small columns of protein A-Sepharose (see Table I; Eisen, 1980). The immune complexes adsorbed by protein A may represent 1:1 complexes between IgG and the receptor; if this assumption is correct, the anti-receptor antibodies account for approximately 0.4% of the total IgG in immune serum.

## IV. IMMUNOAFFINITY CHROMATOGRAPHY OF THE RAT LIVER [$^3$H]TRIAMCINOLONE–RECEPTOR COMPLEX

In the previous section, several independent methods were described for detecting antibody–receptor complexes. Since IgG accounted for all of the anti-receptor activity, purified IgG was covalently immobilized on

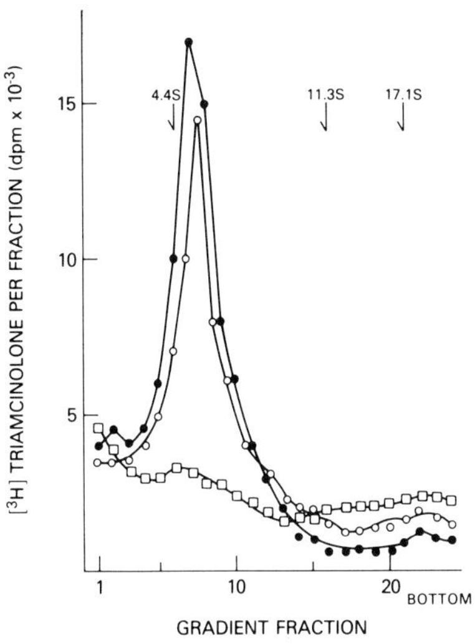


FIG. 2. Effect of immune IgG on the sedimentation of the rat liver [$^3$H]triamcinolone–receptor complex. Rat liver cytosol was incubated with 100 n$M$ [$^3$H]triamcinolone for 2 hours at 4°C and then treated with dextran–charcoal. Cytosol (50 $\mu$l) and immune IgG (10 $\mu$l) at the indicated dilutions were incubated for 2 hours at 4°C. The samples were centrifuged on linear 5–20% sucrose density gradients prepared in HEDG buffer. Gradients were centrifuged at 2°C for 16 hours at 48,000 rpm in a Beckman SW60Ti rotor ($g_{av}$ = 235,000). After centrifugation, 200 $\mu$l gradient fractions were collected. [$^{14}$C]Albumin was included as an internal sedimentation marker; other markers centrifuged in separate gradients were aldolase (11.3 S) and ferritin (17.1 S). Immune IgG ($\mu$g/10 $\mu$l) (●) none; (○) 0.6; (□) 6. The serum was obtained from one of the rabbits in the second immunized group.

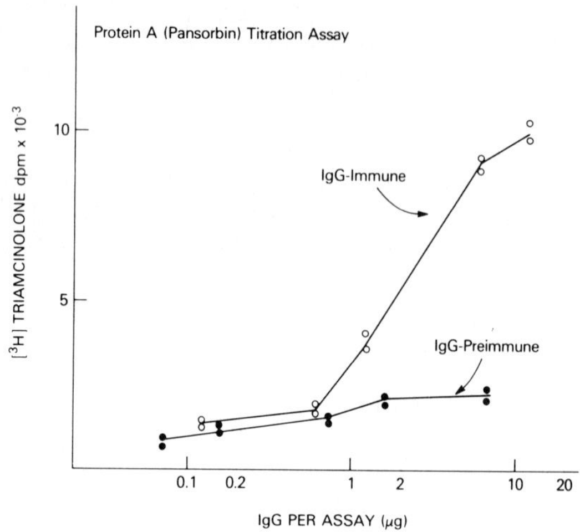


FIG. 3. Titration of anti-glucocorticoid receptor antibodies using formalin-treated staphylococci (Pansorbin). Rat liver cytosol was incubated with 100 n$M$ [$^3$H]triamcinolone for 2 hours at 4°C and then chromatographed on a column of Sephacryl S-200 (see Fig. 6). Fractions from the void volume containing the [$^3$H]triamcinolone–receptor complex were used as the source of receptor for titration. Receptor (50 μl) and IgG (10 μl) were incubated for 2 hours at 4°C. Pansorbin (100 μl packed volume) in 200 μl of HEDG buffer was added to the incubation mixture for 30 minutes. After the addition of 1 ml of HEDG buffer, the Pansorbin was separated by centrifugation in a Beckman ultrafuge and then washed with additional 1 ml of HEDG buffer. The Pansorbin was suspended in 200 μl water and the mixture was added directly to vials containing Aquasol (New England Nuclear) for determination of radioactivity. The assays were performed in duplicate. The amount of [$^3$H]triamcinolone–receptor complex added per assay tube was 13,500 dpm. The sera were obtained from a rabbit in the second immunization group. The immune IgG was prepared from serum obtained 1 month after the final immunization.

Sepharose CL-4B and this matrix was used as an immunoadsorbant. The IgG was coupled at a ratio of 10mg/gm CNBr-activated Sepharose CL-4B (Pharmacia). The coupling reaction was carried out at room temperature (15°C) for 2 hours; the remaining reactive groups were blocked with glycine or ethanolamine. The IgG-Sepharose prepared in this manner is quite stable and little leakage of IgG occurs. Several immunoaffinity columns have been used for over a year and have shown little loss in their capacity to adsorb the glucocorticoid receptor.

The adsorption of the rat liver [$^3$H]triamcinolone–receptor complex by immune IgG-Sepharose is shown in Fig. 4. Approximately 70% of the receptor complex is adsorbed by the column; and protein and radioactivity adsorbed can be eluted by dilute acids (e.g., 0.1 $M$ acetic acid). Control adsorbants containing preimmune IgG, or IgG from unimmunized rabbits did not adsorb the [$^3$H]triamcinolone–receptor complex.

The [$^3$H]triamcinolone–receptor complex is denatured by 0.1 $M$ acetic acid. For many purposes, it would be desirable to recover the [$^3$H]triamcinolone–receptor complex in nondenatured form from the immunoaffinity column. Although NaCl at high concentrations (1.5 *M*) does not elute the receptor, 1.5 *M* NaSCN can be used to elute the [$^3$H]triamcinolone–receptor complex. Approximately 20% of the adsorbed [$^3$H]triamcinolone–receptor complex can be recovered after elution with with NaSCN. As demonstrated by gel permeation chromatography, the receptor complex has an $R_s$ of ~55 Å following elution by 1.5 *M* NaSCN (results not shown).

## V. SPECIFICITY OF THE ANTISERA

### A. Reactivity with Various Forms of the Rat Liver Glucocorticoid Receptor

As the first step in analyzing the specificity of the antisera, it was important to determine the reactivity of the antibodies with the ligand-free recep-

TABLE I

Adsorption of the Rat Liver Glucocorticoid Receptor by Immune IgG Immobilized on Protein A-Sepharose

| Experiment[a] | [$^3$H]Triamcinolone adsorbed (dpm × $10^{-6}$)[b] |
|---|---|
| A. Ligand-free receptor | |
| 1. 300 μg IgG | 1.0 |
| 2. 500 μg IgG | 1.6 |
| B. [$^3$H]Triamcinolone–receptor complex | 0.9 |
| C. [$^3$H]Triamcinolone (buffer control) | 0.0 |

[a] Immune IgG (300 μg or 500 μg) and 0.5 ml of protein A-Sepharose in 2 ml of HEDG buffer were mixed for 1 hour. The protein A-Sepharose was then pelleted by centrifugation and washed twice in 15 ml of HEDG buffer. The mixture was divided and the pellets used for the subsequent experiments. (A) Rat liver cytosol (2.5 ml) was added to each pellet and the mixture was rotated end over end for 1 hour. The mixture was centrifuged and the pellet resuspended and washed twice in HEDG buffer. The pellets were suspended in HEDG buffer containing 100 n*M* [$^3$H]triamcinolone or 100 n*M* [$^3$H]triamcinolone plus 1 μ*M* unlabeled triamcinolone. After 1 hour, the pellet was separated by centrifugation and washed twice in HEDG buffer. The pellets were suspended in 2 ml of 0.1 *M* acetic acid and radioactivity determined. (B) Rat liver cytosol was incubated with 100 n*M* [$^3$H]triamcinolone or with 100 n*M* [$^3$H]triamcinolone plus 1 μ*M* unlabeled triamcinolone and adsorption was measured as in A1. (C) HEDG buffer containing 100 n*M* [$^3$H]triamcinolone or 100 n*M* [$^3$H]triamcinolone plus 1 μ*M* unlabeled triamcinolone was mixed with the pellets as described in A1.

[b] dpm adsorbed in presence of 1 μ*M* triamcinolone subtracted to correct for nonspecific adsorption.

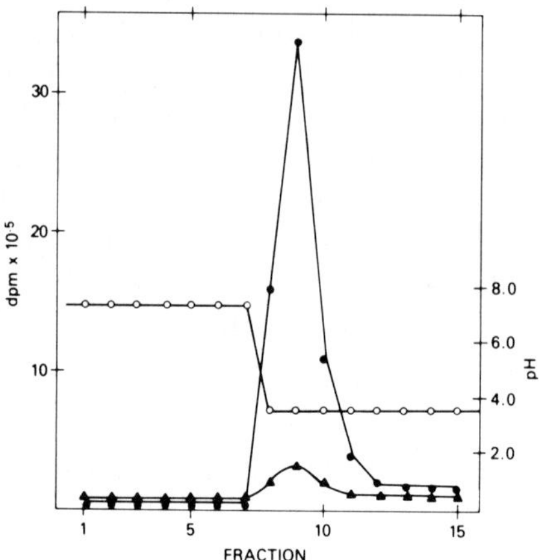


FIG. 4. Chromatography of rat liver [$^3$H]triamcinolone–receptor complex on IgGSepharoses. Cytosol was prepared in HEDG buffer containing 0.1 *M* NaCl and 50 n*M* [$^3$H]-triamcinolone. After adjustment to 0.5 *M* NaCl, samples (20 ml) were applied to 3 ml bed volume columns of immune and nonimmune IgG-Sepharose. The columns were washed with 50 ml of HEDG buffer (0.5 *M* NaCl) and then eluted with 0.1 *M acetic acid.* ●, *immune IgG-Sepharose;* ▲, *nonimmune IgG-Sepharose;* ○, *pH of fractions marking position of buffer shift. Only fractions (0.8 ml) from the 0.1 M* acetic acid eluate are shown in the figure (from Eisen, 1980).

tor and with the nonactivated and activated forms of the [$^3$H]triamcinolone–receptor complex. In the previous sections, the [$^3$H]triamcinolone–receptor complex was examined under conditions that tend to activate the receptor complex (i.e., high ionic strength). The capacity of the receptor to bind glucocorticoids is rapidly lost in high ionic strength buffers (Nielson *et al.*, 1977). Experimental conditions were therefore modified to preserve the capacity of the receptor to bind glucocorticoids and to prevent activation of the [$^3$H]triamcinolone–receptor complex.

In order to demonstrate that the ligand-free form of the receptor binds to immune IgG, an antibody "sandwich" technique was devised. Protein A-Sepharose was mixed with purified IgG, and the matrix was washed and centrifuged to remove unadsorbed IgG. In buffers containing 0.1 *M* NaCl, the Sepharose-protein A-IgG sandwich was mixed with crude liver cytosol. This material was washed to remove unadsorbed cytosol protein and treated with [$^3$H]triamcinolone. As a result of adsorption of the ligand-free receptor, the Sepharose-protein A-IgG sandwich now contained saturable binding sites for [$^3$H]triamcinolone (Table I). The capacity of the Sepharose-protein A IgG to bind preformed [$^3$H]triamcinolone receptor complexes was determined, as was its capacity to bind [$^3$H]triamcinolone in buffer. As shown in Table I, the capacity of the Sepharose-protein A-IgG is a function of the amount of IgG adsorbed. The antibodies clearly react with the ligand-free form of the receptor and also do not appear to block the glucocorticoid binding site.

In order to distinguish rigorously between the nonactivated and activated forms of the [$^3$H]triamcinolone–receptor complex, it was necessary to perform experiments using buffers such as potassium phosphate, pH 6.8, which stabilize the nonactivated form (Litwack and Parchman, 1977; Sakaue and Thompson, 1977). The activation state of the [$^3$H]triamcinolone–receptor complex was determined by rapid anion-exchange chromatography and by adsorption to DNA-cellulose (Markovic *et al.*, 1980). The nonactivated form of the [$^3$H]triamcinolone–receptor complex was quantitatively adsorbed by the immune IgG-Sepharose column. Following heat activation, the [$^3$H]triamcinolone receptor complex also was quantitatively adsorbed.

These experiments demonstrate that all three "forms" (ligand-free, nonactivated, and activated form) of the major glucocorticoid receptor from rat liver are adsorbed by the immune IgG-Sepharose column. It is evident that the immunochemical reaction does not block the steroid binding site of the receptor. Also the antibodies do not block DNA-binding of the activated [$^3$H]triamcinolone–receptor complex (data not shown). This evidence suggests that the antibodies do not effect either of these functional "domains" of the glucocorticoid receptor. Additional evidence regarding the probable antigenic site on the receptor can be obtained from studying the reactivity of the antiserum with proteolytic fragments of the major liver glucocorticoid receptor.

### B. Lack of Reactivity with Proteolytic Fragments of the Rat Liver Glucocorticoid Receptor

As noted previously, the major glucorticoid receptor in rat liver has an $R_s$ ~55 Å as determined by gel permeation chromatography on calibrated columns of Sephacryl S-300 (Eisen, 1980). Smaller moieties that bind synthetic and flourinated glucocorticoids have been described. Carlstedt-Duke *et al.* (1977) have shown that these smaller moieties can be produced during the preparation of rat liver cytosol, and that lysosomal proteases are probably responsible for the production of these forms. Hypertonic buffers (such as those in this work) prevent the leakage of lysosomal proteases and can be used to prepare the undegraded form of the glucocorticoid receptor.

Gustafsson and Wrange (1978) also showed that exogenous proteases can degrade the rat liver glucocorticoid receptor into various fragments. Treatment of rat liver cytosol with chymotrypsin results in the formation of a smaller receptor that contains both glucocorticoid- and DNA-binding sites.

Trypsin treatment results in the formation of an even smaller fragment that binds glucocorticoids but does not bind DNA. These forms have been characterized extensively by Gustafsson and Wrange (1978). The chymotrypsin fragment was found by Gustafsson and Wrange (1978) to have an $R_s$ of ~35 Å. As determined by gel permeation chromatography on a column of Sephacryl S-200, the chymotrypsin fragment has an $R_s$ of ~28 Å. Stevens *et al.* (1981) have also found that the chymotrypsin fragment of the rat liver receptor has an $R_s$ of ~28 Å. The trypsin fragment has an $R_s$ of ~ 19 Å (Fig. 5). Although 72% of the 55 Å rat liver receptor is adsorbed by the immunoaffinity column, only 5% of the chymotrypsin fragment and 1% of the trypsin fragment are adsorbed (Table II). These values were not corrected for nonspecific adsorption, and it is also possible that a small amount of the 55 Å form is present in the chymotrypsin-treated sample. Adsorption of these smaller forms, however, is greatly reduced.

### C. Species and Tissue Specificity: Evidence That Size of the Receptor Is a Major Factor in Determining Reaction with Antibody

Although the initial studies with the antiserum were limited to rat liver, it was obviously of interest to examine the reactivity of the antiserum with glucocorticoid receptors from other tissues and other mammalian species. Since antisera often contain a heterogeneous population of antibodies, it was necessary to develop quantitative assays to measure cross-reactivity. In our initial studies, large quantities of mouse or hamster liver cytosol were chromatographed on an immune IgG-Sepharose column (Eisen, 1980). Although some hamster and mouse receptor was adsorbed, the proportion of receptor adsorbed was lower than that determined for rat liver.

Many of the interesting model systems for studying glucocorticoid action are derived from mouse or human cells; hence, it was important to define conditions that would permit quantitative adsorption of these receptors. Since the number or affinity of these cross-reacting antibodies appeared to be the limiting factor in the experiments with the immunoaffinity column, the amount of receptor loaded onto the column was greatly reduced. Under these conditions (equivalent to conditions of antibody excess), we were able to obtain quantitative adsorption of receptors from mouse and human sources (Stevens *et al.*, 1981).

One of the model systems chosen for detailed analysis was the mouse lymphoma P1798 (Stevens *et al.*, 1981). The CS strain of the transplantable mouse lymphoma P1798 is sensitive to the cytolytic effects of glucocorticoids. The CR strain is resistant to glucocorticoids. Lymphoid cells isolated

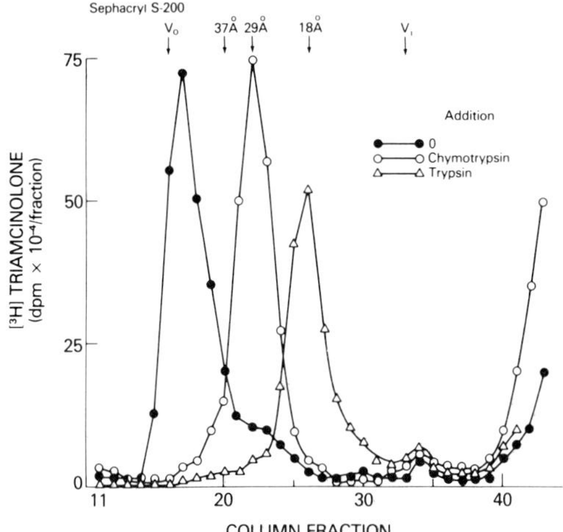


FIG. 5. Separation of proteolytic fragments of the rat liver [$^3$H]triamcinolone–receptor complex. Rat liver cytosol was incubated with 100 n*M* [$^3$H]triamcinolone for 2 hours at 4°C. Samples were treated with chymotrypsin or trypsin essentially as described by Gustafsson and Wrange (1978). The rat liver cytosols ($A_{280}$/ml = 40) were incubated with 4 $\mu$g/ml trypsin or 20 $\mu$g/ml chymotrypsin for 30 minutes at 10°C. Soybean trypsin inhibitor (40 $\mu$g/ml) was added to the trypsin-treated cytosol. Control and treated cytosols (2 ml) were chromatographed on a column of Sephacryl S-200 superfine (1.5 × 50 cm). Proteins used for calibration were albumin (37 Å), ovalbumin (29 Å), and cytochrome *c* (18 Å).

from the CS strain contain glucocorticoid receptors with physiocochemical properties of the 55 Å glucocorticoid receptor present in normal mouse thymic lymphocytes (Stevens and Stevens, 1981). The CR strain contains a form of receptor with an $R_s$ of ~ 28 Å (Stevens *et al.*, 1981). The receptor in both strains undergoes nuclear translocation; however, the normal cytolytic action of glucocorticoids does not take place in the CR strain. The activated form of the [$^3$H]triamcinolone–receptor complex from the CR strain has been shown to have higher affinity for nuclei and DNA than the CS receptor (Stevens *et al.*, 1978). Even though the CR receptor undergoes translocation to the nucleus, therefore, the CR receptor may not initiate the subsequent steps involved in glucocorticoid action. The receptor from the CS strain (Fig. 6) is adsorbed by the immune IgG-Sepharose column, but not by a control column. In contrast, the CR receptor is not adsorbed by the immune column. As discussed above, small quanties of CS and CR receptors were chromatographed for these studies, and a high proportion of the CS receptor was adsorbed by the column.

The CR receptor may represent a proteolytic product of a larger form of receptor that is identical to the CS receptor. Stevens and Stevens (1981) have presented evidence from mixing experiments that CR cytosol does not

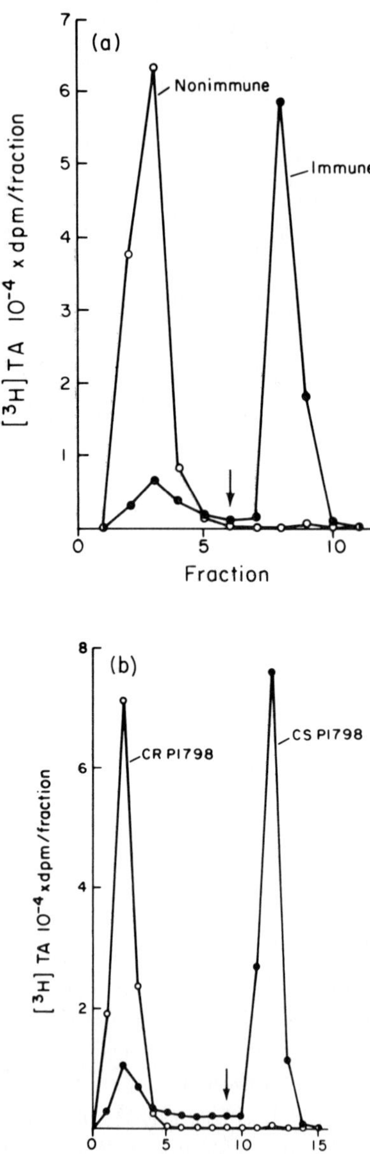


FIG. 6. Immunoaffinity chromatography of glucocorticoid receptors obtained from CS and CR P1798 tumor lymphocytes. (a) Chromatography of $[^3H]$triamincolone-labeled cytosol from CS P1798 tumor lymphocytes on "immune" (●) and "nonimmune" (○) IgG-Sepharose CL-4B. The arrow indicates start of elution with 0.1 *M* acetic acid. (b) Chromatography of $[^3H]$triamincolone-labeled cytosol from CS (●) and CR P1798 (○) tumor lymphocytes on "immune" IgG-Sepharose CL-4B. The arrow indicates start of elution with 0.1 *M* acetic acid (from Stevens *et al.*, 1981).

cause proteolysis of the CS receptor. In any case, the CR receptor does not cross-react with the immune IgG-Sepharose column, and this observation provides further evidence that the size of the receptor is a major factor determining reactivity with the antibodies.

Rat kidney contains a form of the glucocorticoid receptor that appears to differ from the major 55 Å receptor found in rat liver (Markovic *et al.*, 1980). This receptor undergoes temperature-dependent activation, but the activated form is smaller ($R_s \sim 28$ Å) and more basic than the activated form of the major rat liver glucocorticoid receptor. Although this form is also similar to the 28 Å chymotrypsin fragment of the 55 Å liver receptor, Markovic *et al.* (1980) found that renal cytosol did not degrade the 55 Å liver receptor. The renal cortex glucocorticoid receptor was not adsorbed by the immunoaffinity column (Markovic *et al.*, 1980).

Thus, in three independent situations the immunoaffinity column does not adsorb 28 Å species of the glucocorticoid receptor. Although the CR receptor and the renal receptor (corticosteroid binder IB) may represent proteolytic products of a 55 Å form of the receptor, further work is needed to distinguish between this and other possible origins of these receptor forms.

## VI. DISCUSSION AND DIRECTIONS FOR FUTURE RESEARCH

The antiserum to the estrogen receptor recently described by Green *et al.* (1977) were also produced with a partially purified receptor. This antiserum to the estrogen receptor does not produce immunoprecipitation reactions and contains relatively low titers of anti-receptor antibodies. Immunoprecipitation reactions require conditions of antibody excess and multivalent binding sites on the antigen and antibody. In the titration experiments shown in Fig. 3, very high concentrations of IgG are required to reach a region of antibody excess, and this fact alone may account for the lack of immunoprecipitation. Alternatively, either the antibody or the antigen (receptor) may be monovalent. It is clearly important to develop methods for selectively purifying the anti-receptor IgG. Since the purification of large quantities of receptor presents obvious difficulties, it may not be practical to use the receptor as a specific adsorbant. These problems could be resolved by the production of monoclonal antibodies to the receptor.

One of the most interesting features of the anti-glucocorticoid receptor antisera is their lack of reactivity with several smaller species of glucocorticoid receptors. Although the antisera react with the 55 Å form of the receptor in various mouse, rat, and human cells (Stevens *et al.*, 1981), the antisera do not react with the 28 Å species present in rat kidney cortex

TABLE II
IMMUNOAFFINITY CHROMATOGRAPHY OF PROTEOLYTIC FRAGMENTS OF THE RAT LIVER [$^3$H]TRIAMCINOLONE–RECEPTOR COMPLEX[a]

| | | dpm × $10^{-3}$ | | |
|---|---|---|---|---|
| | $R_s$ (Å) | Applied | Adsorbed | % adsorbed |
| Control | 55 | 290 | 208 | 72 |
| Chymotrypsin | 28 | 307 | 16 | 5 |
| Trypsin | 18 | 210 | 2 | 1 |

[a]Sample (0.5 ml) from the peak fractions shown in Fig. 6 were chromatographed on an immune IgG-Sepharose column (see Fig. 4).

(Markovic *et al.*, 1980) and in the CR strain of mouse lymphoma P1798 (Stevens *et al.*, 1981). The antisera also do not react with the chymotrypsin fragment of the rat liver receptor, which under the conditions of these experiments has an $R_s$ of 28 Å (Fig. 6, Table II).

It is possible that endogenous proteases generate these smaller forms of the glucocorticoid receptor present in kidney cortex and in the CR strain of mouse lymphoma P1798. Although various mixing experiments involving these cytosols do not result in cleavage of the 55 Å form of the receptor (Markovic *et al.*, 1980; Stevens and Stevens, 1981), the proteases may have extremely short half-lives after homogenization of tissues or they may be affected by inhibitors. In order to detect nondegraded forms of the glucocorticoid receptors in these tissues, it may be necessary to denature rapidly all of the proteins in order to inactivate endogenous proteases. Immunochemical methods may be required, then, to detect the receptor. If these 28 Å receptors are derived from a larger form, it may be possible to detect the other fragment(s) of the receptor that contain the antigenic site.

The rat liver glucocorticoid receptor has been purified and partially characterized by Wrange *et al.* (1979) and by Govindan and Sekeris (1978). The receptor is an asymmetric protein with an $R_s$ of 60 Å and MW of ~ 90,000 (as determined by SDS-polyacrylamide gel electrophoresis). Govindan and Sekeris (1978) have developed an antiserum to the purified glucocorticoid receptor. The antibodies produce immunoprecipitation reactions and are high in titer. These antibodies react with both the MW ~ 44,000 fragment and the MW ~ 90,000 form of the receptor; hence, it is likely that the antigenic site for these antibodies is located on the MW ~ 44,000 fragment of the receptor that contains the steroid and DNA-binding sites. It would be interesting to determine if these antibodies block the steroid and DNA-binding sites of the glucocorticoid receptor or interact with the various 28 Å forms of the glucocorticoid receptor.

The studies reviewed in this chapter represent the initial steps in the characterization of these antisera to the glucocorticoid receptor. The properties of these antisera differ considerably from the antisera reported by Govindan and Sekeris (1978). Since the methods used to purify the receptor are quite different, it is interesting to speculate that the antigenicity of the receptor may be affected by the methods used for purification and antibody production.

The experiments described in this chapter do not deal with the important problem of identifying the receptor moiety by immunochemical methods. Methods must be developed to identify unequivocally the receptor protein under the various conditions used for immunochemical experiments. Since these conditions often involve denaturing the receptor and may (inadvertently) expose the receptor to proteases, it would be useful to label the receptor covalently with an affinity label (Simons *et al.*, 1978). It may be possible to combine the two "technologies" of immunochemistry and affinity labeling to develop highly selective procedures for isolating and identifying covalently labeled receptors.

NOTE ADDED IN PROOF: With the use of [$^3$H]dexamethasone 21-mesylate as an affinity label, we have shown that the antibody selectively adsorbs the 90,000 MW glucocorticoid receptor from rat liver cytosol [Eisen, H. J., Schleenbaker, R., and Simons, S. S. (1981) *J. Biol. Chem.* **256**, 12290–12296].

## ACKNOWLEDGMENT

The expert secretarial assistance of Ms. K. Kunkle is greatly appreciated.

## REFERENCES

Carlstedt-Duke, J., Gustafsson, J.-A., and Wrange, O. (1977). *Biochim. Biophys. Acta* **97**, 507–524.

Colman, P., and Feigelson, P. (1976). *Mol. Cell. Endocrinol.* **5**, 33–40.

Dolan, K. P., and Litwack, G. (1978) *Proc. 60th Annu. Meet. Endocrinal. Soc., Miami, Beach*, p. 308.

Eisen, H. J. (1980). *Proc. Natl. Acad. Sci. U.S.A.* **77**, 3893–3987.

Eisen, H. J., and Glinsmann, W. (1978). *Biochem. J.* **171**, 177–183.

Goding, J. W. (1976). *J. Immunol. Methods* **13**, 215–226.

Govindan, M. W., and Sekeris, C. E. (1978). *Eur. J. Biochem.* **89**, 95–104.

Greene, G. L., Closs, D. E., Fleming, H., DeSombre, E. R., and Jensen, E. V. (1977). *Proc. Natl. Acad. Sci. U.S.A.* **74**, 3681.-3685.

Gustafsson, J.-A., and Wrange, O. (1978). *J. Biol. Chem.* **253**, 856–865.

Litwack, G., and Parchman, L. G. (1977). *Arch. Biochem. Biophys.* **183,** 374–382.

Markovic, C. A., Eisen, H. J., Parchman, L. G., Barnett, C. A., and Litwack, G. (1980). *Biochemistry* **19,** 4556–4564.

Nielson, C. J., Sando, J. J., and Pratt, W. B. (1977). *Proc. Natl. Acad. Sci. U.S.A.* **74,** 1398–1402.

Rousseau, G. G., Higgins, S. J., Baxter, J. C., Gelfand, D., and Tomkins, G. M. (1975). *J. Biol. Chem.* **250,** 6015–6021.

Sakaue, V., and Thompson, E. B. (1977). *Biochem. Biophys. Res. Commun.* **77,** 533–541.

Simons, S. S., Thompson, E. B., and Johnson, D. F. (1978). *Biochemistry* **18,** 4915–4922.

Simons, S. S., Martinez, H. M., Garcea, R. L., Baxter, J. D., and Tomkins, G. M. (1976). *J. Biol. Chem.* **251,** 334–343.

Stevens, J., Stevens, Y.-W. Rhodes, J., and Steiner, G. (1978). *J. Natl. Cancer Inst.* **61,** 1477–1485.

Stevens, J., and Stevens, Y.-W. (1979). *Cancer Res.* **39,** 4011–4021.

Stevens, J., and Stevens, Y.-W. (1981). Cancer Res. **41,** 125–133.

Stevens, J., Eisen, H. J., Stevens, Y.-W. Haubenstock, H., Rosenthal, R., and Artishevsky, A. (1981). *Cancer Res.*, **41,** 134–137.

Wrange, O., Carlstedt-Duke, J., and Gustafson, J.-A. (1979). *J. Biol. Chem.* **254,** 9284–9290.

# CHAPTER 10

# The Properties and the Endocrine Control of the Production of the Steroid Sulfotransferases

*Sanford S. Singer*



## I. INTRODUCTION

Sulfotransferases are enzymes that transfer sulfate from 3′-phosphoadenosine 5′-phosphosulfate (PAPS), the universal sulfate donor (Hilz and Lipmann, 1955; Robbins and Lipmann, 1956; Lipmann, 1958), to suitable hydroxylated acceptor compounds. This reaction is shown below.

$$\text{ROH} + \text{PAPS} \rightarrow \text{ROSO}_3^- + \text{Adenosine } 3',5'\text{-diphosphate}$$



BIOCHEMICAL ACTIONS OF HORMONES, VOL. IX

ISBN 0-12-452809-0

It has been known for many years that phenols, steroids, peptides, complex carbohydrates, and many other important physiological and pathological biomolecules were sulfated by sulfotransferase activities in a wide variety of organs in many animal species. However, the examination of the enzymes responsible lagged far behind study of many other areas of metabolism. This was largely due to the great instability of the sulfotransferases and the fact that PAPS was not commercially available. The great cost and low yields of the methods available for in-house PAPS preparation (Robbins and Lipmann, 1958; Brunngraber, 1958; Cherniak and Davidson, 1964) limited the studies carried out during the first two-thirds of the twentieth century to relatively rudimentary ones. This led to great uncertainty as to the number and specificity of the different kinds of sulfotransferases.

Despite these problems, long-standing interest in the sulfation of xenobiotic phenols led several pioneering laboratories to purify the phenol sulfotransferases from several species extensively by the early 1970's (Banerjee and Roy, 1968; McEvoy and Carroll, 1971; Yang and Wilkenson, 1973). These research efforts have been reviewed elsewhere (Roy, 1971), and are not described in depth here.

The steroid sulfotransferases were still largely ignored at that time, due to accepted dogma stating that steroid sulfates were simply excretion products and that steroid sulfotransferases served only to solubilize steroids to facilitate their excretion. However, in the last two decades the steady accumulation of evidence (see Section II) supporting physiological and pathological roles for sulfated steroids has stimulated interest in the steroid sulfotransferases.

## II. THE IMPORTANCE OF STEROID SULFATES

A role for steroid sulfates in hormone synthesis was first suggested by the work of Lieberman's group with human neoplastic tissues in the 1960's (Calvin *et al.*, 1963; Calvin and Lieberman, 1964; Roberts *et al.*, 1964; Drayer and Lieberman, 1965; Roberts and Lieberman, 1970). These studies essentially pointed out the existence of a pathway for the direct conversion of cholesterol sulfate to other sulfated steroids including pregnenolone sulfate, 17$\alpha$-hydroxypregnenolone sulfate, and dehydroepiandrosterone sulfate. Other such "direct sulfate" pathways have also been described in the metabolism of hormonal steroids including estrogens and androgens (Siiteri and MacDonald, 1963; Baulieu and Dray, 1963; Aakvaag *et al.*, 1964; Payne and Mason, 1965; Miyazaki *et al.* 1969; Brooks and Horn, 1971). One of the best known of these was the classical report by Miyazaki *et al.* (1969), confirmed by Brooks and Horn (1971), demonstrating that estrone sulfate was required for the conversion of estrone to catechol estrogens in the rat. More recently, Hobkirk and co-workers (1978) have shown the potential importance of estrogen sulfates in the 16-hydroxylation of estrogens in mammalian liver, and Dominguez *et al.* (1975) have reviewed the role of steroid sulfates in hormone biosynthesis.

Additional indications of potential roles for steroid sulfates in life processes have come from a variety of sources, including the observations by Baulieu *et al.* (1965) and others that dehydroepiandrosterone sulfate is a major secretion product of the adrenals and comprises much of the circulatory form of dehydroepiandrosterone. As pointed out by Payne and Singer (1979), there is also evidence that a variety of steroid sulfates serve as precursor pools for gonadal hormone synthesis in man. Furthermore, a role for steroid sulfates in enzyme regulation can be inferred from reports (Mason and Gullekson, 1960; Mason and Schirch, 1961) that estrogen sulfates inhibited a number of enzymes *in vitro*. Also, Burck and Zimmerman (1980) have proposed a role for steroid sulfates in sperm capacitation.

Abnormal accumulation of steroid sulfates has also been linked to cancer by the demonstration that these compounds were present in adrenal tumor homogenates (Baulieu, 1962; Lebeau and Baulieu, 1963), and by the demonstration that mammary tumor extracts exhibited much elevated steroid sulfotransferase activity compared to normal mammary tissue (Adams, 1964; Dao and Libby, 1969; Godefroi *et al.*, 1975). Moreover, correlations have been shown to exist between steroid sulfate concentrations and responses to adrenal ablation by mammary neoplasms in man (Dao and Libby, 1969; Godefroi *et al.*, 1975), and Adams (1977) has proposed that dehydroepiandrosterone sulfate may be involved in human breast cancer in an important way.

Another potentially important case in point comes from observations concerning glucocorticoid sulfates. These compounds are abundant in the blood and urine of people of all ages (Kornel, 1960; Schweitzer *et al.*, 1969; Klein *et al.*, 1969; Kornel *et al.*, 1975). In rats, they have been shown to form soon after the administration of near-physiological doses of [$^3$H]cortisol (Litwack and Singer, 1972) or [$^3$H]corticosterone (Carlstedt-Duke *et al.*, 1975). Furthermore, their involvement in pathological processes has been supported by many observations. Glucocorticoid sulfates were found in homogenates from adrenal neoplasms (Baulieu, 1962; Lebeau and Baulieu, 1963), and several laboratories have reported their concentrations to be elevated in urine from patients with breast, colon, and prostate cancers (Ghosh *et al.*, 1973; Fahl *et al.*, 1974; Rose *et al.*, 1975). Evidence from Kornel's laboratory (Kornel, 1960; Kornel and Mitohashi, 1965; Kornel *et al.*, 1969; Kornel *et al.*, 1975) showed that glucocorticoid sulfate concentrations in blood and urine were elevated in human essential hypertensives. More recently, a report by Stancakova *et al.* (1978) pointed out that glucocorticoid sulfate excretion was elevated in urine from human diabetics and patients with peripheral vascular disease. It appeared possible that this elevation was caused by increased production of the sulfotransferases which synthesized them, as Singer *et al.* (1977) and Turcotte and Shilah (1970) have shown that glucocorticoid sulfotransferase activity was elevated in hypertensive rats, and Singer *et al.* (1981) have demonstrated increased cortisol sulfation in diabetic rats.

There is also evidence for the involvement of glucocorticoid sulfates in the metabolism of related steroids by steroid reductases and steroid hydroxylases that use them as substrates, and in some cases prefer them to unconjugated steroids. Such a role for these compounds was first demonstrated for the corticosteroid-dependent steroid 16$\alpha$-hydroxylase in female rats (Gustafsson and Ingelman-Sundberg, 1974; Gustafsson and Ingelman-Sundberg, 1975; Einarsson *et al.*, 1976). More recently, Ingelman-Sundberg (1976) showed that several steroid reductases also used sulfated steroids as substrates to varying extents. Impressively, the steroid 20$\beta$-reductase, found only in males, required the sulfated corticosteroids as substrates, and bile from males, but not females, contained pregnane-3,11,20,21-tetraol sulfates. This lent support for a physiological role for glucocorticoid sulfates in controlling some facets of corticosteroid metabolism.

Reports from Litwack's laboratory starting in the 1960's (Fiala and Litwack, 1966; Litwack, 1967; Singer *et al.*, 1970) suggested that glucocorticoid sulfates could also be involved in hepatic enzyme inductions mediated by glucocorticoids. By the early 1970's they had demonstrated that three of the four rat liver glucocorticoid binding proteins they had described—Binders I, III, and IV (Litwack and Singer, 1972)—associated with sulfated glucocorticoids soon after injection of near-physiological doses of glucocorticoid (Morey and Litwack, 1969; Litwack *et al.*, 1973). Interestingly, fetal rats and newborns were relatively unresponsive to the enzyme inducing action of cortisol, measured as tyrosine aminotransferase induction (Singer and Litwack, 1971). In these animals the concentration of complexes between sulfated glucocorticoid metabolites and Binders I and III were much diminished compared to adult rats (Singer and Litwack, 1971).

As rats grew they developed the ability for cortisol-mediated tyrosine aminotransferase induction in close parallel with the increase of the hepatic concentration of glucocorticoid sulfate–Binder complexes to concentrations found in adult rats. By contrast, the concentration of the complex between rat liver Binder II—the glucocorticoid receptor (Litwack *et al.*, 1973; Singer *et al.*, 1973)—and unmetabolized hormone was similar in rats of all ages. Very markedly reduced concentrations of complexes between sulfated glucocorticoids and equivalent glucocorticoid Binders in guinea pigs, compared to adult rats, were also demonstrated by Singer *et al.* (1975). In these animals the hepatic concentration of sulfated glucocorticoid was also much diminished. This observation was significant because tyrosine aminotransferase induction by glucocorticoids was much less extensive in guinea pigs than in rats (Chan and Cohen, 1964; Singer *et al.*, 1975).

## III. STEROID SULFOTRANSFERASES

The first proof of the existence of distinct steroid sulfotransferase activity came from a report by Gregary and Nose (1957) of partial resolution of phenol sulfotransferase activity from enzyme activity that sulfated dehydroepiandrosterone and other 3$\beta$-hydroxysteroids. The next year, Nose and Lipmann (1958) resolved the steroid sulfotransferase activity to components that sulfated estrogen and dehydroepiandrosterone, respectively. However, the separation of the two enzyme activities was not complete and the methodology used was very complicated. Eight years later, some additional progress was reported by Roy's laboratory (Banarjee and Roy, 1966), where the estrogen and dehydroepiandrosterone sulfotransferase activities of guinea pig liver were purified 70-fold and 20-fold, respectively. Evidence for the possible existence of androgen and mineralocorticoid sulfotransferase activities was also presented.

However, few definitive reports of steroid sulfotransferase purification and characterization appeared until the 1970's yielded a cluster of such efforts. These began with reports from Adams' laboratory on "purified" *estrogen sulfotransferase* from bovine adrenals, ovary, and placenta (Adams and Poulos, 1967; Adams and Chulavatnatol, 1967; Adams *et al.*, 1974; Adams and Low, 1974). The extent of purification of this enzyme is not clear. However, it was found to be a monomer of molecular weight 74,000, specific for estrogens. It sulfated only the phenolic hydroxyl group of these compounds and its pH optimum was between 8 and 10. Rozhin *et al.* (1974) independently provided evidence supporting many of the observations of Adams' group on the properties and specificity of the estrogen sulfotransferase.

The $K_m$ of the estrogen sulfotransferase for PAPS was 37 $\mu M$, and that for estrone was estimated as 15 $\mu M$. However, the enzyme was difficult to study, exhibiting very complex kinetics. These were attributed by Adams *et al.* (1974) as being due to its existence as four isozymes present as a number of conformers differing in the accessibility of a single sulfhydryl group, and in their affinity for estrogen. As a result of the observed complex kinetics it was proposed that the estrogen sulfotransferase plays a regulatory role in metabolism.

A second steroid sulfotransferase that has been partly described is the *3β-hydroxysteroid sulfotransferase* of rat liver (Ryan and Carroll, 1976), human liver (Gugler *et al.*, 1970), and human adrenals (Adams and MacDonald, 1979). Dehydroepiandrosterone is usually used for assay of 3β-hydroxysteroid sulfotransferase activity, although epiandrosterone is an even better substrate (Ryan and Carroll, 1976; Adams and MacDonald, 1979). The rat liver enzyme was purified approximately 60-fold from cytosol. It was not completely characterized. However, its pH optimum was quite acid at pH 5.0, and its $K_m$ values for PAPS and dehydroepiandrosterone were 13 $\mu M$ and 6 $\mu M$, respectively. Like the estrogen sulfotransferase, it contained essential sulfhydryl groups. It was reported to sulfate 3β-hydroxysteroids almost exclusively. Unlike the estrogen sulfotransferase, the Ryan–Carroll enzyme was shown to exhibit simple Michealis–Menten kinetics. It was strongly inhibited by adenosine 3′, 5′-diphosphate, one of its reaction products.

The rat liver 3β-hydroxysteroid sulfotransferase was very similar to the less extensively purified enzyme preparation isolated from human liver by Gugler *et al.* (1970). Very recently, Adams and MacDonald (1979) reported the 250-fold purification of a 3β-hydroxysteroid sulfotransferase from human adrenal cytosol by a method using affinity chromatography on dehydroepiandrosterone-Sepharose 4B. This enzyme had properties similar to the 3β-hydroxysteroid sulfotransferases already reported. In addition, it was reported to exhibit a molecular weight of 68,000, and to be a dimeric protein composed of 38,000 dalton monomers. Adams and MacDonald also reported that the human adrenal enzyme exhibited complex kinetics reminiscent of the bovine estrogen sulfotransferase (Adams *et al.*, 1974). However, they mentioned in passing that the human liver 3β-hydroxysteroid sulfotransferase exhibited simple Michealis–Menten kinetics when isolated by the same method.

Another steroid sulfotransferase isolated from rat liver (Chen *et al.*, 1977) was reported to be specific for bile acids. This *bile acid sulfotransferase* was purified 35-fold from rat liver cytosol. Its apparent $K_m$ values for PAPS and taurolithcholate were 8 $\mu M$ and 50 $\mu M$, respectively. The bile acid sulfotransferase also appeared to contain several essential sulfhydryl groups, and its "apparent molecular weight," estimated on Sephadex G-100, was 130,000. A somewhat more extensively purified bile acid sulfotransferase from rat kidney (Chen *et al.*, 1978) had somewhat similar properties. However, its molecular weight was estimated to be 80,000. A preliminary report (Loof and Hjerten, 1980) on the human bile acid sulfotransferase activity has just appeared.

Beginning in 1976, this laboratory (Singer *et al.*, 1976) reported on three rat liver steroid sulfotransferases that sulfated adrenal glucocorticoids. These

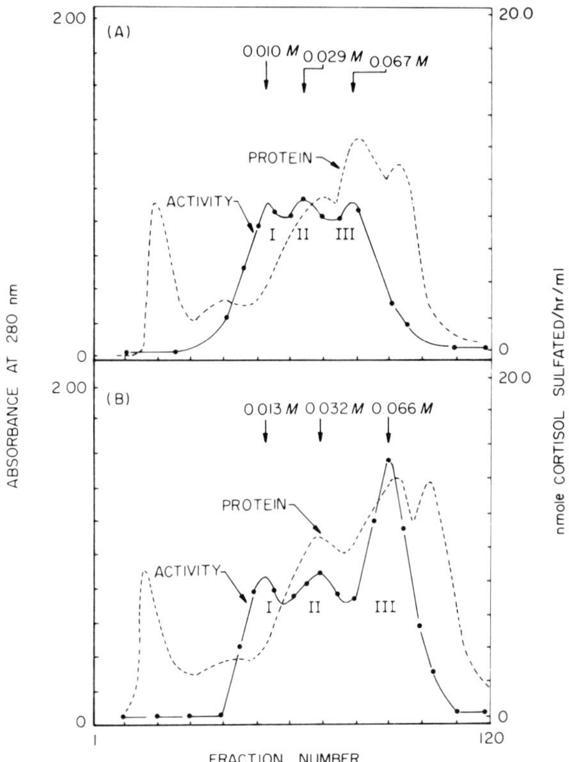


FIG. 1. DEAE Sephadex A-50 chromatography of the hepatic cortisol sulfotransferase activity in cytosols from female rats of two different strains. Three-milliliter samples of liver cytosol from female Fisher 344 rats (A) and female Sprague Dawley rats (B), purchased from Charles River Labs, were eluted from 2 × 50 cm columns of DEAE Sephadex A-50 as in Singer *et al.* (1976). All methods for enzyme assays and protein and salt concentration measurements are in Singer *et al.* (1976) and Singer and Sylvester (1976). I, II, III indicate sulfotransferases I, II, and III. The molar concentrations represent the KCl concentrations, in a linear 0–0.30 *M* salt gradient, at which enzyme peak tubes eluted from the columns.

enzymes were named *sulfotransferases I, II, and III* (STI, STII, and STII) in order of their elution from DEAE Sephadex A-50 columns to which cytosol from female rats had been applied. Figure 1 shows DEAE Sephadex A-50 elution profiles from liver cytosols prepared from females of two different rat strains.

STII (Singer *et al.*, 1978) appears to be the 3β-hydroxysteroid sulfotransferase reported by Ryan and Carroll (1976). Therefore, we have not pursued its purification and characterization actively. STIII is the most glucocorticoid-preferring of the enzymes. We have purified it 250-fold from liver homogenates from male rats (Singer *et al.*, 1978) and more than 1000-

TABLE I

COMPARISON OF SOME PROPERTIES OF SULFOTRANSFERASES I AND III FROM FEMALE RATS[a]

| Enzyme utilized | STIII[b] | STI[c] |
|---|---|---|
| Fold purified | 1010–1300 | 1000–1250 |
| Molecular weight | 68,300 ± 4,900 (GF) | 156,000 (UC) |
| Subunit molecular weight | ~30,000[d] | ~31,000[d] |
| pH optimum | 6.0 ± .1 | 6.0 ± .1 |
| Cortisol $K_m(\mu M)$ | 6.82 ± 1.2 | 7.09 ± .65 |
| PAPS $K_m(\mu M)$ | 6.28 ± .64 | 10.6 ± 1.1 |
| Reaction mechanism | Ordered sequential or iso Theorell–Chance | Sequential |
| Effects of 5 m*M* | | |
| $MgCl_2$ | + | + |
| $MnCl_2$ | + | + |
| $CrCl_2$ | + | + |
| $ZnCl_2$ | – | – |
| $CdCl_2$ | – | – |
| $BaCl_2$ | + | NR |
| $CaCl_2$ | + | ? |
| $NiCl_2$ | + | NR |
| Ratio, sulfation of 40 $\mu M$ cortisol compared to 40 $\mu M$ of | | |
| Dehydroepiandrosterone | ~3.3 | ~.60 |
| Estradiol | ~3.3 | ~2.0 |
| Testosterone | ~10 | ~3.3 |

[a]GF, gel filtration; UC, ultracentrifugal sedimentation velocity analysis; +, activation; –, inactivation; NR, no reaction; ?, indefinite results.

[b]Data from Singer and Bruns (1980).

[c]Data from Singer (1979)

[d]Data from S. S. Singer, M. Federspiel, W. Lewis, V. Martin, A. Moshtaghie, J. Tappel, and K. Witt (unpublished results).

fold from homogenates from female rats (Singer and Bruns, 1980). Presently, we have prepared essentially homogeneous, ~ 2500-fold purified STIII from female rats (Singer *et al.*, 1980a) and are characterizing it (S. S. Singer, M. Federspiel, W. Lewis, V. Martin, A. Moshtaghie, J. Tappel, and K. Witt, unpublished results). We have also studied STI, which is restricted to female rats, extensively (Singer, 1979). This enzyme has been purified approximately 1000-fold from homogenates from female rats (Singer, 1979). It is not found in males in large quantities unless they are feminized with estrogen (Singer and Sylvester, 1976). The properties of STI and STIII are summarized in Table I. Although there are differences in the enzymes, several of their listed properties (similar pH optima, subunit size, and $K_m$ for cortisol) suggest their common origin. However, they differ greatly in substrate preference, $K_m$ for PAPS, and responses to metal ions.

We have also just reported the isolation of a new *mineralocorticoid sulfotransferase* from livers from female rats (Lewis *et al.*, 1981). Although this enzyme, which sulfates deoxycorticosterone, has not yet been well characterized, it appears to differ from STI, STII, and STIII.

Very recently, Jakoby's group (Lyon and Jakoby, 1980) has described the purification of a sulfotransferase that sulfates steroids and aliphatic alcohols to apparent homogeneity. This enzyme, molecular weight 180,000, was isolated in very low yield from livers of female rats. Its best substrate was dehydroepiandrosterone ($K_m$ 12 $\mu M$). Thus, it appears likely that this enzyme is a purified preparation of one of the 3$\beta$-hydroxysteroid sulfotransferase isozymes mentioned by Ryan and Carroll (1976). Its 17$\beta$-sulfation of estradiol is of interest. However, its sulfation of alcohols ($K_m$ between 1 and 50 m$M$) and steroids other than dehydroepiandrosterone at $K_m$'s 20- to 75-fold higher than reported by other groups (as cortisol, $K_m = 440$ $\mu M$, compared to 7 $\mu M$ in Table I), is not suprising due to the earlier report of the substrate preference of the 3$\beta$-hydroxysteroid sulfotransferase (Ryan and Carroll, 1976).

Thus, there is currently evidence for the probable existence of at least six different steroid sulfotransferases in mammalian tissues: estrogen (Adams *et al.*, 1974; Adams and Low, 1974), bile acid (Chen *et al.*, 1977, 1978), 3$\beta$-hydroxysteroid (Ryan and Carroll, 1976, Adams and MacDonald, 1979), sulfotransferases STI (Singer, 1979), STIII (Singer *et al.*, 1978; Singer and Bruns, 1980; Singer *et al.*, 1980a), and the enzyme that sulfates mineralocorticoid in livers from female rats (Lewis *et al.*, 1981). The individual enzymes can be partly distinguished from one another on the basis of their kinetic and physiocochemical properties (see Tables I and II). However, prior to the definitive assignment of the absolute number of known steroid sulfotransferases, their direct comparison will be required.

This comparison is needed for several reasons. First, the great differences of preparative procedures reported for different sulfotransferases complicates comparison of the several existing enzyme preparations. Second, the use of different buffers for pH optimum determinations leads to problems because of variations of pH optima of single sulfotransferases observed when buffer composition was varied (Sekura and Jakoby, 1979; S. S. Singer, M. Federspiel, W. Lewis, V. Martin, A. Mostaghie, J. Tappel, and K. Witt, unpublished results). Furthermore, problems also arise from the common practice of measuring steroid sulfotransferase substrate preferences with one concentration of all test steroids (generally the optimum concentration for the particular enzyme activity being studied), as many steroids are inhibitors

TABLE II

Some Properties of Bovine Adrenal Estrogen Sulfotransferase, Rat Liver 3$\beta$-Hydroxysteroid Sulfotransferase, and Rat Liver Bile Acid Sulfotransferase

| Enzyme | Molecular weight | pH optimum | Substrate used, $K_m$ ($\mu M$) | PAPS $K_m$ ($\mu M$) | Essential sulfhydryl | Metal ion effects | Reference |
|---|---|---|---|---|---|---|---|
| Estrogen sulfotransferase | 74,000 | 8 | Estrone, 15 | 37 | + | Many reported | Adams and Poulos, 1967; Adams *et al.*, 1974 |
| 3$\beta$-Hydroxysteroid sulfotransferase | 68,000 | 5 | Androstenolone, 7 | 13 | + | None observed | Gugler *et al.*, 1970; Ryan and Carroll, 1976 |
| Bile acid sulfotransferase | 130,000 | 6.5 | Taurolithcholate, 50 | 8 | + | None observed | Chen *et al.*, 1977 |

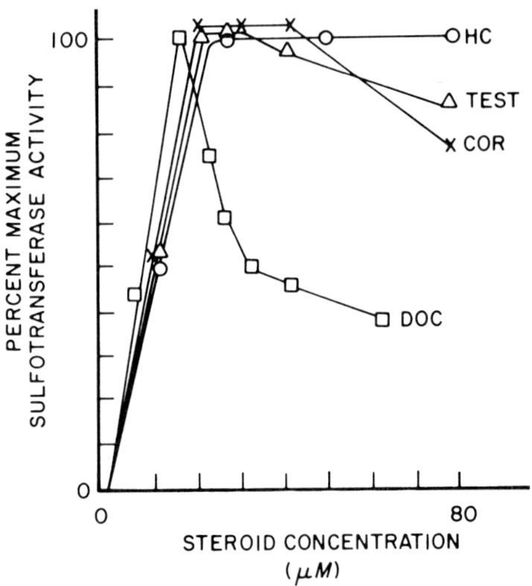


FIG. 2. Sulfation of several steroids by the sulfotransferases of rat liver cytosol. Assay of the cortisol (HC), corticosterone (COR), deoxycorticosterone (DOC), and testosterone (TEST) sulfotransferase of cytosol from female rats was as in Singer *et al.* (1976) and Singer (1978a). The data are shown as the percent of the maximum activity obtained when the steroid concentrations were varied as shown.

of their own sulfation to varying extents (see Figure 2; Carlstedt-Duke and Gustafsson, 1973; Adams *et al.*, 1974; Payne and Singer, 1979; Lewis *et al.*, 1981). Such substrate inhibition of sulfotransferases could lead to misconceptions about their absolute abilities to sulfate various steroids. Finally, similarities between the carcinogen sulfotransferase of Wu and Straub (1976), the phenol sulfotransferases (McEvoy and Carroll, 1971; Sekura and Jakoby, 1979), and the steroid sulfotransferases point out that the relationship of all of these enzymes to one another must also be defined. Such studies are presently in progress in this laboratory.

## IV. SEX DIFFERENCES OF HEPATIC STEROID SULFOTRANSFERASE CONTENT AS EVIDENCE FOR ENDOCRINE CONTROL OF THE PRODUCTION OF THE ENZYMES

Sex differences of steroid sulfation were observed as early as the late 1950's, in reports (Roy, 1956; Wengle, 1963) that crude rat liver preparations from female rats contained much larger amounts of dehydroepiandrosterone sulfotransferase activity than those from males. Later, other steroid sulfotransferase activities tested (Torday *et al.*, 1971; Carlstedt-Duke and Gustafsson, 1973; Singer *et al.*, 1976; Lewis *et al.*, 1981) were also found to be present at higher concentrations in tissues from females than in those from males. Interestingly, phenol and carcinogen sulfotransferases (McEvoy and Carroll, 1971; Wu and Straub, 1976; Sekura and Jakoby, 1979) have been shown to be present at higher concentrations in males than in females.

The early observations of sex effects on steroid sulfotransferase activities led us to consider the probable importance of gonadal secretions in control of sulfotransferase production. Our first explorations in this direction led us to fractionate the glucocorticoid sulfotransferase activity from male rats (Singer *et al.*, 1976). As shown in Fig. 3, cytosol from males contained relatively small amounts of STIII compared to females (Fig. 1), tiny amounts of STII, and no detectable STI. The examination of the developmental production of the glucocorticoid sulfotransferases (Singer *et al.*, 1976) pointed out that STII predominated in both sexes prior to puberty. Postpubertal ovarian secretions appeared to be a probable source of a general stimulation of the production of all three glucocorticoid sulfotransferases in females during maturation. It also appeared probable that maturation of the testes prevented such stimulation of glucocorticoid sulfotransferase production in males, resulting in the absence of major amounts of STI and STII in adult rats of this sex. Figure 4 shows the relative amounts of STI, STII, and STIII in livers from male rats at various stages of development.

The recent report from Jakoby's laboratory (Sekura and Jakoby, 1979) of two hepatic $\beta$-naphthol sulfotransferases, contrasted with McEvoy and Carrol's earlier report of a single $p$-nitrophenol sulfotransferase in females (McEvoy and Carroll, 1971) suggested the presence of sexual dimorphism of the phenol sulfotransferase, and led us to examine the rat liver phenol sulfating enzymes in both sexes briefly (S. S. Singer, M. Federspiel, W. Lewis, V.

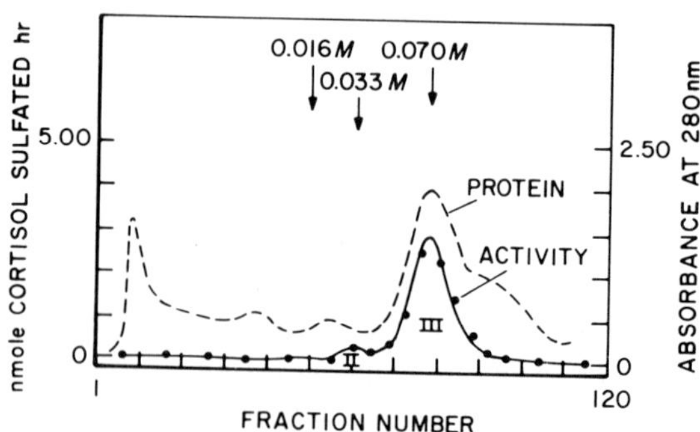


FIG. 3. Fractionation of the hepatic cortisol sulfotransferase activity from a male Fisher 344 rat on DEAE Sephadex A-50. A three-milliliter sample of cytosol from a male rat was fractionated on a 2 × 50 cm column of DEAE Sephadex A-50 as described in the legend for Fig. 1.

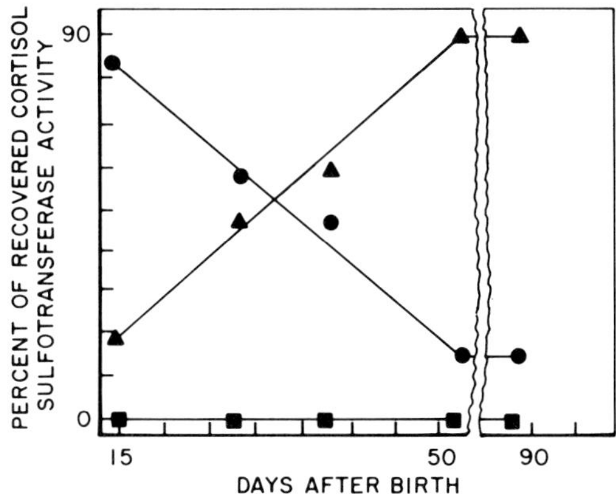


FIG. 4. The relative amounts of sulfotransferases I, II, and III in livers of male rats at various times after birth. This is an estimation of the percentage of the activity recovered from DEAE Sephadex A-50 columns when cytosol from representative rats of different ages were fractionated in the ion exchanger. More detailed data are shown in Singer *et al.* (1976). ■, ●, and ▲ represent STI, STII, and STIII, respectively.

Martin, A. Moshtaghie, J. Tappel, and K. Witt, unpublished results). We found two phenol sulfotransferases in both sexes. We assume that they are the Jakoby group's transferases I and II. However, there was only a very small amount of transferase II in female rats (S. S. Singer, M. Federspiel, W. Lewis, V. Martin, A. Moshtaghie, J. Tappel, and K. Witt, unpublished results).

The existence of multiple phenol and glucocorticoid sulfotransferases in different proportions in male and female rats suggests a plausible role for the gonads in controlling general sulfotransferase production. If the multiple forms of the various enzymes have differing substrate preferences as do phenol (Sekura and Jakoby, 1979) and glucocorticoid sulfotransferases (Singer *et al.*, 1976; Singer, 1979; Singer and Bruns, 1980), the observed gonadal regulation could have important consequences as a result of the modification of the extent of sulfation of important biomolecules.

## V. GONADAL CONTROL OF STEROID SULFOTRANSFERASE PRODUCTION

The first report of gonadal control of the production of a steroid sulfotransferase was communicated by Torday *et al.* (1971), who demonstrated that ovariectomy resulted in decreased hepatic corticosterone sulfation in female rats. This effect was reversed by administration of estrogen to

TABLE III
THE EFFECTS OF GONADECTOMY AND GONADAL HORMONES ON THE HEPATIC CORTISOL SULFOTRANSFERASE ACTIVITY IN MALE AND FEMALE RATS[a]

| Surgery | Hormone treatment | % of cortisol sulfotransferase activity found in untreated rats[b] | |
|---|---|---|---|
| | | Males | Females |
| Gonadal ablation | None | 210–260 | 65–75 |
| None | Estradiol-17β | 900–1100 | 85–115 |
| None | Testosterone | 170–190 | 30–40 |

[a]Injections or castrations began approximately a month after birth. Animals were sacrificed 45 to 90 days after start of experiments. Androgen treated rats were given testosterone (1 mg) or estradiol-17β (0.20 mg) in sesame oil, daily, subcutaneously. For exact conditions see Singer and Sylvester (1976).

[b]The mean cortisol sulfotransferase activity in male and female rats was 20 and 330 nmol of cortisol sulfated $hour^{-1}$ per ml of cytosol, respectively.

ovariectomized animals. Furthermore, it was shown that the much smaller amount of hepatic corticosterone sulfotransferase activity in male rats was greatly elevated after castration. The effects of this testectomy on the enzyme activity were further enhanced by estrogen administration.

Later, Singer and Sylvester (1976) reported similar effects of gonadectomy and gonadal hormones on the rat liver cortisol sulfotransferase activity. These results have been summarized in Table III. As shown, ovariectomy resulted in 25–35% decreases of the hepatic cortisol sulfotransferase activity in females. In contrast, removal of the testes was followed by 110–160% increases of the enzyme activity compared to intact males. Table III also shows that estrogen administration to males elevated the cortisol sulfotransferase concentration in liver to 9–11 times that normally found in this sex, resulting in enzyme concentrations usually restricted to females. However, the ovarian hormone had no effect on the cortisol sulfotransferase activity in females. On the other hand, after administration of androgen to males the cortisol sulfotransferase activity nearly doubled compared to controls. In females the male hormone decreased the enzyme activity as much as 70%.

The similar gonadal control of the production of the cortisol and corticosterone sulfotransferase activities (Torday *et al.*, 1971; Singer and Sylvester, 1976), led us to examine the individual enzymes that sulfated the two glucocorticoids (Singer, 1978a). We found that both hormones were sulfated by STI, STII, and STIII. Therefore, these enzymes appeared to be glucocorticoid sulfotransferases. It was of interest that the corticosterone sulfotransferase activity of STI, STII, and STIII was markedly inhibited by this glucocorticoid, implying the possibility of self-regulation of corticosterone sulfation.

Our study of gonadal control of cortisol sulfation (Table IV) pointed out that the gonads and their secretions had very specific effects on hepatic concentrations of the individual glucocorticoid sulfotransferases. Ovariectomy resulted in diminished STI and STII activity in female rats. In contrast, testicular ablation led to the elevation of the STII activity above that usually

TABLE IV

THE TOTAL CORTISOL SULFOTRANSFERASE ACTIVITY AND THE RELATIVE AMOUNTS OF STI, STII, AND STIII IN LIVERS FROM INTACT, GONADECTOMIZED, AND ANDROGEN- OR ESTROGEN-TREATED MALE AND FEMALE RATS[a]

| Experiment, surgery, and hormone given | Total CSA | % of recovered CSA in: | | | Estimated mean CSA in: | | |
|---|---|---|---|---|---|---|---|
| | | STI | STII | STIII | STI | STII | STIII |
| A. Females | | | | | | | |
| Intact control | 230–385 (330) | 25–30 | 30–38 | 30–38 | 99 | 112 | 116 |
| Ovariectomized female | 160–270 (236) | 18–24 | 15–25 | 40–58 | 47 | 49 | 122 |
| Intact female given testosterone | 100–150 (121) | 5.0–10 | 15–21 | 53–75 | 9.1 | 19 | 91 |
| Intact female given estradiol-17$\beta$ | 210–392 (315) | — | — | — | — | — | — |
| B. Males | | | | | | | |
| Intact control | 10–25 (20) | 0 | 10–25 | 75–90 | 0 | 4.0 | 16 |
| Orchidectomized male | 21–43 (38) | 0 | 40–51 | 50–60 | 0 | 16 | 22 |
| Intact male given testosterone | 25–45 (38) | 0 | 5–10 | 90–95 | 0 | 3.4 | 35 |
| Intact male given estradiol-17$\beta$ | 240–375 (300) | 28–41 | 33–49 | 13–19 | 105 | 120 | 42 |

[a]The rats used were described in Table III. The total CSA is the cortisol sulfotransferase activity in n moles/hour/ml of original cytosol. The ranges of the % CSA associated with STI, STII, and STIII were estimated from DEAE Sephadex A-50 chromatograms. The mean CSA associated with each enzyme was estimated by multiplying the mean CSA, shown in parentheses, by the mean % CSA associated with each sulfotransferase.

found in males. Table IV also shows that the more extensive effects of gonadal hormones on the cortisol sulfotransferase activity were due to differential responses of the three glucocorticoid sulfotransferases.

For example, testosterone administration to female rats resulted in diminished STI and STII activity compared to controls, although this treatment had no major effect on STIII. In males the androgen behaved differently, resulting in the accumulation of STII activity. Estradiol-17$\beta$ administration to females, on the other hand, had no effect on the enzyme activity. However, in males, its effects were very extensive, and differed depending on whether intact or castrated animals were used. In intact males, the estrogen elevated STI and STII to concentrations usually found in females, although STIII was not elevated as extensively. In male castrates (not shown), we found that all three enzyme activities were elevated extensively, resulting in glucocorticoid sulfotransferase profiles identical to those found in females.

The different estrogen effects on STIII in intact and castrated males pointed out that physiological androgen concentrations could override pharmacological estrogen effects on the enzyme. This suggested that testicular secretions determined STIII concentrations in the livers of male rats.

As a consequence of the studies described in Tables III and IV, it appeared that the gonads did not serve as the main factor involved in the maintenance of the characteristic glucocorticoid sulfotransferase patterns observed in adult rats. However, the gonadal hormones appeared to possess the control properties needed to cause the developmental changes of rat liver glucocorticoid sulfotransferase activity observed in growing rats (Singer *et al.*, 1976). Other endocrine factors involved in maintenance of adult glucocorticoid sulfotransferase activity are described in Sections VI–VIII.

A somewhat different pattern of sex effects on hepatic steroid sulfation was reported for deoxycorticosterone by Carlstedt-Duke and Gustafsson (1973). These researchers found that the relative amounts of deoxycorticosterone sulfotransferase activity in male and female rats were similar to those described for cortisol and corticosterone sulfotransferase activities (cf. Torday *et al.*, 1971; Singer and Sylvester, 1976). However, unlike the glucocorticoids, sulfation of the mineralocorticoid was not diminished after ovariectomy. Other than this, the gonadal control of deoxycorticosterone sulfation was similar to that described for the other corticosteroids, testectomy resulting in elevated enzyme activity, and gonadal hormones causing effects of the sort already mentioned.

The different effects of ovariectomy on rat liver deoxycorticosterone and glucocorticoid sulfotransferase activities led us to examine the individual sulfotransferases involved (Lewis *et al.*, 1981). Interestingly, we found that while all of the hepatic deoxycorticosterone sulfotransferase activity in male

TABLE V
THE RELATIVE AMOUNTS OF CORTISOL, DEHYDROEPIANDROSTERONE, ESTRADIOL, AND TESTOSTERONE SULFOTRANSFERASE ACTIVITIES IN LIVERS FROM MALE AND FEMALE RATS[a]

| | Livers from males | | Livers from females | |
|---|---|---|---|---|
| Steroid sulfated | Activity per ml[b] | % activity with HC[c] | Activity per ml[b] | % activity with HC[c] |
| Cortisol | 28.1 | 100 | 301 | 100 |
| Dehydroepiandrosterone | 34.2 | 122 | 750 | 250 |
| Estradiol-17$\beta$ | 395 | 1,400 | 451 | 150 |
| Testosterone | 15.4 | 55 | 210 | 70 |

[a]This is one of six similar experiments.
[b]Enzyme activity units are nmoles of steroid sulfated/ml cytosol/hour, when 40 $\mu M$ steroid is used as substrate in standard reaction mixtures described in Singer *et al.* (1976).
[c]Cortisol.

rats appeared to be due to STIII, the deoxycorticosterone sulfotransferase activity in females was divided equally between presumptive STIII and a new mineralocorticoid sulfotransferase.

Little is known about the gonadal control of sulfation of other steroids. However, in contrast to the extensive gonadal control of the sulfation of the corticosteroids, Adams' group (Adams *et al.*, 1974) has reported that the bovine estrogen sulfotransferase activity consisted of four "isozymes" present in equal proportions in both sexes. This observation agreed with our study (Singer *et al.*, 1976; S. S. Singer, M. Federspiel, W. Lewis, V. Martin, A. Moshtaghie, J. Tappel, and K. Witt, unpublished results) showing that rat liver estrogen sulfotransferase activity was very similar in males and females (see Table V). Thus it appeared that the estrogen sulfotransferase activity was not affected by the gonads.

As a consequence of the great difference between the amounts of cortisol sulfotransferase activity observed in female rats, the ratios of glucocorticoid to estrogen sulfotransferase activity were 14 and 1.5 in males and females, respectively. This pointed out that rat liver estrogen sulfotransferase, like its bovine counterpart, was probably a protein unrelated to the glucocorticoid sulfotransferases. Table V also shows that dehydroepiandrosterone and testosterone sulfation are controlled by the gonads in a fashion similar to gonadal control of corticosteroid sulfation. Several additional studies supported similarities between testosterone (S. S. Singer, M. Federspiel, W. Lewis, V. Martin, A. Moshtaghie, J. Tappel, and K. Witt, unpublished results) and dehydroepiandrosterone (Singer *et al.*, 1978) sulfotransferases and STI, STII, or STIII.

## VI. ADRENAL CONTROL OF GLUCOCORTICOID SULFOTRANSFERASE PRODUCTION

Our examination of adrenal control of glucocorticoid sulfotransferase production (Singer, 1978b) is the only report of adrenal effects on a steroid sulfotransferase that we are aware of. The study was a consequence of our conclusion (Section V) that nongonadal factors were involved in endocrine control of STI, STII, and STIII production, and our observation (Singer *et al.*, 1977) that hypertension-producing doses of corticosteroids resulted in the elevation of the glucocorticoid sulfotransferase activity in livers of male rats.

Initial studies with female rats (Singer, 1978b) pointed out that a month or more after adrenalectomy, the hepatic glucocorticoid sulfotransferase activity was diminished 63–67% compared to unoperated controls. As shown in Table VIA, adrenalectomy affected the hepatic concentrations of all three glucocorticoid sulfotransferases in a major way. However, STIII activity was diminished most (80–88%). STII was affected less, decreasing by 65–77%,

TABLE VI

THE EFFECTS OF ADRENALECTOMY OR ADRENALECTOMY AND CASTRATION ON THE TOTAL CORTISOL SULFOTRANSFERASE ACTIVITY AND THE RELATIVE AMOUNTS OF STI, STII, AND STIII IN LIVERS FROM MALE AND FEMALE RATS[a]

| Experiment, and surgery | Total CSA | % of recovered CSA in: | | | Estimated mean CSA in: | | |
|---|---|---|---|---|---|---|---|
| | | STI | STII | STIII | STI | STII | STIII |
| A. Females | | | | | | | |
| None | 197–355 (260) | 24–29 | 30–36 | 30–38 | 72 | 88 | 98 |
| Adrenalectomy | 37.5–103 (70.7) | 40–50 | 30–35 | 15–25 | 32 | 23 | 14 |
| Adrenalectomy and ovariectomy | 40.8–121 (69.9) | 45–45 | 25–31 | 11–22 | 35 | 19 | 11 |
| B. Males | | | | | | | |
| None | 17.9–56.1 (31.5) | 0 | 10–25 | 75–90 | 0 | 5.6 | 27 |
| Adrenalectomy | 8.72–17.9 (13.8) | 22–27 | 30–35 | 35–42 | 3.8 | 4.0 | 5.6 |
| Adrenalectomy and orchidectomy | 38.5–88.5 (63.1) | 0 | 55–71 | 29–46 | 0 | 39 | 24 |

[a]The rats used were described in Singer (1978b). All details and abbreviations are as described in footnote *a* for Table IV.

while the STI activity decreased by only 54–67%. The effects of simultaneous adrenalectomy and castration of female rats shown were similar to those of adrenalectomy alone. This suggested that the maintenance of the glucocorticoid sulfotransferase populations found in adult female rats (Singer *et al.*, 1976) required the synergistic action of both adrenals and gonads. The major control factor in such rats appeared to be an adrenal secretion.

In male rats (Singer, 1978b) adrenalectomy also resulted in dramatic decreases of the hepatic glucocorticoid sulfotransferase activity. Within a month or more after surgery the enzyme activity was found to be decreased by 51–61% compared to intact controls. Table VIB shows that STIII activity decreased greatly (75–86%) in these animals, while STII decreased by only 24–35%. It is of interest that very small amounts of STI, which we had not seen in males before this, were present in livers of adrenalectomized males. At this point it appeared that the adrenals were the major control factor involved in the production of the hepatic glucocorticoid sulfotransferases in both male and female rats.

Examination of male adrenalectomized castrates showed that the endocrine control of glucocorticoid sulfotransferase production in the two sexes was actually somewhat different. This was pointed out by the fact that the hepatic glucocorticoid sulfotransferase concentration in the double-operated males was much higher than that in either intact or adrenalectomized males (Table VIB). Table VIB also shows that this was due mostly to STII elevation, as the concentration of this enzyme was 8–10 times greater than in either adrenalectomized or intact males. Furthermore, the double-operated animals exhibited STIII concentrations similar to those in intact rats. This pointed out that other regulatory factors in addition to adrenal and gonadal hormones operated in male rats. These factors are discussed in a preliminary fashion in Sections VII and VIII.

The nature of the adrenal secretions that controlled the production of the glucocorticoid sulfotransferases were also tested briefly (Singer, 1978b). The administration of daily, 1 mg doses of cortisol for a month partly reversed the decrease of the enzyme activity we observed after adrenalectomy. As shown in Fig. 5, this was due to the elevation of the hepatic concentrations of all three glucocorticoid sulfotransferases. Similar treatment with deoxycorticosterone also elevated the glucocorticoid sulfotransferase activity and STI, STII, and STIII in treated adrenalectomized rats. However, it was not deemed likely that the mineralocorticoid was normally involved in adrenal control of production of the glucocorticoid sulfotransferases, as it had no effect on the production of the enzymes in intact males in the absence of a saline-loaded diet (Singer *et al.*, 1977). In contrast, glucocorticoids elevated the sulfotransferases either in the presence or absence of a high NaCl diet.

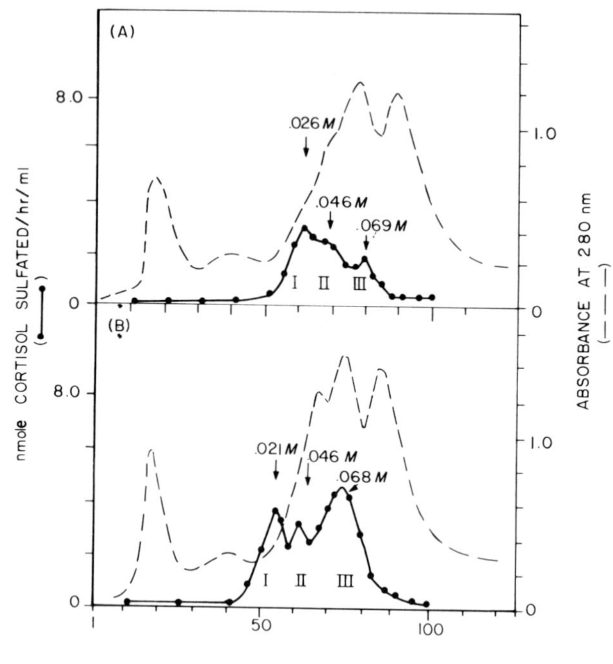


FIG. 5. Fractionation of the cortisol sulfotransferase activity of cytosols from untreated and cortisol injected adrenalectomized rats. Three-milliliter samples of cytosol from an untreated female adrenalectomized rat (A) and an adrenalectomized female given 1 mg cortisol daily for 40 days were fractionated in 2 × 50 cm columns of DEAE Sephadex A-50. All conditions were as described in the legend for Fig. 1. Reproduced from Singer (1978b) with permission.

Unfortunately it was not possible to test other adrenal hormones. In females, repeated injections of all other adrenal hormones tested were lethal within a few days. Higher doses of cortisol were also lethal. Male adrenalectomized rats did not survive the injection of any test hormone for more than a few days.

## VII. PITUITARY CONTROL OF GLUCOCORTICOID SULFOTRANSFERASE PRODUCTION

After examination of the roles of the adrenals and the gonads in control of rat liver glucocorticoid sulfotransferase production, several aspects of control of the production of the enzymes remained unclear. These included the identity of the regulatory factor that emerged in males after simultaneous adrenalectomy and castration (Singer, 1978b). Study of the effects on hypophysectomy in both sexes was carried out at that time (Singer *et al.*, 1979) for several reasons. First, we hoped to ascertain whether the effects of pituitary ablation in either sex exceeded those expected due to adrenal and gonadal atrophy. Second, we envisioned a method for use of hypophysectomized rats to screen the effects of the many hormones produced by the pituitary (or dependent on its action) on glucocorticoid sulfotransferase production.

In female rats (Singer *et al.*, 1979) the effects of hypophysectomy on the sulfotransferases were very similar to those obtained after adrenalectomy. Within a month after surgery the enzyme activity in hypophysectomized females had dropped to 8–25% of that in intact controls. Furthermore, as in adrenalectomized females (Singer, 1978b) enzyme profiles after pituitary ablation showed much diminished amounts of STI, STII, and STIII compared to controls (see Fig. 6B). However, the study suggested that responses of the enzymes to endocrines were more rapid than we had thought, as hypophysectomy was followed by 50–70% decreases of the cortisol sulfotransferase activity in 15–25 days.

The study of the response of the glucocorticoid sulfotransferases to hypophysectomy in females also established the temporal order of the decrease of the concentrations of the three enzymes. It appeared that STIII was

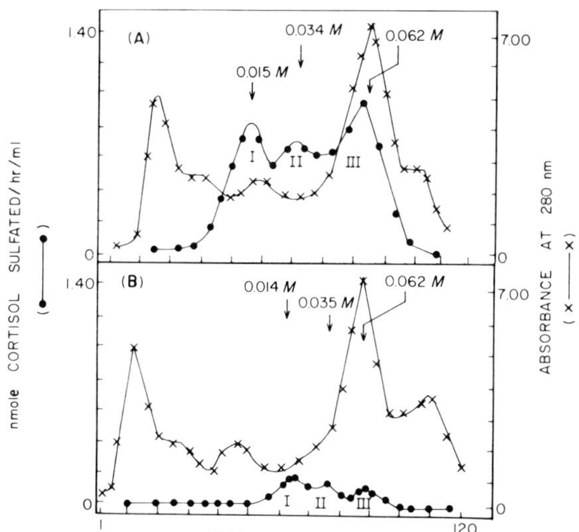


FIG. 6. Fractionation of the cortisol sulfotransferase activity of livers from intact and hypophysectomized female rats. Three-milliliter samples of cytosol from an intact female (A) and a female hypophysectomized 47 days prior to surgery (B) were used. They were fractionated as described in the legend for Fig. 1.

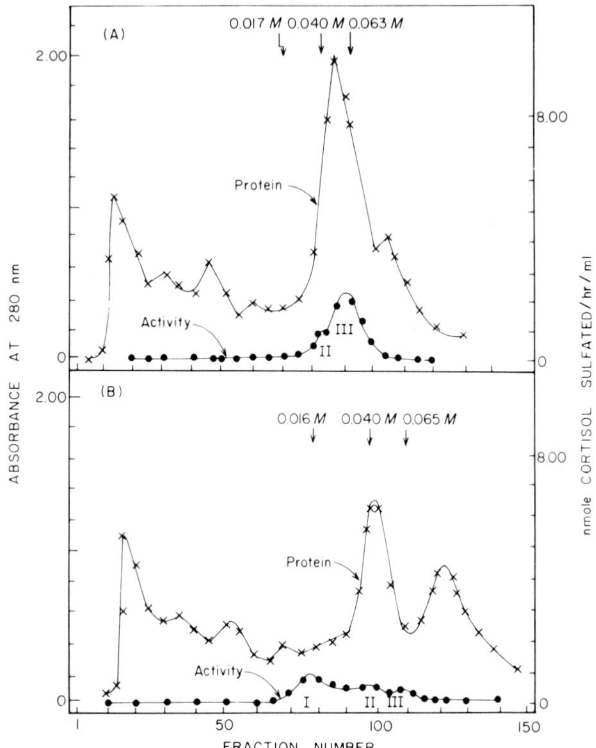


FIG. 7. DEAE Sephadex A-50 fractionation of the cortisol sulfotransferase activity in livers from intact and hypophysectomized male rats. Three-milliliter samples of cytosol from an intact male (A) and a hypophysectomized male (B) were chromatographed as described in the legend for Fig. 1. Reproduced with permission from Singer *et al.* (1979).

affected first, STII next, and STI last. Moreover, the response to pituitary ablation was the same whether female rats were operated as adults, or prior to puberty. Thus, the result of hypophysectomy appeared to have components due to both loss of preexisting enzyme in adults and prevention of the development of "adult" enzyme populations due to the maturation process. It also appeared that the adrenal–pituitary axis was the major endocrine component of the control system involved with the production of the glucocorticoid sulfotransferases in female rats.

In males (Singer *et al.*, 1979) hypophysectomy had very different results. There, the apparent cortisol sulfotransferase activity in liver cytosols did not differ significantly from that in unoperated males. Also, the result of pituitary ablation was similar whether male rats were operated when immature or as adults. However, DEAE Sephadex A-50 fractionation of the glucocorticoid sulfotransferases of livers from male hypophysectomized rats (Fig. 7B) showed that STI, STII, and STIII were present in proportions similar to those in hypophysectomized females.

Thus, pituitary ablation appeared to remove the factor that emerged to elevate STII and STIII concentrations in adrenalectomized–castrated male rats (Table VIB), supporting its pituitary origin. The nature of this factor has not yet been elucidated, as hypophysectomized rats did not survive repeated hormone injections for more than a few days. However, some interesting effects of purified pituitary hormones and progesterone have emerged in intact rats. These are briefly described next.

## VIII. OTHER ASPECTS OF ENDOCRINE CONTROL OF GLUCOCORTICOID SULFOTRANSFERASE PRODUCTION

Two other kinds of hormone effects on rat liver glucocorticoid sulfotransferases have presently been examined briefly. These were the results of the administration of multiple doses of progestin or anterior pituitary hormones. Study of the progestin effects (Singer *et al.*, 1980b) used progesterone because of its central role in steroid hormone biosynthesis, its role *in situ* and in tissue culture as an antiglucocorticoid (Samuels and Tomkins, 1970; DiSorbo *et al.*, 1977), and its action as an inhibitor of purified STI (Singer, 1979) and STIII (Singer *et al.*, 1978; Singer and Bruns, 1980).

Progesterone doses varying from 2.5–12 mg per male rat (Singer *et al.*, 1980b) resulted in statistically significant elevation of the hepatic glucocorticoid sulfotransferase activity. The maximum effect, obtained after a month or more of daily 12 mg intramuscular injections, averaged 342%. However, administration of the daily 12 mg dose for a week more than doubled the enzyme activity. The results of progesterone administration to adrenalectomized or castrated males supported the direct action of the injected progestin, or a closely related metabolite, rather than adrenal or testicular hormones produced by its metabolism.

Table VII shows that the increased glucocorticoid sulfotransferase activity observed after progesterone administration was largely due to the elevation of STIII activity. However, the hepatic concentrations of STI and STII were also elevated significantly compared to control rats. The profile of glucocorticoid sulfotransferases obtained after progesterone administration differed markedly from that seen in females (compare Fig. 1A with the data, as Fischer 344 rats were used for all hormone studies) or in males treated with

TABLE VII
THE EFFECT OF THE REPEATED DAILY ADMINISTRATION OF PROGESTERONE ON THE TOTAL CORTISOL SULFOTRANSFERASE ACTIVITY AND THE RELATIVE AMOUNTS OF STI, STII, AND STIII IN LIVERS FROM MALE RATS[a]

| Progesterone dose | Total CSA | % of recovered CSA in: STI | STII | STIII | Estimated mean CSA in: STI | STII | STIII |
|---|---|---|---|---|---|---|---|
| None | 21.2–54.0 (31.8) | 0 | 6.0–15 | 85–94 | 0 | 3.2 | 29 |
| 12 mg | 108–177 (141) | 10–18 | 20–35 | 45–62 | 17 | 49 | 75 |

[a]Rats used were described in Singer *et al.* (1980b). Progesterone was given daily, IM, for 30–56 days. Otherwise all details and abbreviations are as indicated in footnote *a* for Table IV.

estrogen (Table IVB). Furthermore, long-term treatment of female rats with daily 12 mg doses of progesterone did not affect their hepatic cortisol sulfotransferases in a major way. Therefore, it also appeared that neither the action of estrogens, nor estrogen-masking actions of progesterone were involved in the progestin effects.

The study with progesterone also suggested a plausible explanation for our puzzling observation (Singer and Sylvester, 1976) that while estradiol-17$\beta$ administration elevated STI, STII, and STIII activity in castrated male rats to concentrations usually found in females, ovariectomy did not have a large effect on the enzymes. It now appeared that physiological progestin might facilitate the maintenance of high STI and STII concentrations in adult females and act synergistically with estrogen to induce and maintain female sulfotransferase profiles. Such synergism between estrogen and progestin appeared a likely explanation for the fact that STI elevation without progestin administration had not been possible in male rats unless they were treated with estrogen. The proposed role for the progestin replaced our earlier supposition (Singer, 1978b) that the corticosteroids were responsible for such effects. This had never been satisfying, as it was difficult to see how adrenal hormones could maintain high STI and STII concentrations when their major observed effects were on STIII.

Preliminary study of the effects of anterior pituitary hormones have presently been confined to prolactin, follicle stimulating hormone, and lutenizing hormone (S. S. Singer, M. Federspiel, W. Lewis, V. Martin, A. Moshtaghie, J. Tappel, and K. Witt, unpublished results). Of these, only prolactin was found to elevate the hepatic glucocorticoid sulfotransferase activity in a significant fashion.

## IX. GLUCOCORTICOID SULFOTRANSFERASES IN HYPERTENSION, DIABETES, AND AGING

The potential involvement of glucocorticoid sulfates in pathological processes (Section II) led us to test for relationships between such processes and the hepatic glucocorticoid sulfotransferases in male rats. It was hoped that the results of these studies would be of use in explaining the elevated glucocorticoid sulfate concentrations observed in such instances and/or provide a rationale for changes in glucocorticoid-mediated processes that were not explainable in terms of known control processes. Although much remains to be done, information of interest has resulted from the studies already carried out.

### A. Hypertension

As already pointed out, the concentration of glucocorticoid sulfates in blood and urine has long been known to increase in human hypertensives (Kornel and Mitohashi, 1965; Kornel *et al.*, 1969; Kornel *et al.*, 1975). Furthermore, a brief study by Turcotte and Silah (1970) showed that hepatic corticosterone sulfotransferase activity in male rats was elevated when they were made hypertensive by the method of Grollman. These observations led us to study the effects of hypertension on the glucocorticoid sulfotransferases of male rats (Singer *et al.*, 1977). Our study extended the earlier report and showed that the development of Grollman hypertension was paralleled by the elevation of the hepatic cortisol sulfotransferase activity.

Moreover, we also found that the elevation of the blood pressure elicited by chronic injection of 9 $\alpha$-fluorocortisol and the spontaneous hypertension of Okamoto rats were accompanied by increased hepatic cortisol sulfotransferase activity. All three types of hypertension-induced increase of the enzyme activity were shown to be due mostly to STIII elevation. This was exemplified by the data obtained with Grollman hypertensives (Table VIII). The maturation of Okamota rats, or treatment with 9$\alpha$-fluorocortisol each resulted in increases of the systolic blood pressure that averaged approximately 50 mm. These were accompanied by statistically significant increases of the hepatic glucocorticoid sulfotransferase activity that averaged 50% in the spontaneous hypertensives and 150% in the steroid hypertensives.

In the same study we also tested the effects of repeated injection of cortisol, corticosterone, deoxycorticosterone, and several doses of 9$\alpha$-fluorocortisol. As shown in Table IX, the hypertensive effects of the test steroids were not separable from the elevation of the sulfotransferase activity. In all cases the increased enzyme activity was due mostly to STIII

TABLE VIII
THE HEPATIC CORTISOL SULFOTRANSFERASE ACTIVITY AND ESTIMATED STIII CONCENTRATION IN INTACT AND GROLLMAN HYPERTENSIVE MALE RATS[a]

| Rats | Systolic blood pressure (mm) | Hepatic CSA[b] | Estimated mean CSA in STIII |
|---|---|---|---|
| Normal | 92 ± 8.9 (76–105) | 21.6 ± 7.8 | 17.3 |
| Grollman | 130 ± 19.3[c] (102–195) | 37.0 ± 14[c] | 31.5[c] |

[a]Rats used were described in Singer *et al.* (1977). The body and liver weight ranges of experimental and control rats did not vary significantly.
[b]CSA and the estimated mean CSA are as defined in Table 4
[c]Statistically significant difference between control and hypertensive groups ($P<0.01$).

elevation. It was notable that the well-known elevation of the blood pressure in deoxycorticosterone-treated rats maintained on 1% NaCl as drinking water was accompanied by elevation of the glucocorticoid sulfotransferase activity. However, neither the blood pressure nor the enzyme activity was affected by the mineralocorticoid when rats were fed tap water instead of 1% NaCl.

The data from our study of hypertensive rats suggested that the elevation of the concentration of a STIII-like human enzyme might explain reports by

TABLE IX
THE BLOOD PRESSURE AND HEPATIC CORTISOL SULFATION IN RATS GIVEN CORTISOL, CORTICOSTERONE, DEOXYCORTICOSTERONE, OR 9α-FLUOROCORTISOL[a]

| | | Average increase of the: | |
|---|---|---|---|
| Steroid[b] (dose) | Days of treatment | Blood pressure (mm) | CSA (%) |
| FLHC (.60 mg) | 30–45 | 50[c] | 152[c] |
| FLHC (.20 mg) | 33–40 | 8 | 21 |
| HC (6.0 mg) | 35–53 | 46[c] | 112[c] |
| COR (3.0 mg) | 35–53 | 31[c] | 216[c] |
| DOC, no NaCl (3.0 mg) | 35–53 | 8 | 12 |
| DOC, no NaCl (3.0 mg) | 64–80 | 9 | 10 |
| DOC, with NaCl (3.0 mg) | 64–80 | 32[c] | 162[c] |

[a]The data come from studies described in Singer *et al.* (1977).
[b]FLHC, 9α-fluorocortisol; HC, cortisol; COR, corticosterone; DOC, deoxycorticosterone.
[c]Statistically significant difference between control and experimental groups ($P < 0.01$).

other laboratories that glucocorticoid sulfate concentrations increased in various tissues and excreta of hypertensives. Furthermore, a relationship among glucocorticoid sulfates, STIII, and hypertension was supported; and a previously unsuspected connection between sulfotransferases, glucocorticoid hypertension, and mineralocorticoid hypertension appeared to be possible.

### B. Diabetes

These studies were carried out because several laboratories including Adelman's (Adelman *et al.*, 1973) suggested that insulin was required for maximal glucocorticoid effects. Furthermore, it is well known that glucocorticoid effects on gluconeogenesis can exacerbate the effects of insulin deficiency. It was hoped that a useful relationship between the glucocorticoid sulfotransferases and insulin action would be obtained. We found (Singer *et al.*, 1981) that streptozotocin, a specific $\beta$-cell blocker, elevated the hepatic glucocorticoid sulfotransferase activity in male rats by up to 300%, 20–25 days after a single intraperitoneal dose of the drug. Figure 8 shows the time course of the response, pointing out that the cortisol sulfotransferase activity was doubled 10–11 days after streptozotocin administration. Additional studies (Singer *et al.*, 1981) (not shown) indicated that the effect of the drug was prevented or reversed by insulin administration.

The response of the glucocorticoid sulfotransferase activity to streptozotocin was much slower than the reported hyperglycemic effect of the drug (Kawashima *et al.*, 1978). Thus, it seemed to be a secondary consequence of the disease, due to insulin depletion. However, it appears that the streptozotocin-mediated glucocorticoid sulfotransferase elevation may be important for several reasons. First, the temporal course of the elevation of the enzyme activity closely paralleled the hypertensive response of rats to streptozotocin reported by another laboratory (Kawashima *et al.*, 1978). This could be of use in obtaining needed information about the relationship between the hypertension observed in some diabetics and diabetes. Furthermore, the data we obtained pointed out an interesting connection among diabetes, the glucocorticoid sulfotransferases, and hypertension. This was substantiated by a recent report by Stancakova *et al.* (1978), which demonstrated that glucocorticoid sulfate concentrations in urine were elevated in human diabetics and patients suffering from peripheral vascular disease. Finally, if glucocorticoid sulfates and sulfotransferases are involved in glucocorticoid effects, increased gluconeogenic actions of the hormone could exacerbate diabetic symptoms and effects.

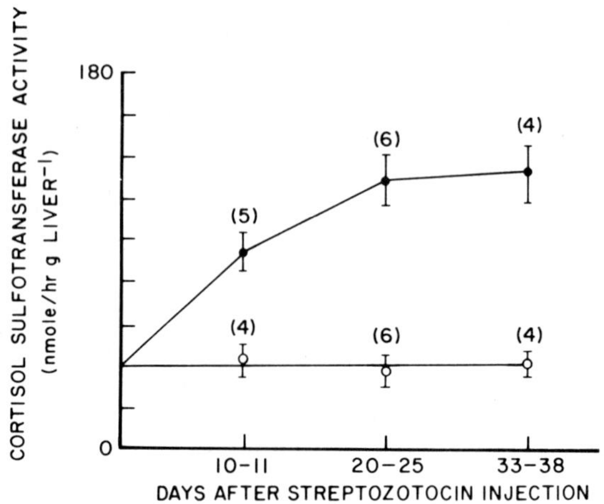


FIG. 8. The effect of of streptozotocin on hepatic cortisol sulfotransferase activity in male rats. Rats were injected intraperitoneally with 75 mg of streptozotocin per kg bodyweight (●) or they were uninjected controls (○). At the indicated times, they were sacrificed and liver cytosols were assayed for cortisol sulfotransferase activity. The vertical bars are the standard deviations and the numbers in parentheses are the number of experimental points. The data come from studies described in Singer *et al.* (1981).

## C. AGING

One effect of aging in rodents is a decreased ability to respond to near-physiological amounts of glucocorticoids (Finch *et al.*, 1969; Adelman, 1975). This was exemplified in study of the effects of cold stress on mouse liver tyrosine aminotransferase activity (Finch *et al.*, 1969). Old animals responded slowly and did not attain the maximum effect observed in young mice. In contrast, the response to large pharmacological doses of the glucocorticoids was similar in time course and extent in amimals of all ages. This suggested that an essential factor needed for glucocorticoid action was depleted in old animals. The extensive production of this factor appeared to occur after a lag, when they were stressed. However, it did not appear to be replaced completely, or to be maintained as long as in young animals. The results of administration of pharmacological hormone doses already cited suggested that when old rodents were given a large dose of glucocorticoid, enough of the proposed factor was produced to enable the basic induction mechanism, which was not affected by age, to function optimally.

The lesion caused by aging could involve glucocorticoid secretion or metabolism. However, studies by several laboratories (Rapaport *et al.*, 1964; Grad *et al.*, 1967; Finch *et al.*, 1969) did not demonstrate major changes of glucocorticoid levels or ACTH responsiveness that could have been responsible. On the basis of the potential role we proposed for glucocorticoid sulfation in enzyme induction, we tested the effect of aging on glucocorticoid sulfotransferase activity in rats aged 2–5 months (young) and 20–27 months (old) (Singer and Bruns, 1978). Because of the large spread of values observed in old rats, the difference between the cortisol sulfotransferase activity observed in cytosols from the two groups was not statistically significant. However, DEAE Sephadex A-50 column profiles of the old group showed that in all old rats tested (Fig. 9), decreased relative amounts of STIII and larger amounts of STII were present. STI was also present in old rats.

Additional evidence for this shift of sulfotransferase populations came from our examination of the substrate preference of liver cytosols from old and young rats (Singer and Bruns, 1978) (not shown). We found that the dehydroepiandrosterone sulfotransferase activity in old rats increased up to 6-fold. This was expected from Fig. 9, as STII sulfates dehydroepiandrosterone preferentially (Singer *et al.*, 1978). Estradiol-17$\beta$ sulfation was virtually unaffected by age. Cortisol, corticosterone, testosterone, and deoxycorticosterone sulfation were all elevated similarly in aged rats, suggesting that the sulfation of androgens and corticosteroids might be carried out by the same enzymes in males. This supported our later conclusions about the number and relationship between the steroid sulfotransferases, already described in Section III.

Our data slso suggested that the hepatic sulfation of near-physiological amounts of glucocorticoid was likely to be diminished in old rats due to the

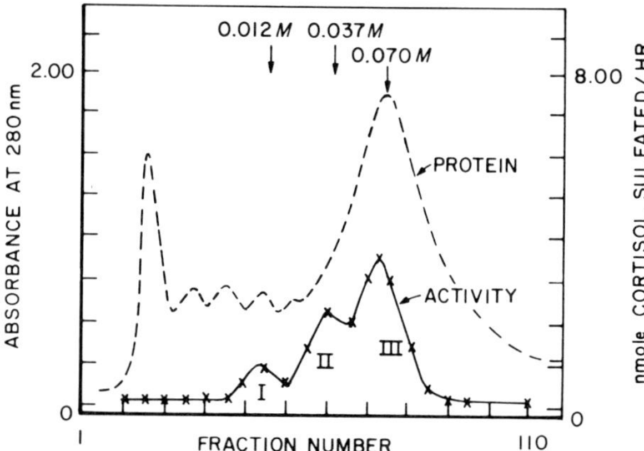


FIG. 9. Fractionation of the glucocorticoid sulfotransferases from the liver of an old rat. A 3 ml aliquot of liver cytosol from an old rat was chromatographed on an 2 × 50 cm column of DEAE Sephadex A-50. All methodology and abbreviations are as described in the legend for Fig. 1. A column containing an equal volume of cytosol from a young rat was chromatographed at the same time. The data from that column (not shown) were similar to those shown for untreated males in Figs. 3 and 7A.

presence of large amounts of STI, which supported the sulfation of steroids like dehydroepiandrosterone at the expense of glucocorticoid sulfation. If sulfated glucocorticoids were involved in the actions of the hormones, this could lead to the decreased basal tyrosine aminotransferase concentrations (Finch *et al.*, 1969) and other cited effects of near-physiological amounts of the hormones observed in old rodents. Pharmacological doses of the glucocorticoids, however, would be expected to compete successfully with other steroids for sulfation. Thus they would be expected to cause similar effects in rodents of all ages, as already reported by several researchers and cited above.

## X. SUMMARY

Presently, the exact basis for the actions of steroid hormones is not entirely clear. The last two decades have produced information suggesting previously unexpected roles for sulfated steroid hormone metabolites in many physiological and pathological actions of the hormones. Such roles could be due to control of production of other essential hormone metabolites in "sulfated" biosynthetic pathways, control of the action of key enzymes of intermediary metabolism, and direct action of sulfated steroids as active hormones, to name only a few possibilities.

Regardless of the actual mechanism involved, understanding of the enzymes that sulfate steroids has become a topic germane to the explanation of steroid hormone action. These enzymes, steroid sulfotransferases, are found in many animal tissues, but are usually most plentiful in liver. At this time, six mammalian steroid sulfotransferases have been purified extensively and described. These enzymes include sulfate estrogens, bile acids, mineralocorticoids, 3$\beta$-hydroxysteroids, and glucocorticoids. They can be differentiated partially on the basis of their substrate preferences and their physicochemical properties. However, more complete understanding of the relationship, or lack of relationship, between the sulfotransferases will require additional research efforts.

With the exception of the estrogen sulfotransferase, production of all of the reported steroid sulfotransferases appears to be controlled in part by the gonads, as much more of their activity is observed in female animals than males. Extensive study of the endocrine control of steroid sulfotransferase production has thus far been carried out only with STI, STII, and STIII, the three rat liver enzymes that sulfate the glucocorticoids. It has been shown that their production is controlled in a very complex fashion by adrenal, gonadal, and pituitary hormones, and progestins. Moreover, there is evidence for additional control factors that have not yet been identified.

Variation of the hepatic concentrations of STI, STII, and STIII also appears to be related to hypertension, the aging process, and diabetes in a fashion that may link these pathological processes and shows promise of being integrated with hormone action. It is hoped that future studies of steroid sulfotransferases will allow elucidation of the relationship between the enzymes and the actions of the various steroid hormones.

## ACKNOWLEDGEMENTS

Research carried out in the author's laboratory is supported by grant AM-19669 from the National Institute of Arthritis, Metabolism and Digestive Diseases, and funds from the University of Dayton Research Council.

## REFERENCES

Aakvaag, A., Hagen, A. A., and Eik-Nes, K. B. (1964). *Biochim. Biophys. Acta* **82**, 622.
Adams, J. B. (1964). *J. Clin. Endocrinol. Metab.* **24**, 988.
Adams, J. B. (1977). *Cancer (Brussels)* **40**, 325.
Adams, J. B., and Chulavatnatol, M. (1967). *Biochim. Biophys. Acta* **146**, 509.
Adams, J. B., and Low, J. (1974). *Biochim. Biophys. Acta* **370**, 189.
Adams, J. B., and McDonald, D. (1979). *Biochim. Biophys. Acta* **567**, 144.
Adams, J. B., and Poulos, A. (1967). *Biochim. Biophys. Acta* **146**, 493.
Adams, J. B., Ellyard, R. K., and Low, J. (1974). *Biochim. Biophys. Acta* **370**, 160.
Adelman, R. C. (1975). *Fed. Proc. Fed. Am. Soc. Exp. Biol.* **34**, 179.
Adelman, R. C., Freeman, C., and Rotenberg, S. (1973). *Prog. Brain Res.* **40**, 509.
Banerjee, R. K., and Roy, A. B. (1966). *Mol. Pharmacol.* **2**, 56.
Banerjee, R. K., and Roy, A. B. (1968). *Biochim. Biophys. Acta* **151**, 573.
Baulieu, E. E. (1962). *J. Clin. Endocrinol. Metab.* **22**, 501.
Baulieu, E. E., and Dray, F. (1963). *J. Clin. Endocrinol. Metab.* **23**, 1298.
Baulieu, E. E., Corpechot, C., Dray, F., Emiliozzi, P., Lebeau, M. C., Jarvis, P. M., and Robel, P. (1965). *Recent Prog. Horm. Res.* **21**, 411.
Brooks, S. C., and Horn, L. (1971). *Biochim. Biophys. Acta* **231**, 233.
Brunngraber, E. G. (1958). *J. Biol. Chem.* **233**, 472.
Burck, P. J., and Zimmerman, R. E. (1980). *J. Reprod. Fertil.* **58**, 121.
Calvin, H. I., and Lieberman, S. (1964). *Biochemistry* **3**, 259.
Calvin, H. I., VandeWiele, R. L., and Lieberman, S. (1963). *Biochemistry* **2**, 648.
Carlstedt-Duke, J., and Gustafsson, J.-A. (1973). *Eur. J. Biochem.* **36**, 172.
Carlstedt-Duke, J., Gustafsson, J.-A., and Gustafsson, S. A. (1975). *Biochemistry* **14**, 639.
Chan, S., and Cohen, P. P. (1964). *Arch. Biochem. Biophys.* **104**, 355.
Chen, L., Bolt, R. J., and Admirand, W. H. (1977). *Biochim. Biophys. Acta* **480**, 219.
Chen, L., Imperato, T. J., and Bolt, R. J. (1978). *Biochim. Biophys. Acta* **522**, 443.
Cherniak, R., and Davidson, E. A. (1964). *J. Biol. Chem.* **239**, 2986.
Dao, T. L., and Libby, P. R. (1969). *Surgery* **66**, 162.
DiSorbo, D., Rosen, F., McPartland, R. P., and Millholland, R. J. (1977). *Ann. N.Y. Acad. Sci.* **286**, 355.

Dominguez, O. V., Valencia, S. A., and Loza, A. C. (1975). *J. Steroid Biochem.* **6,** 301.
Drayer, N. M., and Lieberman, S. (1965). *Biochem. Biophys. Res. Commun.* **18,** 126.
Einarsson, K., Gustafsson, J.-A., Ihre, T., and Ingelman-Sundberg, M. (1976). *J. Clin. Endocrinol. Metab.* **43,** 56.
Fahl, W. E., Rose, D. P., Liskowski, L., and Brown, R. R. (1974). *Cancer (Brussels)* **34,** 1691.
Fiala, E. S., and Litwack, G. (1966). *Biochim. Biophys. Acta* **124,** 260.
Finch, C. E., Foster, J. R., and Mirsky, A. E. (1969). *J. Gen. Physiol.* **54,** 690.
Ghosh, P. C., Lockwood, E., and Pennington, G. W. (1973). *Br. Med. J.* **1,** 328.
Godefroi, V. C., Locke, E. R., Singh, D. V., and Brooks, S. C. (1975). *Cancer Res.* **35,** 1791.
Grad, B., Kral, V. A., Payne, R. C., and Berenson, J. (1967). *J. Gerontol.* **22,** 66.
Gregory, J. D., and Nose, Y. (1957). *Fed. Proc. Fed. Am. Soc. Exp. Biol.* **16,** 189.
Gugler, R., Rao, G. S., and Breuer, H. (1970). *Biochim. Biophys. Acta* **220,** 69.
Gustafsson, J.-A., and Ingelman-Sundberg, M. (1974). *J. Biol. Chem.* **249,** 1940.
Gustafsson, J.-A., and Ingelman-Sundberg, M. (1975). *J. Biol. Chem.* **250,** 3451.
Hilz, H., and Lipmann, F. (1955). *Proc. Natl. Acad. Sci. U.S.A.* **41,** 880.
Hobkirk, R., Nilsen, M., and Mori, J. (1978). *Endocrinology* **103,** 1227.
Ingleman-Sundberg, M. (1976). *Biochim. Biophys. Acta* **431,** 592.
Kawashima, H., Igarishi, T., Nakajima, Y., Akiyama, Y., Usuki, K., and Ohtake, S. (1978). *Arch. Pharmacol.* **305,** 123.
Klein, G. P., Chan, S. K., and Giroud, C. J. P. (1969). *J. Clin. Endocrinol. Metab.* **28,** 1448.
Kornel, L. (1960). *J. Clin. Endocrinol. Metab.* **20,** 1445.
Kornel, L., and Mitohashi, K. (1965). *J. Clin. Endocrinol. Metab.* **25,** 904.
Kornel, L., Starnes, W. R., Hill, S. R., and Hill, A. R. (1969). *J. Clin. Endocrinol. Metab.* **29,** 1608.
Kornel, L., Miyabo, S., Saiti, Z., Cha, R. N., and Wu, F. T. (1975). *J. Clin. Endocrinol. Metab.* **40,** 949.
Lebeau, M. C., and Baulieu, E. E. (1963). *Endocrinology* **73,** 832.
Lewis, W., Witt, K., and Singer, S. S. (1981). *Proc. Soc. Exp. Biol. Med.,* **166,** 70.
Lipmann, F. (1958). *Science* **128,** 575.
Litwack, G. (1967). *Top. Med. Chem.* **1,** 3.
Litwack, G., and Singer, S. S. (1972). *In* "Biochemical Actions of Hormones" (G. Litwack, ed.), Vol. 2, p. 113. Academic Press, New York.
Litwack, G., Filler, R., Lichtash, E., Rosenfield, S. A., Wishman, C. A., and Singer, S. S. (1973). *J. Biol. Chem.* **248,** 7481.
Loof, L., and Hjerten, S. (1980). *Biochim. Biophys. Acta* **617,** 192.
Lyon, E. S., and Jakoby, W. B. (1980). *Arch. Biochem. Biophys.* **202,** 474.
McEvoy, F. A., and Carroll, J. (1971). *Biochem. J.* **123,** 901.
Mason, M., and Gullekson, E. H. (1960). *J. Biol. Chem.* **235,** 1312.
Mason, M., and Schirch, L. (1961). *Fed. Proc. Fed. Am. Exp. Biol.* **20,** 200.
Miyazaki, M., Yoshizawa, I., and Fishman, J. (1969). *Biochemistry* **8,** 1669.
Morey, K. S., and Litwack, G. (1969). *Biochemistry* **8,** 4813.
Nose, Y., and Lipmann, F. (1958). *J. Biol. Chem.* **233,** 1348.
Payne, A. H., and Mason, M. (1965). *Steroids* **6,** 323.
Payne, A. H., and Singer, S. S. (1979). *In* "Steroid Biochemistry" (R. Hobkirk, ed.), Vol. I, p. 111. CRC Press, Boca Raton.
Rapaport, A., Allaire, Y., Bourliere, F., and Gerard, F. (1964). *Gerontologia* **10,** 20.
Roberts, K. D., Bandi, L., Calvin, H. I., Drucker, W. D., and Lieberman, S. (1964). *J. Am. Chem. Soc.* **86,** 958.
Roberts, K. D., and S. Lieberman (1970). *In* "Chemical and Biological Aspects of Steroid Conjugation" (S. Bernstein and S. Solomon, eds.), p. 219. Springer-Verlag, Berlin and New York.

Robbins, P. W., and Lipmann, F. (1956). *J. Am. Chem. Soc.* **78**, 2653.
Robbins, P. W., and Lipmann, F. (1958). *J. Biol. Chem.* **233**, 686.
Rose, D. P., Fahl, W. E., and Liskowski, L. (1975). *Cancer (Brussels)* **36**, 2060.
Roy, A. B. (1956). *Biochem. J.* **63**, 294.
Roy, A. B. (1971). *In* "Concepts in Biochemical Pharmacology" (B. B. Brodie and J. R. Gillette, eds.), Part 2, p. 536. Springer-Verlag, Berlin and New York.
Rozhin, J., Soderstrom, R. L., and Brooks, S. C. (1974). *J. Biol. Chem.* **249**, 2079.
Ryan, R., and Carroll, J. (1976). *Biochim. Biophys. Acta* **429**, 391.
Samuels, H. H., and Tomkins, G. M. (1970). *J. Mol. Biol.* **52**, 57.
Schweitzer, M., Branchaud, C., and Giroud, C. J. P. (1969). *Steroids* **14**, 519.
Sekura, R. D., and Jakoby, W. B. (1979). *J. Biol. Chem.* **254**, 5658.
Siiteri, P. K., and MacDonald, P. C. (1963). *Steroids* **2**, 713.
Singer, S. S. (1978a). *Biochim. Biophys. Acta* **539**, 19.
Singer, S. S. (1978b). *Endocrinology* **103**, 66.
Singer, S. S. (1979). *Arch. Biochem. Biophys.* **196**, 340.
Singer, S. S., and Bruns, L. (1978). *Exp. Gerontol.* **13**, 425.
Singer, S. S., and Bruns, L. (1980). *Can. J. Biochem.* **58**, 660.
Singer, S. S., and Litwack, G. (1971). *Endocrinology* **88**, 1448.
Singer, S. S., and Sylvester, S. (1976). *Endocrinology* **99**, 1346.
Singer, S. S. Morey, K. S., and Liteack, G. (1970). *Physiol. Chem. Phys.* **2**, 117.
Singer, S. S., Becker, J. E., and Litwack, G. (1973). *Biochem. Biophys. Res. Commun.* **52**, 943.
Singer, S. S., Gebhart, J., and Krol, J. (1975). *Eur. J. Biochem.* **56**, 595.
Singer, S. S., Giera, D., Johnson, J., and Sylvester, S. (1976). *Endocrinology* **98**, 963.
Singer, S. S., Hess, E., and Sylvester, S. (1977). *Biochem. Pharmacol.* **26**, 1033.
Singer, S. S., Gebhart, J., and Hess, E. (1978). *Can. J. Biochem.* **56**, 1028.
Singer, S. S., Kutzer, T., and Lee, A. (1979). *Endocrinology* **104**, 571.
Singer, S. S., Bruns, L., and Kutzer, T. (1980a). *Fed. Proc. Fed. Am. Exp. Biol.* **39**, 1722.
Singer, S. S., Moshtaghie, A., Lee, A., and Kutzer, T. (1980b). *Biochem. Pharmacol.* **29**, 3181.
Singer, S. S., Martin, V., and Federspiel, M. (1981). *Horm. Metab. Res.* **13**, 45.
Stancakova, A., Merstenova, E., Vajo, J., and Valkova, M. (1978). *Horm. Metabol. Res.* **10**, 539.
Torday, J. S., Klein, G. P., and Giroud, C. J. P. (1971). *Can. J. Biochem.* **49**, 437.
Turcotte, G., and Silah, J. G. (1970). *Endocrinology* **87**, 723.
Wengle, B. (1963). *Acta Soc. Med. Ups.* **68**, 154.
Wu, S. G., and Straub, K. D. (1976). *J. Biol. Chem.* **251**, 6529.
Yang, R. S. H., and Wilkenson, C. F. (1973). *Biochem. J.* **130**, 487.

# CHAPTER 11

# Chemical Substitution of Steroid Hormones: Effect on Receptor Binding and Pharmacokinetics

*Jean-Pierre Raynaud, Tiiu Ojasoo, Jacques Pottier, and Jean Salmon*





BIOCHEMICAL ACTIONS OF HORMONES, VOL. IX

ISBN 0-12-452809-0

## I. INTRODUCTION

The ability to improvise on paper the molecule that will induce a specific biological response in man is an ever-inspiring goal of the scientist, especially in the drug industry. As technological improvements, such as the use of computers for information storage and analysis, bring to light wider and finer correlations between structure and response, this goal seems to become more readily attainable, but then recedes again as new problems arise from a deeper understanding of molecular mechanisms of action.

In the field of steroid hormones, the concept of a receptor and later its partial isolation led to the notion that a steroid is active on the condition that it interacts with the receptor and to the implication that the strength of the interaction might determine the magnitude of the response. Thus, it was assumed that a good fit between the ligand and the receptor protein yielded a complex endowed with potency. In accordance with this concept we have since 1974 systematically screened newly synthetized molecules for binding to the receptors of several steroid hormone classes. Lately, experimental conditions have been refined to include an evaluation of the dynamics of these interactions. However, in this search for the perfect ligand, other factors intervening in the biological response and establishing the suitability of the ligand as a drug have received slightly less attention. For instance, the bioavailability of the ligand at the target site is as decisive as the receptor interaction and, consequently, a study of the influence of chemical substitution of endogenous hormones on their plasma binding and metabolism is of crucial importance. Like the endogenous hormone, the ligand may not only bind to the receptor protein but also to plasma transport proteins that are either specific (e.g., sex-steroid binding protein) or nonspecific (e.g., albumin) and to degradative enzymes.

In this chapter, we shall first consider some of the relationships that can exist between affinity for the receptor, plasma binding, biotransformations, and activity. We shall then illustrate these relationships by analyzing the influence of systematic chemical substitution of progesterone and testosterone on their receptor binding, metabolic fate, and bioavailability.

## II. CONTRIBUTION OF RECEPTOR AFFINITY, PLASMA BINDING, AND METABOLISM TO ACTIVITY

### A. Is the Strength of the Steroid–Receptor Interaction Correlated with End-Organ Response?

#### *1. Factors to Be Considered in the Correlation*

The existence of a correlation between the affinity of a ligand for a steroid receptor and its biological activity is implicit in the work of many authors (for review, see Raynaud *et al.*, 1978), but proof of a strict relationship is lacking for obvious reasons. (1) First, the study has to be restricted to responses mediated directly via the receptor, leaving aside indirect biological actions or regulatory mechanisms such as inhibition or stimulation of hormone biosynthesis. (2) Then, the distribution factors (absorption, plasma binding, metabolism, etc.) that influence the concentration of free, i.e., active, ligand at the tissue binding site have to be taken into account. In this context, correlations with early cellular responses, e.g., the induction of the *in situ* synthesis of specific proteins, or with responses in closed systems like tissue culture cell lines, where these factors do not intervene or are minimized, are particularly relevant. (3) Many biological responses are studied in systems under multihormonal control. Several peripheral and central target tissues (uterus, pituitary, hypothalamus, etc.) contain appreciable quantities of receptors of more than one hormone class. For ligands that bind simultaneously but with different affinities to several of these receptors, the contribution of each binding component to the gross responses measured is uncertain. These responses depend on the relative concentrations of the different receptor sites in the target tissue and on the sensitivity of each receptor. (4) To further complicate matters, biological response and receptor affinity are rarely measured under the same experimental conditions. Relative binding affinities (RBAs), even when evaluated on cytosol from the corresponding species and tissues, may depend on the medium, the radioligand, etc., and do depend on the interaction kinetics of the competitor and radioligand with the receptors (Shutt and Cox, 1972; Bouton and Raynaud, 1978; Bell and Jones, 1979; Aranyi and Quiroga, 1980). Compounds with comparable association rates compete similarly after short-time incubation. However, on increasing incubation time or temperature, their inhibition of radioligand binding increases if the complex between competitor and receptor dissociates slower than that between radioligand and receptor, and decreases if it dissociates faster. Consequently, by measuring RBAs under different incubation conditions, it is possible to obtain insight into the binding kinetics of the test substance with respect to that of the radioligand.

The importance of binding kinetics should not be underestimated since several studies have indicated that differences in rates of interaction are generally reflected in different intensity biological responses. Compounds that dissociate slowly from the receptor form long-lived complexes with the receptor, are able to sustain the biological events following binding and, as long as they do not interfere adversely with subsequent steps such as nuclear binding, tend to be potent agonists with steep dose–response curves. Compounds that dissociate fast form short-lived complexes and are poor agonists with shallow dose–response curves. Moreover, if these compounds with fast association and dissociation rates transiently occupy available binding sites without induction of a full response, it can be supposed that the natural hormone will have difficulty in gaining adequate access to its binding sites and that the outcome will be reflected in antihormonal action. Indeed, the validity of this hypothesis has been demonstrated for steroid and non-steroid estrogens and antiestrogens (Rochefort and Capony, 1977; Raynaud 1978; Bouton and Raynaud, 1979; Raynaud and Bouton, 1980; Shyamala and Leonhard, 1980; Weichman and Notides, 1980; Rochefort and Borgna, 1981), androgens and antiandrogens (Raynaud *et al.*, 1979a), and is under close scrutiny for the corticoids (Bell, 1977; Simons *et al.*, 1979; Raynaud *et al.*, 1980b, d, 1981b). The few apparent exceptions encountered so far such as certain hydroxylated triphenylethylene derivatives (Black *et al.*, 1981; Wakeling and Slater, 1981) could be tentatively explained by the high reactivity of a substituent forming a quasi-covalent bond with the receptor (Raynaud, 1978; Rochefort and Borgna, 1981), thus destroying the equilibrium conditions on which RBA determinations are based (Aranyi and Quiroga, 1980). Other explanations that can be put forward are interaction with another binding site (Sutherland *et al.*, 1980) or the formation of a receptor complex with a conformation that may interact adversely with the acceptor site.

2. *In Vitro Screening for Receptor Binding*

In view of the unelucidated aspects of receptor binding studies, two courses remain open to the scientist: either pursue the in-depth study of the molecular mechanism of action of only a few molecules using increasingly sophisticated biochemical approaches (in this context one can cite the work of J. H. Clark and B. S. Katzenellenbogen on estrogens and antiestrogens) or choose a totally different approach and study a large number of molecules under standardized conditions. These two approaches are nevertheless complementary since knowledge obtained from the more fundamental studies governs the choice of standardized conditions for the screening system.

Accordingly, initial structure-affinity studies on a limited number of compounds have led to the systematic screening of chemically related compounds by the drug industry (Broek *et al.*, 1977; Reel *et al.*, 1979; Ariëns, 1979; Zeelen and Bergink, 1980) and even to the setting-up of large-scale multireceptor screening programs to establish the binding profiles of available and newly synthetized molecules (Kolata, 1977; Kato, 1980; Gund *et al.*, 1980). Thus, for instance, since the early 1970s, competitive binding of test substances to the estrogen, progestin, androgen, mineralocorticoid, and glucocorticoid receptors, present in the cytosols of organs routinely used as end-points in biological activity tests, have been systematically measured at Roussel-Uclaf to select potentially active hormones (Raynaud, 1977; Raynaud *et al.*, 1974b, 1975, 1978, 1980a,b,d; Ojasoo and Raynaud, 1978).

In our screening system, the estrogen receptor is radiolabeled with estradiol in mouse uterus cytosol because uterine growth is a traditional measure of estrogenicity and because estradiol binding protein (EBP) is present in very low concentrations in the mouse compared to the rat. The progestin receptor is labeled with promegestone (R 5020) in rabbit uterus cytosol since histological grading of the proliferation of rabbit endometrium is considered one of the more sensitive tests of progestational activity and since promegestone binds minimally to corticosteroid binding globulin (CBG) and forms a much more stable receptor complex than progesterone (Philibert *et al.*, 1977). The androgen receptor is identified in rat prostate cytosol with metribolone; this organ and species present few problems as sex-steroid binding protein (SBP) is undetected in the rat and the prostate of the young animal does not appear to contain any progestin receptor binding metribolone (Bonne and Raynaud, 1975; Asselin *et al.*, 1979; Zava *et al.*, 1979). In the absence of SBP it is also possible to use testosterone but not dihydrotestosterone, which is degraded in the incubation medium (Raynaud *et al.*, 1979b). The most difficult receptors to identify conclusively without misinterpretation are the mineralocorticoid and glucocorticoid receptors, since they are often present concurrently and since most ligands that bind firmly to one of these receptors also bind, even if less firmly, to the other. We have used labeled aldosterone in the presence of a highly specific unlabeled glucocorticoid, RU 26988 ($11\beta,17\beta$-dihydroxy-$17\alpha$(1-propionyl)-androsta-1,4,6-trien-3-one) that saturates only glucocorticoid binding sites (Moguilewsky and Raynaud, 1980) to identify mineralocorticoid receptor binding in rat kidney cytosol (Raynaud *et al.*, 1980a) and labeled dexamethasone to identify glucocorticoid receptors in rat thymus cytosol. Binding is evaluated by a dextran-coated charcoal adsorption method which leads to the dissociation of all low-affinity binding ($< 10^6 M^{-1}$). Graded concentrations of a steroid are placed in competition with a given concentration of radioligand and the displacement of bound radioligand is measured under two sets of appropriately chosen incubation conditions for each hormone class (Raynaud, 1978; Raynaud *et al.*, 1980a). From these measurements binding curves are constructed and RBAs determined.

The results of this screening shed light on the structural requirements for the receptor binding of ligands. By identifying a sufficient number of different ligands interacting with a receptor protein, it can be assumed that a mold of the volume occupied by their likeliest conformations, deduced by X-ray crystallography (Mornon *et al.*, 1977; Duax *et al.*, 1978b) or by energy minimizing calculation techniques (Schmit and Rousseau, 1978; Schmit *et al.*, 1980), might fairly accurately represent the binding site. Thus, data on binding affinity and specificity viewed in the light of molecular conformation can lead to the mapping of binding sites (Delettré *et al.*, 1980c) and ultimately to the design of new specific ligands with an optimum fit. That these ligands might also possess considerably enhanced activity is shown in Fig. 1, which illustrates the correlations between RBAs for the rabbit uterine pro-

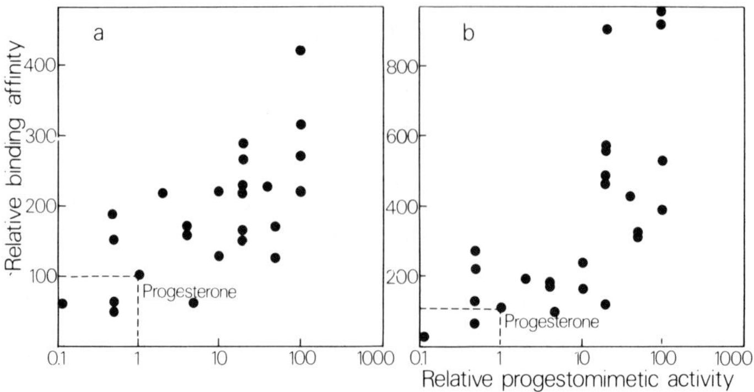


FIG. 1. Correlation between relative binding affinity for the rabbit uterine progestin receptor and progestomimetic potency. Relative binding affinities were determined after incubation for 2 hours at 0°C (a) or 24 hours at 0°C (b) as described in the footnote to Table III. Progestomimetic activity was evaluated by grading the endometrial response histologically according to McPhail's scale after s.c. administration of the test substances for 5 days to estradiol-primed immature rabbits.

gestin receptor after 2 and 24 hours incubation and progestomimetic activity. Steroids with high affinities tend to be potent progestins. Similar correlations between binding affinity and activity have been published for estrogens, androgens (Raynaud *et al.*, 1978), and corticoids (Rousseau *et al.*, 1972).

### B. Influence of Specific Plasma Binding on Pharmacokinetics and on End-Organ Responses

Available experimental models to study the role of high affinity steroid binding in plasma are limited. In only a few instances, the fate of a molecule can be readily compared in the absence and in the presence of the plasma binder which, in general, is continuously present, albeit at different concentrations. However, at least two notable animal models have received a fair amount of study, namely, progesterone binding globulin (PBG) in the pregnant guinea pig (Westphal, 1980) and the $\alpha$-fetoprotein binding estradiol (EBP) in the young rodent.

#### 1. *Influence of Binding to PBG on Progesterone Pharmacokinetics*

In the pregnant guinea pig, PBG appears on about day 17 of pregnancy, increases rapidly until day 30, remains stable until day 68, then falls drastically at parturition. Among the main progesterone metabolites, only allopregnanedione and 20α-hydroxy-5α-pregnan-3-one compete more effectively than progesterone for binding to PBG (Table I). During pregnancy, the apparent initial volumes of distribution (AIVD) of plasma progesterone (Illingworth *et al.*, 1970) and allopregnanedione decrease resulting in slower clearance (Fig. 2) and also in changed metabolic profiles (Fig. 3). After injection of labeled progesterone to pregnant guinea pigs, the progesterone level decreases fairly uniformly with time and the allopregnanedione and pregnanediol levels increase correspondingly, whereas, in the virgin animal, in the absence of PBG, a drastic drop in progesterone level occurs within 15 minutes of administration with no accompanying rise in allopregnanedione but an abrupt increase in pregnanediols instead. Similarly, after injection of labeled allopregnanedione, which is also bound by PBG, to pregnant guinea-pigs, both the dissappearance of allopregnanedione and the appearance of pregnanediols are gradual; in the nonpregnant animal, allopregnanedione is virtually instantaneously metabolized and rapidly yields a high level of pregnanediols. The differences in pharmacokinetic parameters (Table II) resulting from high PBG levels (1 g/liter) during pregnancy are thus reflected

TABLE I

BINDING TO PROGESTERONE BINDING GLOBULIN (PBG) IN PREGNANT GUINEA PIG PLASMA AS DETERMINED BY EQUILIBRIUM DIALYSIS[a]

| | Relative affinity |
|---|---|
| 5α-Pregnane-3,20-dione (Allopregnanedione) | 210 |
| 20α-Hydroxy-5α-pregnan-3-one | 160 |
| Progesterone | 100 |
| 20α-Hydroxy-4-pregnen-3-one | 65 |
| 5β-Pregnane-3,20-dione | 7 |
| 20β-Hydroxy-4-pregnen-3-one | 7 |
| 3α-Hydroxy-5α-pregnan-20-one | 5 |
| 3α-Hydroxy-5β-pregnan-20-one | 4 |
| 17α-Hydroxy-4-pregnen-3,20-dione | 1 |
| 5β-Pregnane-3α,20α-diol | 0.5 |
| 5α-Pregnane-3α,20β-diol | 0.5 |
| Cortisol | 0.5 |

[a] 1 ml diluted plasma was placed in a Nojax dialysis bag and dialyzed for 48 hours at 4°C against 15 ml of 0.1 *M* phosphate buffer (pH 7.4) containing 0.2 n*M* [$^3$H]progesterone or [$^3$H]allopregnanedione and 1–250 n*M* unlabeled homologous steroid. Three 0.2 ml samples from the inner and outer solutions were counted. The intrinsic dissociation constant ($K_d$) was evaluated from a proportion graph ($K_d$ progesterone = $1.3 \times 10^{-9}$ *M*; $K_d$ allopregnanedione = $0.8 \times 10^{-9}$ *M*). In competition experiments, 1–250 n*M* unlabeled competitor was added to 0.5 n*M* [$^3$H]progesterone and the concentration required to reduce bound [$^3$H]progesterone by half (logit fraction bound = 0) was determined from logit curves.

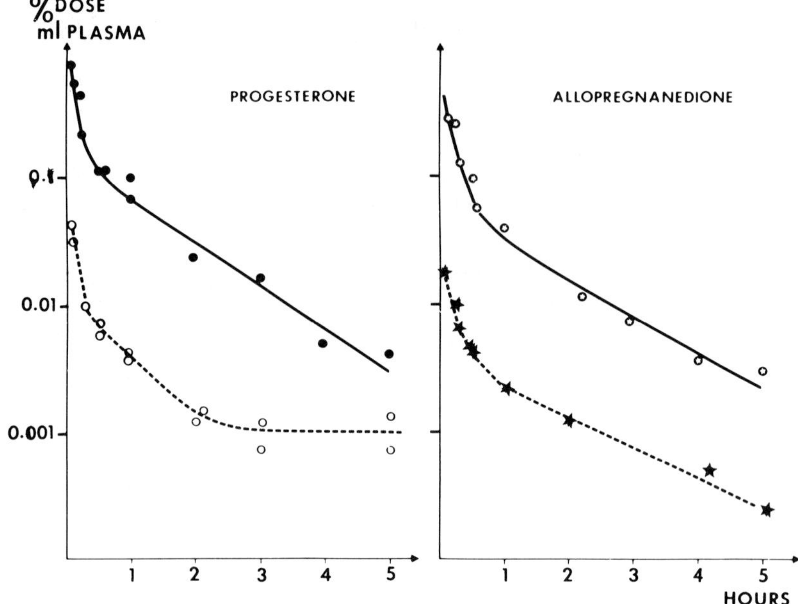


FIG. 2. Disappearance of progesterone and allopregnanedione from guinea pig plasma. 2 μg of labeled compound were injected i.v. into pregnant (solid lines) or virgin (dotted lines) guinea pigs. The plasma radioactivity of the parent compound, identified by TLC, was measured at various times after injection.

in the rates of appearance and disappearance of progesterone metabolites (Raynaud and Philibert, 1972).

Trapping of progesterone and its first metabolite by PBG slows down progesterone elimination in the pregnant animal, leads to the formation of reservoirs of free (active) hormone and efficiently ensures an adequate hormone supply in the target tissue over time. Similarly, the increase in plasma corticosteroid binding globulin (CBG) in pregnant women may, by impeding

TABLE II
PHARMACOKINETIC PARAMETERS FOLLOWING I.V. INJECTION OF 2 μG OF LABELED STEROID TO GUINEA PIGS

| | | Apparent initial volume of distribution (liters) | Clearance (ml/hour) |
|---|---|---|---|
| Progesterone | Virgin | 1.5 | 5.6 |
| | Pregnant | 0.1 | 0.3 |
| Allopregnanedione | Virgin | 4.0 | 9.0 |
| | Pregnant | 0.2 | 0.6 |

progesterone elimination, meet the need for elevated progesterone concen trations. Conversely, reduced CBG capacity affects cortisol levels and has been described in association with Cushing's syndrome (De Moor *et al.*, 1965). Saturation of available sex-steroid binding protein (SBP) sites in the adult male by pathologically increased testosterone concentrations destroys normal feedback control. In the healthy male these sites are only half-saturated by circulating testosterone, conditions needed for continuous hormone release (Raynaud, 1971b). In any investigation into the fate of synthetic steroid hormones in humans it is therefore necessary to determine,

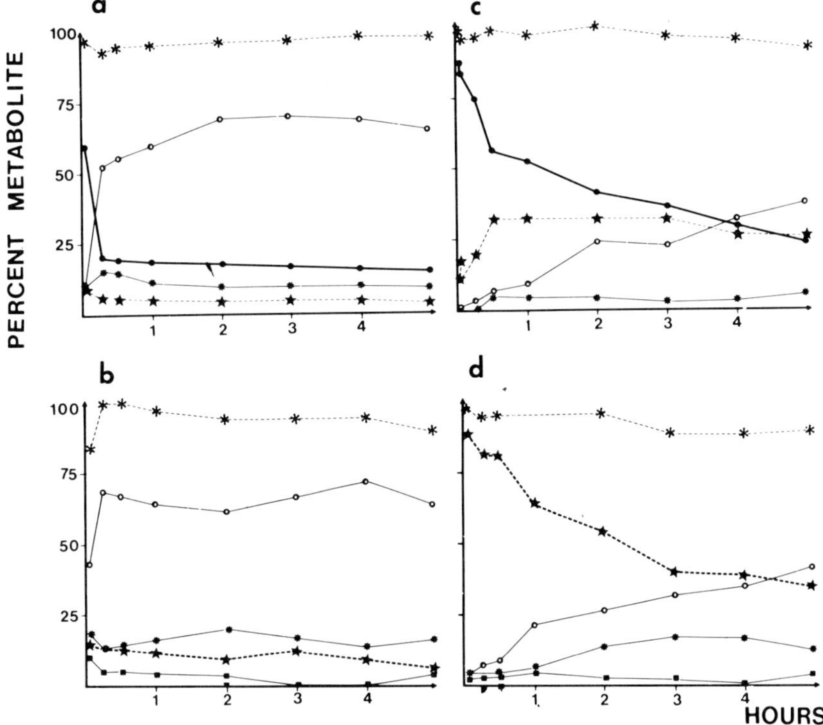


FIG. 3. Profile of metabolites recovered in the plasma of virgin (a and b) and pregnant (c and d) guinea pigs following i.v. injection of progesterone (a and c) or allopregnanedione (b and d). Anesthetized virgin and pregnant guinea pigs (between day 58 and day 62 of pregnancy) received the labeled compound i.v. in 0.5 ml saline containing 10% ethanol. Plasma aliquots were used to monitor total radioactivity during the 5 hours following injection. The remainder was alkalinized with 0.2 *N* NaOH. Free steroids were extracted with ethyl acetate (3 × 1 ml) and then separated and identified by TLC on silicagel plates by comparing their $R_f$ values with those of reference standards. Bands 5 mm wide were scraped and the radioactivity of steroids eluted with 1 ml ethanol was counted. *, total radioactivity recovered; ●, progesterone, ★, allopregnanedione; ○, pregnanediols; ✳, 17α-hydroxyprogesterone; ■, allopregnanolone.

by measuring the strength of their binding to plasma proteins, the likelihood of this "reservoir phenomenon."

### 2. *Influence of Binding to EBP on End-Organ Responses*

The second model of choice to study the effect of a plasma binding protein on steroid action is the rat where EBP appears during fetal life, declines after parturition and is undetectable during later pubescence (Raynaud, 1973; Nunez *et al.*, 1976). The comparison of the effects of the natural hormone estradiol that binds EBP and of a potent synthetic estrogen that does not, e.g., moxestrol (11β-methoxy-19-nor-17α-pregna-1,3,5(10)-trien-20-yne-3,17β-diol), in the neonate, immature, and adult rat has revealed the influence of this plasma protein on various biological responses and a possible explanation for its role. The presence of EBP reduces the full expected estradiol response whether the end-point considered is progesterone receptor induction, uterine growth or control of plasma LH, whereas it has no effect on the moxestrol response (Raynaud, 1973; Andrews and Ojeda, 1977, Raynaud *et al.*, 1980e). As the EBP concentration decreases in the immature rat, the ratio of the estradiol to moxestrol response increases. Furthermore, it has been shown that on administration of estradiol to the pregnant rat, retention of estradiol by maternal and fetal EBP protects the fetus from the possible deleterious effects of high concentrations of endogenous hormone, as evidenced by histological examination of the fetal genital tract (Vannier and Raynaud, 1975) and a study of the fertility and reproductive performance of the offspring (Vannier and Raynaud, 1980).

## C. Influence of Biotransformations on End-Organ Responses

Synthetic hormones, many of which, unlike progesterone and testosterone, are active on oral administration, can undergo enzyme attack not only to give degradation products but also, in some instances, active metabolites that contribute toward the potency of the parent compound. For example, the presence of a Δ9 double bond in promegestone seriously limits the ring A reduction undergone by progesterone. Nevertheless, like progesterone, promegestone undergoes C-21 hydroxylation but, because of the asymmetric carbon atom, two metabolites are formed (see Table III), one with an S configuration (RU 27987) with enhanced and stable progestin binding, the other with an R configuration (RU 27988) which has very limited affinity for the progestin receptor. Following the injection of promegestone for 5 days to rabbits, only trace amounts of these two metabolites are found in the plasma, but bound levels of both RU 27987 and promegestone

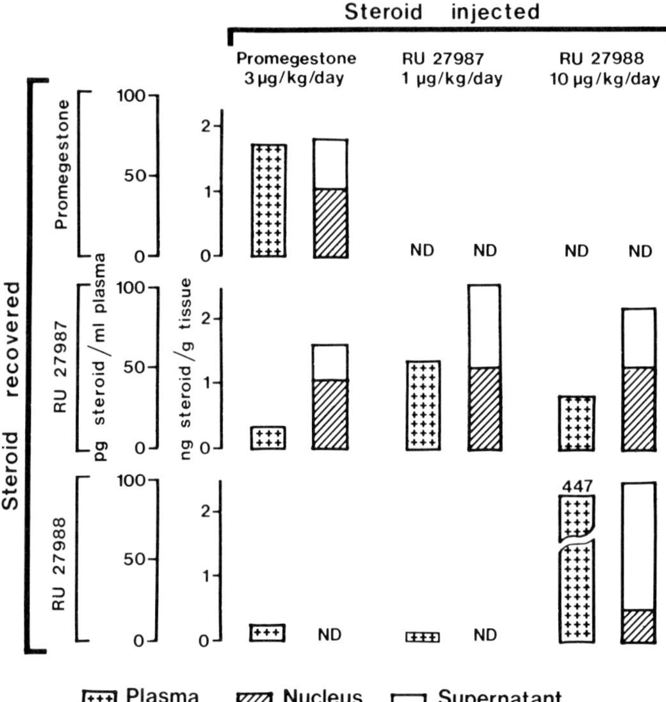


FIG. 4. Distribution of the progestins RU 27987, promegestone, and RU 27988 in the rabbit. Estradiol-primed immature rabbits received the 6,7-tritiated progestins (50 Ci/mmol) s.c. for 5 days and were killed 4 hours after the last injection. The amounts of each steroid recovered are expressed as pg/ml for plasma levels and ng/g tissue for uterine levels. Uterine concentrations are subdivided into the relative amounts observed in the nuclear pellet and supernatant. ND, nondetectable. From Raynaud *et al.* (1980c). By courtesy of Elsevier/North-Holland Biomedical Press.

are high in uterine supernatant and nuclei (Fig. 4). RU 27988 is undetectable.

According to the RBA of RU 27988 for the progestin receptor, this steroid would be expected to have little biological action. However, RU 27988 is active on the endometrial proliferation test in the rabbit, less active than RU 27987 and promegestone, but nevertheless more active than progesterone (Fig. 5). This unexpectedly high biological activity can be explained by the finding that, following s.c. injection of RU 27988, some of the steroid undergoes conversion to the 21 S isomer. As shown in Fig. 4, after injection of RU 27988, plasma levels of the steroid were found to be extremely high whereas uterine levels were comparatively low, nuclear bound RU 27988 representing only 19% of the total uterine concentration. However, a high concentra-

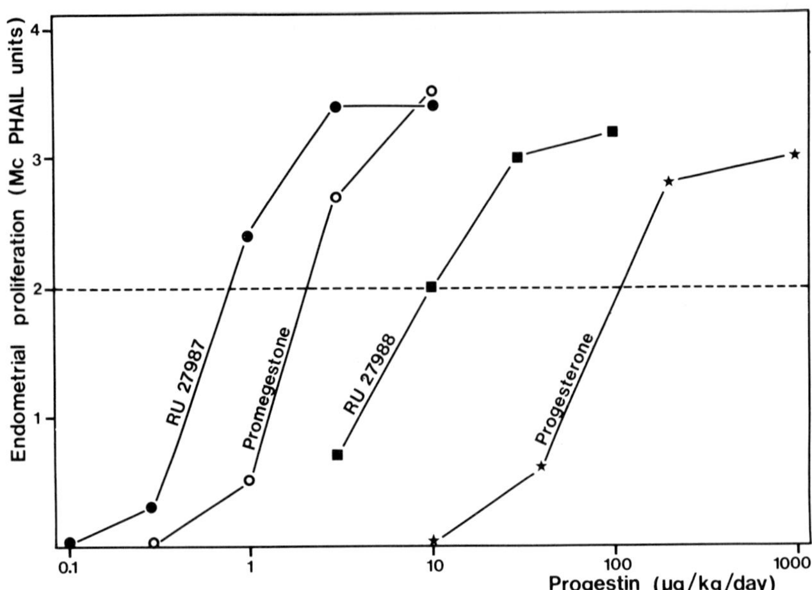


FIG. 5. Endometrial proliferation in the rabbit uterus (Clauberg test). Endometrial response was graded according to McPhail's scale after s.c. administration of the test substances for 5 days to estradiol-primed immature rabbits. RU 27987 (●), promegestone (□), RU 27988 (■), and progesterone (★). From Raynaud *et al.* (1980c). By courtesy of Elsevier/North-Holland Biomedical Press.

tion of the more potent 21 S isomer RU 27987 was also found in the uterus, 50% of this being recovered in the nuclear fraction. When RU 27987 was injected, no conversion to RU 27988 occurred and nuclear bound RU 27987 accounted for 55% of the total uterine concentration (Raynaud *et al.*, 1980c).

Although the tissue bound concentrations of steroids presented here do not represent specifically bound steroid, they suggest that while promegestone is biologically active per se, its high activity is even further enhanced by the potency of its 21 S hydroxy metabolite.

## III. EFFECT OF CHEMICAL SUBSTITUTION ON RECEPTOR AFFINITY, PLASMA BINDING, AND METABOLISM

In order to analyze the effect of substitution of the natural hormones progesterone and testosterone on the various parameters discussed above (affinity for the cytosolic steroid hormone receptors, interaction with plasma binders and metabolism), we have chosen a homologous series of pregnane and androstane derivatives (Table III and Appendix) differing by single substituents and which have yielded molecules of clinical interest. We now propose to review in the light of the above observations available data on these molecules.

### A. Receptor Binding Profiles of Homologous Progesterone and Testosterone Derivatives

The routine screening system reveals the specificity profile of the test substance (i.e., to which classes of receptor protein it binds) and also gives some indication of the dynamics of these interactions (i.e., potential agonist or antagonist activities (Table III).

As expected, the three well-known pregnane derivatives used clinically as progestins (medroxyprogesterone, megestrol, and chlormadinone acetates) bind firmly to the progestin receptor with RBAs that vary little or increase with time, thus implying the formation of a more slowly dissociating steroid–receptor complex than formed by progesterone. The removal of the C-19 methyl of progesterone gives rise to a compound (norprogesterone) with considerably enhanced binding to the progestin receptor compared to progesterone, more so than the introduction of an additional double bond at C-9 (RU 3163). The further introduction into RU 3163 of a 17$\alpha$-methyl group alone (demegestone) or together with a C-21 methyl group (promegestone) yields compounds with RBAs that increase with incubation time as notably as for norprogesterone. C-21 hydroxylation of demegestone (RU 28389) decreases its progestin binding to a level comparable to that of progesterone. As stated above, C-21 hydroxylation of promegestone gives two derivatives, RU 27987 (*S* configuration) with enhanced progestin binding and RU 27988 (*R* configuration) with limited affinity for the progestin receptor. RU 27987, unlike RU 27988, binds appreciably to the progestin receptor because its 17$\beta$ side chain is able to adopt a position on the $\beta$ face above ring D toward C-16 (Fig. 6), which is compatible with hydrogen bonding within the proposed locations for hydrogen bond donors to the progestin receptor deduced from a large number of steroid conformations (Delettré *et al.*, 1980c). In accordance with their affinity, demegestone, promegestone, and in particular RU 27987 are able, for instance, to induce high levels of endometrial proliferation and uteroglobin synthesis, whereas the activity of RU 27988 is lower but, as a result of partial *in vivo* bioconversion to RU 27987 (see above), not as poor as would be expected merely on the basis of RBA values (Raynaud *et al.*, 1980c).

The C-6 substituted Δ6-progesterone acetates bind weakly to the androgen

TABLE III

RELATIVE BINDING AFFINITIES IN A ROUTINE SCREENING SYSTEM[a]

| | Structural modifications | | | X-Ray crystallography | ES[b] | PG[b] | | AND[b] | | MIN[b] | | GLU[b] | | |
|---|---|---|---|---|---|---|---|---|---|---|---|---|---|---|
| | | | | | 2 h 0°C | 2 h 0°C | 24 h 0°C | 30 min 0°C | 2 h 0°C | 1 h 0°C | 24 h 0°C | 1 h 0°C | 4 h 0°C | 24 h 0°C |
| Progesterone | | — | | | <0.1 | 100 | 100 | 20 | 5.5 | 165 | 20 | 70 | 40 | 15 |
| Medroxyprogesterone acetate | | 6α—$CH_3$ | 17α—$OCOCH_3$ | Duax *et al.*, 1978a | <0.1 | 125 | 305 | 40 | 50 | 15 | 1 | 280 | —[c] | 45 |
| Megestrol acetate | Δ6 | 6—$CH_3$ | 17α—$OCOCH_3$ | — | <0.1 | 150 | 120 | 65 | 20 | — | — | — | — | — |
| Chlormadinone acetate | Δ6 | 6—Cl | 17α—$OCOCH_3$ | Chandross and Bordner, 1975 | <0.1 | 175 | 320 | 80 | 20 | 2 | 0.1 | 130 | — | 8 |
| Norprogesterone | | — | | — | <0.1 | 230 | 560 | — | 6 | — | — | 80 | 35 | — |
| RU 3163 | Δ9 | | | — | <0.1 | 180 | 245 | 30 | 9 | — | — | — | — | — |
| Demegestone | Δ9 | 17α—$CH_3$ | | Courseille *et al.*, 1975 | <0.1 | 230 | 420 | 7.5 | 1 | 25 | 0.1 | 20 | 10 | 2.5 |
| RU 28389 | Δ9 | 17α—$CH_3$ | 21—OH | Raynaud *et al.*, 1980c | <0.1 | 105 | 115 | — | 1.5 | 215 | 25 | — | 5 | 1.5 |
| Promegestone | Δ9 | 17α,21—$CH_3$ | | Busetta *et al.*, 1974 | <0.1 | 220 | 535 | 10 | 1.5 | 35 | 2.5 | — | 20 | 7 |
| RU 27987 | Δ9 | 17α,21—$CH_3$ | 21S—OH | Raynaud *et al.*, 1980c | <0.1 | 175 | 625 | — | 2 | 125 | 15 | — | 40 | 10 |
| RU 27988 | Δ9 | 17α,21—$CH_3$ | 21R—OH | Raynaud *et al.*, 1980c | <0.1 | 15 | 10 | — | 0.5 | 1.5 | 0.1 | — | 1 | 0.3 |
| Testosterone | | — | | — | <0.1 | 1 | 1 | 100 | 100 | 25 | 4 | 3 | 1 | 0.5 |
| Methyltestosterone | | 17α—$CH_3$ | | — | <0.1 | 3 | 2 | 90 | 45 | 15 | 1 | — | 1 | 0.3 |

| | | | | | | | | | | | | | | |
|---|---|---|---|---|---|---|---|---|---|---|---|---|---|---|
| Ethynyl testosterone | | 17α—C≡CH | | — | <0.1 | 35 | 15 | 7 | 0.1 | 0.1 | — | — | 1 | 0.1 |
| Nortestosterone | | — | | — | <0.1 | 20 | 14 | 230 | 155 | 25 | 1.5 | 2.5 | 0.5 | 0.1 |
| Methylnortestosterone | | 17α—$CH_3$ | | — | <0.1 | 100 | 110 | 170 | 145 | 15 | 1 | — | 1 | 0.3 |
| Norethindrone | | 17α—C≡CH | | Mornon *et al.*, 1976 | <0.1 | 155 | 265 | 75 | 45 | 3.5 | 0.2 | 10 | — | 1 |
| Norgestrel | | 17α—C≡CH | 13—$C_2H_5$ | De Angelis *et al.*, 1975 | <0.1 | 170 | 905 | 110 | 85 | 25 | 1 | 130 | — | 10 |
| RU 1364 | | 17α—C≡CH | 13—$C_3H_7$ | Delettré *et al.*, 1980a | <0.1 | 75 | 85 | 90 | 45 | 2 | 0.1 | — | 35 | 10 |
| Trenbolone | Δ9,11 | | | Précigoux, 1978 | <0.1 | 75 | 15 | 250 | 190 | 25 | 2.5 | 5 | — | 0.5 |
| Metribolone | Δ9,11 | 17α—$CH_3$ | | Précigoux, 1978 | <0.1 | 210 | 190 | 160 | 205 | 565 | 40 | 35 | 10 | 5 |
| Norgestrienone | Δ9,11 | 17α—C≡CH | | Lepicard *et al.*, 1974 | <0.1 | 65 | 45 | 95 | 70 | 45 | 1.5 | 35 | — | 4 |
| Gestrinone | Δ9,11 | 17α—C≡CH | 13—$C_2H_5$ | Delettré *et al.*, 1975 | <0.1 | 75 | 50 | 95 | 85 | 25 | 2 | 160 | — | 35 |
| RU 2715 | Δ9,11 | 17α—C≡CH | 13—$C_3H_7$ | Mornon *et al.*, in press | 0.5 | 60 | 30 | 35 | 65 | 5 | 0.3 | — | 8 | 2.5 |

[a] The RBAs of estradiol, progesterone, testosterone, aldosterone, and dexamethasone were, respectively, taken as equal to 100. Results are expressed as the means of three or more determinations. The following organs were homogenized in 10 m*M* Tris-HCl (pH 7.4), 0.25 *M* sucrose buffer: immature mouse uteri (1/25, wt/vol), estradiol-primed rabbit uteri (1/50, wt/vol), castrated rat prostates (1/5, wt/vol) and adrenalectomized rat thymuses (1/10, wt/vol). Perfused kidneys from the adrenalectomized rats were homogenized (1/3, wt/vol) in Krebs–Ringer phosphate buffer containing glucose. The Tris-sucrose homogenates were centrifuged at 105,000 *g* for 60 min at 0°–4°C to obtain cytosols, which were incubated as indicated with [$^3$H]estradiol, [$^3$H]promegestone, [$^3$H]metribolone, and [$^3$H]dexamethasone, respectively, in the presence or absence of 0–2500 n*M* unlabeled steroid. The rat kidney homogenates were incubated with [$^3$H]aldosterone at 0°C with or without unlabeled steroid, and in the presence of an excess of a specific glucocorticoid, RU 26988, then centrifuged at 800 *g* for 10 min at 0°C. Bound radioactivity was measured by a dextran-coated charcoal adsorption technique. (RU 26988 = 11$\beta$,17$\beta$-dihydroxy-17$\alpha$(1-propionyl)-androsta-1,4,6-trien-3-one.)

[b] ES, PG, AND, MIN, GLU: Estrogen, progestin, androgen, mineralocorticoid and glucocorticoid receptors, respectively.

[c] Not determined.

receptor, the norprogesterone derivatives even less so. The RBA values, which are already low after 30 minutes incubation, are even lower after 2 hours, suggesting that the interaction is fleeting and that the compounds are potential antiandrogens, as verified experimentally (Raynaud *et al.*, 1981b). An exception is, however, medroxyprogesterone acetate, which has a stable RBA for the androgen receptor and which, as expected, can inhibit nuclear testosterone uptake in kidney nuclei (Brown *et al.*, 1979) and at high doses stimulate prostate growth in the castrated rat (Raynaud *et al.*, 1980a,d).

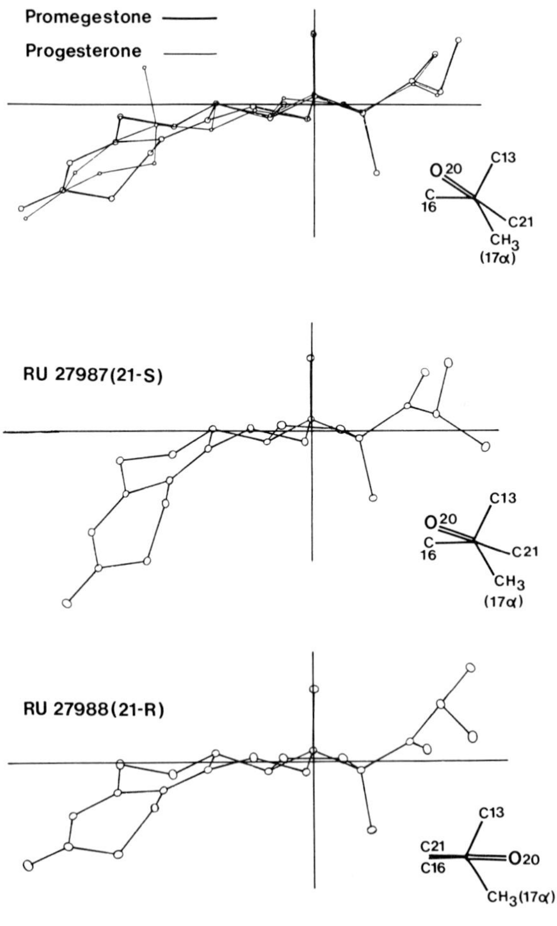


FIG. 6. Crystalline conformations of progesterone, promegestone, and their two C-21 hydroxylated metabolites RU 27987 and RU 27988. (For methodology, see Raynaud *et al.*, 1980c.)

The removal of the C-13 methyl of testosterone yields nortestosterone that has considerably enhanced binding to the androgen receptor. On the other hand, the introduction into either the testosterone or nortestosterone molecules of a 17$\alpha$-methyl or especially 17$\alpha$-ethynyl group slightly diminishes this androgen binding but, in the case of the nortestosterone derivatives, markedly favors binding to the progestin receptor. The presence of a C-13 ethyl (norgestrel) but not propyl (RU 1364) group is even more conducive to stable progestin binding. Norethindrone and norgestrel exhibit substantial progestomimetic activity, but are also fairly potent androgens. They promote prostate growth in the castrated rat and inhibit LH response to LHRH in rat pituitary cells in culture (Labrie *et al.*, 1977; Raynaud *et al.*, 1980a). Removal of the C-13 methyl group of testosterone also engenders binding to the progestin receptor and the presence of two additional double bonds ($\Delta$9,11) (trenbolone) slightly increases this binding (compare trenbolone and nortestosterone) as does the further introduction of a 17$\alpha$-methyl group (metribolone). However, unlike norethindrone, the 17$\alpha$-ethynyl derivative of trenbolone has only a limited relative binding affinity for the progestin receptor, which is not greatly modified by the presence of a C-13 ethyl (gestrinone) or propyl (RU 2715) radical. Both trenbolone and metribolone are highly potent androgens but, at high doses, metribolone and, to a lesser extent, trenbolone can induce endometrial proliferation in the rabbit uterus (Raynaud *et al.*, 1981b). Norgestrienone and gestrinone are weak progestins with some androgenic properties. Under certain experimental conditions, gestrinone because of its weak and fast dissociating interaction with the progestin receptor can act as an antiprogesterone agent (Sakiz *et al.*, 1974). Its androgenic binding explains its pituitary inhibitory activity, also observed with norethindrone but not with nonandrogenic progestins such as chlormadinone acetate and megestrol acetate (Labrie *et al.*, 1977).

A general examination of glucocorticoid binding values for all these compounds suggests that, although most can bind to the glucocorticoid receptor (see RBAs at 1 and 4 hours), none is able to maintain this binding over time. In some cases, values at 24 hours are still high but decreasing. Previous experiments have in fact suggested that many of these progestins can act as antiglucocorticoids (Raynaud *et al.*, 1980b). Furthermore, most increase the dissociation of a labeled glucocorticoid, e.g., tritiated dexamethasone, from the glucocorticoid receptor (Suthers *et al.*, 1976; Jones and Bell, 1980; Svec *et al.*, 1980; Moguilewsky and Deraedt, in press). These direct and indirect kinetic effects may explain the reversal by demegestone of the dexamethasone-induced inhibition of [$^3$H]uridine incorporation into mouse thymocytes (Dausse *et al.*, 1977), the inhibition of tyrosine aminotransferase induction in hepatoma tissue cells in culture by demegestone, promegestone, and gestrinone (Raynaud *et al.*, 1980a), and the pure antagonist

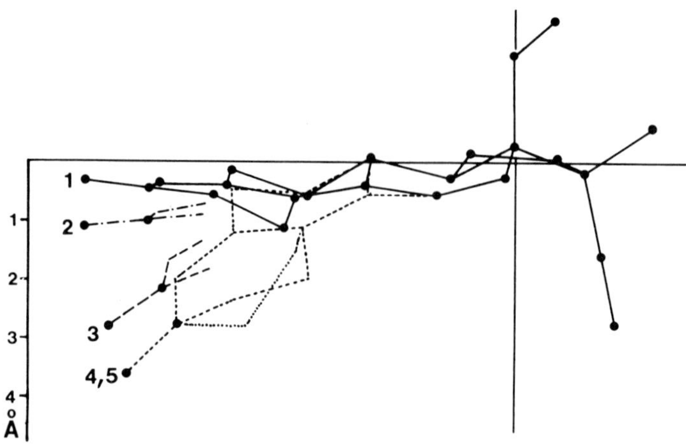


FIG. 7. Crystalline conformations of gestrinone. Superimposition of conformations encountered in the crystal using the D ring reference system, which reveals differences in molecular curvature. (By courtesy of Raven Press. Delettré *et al.*, 1980b,c.)

activity of promegestone, norgestrel, and gestrinone on dexamethasone-induced inhibition of ACTH release in rat anterior pituitary cells in primary culture (Raynaud *et al.*, 1981b).

From all these results it is possible to conclude that whereas both progesterone and nortestosterone derivatives can bind substantially to the progestin receptor, the former interact only fleetingly with the androgen receptor, whereas the latter still exhibit some androgen binding after 2 hours incubation. Furthermore, the combination of marked unsaturation ($\Delta$4,9,11) and 17$\alpha$-ethynylation reduces both progestin and androgen binding, whereas in the case of ethynylated 19-nor compounds progestin binding is enhanced and only androgen binding decreased. Unsaturation is associated with ability to bind to the receptors of several hormone classes (see trenbolone→RU 2715) and a C-13 ethyl group is particularly conducive to glucocorticoid binding.

Conformation studies offer a plausible explanation for the lack of binding specificity of the above 3-ketotrienes (trenbolone→RU 2715). $\Delta$4,9,11 steroids are characterized by a high degree of molecular flexibility (Delettré *et al.*, 1980b), which may increase the chances of hydrogen bond formation with the recognition sites of the receptor of more than one hormone class. Thus, gestrinone can adopt at least five different crystalline conformations with an overall C3-O3 flexibility range of 3 Å (Fig. 7). The transition energy required to pass from a slightly bent to a highly bent conformation is less than 2 kcal (Raynaud *et al.*, 1980f; Delettré *et al.*, 1980b), i.e., far less than the energy of binding to steroid receptors (~ 12 kcal/mole).

### B. Binding of Homologous Testosterone and Progesterone Derivatives to Plasma Proteins

As shown in Fig. 8 and Table IV, among the progestins studied in our routine screening system norgestrel competes for SBP binding in human plasma, as already demonstrated by Victor *et al.* (1976), metribolone considerably less so, and promegestone, medroxyprogesterone acetate, and chlormadinone acetate not at all. On the other hand, promegestone and norethindrone compete weakly for CBG binding in human plasma, fractionally more so than norgestrel, metribolone, medroxyprogesterone acetate, and chlormadinone acetate. The intrinsic association constant of promegestone binding to pure CBG is only $1 \times 10^6\ M^{-1}$ compared to $4 \times 10^8\ M^{-1}$ for progesterone and $2 \times 10^8\ M^{-1}$ for cortisol (Chan and Slaunwhite, 1977).

A compound with high receptor affinity and low plasma binding is a potential tool in receptor studies (Raynaud *et al.*, 1979b, 1981a). When radiolabeled it can be used to track the receptor under various physiological and pathological conditions. Table IV shows that promegestone competes less than progesterone not only for CBG binding but also for PBG binding. It is thus particularly suitable for the study of the progesterone receptor in many human and animal tissues including those of the pregnant guinea pig. Metribolone competes less than testosterone and dihydrotestosterone for binding to SBP and to epididymal androgen-binding protein (ABP). It can consequently be used to identify and study the androgen receptor in the rat epididymis and prostate (Raynaud *et al.*, 1977).

All steroids bind to human serum albumin, the most abundant serum protein, mostly with relatively low affinity. The influence of this binding should not be underestimated since the high binding capacity of albumin compensates for its low affinity. For instance, promegestone, which does not bind appreciably to CBG, nevertheless has an affinity constant of $6 \times 10^5\ M^{-1}$ for human serum albumin compared to $6 \times 10^4\ M^{-1}$ for progesterone and $3 \times 10^3\ M^{-1}$ for cortisol (U. Westphal, personal communication).

### C. Biotransformations of Some Homologous Testosterone and Progesterone Derivatives

The biotransformation pathways of several of the steroids in Table III have been reviewed in some detail (Thijssen, 1972; Fotherby and James, 1972; Breuer, 1977). The following comments will stress unpublished information on some of the steroids synthetized by Roussel-Uclaf.

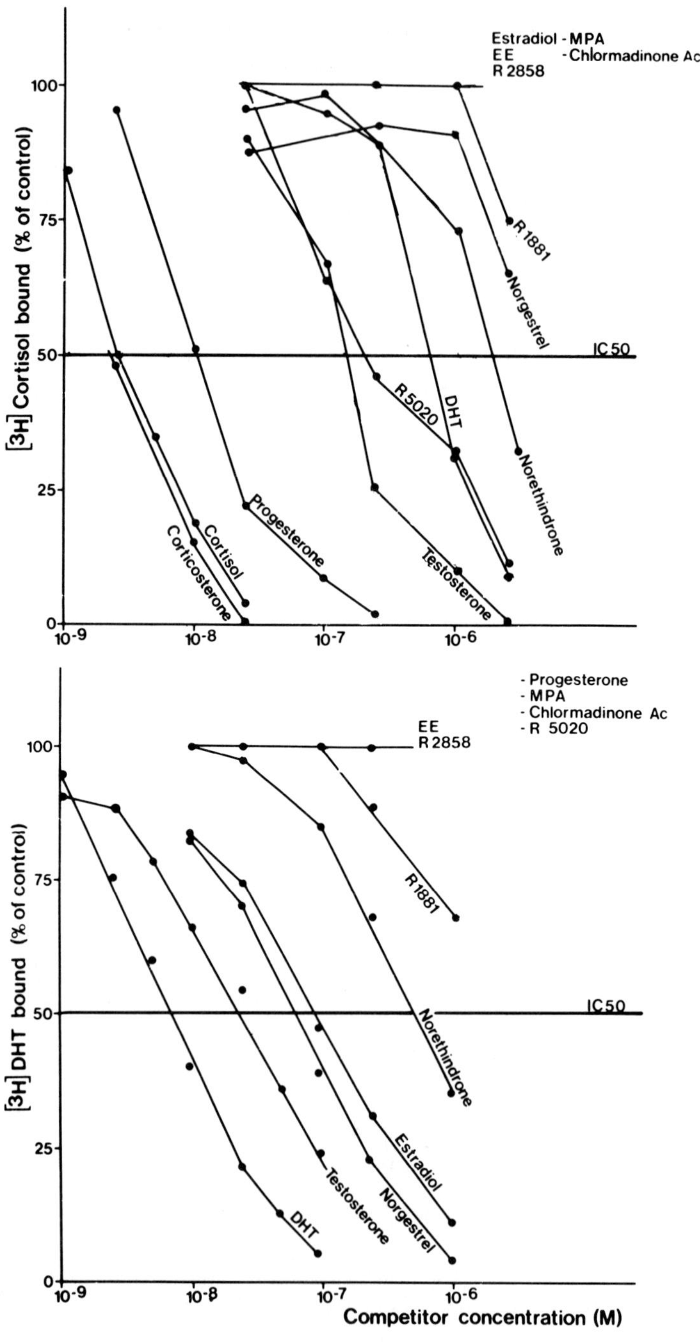

Estradiol - MPA
EE - Chlormadinone Ac
R 2858
100
75
50
25
0
[3H] Cortisol bound (% of control)
R 1881
Norgestrel
IC 50
R 5020
DHT
Norethindrone
Progesterone
Cortisol
Corticosterone
Testosterone
10-9
10-8
10-7
10-6
- Progesterone
- MPA
- Chlormadinone Ac
- R 5020
EE
R 2858
[3H] DHT bound (% of control)
R1881
IC50
Norethindrone
Estradiol
Norgestrel
Testosterone
DHT
Competitor concentration (M)

TABLE IV
COMPETITION FOR BINDING TO PLASMA PROTEINS AND TO ANDROGEN-BINDING PROTEIN IN EPIDIDYMAL FLUID[a]

| | Relative competition for binding to | | | | |
|---|---|---|---|---|---|
| | CBG[b] | SBP[c] | EBP[d] | PBG[e] | ABP[f] |
| Cortisol | 100 | <0.2 | —[g] | <0.1 | <0.1 |
| Progesterone | 25 | <0.2 | <0.1 | 100 | 9 |
| Promegestone | 0.9 | <0.2 | <0.1 | 10 | — |
| Dihydrotestosterone | 0.3 | 100 | <0.1 | 20 | 100 |
| Testosterone | 3 | 26 | <0.1 | 5 | 36 |
| Metribolone | <0.1 | 0.2 | <0.1 | 5 | 10 |
| Estradiol | <0.1 | 9 | 100 | <0.1 | 10 |
| Ethynyl estradiol | <0.1 | <0.2 | 3 | — | — |
| Moxestrol | <0.1 | <0.2 | <0.1 | <0.1 | — |

[a] Competition for binding to CBG and SBP was determined by equilibrium dialysis and charcoal adsorption respectively as described by Ojasoo and Raynaud (1978). Binding to EBP was determined by equilibrium dialysis as described by Raynaud *et al.* (1980e). Binding to ABP was measured as follows: 0.5 ml diluted (1/40) epididymal cytosol from intact rats was placed in a Nojax dialysis bag and dialyzed for 24 hours against 15 ml of TEG buffer (10 m$M$ Tris-HCl, pH 7.4, 2 m$M$ EDTA, 10% glycerol) containing 2.5 n$M$ [$^3$H]metribolone and unlabeled competitor. Three 0.2 ml samples from the inner and outer solutions were counted. The percentage inhibition of [$^3$H]metribolone binding was determined.

[b] Corticosteroid binding globulin (human serum).

[c] Sex-steroid binding protein (human serum).

[d] Estradiol binding protein (immature rat plasma).

[e] Progesterone binding globulin (pregnant guinea pig plasma).

[f] Androgen binding protein (castrated rat epididymis).

[g] Not determined.

### 1. *Testosterone Derivatives*

Testosterone, and also nortestosterone, undergo oxidation of the secondary alcohol to a C-17 ketone, reduction of the C-3 ketone and of the C-4 double bond, and hydroxylation primarily at positions C-6 and C-16. 17$\alpha$ substitution of testosterone by either a methyl or ethynyl group transforms the secondary alcohol in C-17 into a tertiary alcohol far more resistant to degradation (Levedahl and Samuels, 1950; Hyde *et al.*, 1954; Quincey and Gray, 1967; Thijssen, 1972), but nevertheless to molecules susceptible to ring

FIG. 8. Binding to CBG and SBP in human plasma after separation of the proteins by ammonium sulfate precipitation. EE, ethynylestradiol; DHT, dihydrotestosterone; R 2858, moxestrol (11$\beta$-methoxy-19-nor-17$\alpha$-pregna-1,3,5(10)-trien-20-yne-3,17-diol). (For methodology, see Ojasoo and Raynaud, 1978.)

A reduction (Breuer, 1977). Norethindrone and norgestrel, compounds with an unprotected C-3 ketone group, form 5$\alpha$ and 5$\beta$-derivatives like the natural hormones progesterone and testosterone (Fotherby and Keenan, 1969; Gerhards *et al.*, 1971; Sisenwine *et al.*, 1973). The introduction of double bonds limits the reduction of the 4(5) double bond and of the ketone group at C-3. The presence of 3 conjugated double bonds (trenbolone) virtually totally impedes ring A reduction (Pottier *et al.*, 1980, 1981). The combination of conjugated double bonds and 17$\alpha$-substitution thus leads to synthetic hormones (e.g., metribolone, gestrinone) highly resistant to attack by the classic routes and for which the principal biotransformation pathway becomes hydroxylation (Salmon *et al.*, 1971; Raynaud *et al.*, 1973).

*a. Trenbolone Acetate.* The metabolic pathways of trenbolone acetate, an anabolic compound (Velluz *et al.*, 1967) used as a growth-promoting agent in breeding, have been compared in the cow, the recipient species, and in the rat, species used for chronic toxicity testing. In both species, bile is the major route of excretion. Intact trenbolone acetate is not detected in bile, the initial metabolic step being extensive hydrolysis of the ester bond to yield trenbolone.

The high biological stability of the 3-ketotriene structure of trenbolone prevents important biotransformations on ring A. In the rat, testosterone undergoes mainly 17-oxidation to keto derivatives as well as reduction of the double bond and of the ketone function on ring A (Ofner, 1955), whereas 16$\alpha$, 6$\beta$, and 7$\alpha$-hydroxylation are minor pathways (Jacobson *et al.*, 1969). In the case of trenbolone, oxidation of the 17$\beta$-hydroxy to a 17-keto group and hydroxylation in the 16$\alpha$ position yield two main metabolites, the 16$\alpha$ hydroxylated derivatives of trenbolone and the 17-keto compound, triendione. In the heifer (Fig. 9), the major pathway is 17$\alpha$-epimerization of trenbolone as for testosterone (Martin, 1966) and by far the main metabolite is epitrenbolone. In both species, triendione and the other metabolites resulting from either hydroxylation in positions C-1, C-2, or C-6 or A ring aromatization are minor products. Consequently, 60% of the 3-ketotriene structures identified in rat bile are 17$\beta$-hydroxylated, the remainder being 17-keto metabolites, whereas in heifer bile 90% are 17$\alpha$-hydroxylated compounds.

The biological activity of the 17$\alpha$-epimer of testosterone is much weaker than that of testosterone itself (Kincl and Dorfman, 1964). Similarly, the androgenic potency of epitrenbolone is about 2% of that of trenbolone and its anabolic potency about 5%. It can thus be concluded that the major 17$\alpha$ pathway operating in the bovine species leads to a strong decrease in the biological potency of possible residues in tissues used for human consumption.

*b. Metribolone.* Further protection against catabolism has been achieved by introducing a 17$\alpha$-methyl substituent into trenbolone to give

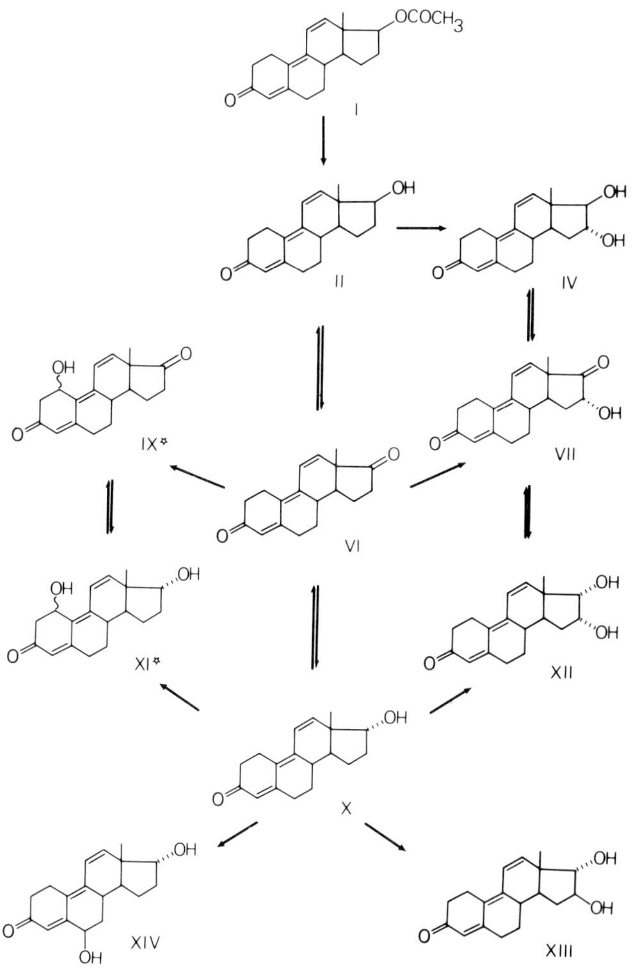

FIG. 9. Proposed biotransformation scheme of trenbolone acetate on the basis of metabolites identified in heifer bile. A Friesian heifer (280 kg) received 6,7-tritiated trenbolone acetate (10 mg/kg in a volume of 0.1 ml/kg) injected i.v. over a period of 5 minutes. Bile was collected for 24 hours via a catheter placed into the bile duct 23 hours previously. Free and conjugated steroids were separated on an Amberlite XAD-2 column and eluted with methanol. Conjugates were hydrolyzed first with Ketodase (48 hours, pH 5.0), next with Helix pomatia juice (48 hours, pH 5.2), then solvolysed in ethyl acetate (48 hours, pH 1.0). The steroids liberated by each hydrolysis were extracted with ethyl acetate. The pooled extracts were submitted to successive chromatographic fractionations, first on a silicagel 20–40 mesh column, next on a Sephadex LH20 column, then on silicagel plates either by partition or by adsorption. Structure identifications were carried out by chemical methods (acetylation of hydroxyl groups with acetic anhydride in pyridine, periodate cleavage of the bond between two carbons carrying an oxygenated function, acetonide formation with acetone in the presence of perchloric acid in the case of a cis $\alpha$-glycol, reduction of carbonyl groups with sodium borohydride) and by physical methods (UV, IR, NMR, and mass spectrometry).

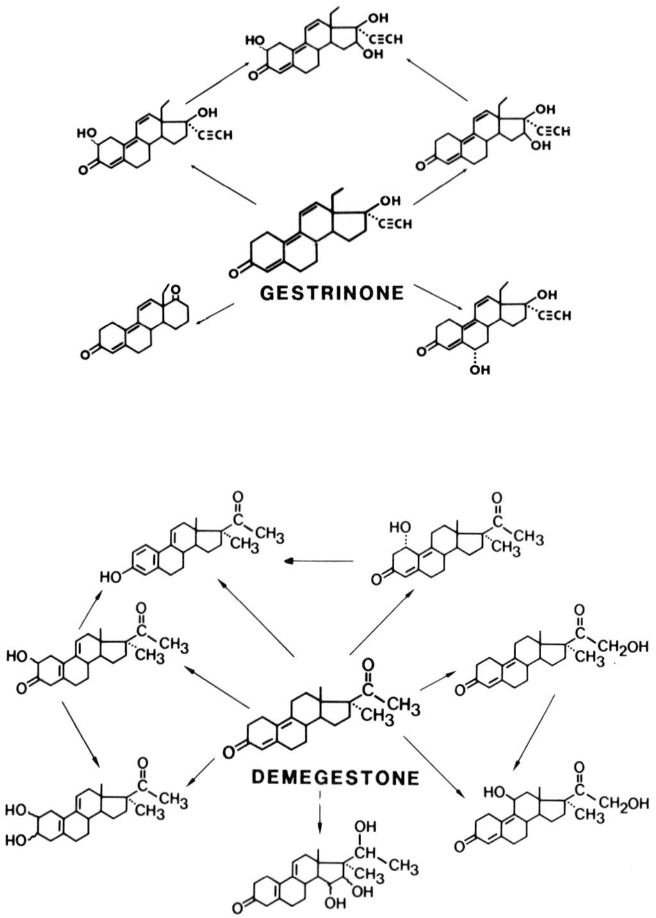

GESTRINONE

DEMEGESTONE

FIG. 10. Proposed biotransformation schemes of gestrinone and demegestone on the basis of metabolites identified in guinea pig bile. Anesthetized guinea pigs received 12.5 mg of 6,7-tritiated gestrinone (I) or demegestone (II) (8 $\mu$Ci/mg) i.v. in 0.25 ml of 92% acetylmethylamine. Bile was collected for 24 hours via a catheter introduced into the bile duct. Free metabolites were extracted with methylene chloride (I) or ethyl acetate (II); glucuroconjugated metabolites were hydrolyzed with $\beta$-glucuronidase (Ketodase) (I) or Helix Pomatia juice (II) and extracted with ethyl acetate; sulfoconjugated metabolites were extracted with ethyl acetate in an acidic medium saturated with ammonium sulfate and then submitted to solvolysis. Metabolites were separated by TLC on silicagel plates using either absorption or partition chromatography. Their $R_f$ values were recorded. Metabolite structure was determined on samples prepared from 2.5 liters of bile subjected to enzymatic cleavage and solvolysis and in the case of gestrinone without prior extraction of free steroids. Steroids were separated from pooled organic phases by chromatography on a silicagel column eluted with a benzene/ethyl acetate gradient and purified by TLC on silicagel plates. Structures were determined by chemical and by physical methods (see legend to Fig. 9).

metribolone, a highly potent androgen (Azadian-Boulanger *et al.*, 1975; Bonne and Raynaud, 1975). Metribolone apparently does not undergo either oxidation at C-17 or reduction of ring A. Three hydroxylated derivatives have been recovered and identified in the bile of the guinea pig: the 6ζ-OH, 16β-OH, and 16α-OH derivatives of metribolone; a fourth dihydroxy product, unidentified, is probably also present (Salmon *et al.*, 1971).

*c. Gestrinone.* Like metribolone, gestrinone, a weak progestin with antiprogesterone and pituitary inhibitory activity (Sakiz *et al.*, 1974), is also protected by Δ4,9,11 conjugated double bonds and a 17α-substituent, in this case a 17α-ethynyl group. The main pathway of gestrinone metabolism in-

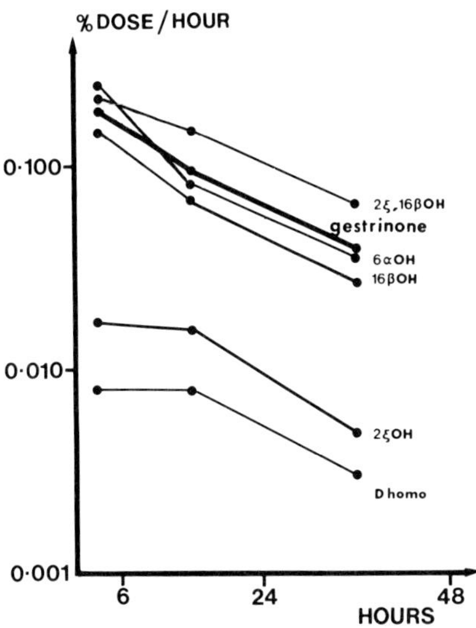


FIG. 11. Excretion of gestrinone and its metabolites in human urine. The subject received 13.8 μCi of 6,7-tritiated gestrinone i.v. Extraction and enzymatic hydrolysis of urine collected in three fractions over 48 hours were carried out as for guinea pig bile (see legend to Fig. 7), but the organic phase from the sulfoconjugated fraction, too impure for direct analysis, was prepurified by column chromatography on silver nitrate-impregnated silicagel; this retains the ethynyl derivatives, which are then eluted with ammonium chloride. The dry extracts obtained after Ketodase treatment (ex-glucuroconjugated steroids) or after purification on silver nitrate-impregnated silicagel (ex-sulfoconjugated steroids) were chromatographed on silicagel plates. Eight bands (beyond D-homo, D-homo, gestrinone, 16β-hydroxy, 6α-hydroxy and 2ζ,16β-dihydroxy derivatives, between 2ζ,16β-dihydroxy derivative and baseline spot, baseline spot) were cut, scraped, and eluted with 3 × 10 ml methylene chloride:acetone (5:5, v/v). An aliquot was counted to evaluate recovery (75–85%); the remainder was spotted on a silicagel plate and chromatographed in the solvent system that gave the best separation. The zones beyond the D-homo compound and between the dihydroxy derivative and baseline spot (3% of the extracted radioactivity) and the baseline spot itself (3–20% of the radioactivity according to fraction) were not analyzed.

volves hydroxylation at positions 2ζ, 6α, and 16β, the principal metabolites in guinea pig bile being the 6α and 16β derivatives (Fig. 10), whereas the 2ζ,16β derivative, as established on a single subject, constitutes the major metabolite in human urine (Fig. 11). A very high proportion of intact gestrinone is also recovered both in bile (Table V) and urine (Fig. 11). A minor metabolite is the monosubstituted 2ζ-derivative, which in all likelihood is rapidly converted to the 2ζ,16β-dihydroxy compound.

The metabolic pathway of gestrinone resembles that described for norgestrel, which also suffers attack at the 2, 6, and 16 positions, as well as being hydroxylated in position 1 (Sisenwine *et al.*, 1973). A further similarity with norgestrel, and also norethisterone (Palmer *et al.*, 1970), ethynyl estradiol, and its 3-methyl ether (Abdel-Aziz and Williams, 1970), is D-homoannulation. This is considered by Abdel-Aziz and Williams (1969) to be an oxidative process but, in the case of gestrinone, the D-homo compound could be an artifact since some is formed *in vitro* on addition of gestrinone to the bile of control animals. However, whereas norgestrel, trenbolone, and metribonole have been found to give rise to a 16α-hydroxy derivative, gestrinone does not appear to undergo such substitution, at least in the guinea pig. This has been confirmed by the synthesis of 16α-hydroxy gestrinone and cochromatography with low concentrations of unidentified metabolites.

### 2. *Progesterone Derivatives*

Progesterone undergoes reduction and hydroxylation to yield over thirty identified metabolites. Reduction can affect the ketone groups at C-20 and C-3 or the C-4 double bond. Hydroxylation occurs primarily at positions C-6, C-11, C-16, C-17, and C-21.

The successive introduction into the progesterone molecule of a 17α-acetoxy group, a 6-methyl group (medroxyprogesterone acetate) and a double bond at C-6 (megestrol acetate) progressively reduces the metabolism of the steroid *in vitro* by liver preparations (Cooke and Vallance, 1964, 1965). The first metabolite of medroxyprogesterone acetate to be identified in human urine was the parent compound with two additional hydroxyl groups, i.e., a 6β- and a 21-hydroxyl group. More recently, several other metabolites have been detected resulting from reduction of the 3-ketone and hydrolysis of the 17-acetate (Fukushima *et al.*, 1979). The three main metabolites of megestrol acetate identified in the urine of human subjects arise from hydroxylations at the 2α-, the 6-methyl, or both positions, but the identified substances only account for a low percentage of the dose given (5–8%) (Cooper and Kellie, 1968). The *in vitro* incubation of chlormadinone acetate with a human liver preparation gave as major metabolites 2α- and 3β-hydroxy derivatives (Handy *et al.*, 1974).

*a. Demegestone.* The introduction of a conjugated Δ9 double bond into the progesterone molecule also hinders the normal biodegradation pathway.

Seven main metabolites of demegestone (Fig. 10) have been isolated from the bile of male guinea pigs and identified (Raynaud *et al.*, 1974a). No reduction of the dienic structure has been noted. The metabolic pathways are essentially 21, 1, and 2 hydroxylation followed by A ring aromatization after 1,2-dehydration. The most abundant metabolite is the 21-hydroxy derivative, which is also the main metabolite in human urine (Fig. 12) and an important metabolite in human plasma (Fig. 13).

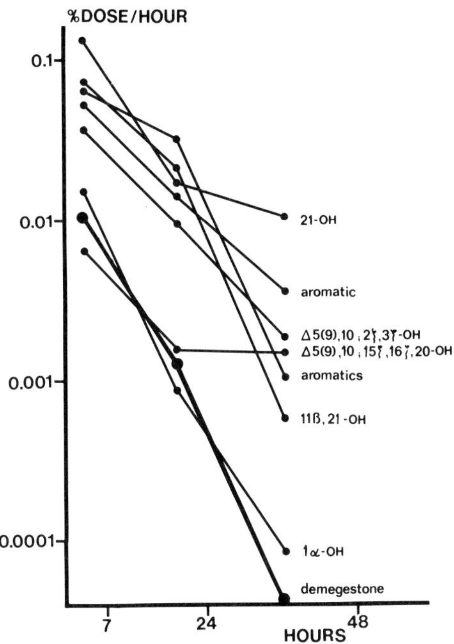


FIG. 12. Excretion of demegestone and its metabolites in human urine. The subjects received 10 μCi of 6,7-tritiated demegestone i.v. Urine was collected in three fractions over 48 hours and run first through an Amberlite XAD-2 column (eluant=methanol, residue taken up in ethanol), then through an Amberlyst 15 column (eluant=ethanol, residue taken up in chloroform:methanol), finally through a Sephadex LH20 column (eluant=chloroform:methanol). Two sets of fractions were collected, the first corresponding to free and glucuroconjugated metabolites, the second to sulfoconjugated metabolites. Free metabolites were extracted with ethyl acetate and bicarbonate and glucuroconjugated metabolites were extracted with ethyl acetate following acidification with 2 *N* HCl. Glucuroconjugated metabolites were extracted from the second set of fractions by ethyl acetate at pH 2 leaving the sulfoconjugated metabolites in the aqueous phase. Pooled glucuroconjugated metabolites were subjected to enzymatic cleavage with β-glucuronidase (Ketodase) and extracted with ethyl acetate; pooled sulfoconjugated steroids were extracted with ethyl acetate in an acidic medium saturated with ammonium sulfate and then submitted to solvolysis. Four zones were separated by TLC on silicagel plates in benzene:ethyl acetate (5:5, v/v) over 15 cm. Each zone was scraped, eluted with methylene chloride:acetone (5:5, v/v), and evaporated to dryness after the radioactivity had been counted on an aliquot. Metabolites within each zone were separated by TLC in various solvent systems.

TABLE V
METABOLITES RECOVERED IN GUINEA PIG BILE

| Gestrinone | % of bile radioactivity | Demegestone | % of bile radioactivity |
|---|---|---|---|
| Gestrinone | 35.5 | Demegestone | N.D.[a] |
| 16β-Hydroxy | 9.7 | 21-Hydroxy | 16.4 |
| 6α-Hydroxy | 7.5 | Aromatics | 13.4[b] |
| 2ζ-Hydroxy | ~1 | 1α-Hydroxy | 9.7 |
| 2ζ, 16β-Hydroxy | 1 | 11,21-Dihydroxy | 4.1 |
| D-Homo | 0.9 | Δ5(9),10-Dien-2ζ-hydroxy | 2.2 |
| | | Δ5(9),10-Dien-2ζ, 3ζ-dihydroxy | 2.0 |
| | | Δ5(9),10-Dien-15ζ,16ζ,20-trihydroxy | 2.0 |
| Total | 55.6 | Total | 49.8 |

[a] Nondetectable.
[b] 4% were accounted for by the aromatic derivative shown in Fig. 10.

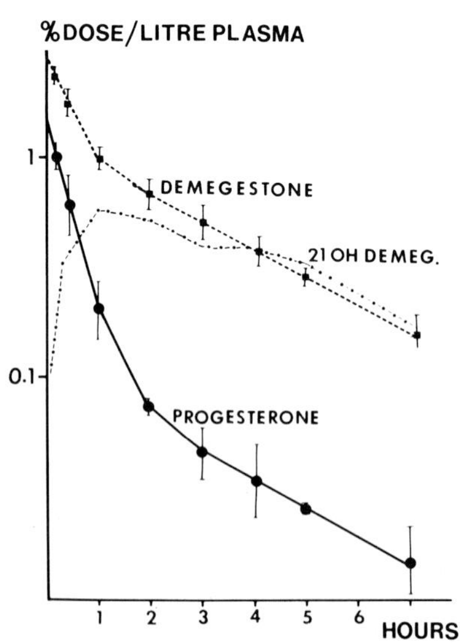


FIG. 13. Plasma disappearance of demegestone and its principal metabolite after i.v. injection of tritiated demegestone to adult male volunteers. Nine blood samples were drawn during the 7 hours following injection. After alkalinization of plasma samples (2% *N* NaOH), steroids were extracted with ethyl acetate and separated and identified by TLC on silicagel plates. (Demegestone:AIVD= 31 liters, Cl = 20 liters/hour.)

*b. Promegestone.* Promegestone, which also has a conjugated Δ9 double bond, undergoes extensive biotransformations in the rat. Six metabolites have been conclusively identified in the bile and probable structures are proposed for three others (Fig. 14). Together they constitute about $\frac{1}{5}$ of excreted radioactivity. The 3-ketodiene structure remains unchanged in $\frac{2}{3}$ of the metabolites. Among these, the quantitatively most important are the 21*R*-hydroxy (RU 27988) and the 2α-hydroxy derivatives. A 2ξ,21-dihydroxy compound has also been identified. Minor hydroxylation products are the 6β and 11α derivatives. The remaining third of the identified radioactivity is constituted of compounds with an aromatic A ring and a Δ9 double bond. They probably arise from the 2α-hydroxy derivative, which is first dehydrated, then aromatized. The aromatic compound is hydroxylated in 2 to give a catechol, which is subsequently methylated probably in this position and then hydroxylated in 15α or 16α.

## D. Plasma Disappearance of Homologous Nortestosterone Derivatives

Plasma binding protects a molecule against enzyme attack and controls the access of unbound, i.e., active, steroid, to target tissues. To increased requirements of endogenous hormone correspond increased plasma binding protein concentrations, whereas under normal physiological conditions, both progesterone and testosterone are not protected to the same extent and are therefore more readily metabolized by the liver.

The effects of plasma binding of natural or synthetic hormones whether to specific proteins (e.g., CBG and SBP) or to nonspecific proteins (e.g., albumin) and the extent of biodegradation are reflected in the plasma disappearance curves of the steroids after intravenous injection. Structural modifications that decrease specific plasma binding and affect lipophility modify the apparent initial volume of distribution (AIVD), the number of compartments and clearance; they can hinder biodegradation without however giving rise to compounds that overpersist in the plasma. Consequently, a comparative analysis of plasma disappearance curves gives an indication of the influence of a given substituent on the bioavailability of the substituted steroid at the target site.

As an illustration, the plasma disappearance curves of the nortestosterone derivatives under study have been compared in the six panels of Fig. 15. Each panel shows the disappearance curve of a different derivative of nortestosterone in comparison to that of the corresponding Δ4,9,11-triene except for the panel comparing methyltestosterone with the parent compound. The pharmacokinetic parameters deduced from these curves on the basis of a two or three compartment open model have been summarized in Table VI.

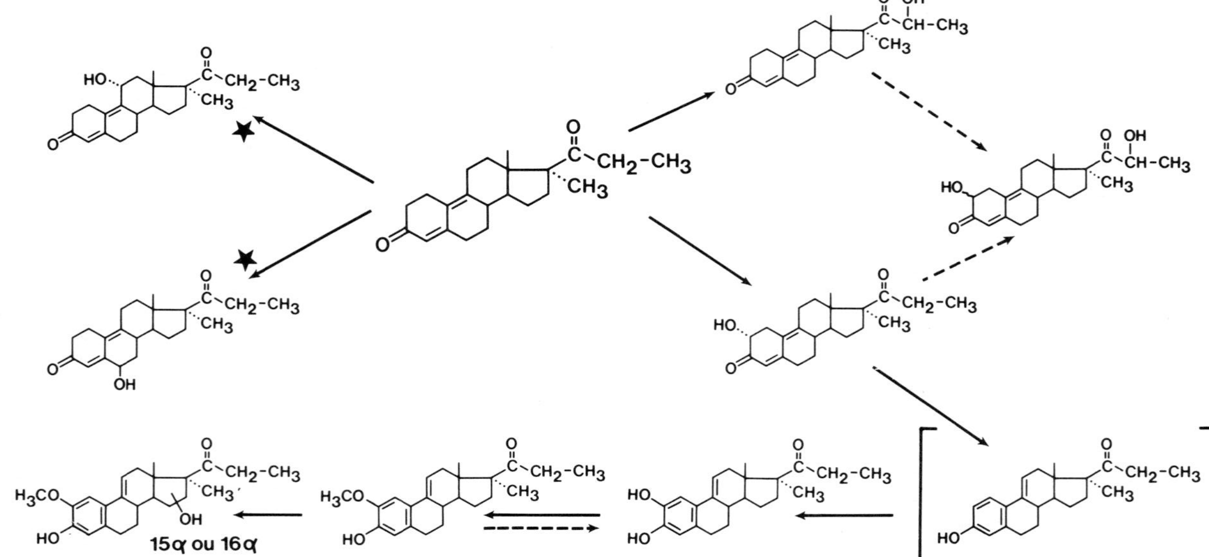


FIG. 14. Proposed biotransformation scheme of promegestone on the basis of metabolites identified in rat bile. Anesthetized rats received 16 mg/kg of 6,7-tritiated promegestone i.v. in 1 ml/kg of 92% acetylmethylamine. Bile was collected for 24 hours via a catheter introduced into the bile duct. Free metabolites were extracted with methylene chloride; glucuroconjugated metabolites were hydrolyzed after purification on an Amberlite XAD2 column with ketodase then Helix Pomatia juice and extracted with ethyl acetate; sulfoconjugated metabolites were extracted with ethyl acetate in an acidic medium saturated with ammonium sulfate and then submitted to solvolysis. Metabolites were separated by silicagel column chromatography, then purified by TCL on silicagel plates. Structures were determined by chemical and by physical methods (see legend to Fig. 9). ★, proposed structure; [ ], probable intermediate.

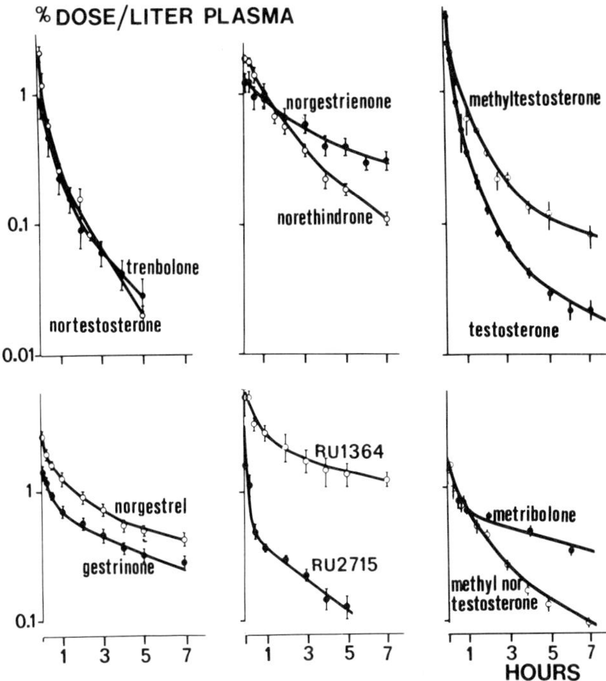


FIG. 15. Plasma disappearance curves following i.v. injection of labeled steroid to adult male volunteers. Ten blood samples were drawn during 7 or 10 hours after injection of labeled steroid. After alkalinization of plasma samples (1 ml 1 *N* NaOH/40 ml plasma), steroids were extracted with chloroform:ether (1:3, v/v), washed with 0.1 *N* NaOH, then deionized water, and separated by gradient elution column chromatography on alumina. From Raynaud (1971a).

The introduction of a 17$\alpha$-methyl group into the testosterone molecule decreases by half the biodegradation of testosterone without modifying the AIVD. Removal of the C-19 methyl (nortestosterone and trenbolone) increases the AIVD since nonspecific and specific plasma binding are decreased, but in the absence of a substituent protecting the 17-hydroxy group from attack, rapid clearance nevertheless ensues. However, clearance is slowed down by the introduction of a 17$\alpha$-ethynyl group (norethindrone) or of a 17$\alpha$-methyl group (methylnortestosterone), especially in the presence of 3 conjugated double bonds (norgestrienone and metribolone). On the other hand, whereas homologation of the C-13 methyl to an ethyl leads to a further decrease in clearance in the case of the monoene norgestrel, it increases the clearance of the triene gestrinone. Homologation to a C-13 propyl increases nonspecific albumin binding thus explaining the lowered AIVD and may also affect specific plasma binding as observed for norgestrel, which also has a relatively low AIVD.

TABLE VI
PHARMACOKINETIC PARAMETERS FOLLOWING A SINGLE I.V. INJECTION OF LABELED SYNTHETIC HORMONES TO ADULT MALE VOLUNTEERS

| Hormone | SBP[a] | Binding to CBG[a] | Albumin[b] | AIVD[c] (liters) | Cl[d] (liters/hour) | $n$[e] |
|---|---|---|---|---|---|---|
| Testosterone | 100 | 8.3 | 100 | 20 | 53 | 3 |
| Methyltestosterone | 39 | <0.1 | — | 20 | 26 | 3 |
| Ethynyltestosterone | — | — | 120 | 16 | 17 | 3 |
| Nortestosterone | 6 | 0.1 | 57 | 36 | 80 | 2 |
| Methylnortestosterone | — | — | — | 48 | 36 | 3 |
| Norethindrone | 11 | 0.3 | 62 | 49 | 25 | 3 |
| Norgestrel | 31 | <0.1 | 65 | 32 | 9 | 3 |
| RU 1364 | — | — | 125 | 15 | 4 | 2 |
| Trenbolone | — | — | — | 86 | 107 | 2 |
| Metribolone | 1.7 | 0.4 | 75 | 59 | 15 | 2 |
| Norgestrienone | — | — | 54 | 76 | 14 | 2 |
| Gestrinone | — | — | 73 | 63 | 19 | 2 |
| RU 2715 | — | — | 130 | 40 | 47 | 2 |

[a] Data taken from Pugeat *et al.* (1981). Binding of cortisol to CBG=100.
[b] Binding to human albumin (3 mg/ml) was determined by equilibrium dialysis (see Raynaud, 1971a).
[c] Apparent initial volume of distribution.
[d] Clearance.
[e] Number of compartments (open model).

## IV. CONCLUSIONS

The above studies have attempted to demonstrate and illustrate the importance of chemical substitution of steroid hormones on several factors to be taken into account in the design of a drug. Chemical substitutions may affect binding to several types of protein, e.g., the receptor protein that triggers hormonal activity, the specific and nonspecific plasma transport proteins that influence distribution, and the enzymes in target and catabolic tissues that govern the fate of the molecules in the organism. The exact nature and significance of each of these forms of binding are not yet completely elucidated. Receptor binding determines activity; in a homoeostatic system, the type of activity, agonist or antagonist, depends on the kinetics of the steroid–receptor interaction if the binding obeys the law of mass action. However, other types of steroid–receptor interaction (e.g., covalent bond formation) might occur and lead to untypical responses. The significance and repercussions of binding in the plasma are, in general, less well understood than receptor binding. Several hypotheses have been advanced, some of which are experimentally verified (see above and Westphal, 1978, 1980). Our understanding of the metabolism of steroids largely depends upon the technological advances in the methods of detection and identification of low concentrations of products and on our knowledge of enzyme pathways. In each of these fields—receptor binding, plasma binding, metabolism—available information is increasing. Some pertinent results have been outlined above. Recently, several teams have studied the binding of large series of molecules to guinea pig progesterone binding globulin (Blanford *et al.*, 1978), corticosteroid binding globulin (Mickelson and Westphal, 1980), rat epididymal androgen binding protein (Kirchhoff *et al.*, 1979, Lobl *et al.*, 1980), human sex-steroid binding protein and corticosteroid binding globulin (Pugeat *et al.*, 1981), and cytosol progesterone receptor (Verma and Laumas, 1981), to mention but a few illustrative studies. As even more experimental data become available, it is pleasing to envisage that, in the future, all this information will be stored in data banks, together of course with data on chemical structure and known biological activities. Multiparametric computer analysis may then reveal new correlations, enable the formulation of original working hypotheses, and avoid a great deal of unnecessary or redundant experimentation. Such interrelated data banks may turn out to be invaluable in both drug design and experimental design.

## APPENDIX:
### Chemical Names of the Test Substances in Table III

| | |
|---|---|
| Chlormadinone acetate | 17α-Acetyloxy-6-chloropregna-4,6-diene-3,20-dione |
| Demegestone (RU 2453) | 17α-Methyl-19-norpregna-4,9-diene-3,20-dione |
| Ethynyl testosterone | 17α-Ethynyl-17β-hydroxy-androst-4-en-3-one |
| Gestrinone (RU 2323) | 13β-Ethyl-17β-hydroxy-18,19-dinorpregna-4,9,11-trien-20-yn-3-one |
| Medroxyprogesterone acetate (MPA) | 17α-Acetyloxy-6α-methylpregn-4-ene-3,20-dione |
| Megestrol acetate | 17α-Acetyloxy-6-methylpregna-4,6-diene-3,20-dione |
| Methylnortestosterone | 17β-Hydroxy-17α-methylestr-4-en-3-one |
| Methyltestosterone | 17β-Hydroxy-17α-methylandrost-4-en-3-one |
| Metribolone (RU 1881, methyltrienolone) | 17β-Hydroxy-17α-methylestra-4,9,11-trien-3-one |
| Norethindrone | 17β-Hydroxy-19-nor-17α-pregn-4-en-20-yn-3-one |
| Norgestrel | 13β-Ethyl-17β-hydroxy-18,19-dinor-17α-pregn-4-en-20-yn-3-one |
| Norgestrienone | 17β-Hydroxy-19-nor-17α-pregna-4,9,11-trien-20-yn-3-one |
| Norprogesterone | 19-Norpregn-4-ene-3,20-dione |
| Nortestosterone | 17β-Hydroxyestr-4-en-3-one |
| Progesterone | Pregn-4-ene-3,20-dione |
| Promegestone (RU 5020) | 17α,21-Dimethyl-19-norpregna-4,9-diene-3,20-dione |
| RU 1364 | 17β-Hydroxy-13α-propyl-18,19-dinor-17α-pregn-4-en-20-yn-3-one |

(*continued*)

| | |
|---|---|
| RU 3163 | 19-Norpregna-4,9-diene-3,20-dione |
| RU 2715 | 17β-Hydroxy-13β-propyl-18,19-dinor-17α-pregna-4,9,11-trien-20-yn-3-one |
| RU 27987 | 17β-[(2*S*)2-hydroxy-1-oxopropyl]-17α-methylestra-4,9-dien-3-one |
| RU 27988 | 17β-[(2*R*)2-hydroxy-1-oxopropyl]-17α-methylestra-4,9-dien-3-one |
| RU 28389 | 17α-Methyl-21-hydroxy-19-norpregna-4,9-diene-3,20-dione |
| Testosterone | 17β-Hydroxyandrost-4-en-3-one |
| Trenbolone (RU 2341) | 17β-Hydroxyestra-4,9,11-trien-3-one |

## ACKNOWLEDGMENTS

The long-standing and extremely valuable collaboration of D. Coussedière and C. Cousty is gratefully acknowledged in the metabolism studies.

## REFERENCES

Abdel-Aziz, M. T., and Williams, K. I. H. (1969). *Steroids* **13,** 809–820.
Abdel-Aziz, M. T., and Williams, K. I. H. (1970). *Steroids* **15,** 695–710.
Andrews, W. W., and Ojeda, S. R. (1977). *Endocrinology* **101,** 1517–1523.
Arányi, P., and Quiroga, V. (1980). *J. Steroid Biochem.* **13,** 1167–1172.
Ariëns, E. J. (1979). *Trends Pharmaceut. Sci.* **1,** 11–15.
Asselin, J., Melançon, R., Gourdeau, Y., Labrie, F., Bonne, C., and Raynaud, J. P. (1979). *J. Steroid Biochem.* **10,** 483–486.
Azadian-Boulanger, G., Bucourt, R., Nédélec, L., and Nominé, G. (1975). *Eur. J. Med. Chem.* **10,** 353–359.
Bell, P. A. (1977). *Biochem. Soc. Trans.* **5,** 639–642.
Bell, P. A., and Jones, T. R. (1979). *In* "Anti-Hormones" (M. K. Agarwal, ed.), pp. 35–50. Elsevier/North-Holland, Amsterdam.
Black, L. J., Jones, C. D., and Goode, R. L. (1981). *Mol. Cell. Endocrinol.* **22,** 95–103.
Blanford, A. T., Wittman, W., Stroupe, S. D., and Westphal, U. (1978). *J. Steroid Biochem.* **9,** 187–201.
Bonne, C., and Raynaud, J. P. (1975). *Steroids* **26,** 227–232.
Bouton, M. M., and Raynaud, J. P. (1978). *J. Steroid Biochem.* **9,** 9–15.
Bouton, M. M., and Raynaud, J. P. (1979). *Endocrinology* **105,** 509–515.
Breuer, H. (1977). *In* "Pharmacology of Steroid Contraceptive Drugs" (S. Garattini and H. W. Berendes, eds.), pp. 73–88. Raven Press, New York.
Broek v.d., A. J., Broess, A. I. A., Heuvel v.d., M. J., de Jongh, H. P., Leemhuis, J., Schönemann, K. H., Smits, J., de Visser, J., van Vliet, N. P., and Zeelen, F. J. (1977). *Steroids* **30,** 481–510.
Brown, T. R., Bullock, L., and Bardin, C. W. (1979). *Endocrinology* **105,** 1281–1287.
Busetta, B., Comberton, G., Courseille, G., and Hospital, M. (1974). *Acta Crystallog. B* **30,** 2759–2761.
Chan, D. W., and Slaunwhite, W. R., Jr. (1977). *J. Clin. Endocrinol. Metab.* **44,** 983–985.
Chandross, R. J., and Bordner, J. (1975). *Acta Crystallog. B* **31,** 928–931.
Cooke, B. A., and Vallance, D. K. (1964). *Biochem. J.* **90,** 31P–32P.
Cooke, B. A., and Vallance, D. K. (1965). *Biochem. J.* **97,** 672–677.

Cooper, J. M., and Kellie, A. E. (1968). *Steroids* **11,** 133–149.

Courseille, C., Busetta, B., Précigoux, G., and Hospital, M. (1975). *Acta Crystallog. B* **31,** 2290–2294.

Dausse, J. P., Duval, D., Meyer, P., Gaignault, J. C., Marchandeau, C., and Raynaud, J. P. (1977). *Mol. Pharmacol.* **13,** 948–955.

De Angelis, N. J., Doyne, T. H., and Grob, R. L. (1975). *Acta Crystallog. B* **31,** 2040–2043.

Delettré, J., Mornon, J. P., and Lepicard, G. (1975). *Acta Crystallog. B* **31,** 450–453.

Delettré, J., Mornon, J. P., and Lepicard, G. (1980a). *Acta Crystallog. B* **36,** 1430–1435.

Delettré, J., Mornon, J. P., Lepicard, G., Ojasoo, T., and Raynaud, J. P. (1980b). *J. Steroid Biochem.* **13,** 45–59.

Delettré, J., Mornon, J. P., Ojasoo, T., and Raynaud, J. P. (1980c). *In* "Perspectives in Steroid Receptor Research" (F. Bresciani, ed.), pp. 1–21. Raven Press, New York.

De Moor, T., Roels, H., Delaere, K., and Crabbé, J. (1965). *J. Clin. Endocrinol. Metab.* **25,** 612–620.

Duax, W. L., Cody, V., Griffin, J., Hazel, J., and Weeks, C. M. (1978a). *J. Steroid Biochem.* **9,** 901–907.

Duax, W. L., Cody, V., Griffin, J. F., Rohrer, D. C., and Weeks, C. M. (1978b). *J. Toxicol. Env. Health* **4,** 205–227.

Fotherby, D., and James, F. (1972). *In* "Advances in Steroid Biochemistry and Pharmacology" (M. H. Briggs and G. A. Christie, eds.), Vol. 3, pp. 67–165. Academic Press, New York.

Fotherby, K., and Keenan, C. A. (1969). *Acta Endocrinol. (Kbh) Suppl.* **188,** Abstr. 83.

Fukushima, D. K., Levin, J., Liang, J. S., and Smulowitz, M. (1979). *Steroids* **34,** 57–72.

Gerhards, E., Hecker, W., Hitze, H., Nieuweboer, B., and Bellmann, O. (1971). *Acta Endocrinol. (Kbh)* **68,** 219–248.

Gund, P., Andose, J. D., Rhodes, J. B., and Smith, G. M. (1980). *Science* **208,** 1425–1431.

Handy, R. W., Palmer, K. H., Wall, M. E., and Piantadosi, C. (1974). *Drug Metab. Disposition* **2,** 214–220.

Hyde, P. M., Elliott, W. H., Doisy, E. A., Jr., and Doisy, E. A. (1954). *J. Biol. Chem.* **208,** 521–528.

Illingworth, D. V., Heap, R. B., and Perry, J. S. (1970). *J. Endocrinol.* **48,** 409–417.

Jacobson, M., Levin, W., and Kuntzman, R. (1969). *Biochem. Pharmacol.* **18,** 2253–2262.

Jones, T. R., and Bell, P. A. (1980). *Biochem. J.* **188,** 237–245.

Kato, G. (1980). *Ind. Eng. Chem. Prod. Res. Dev.* **19,** 569–572.

Kincl, A., and Dorfman, R. I. (1964). *Steroids* **3,** 109–122.

Kirchhoff, J., Soffie, M., and Rousseau, G. G. (1979). *J. Steroid Biochem.* **10,** 487–497.

Kolata, G. B. (1977). *Science* **197,** 36–37.

Labrie, F., Ferland, L., Lagacé, L., Drouin, J., Asselin, J., Azadian-Boulanger, G., and Raynaud, J. P. (1977). *Fert. Steril.* **28,** 1104–1112.

Lepicard, G., Delettré, J., and Mornon, J. P. (1974). *Acta Crystallog. B* **30,** 2751–2753.

Levedahl, B. H., and Samuels, L. T. (1950). *J. Biol. Chem.* **186,** 857–861.

Lobl, T. J., Campbell, J. A., Tindall, D. J., Cunningham, G. R., and Means, A. R. (1980). *Testicular Dev. Struct. Funct.* (Proc. NICHHD Workshop Testis), pp. 323–330.

Martin, R. P. (1966). *Endocrinology* **78,** 907–913.

Mickelson, K. E., and Westphal, U. (1980). *Biochemistry* **19,** 585–590.

Moguilewsky, M., and Deraedt, R. *J. Steroid Biochem.* (in press).

Moguilewsky, M., and Raynaud, J. P. (1980). *J. Steroid Biochem.* **12,** 309–314.

Mornon, J. P., Lepicard, G., and Delettré, J. (1976). *C.R. Acad. Sci. (Paris) C* **282,** 387–390.

Mornon, J. P., Delettré, J., Lepicard, G., Bally, R., Surcouf, E., and Bondot, P. (1977). *J. Steroid Biochem.* **8,** 51–62.

Mornon, J. P., Lepicard, G., and Delettré, J. *Acta Crystallog.* (in press).

Nunez, E. A., Benassayag, C., Savu, L., Vallette, G., and Jayle, M. F. (1976). *Ann. Biol. Anim. Biochem. Biophys.* **16,** 491–501.

Ofner, P. (1955). *Biochem. J.* **61,** 287–297.

Ojasoo, T., and Raynaud, J. P. (1978). *Cancer Res.* **38,** 3044–3050.

Palmer, K. H., Smith, D. J. S., Liepins, L., Feierabend, J. F., and Wall, M. E. (1970). *Pharmacologist* **12,** 254.

Philibert, D., Ojasoo, T., and Raynaud, J. P. (1977). *Endocrinology* **101,** 1850–1861.

Pottier, J., Coussedière, D., and Heitzman, R. J. (1980). *J. Anim. Sci.* **51** (Suppl. 1), no. 508.

Pottier, J., Cousty, C., Heitzman, R. J., and Reynolds, I. P. (1981). *Xenobiotica* **11,** 489–500.

Précigoux, G. (1978). *In* "Analyse radiocristallographique de molécules oestrogènes et androgènes et étude de leur affinité et de leur spécificité." Ph.D. Thesis, Université de Bordeaux I, France.

Pugeat, M. M., Dunn, J. F., and Nisula, B. C. (1981). *J. Clin. Endocrinol. Metab.* **53,** 69–75.

Quincey, R. V., and Gray, C. H. (1967). *J. Endocrinol.* **37,** 37–55.

Raynaud, J. P. (1971a). *Proc. 3rd Int. Congr. Hormonal Steroids, Hamburg 1970,* **ICS 219,** 915–922.

Raynaud, J. P. (1971b). "Distribution, liaison et action de dérivés de l'oestradiol." Ph.D. Thesis, University of Paris.

Raynaud, J. P. (1973). *Steroids* **21,** 249–258.

Raynaud, J. P. (1977). *In* "Medicinal Chemistry" (J. Mathieu, ed.), Vol. 5, pp. 451–456. Elsevier, Amsterdam.

Raynaud, J. P. (1978). *In* "Advances in Pharmacology and Therapeutics" (J. Jacob, ed.), Vol. 1, pp. 259–278. Pergamon Press, Oxford.

Raynaud, J. P., and Bouton, M. M. (1980). *In* "Cytotoxic Estrogens in Hormone Receptive Tumors" (J. Raus, H. Martens, and G. Leclercq, eds.), pp. 49–70. Academic Press, New York.

Raynaud, J. P., and Philibert, D. (1972). *Abstr. 5th Int. Congr. Pharmacol., San Francisco 1972* no. **1132,** 189.

Raynaud, J. P., Salmon, J., Azadian-Boulanger, G., Bucourt, R., and Sakiz, E. (1973). *Abstr. FIP,* Stockholm, 1973.

Raynaud, J. P., Cousty, C., and Salmon, J. (1974a). *J. Steroid Biochem.* **5,** 324, no. 121.

Raynaud, J. P., Philibert, D., and Azadian-Boulanger, G. (1974b). *In* "The Physiology and Genetics of Reproduction" (E. M. Coutinho and F. Fuchs, eds.), Vol. 4a, pp. 143–160. Plenum Press, New York.

Raynaud, J. P., Bonne, C., Bouton, M. M., Moguilewsky, M., Philibert, D., and Azadian-Boulanger, G. (1975). *J. Steroid Biochem.* **6,** 615–622.

Raynaud, J. P., Secchi, J., and Bouton, M. M. (1977). *J. Steroid Biochem.* **8,** xiv, no. 25.

Raynaud, J. P., Ojasoo, T., Bouton, M. M., and Philibert, D. (1978). *In* "Drug Design" (E. J. Ariëns, ed.), Vol. 8, pp. 169–214. Academic Press, New York.

Raynaud, J. P., Bonne, C., Bouton, M. M., Lagacé, L., and Labrie, F. (1979a). *J. Steroid Biochem.* **11,** 93–99.

Raynaud, J. P., Ojasoo, T., and Vaché, V. (1979b). *In* "Steroid Receptors and the Management of Cancer" (E. B. Thompson and M. E. Lippman, eds.), pp. 215–232. CRC Press, Boca Raton, Florida.

Raynaud, J. P., Bouton, M. M., Moguilewsky, M., Ojasoo, T., Philibert, D., Beck, G., Labrie, F., and Mornon, J. P. (1980a). *J. Steroid Biochem.* **12,** 143–157.

Raynaud, J. P., Bouton, M. M., and Ojasoo, T. (1980b). *Trends Pharmaceut. Sci.* **1,** 324–327.

Raynaud, J. P., Brown, N., Coussedière, D., Pottier, J., Delettré, J., and Mornon, J. P. (1980c). *In* "Steroid-Induced Uterine Proteins" (M. Beato, ed.), pp. 217–236. Elsevier/North-Holland, Amsterdam.

Raynaud, J. P., Fortin, M., and Tournemine, C. (1980d). *Actualités de Chimie Thérapeutique* **7,** 293–318.

Raynaud, J. P., Moguilewsky, M., and Vannier, B. (1980e). *In* "Advances in the Biosciences" (A. M. Kaye and M. Kaye, eds.), pp. 59–75. Pergamon Press, Oxford.

Raynaud, J. P., Ojasoo, T., Mornon, J. P., Delettré, J., and Lepicard, G. (1980f). *In* "Pharmacological Modulation of Steroid Action" (E. Genazzani, F. di Carlo, and W. I. P. Mainwaring, eds.), pp. 171–180. Raven Press, New York.

Raynaud, J. P., Ojasoo, T., and Vaché, V. (1981a). *In* "Reproductive Processes and Contraception (K. W. McKerns, ed.), pp. 163–179. Plenum Press, New York.

Raynaud, J. P., Ojasoo, T., and Labrie, F. (1981b). *In* "Mechanisms of Steroid Action" (G. P. Lewis and H. Ginsburg, eds.), pp. 145–158. Macmillan Press, England.

Reel, J. R., Humphrey, R. R., Shih, Y. H., Windsor, B. L., Sakowski, R., Creger, P. L., and Edgren, R. A. (1979). *Fert. Steril.* **31,** 552–561.

Rochefort, H., and Borgna, J. L. (1981). *Nature (London)* **292,** 257–259.

Rochefort, H., and Capony, F. (1977). *Biochem. Biophys. Res. Comm.* **75,** 277–285.

Rousseau, G. G., Baxter, J. D., and Tomkins, G. M. (1972). *J. Mol. Biol.* **67,** 99–115.

Sakiz, E., Azadian-Boulanger, G., and Raynaud, J. P. (1974). *Proc. 6th Int. Congr. Endocrinol., Washington 1972,* **ICS 273,** 988–994.

Salmon, J., Raynaud, J. P., and Pottier, J. (1971). *In* "Symposium sur les Progrès des Techniques Nucléaires en Pharmacodynamie," (G. Valette and Y. Cohen, eds.), pp. 237–248. Masson, Paris.

Schmit, J. P., and Rousseau, G. G. (1978). *J. Steroid Biochem.* **9,** 921–927.

Schmit, J. P., Quivy, J. I., and Rousseau, G. G. (1980). *J. Steroid Biochem.* **13,** 1387–1394.

Shutt, D. A., and Cox, R. I. (1972). *J. Endocrinol.* **52,** 299–310.

Shyamala, G., and Leonhard, L. (1980). *J. Biol. Chem.* **255,** 6028–6031.

Simons, S. S., Jr., Thompson, E. B., and Johnson, D. F. (1979). *Biochem. Biophys. Res. Commun.* **86,** 793–800.

Sisenwine, S. F., Kimmel, H. B., Liu, A. L., and Ruelius, H. W. (1973). *Acta Endocrinol. (Kbh)* **73,** 91–104.

Sutherland, R. L., Murphy, L. C., San Foo, M., Green, M. D., and Whybourne, A. M. (1980). *Nature (London)* **288,** 273–275.

Suthers, M. B., Pressley, L. A., and Funder, J. W. (1976). *Endocrinology* **99,** 260–269.

Svec, F., Yeakley, J., and Harrison, R. W., III (1980). *Endocrinology* **107,** 566–572.

Thijssen, J. H. H. (1972). *In* "Pharmacology of the Endocrine System and Related Drugs: Progesterone, Progestational Drugs and Antifertility Agents" (G. Peters and M. Tausk, eds.), Vol. 2, pp. 217–244. Pergamon Press, Oxford.

Vannier, B., and Raynaud, J. P. (1975). *Mol. Cell. Endocrinol.* **3,** 323–337.

Vannier, B., and Raynaud, J. P. (1980). *J. Reprod. Fertil.* **59,** 43–49.

Velluz, L., Nominé, G., Mathieu, J., Bucourt, R., Nédélec, L., Vignau, M., and Gasc, J. C. (1967). *C. R. Acad. Sci.* (Paris) **264C,** 1396–1401.

Verma, U., and Laumas, K. R. (1981). *J. Steroid Biochem.* **14,** 733–740.

Victor, A., Weiner, E., and Johansson, E. D. B. (1976). *J. Clin. Endocrinol. Metab.* **43,** 244–247.

Wakeling, A. E., and Slater, S. R. (1981). *In* "Mechanisms of Steroid Action" (G. P. Lewis and H. Ginsburg, eds.). pp. 159–172. Macmillan Press, England.

Weichman, B. M., and Notides, A. C. (1980). *Endocrinology* **106,** 434–439.

Westphal, U. (1978). *In* "Receptors and Hormone Action" (B. W. O'Malley and L. Birnbaumer, eds.), Vol. 2, pp. 443–472. Academic Press, New York.

Westphal, U. (1980). *In* "Pharmacological Modulation of Steroid Action" (E. Genazzani, F. Di Carlo, and W. I. P. Mainwaring eds.) pp. 33–47. Raven Press, New York.

Zava, D. T., Landrum, B., Horwitz, K. B., and McGuire, W. L. (1979). *Endocrinology* **104,** 1007–1012.

Zeelen, F. J., and Bergink, E. W. (1980). *In* "Cytotoxic Estrogens in Hormone Receptive Tumors" (J. Raus, H. Martens and G. Leclercq, eds.), pp. 39–48. Academic Press, New York.

# Index

## H



## I

## T

# Contents of Previous Volumes

Volume I

## Volume II

## Volume III

## Volume IV



## Volume V

## Volume VI

## Volume VII

## Volume VIII